An Introduction
to Genetic
Statistics

An Introduction to Genetic Statistics

OSCAR KEMPTHORNE

Professor of Statistics
Iowa State University

THE IOWA STATE UNIVERSITY PRESS / *Ames, Iowa, U.S.A.*

QA
276
.K28
1969

To my mother
   and
   in memory of my father

Preface

THIS BOOK IS SOMEWHAT SPECIALIZED AND IS TO A CERTAIN EX-
tent the product of special circumstances. The author is not a geneticist, but has been spending a considerable part of the past eight
years talking to geneticists pure and applied about their statistical
problems and has for some five years been responsible for a course in
genetic statistics to graduate students and advanced undergraduates.
The worker in genetics needs to know many of the tools of modern
statistics but can hardly be expected to go through many statistical
courses to gather knowledge of these tools. Also the tools should be
presented in terms of genetic situations and problems. For example,
problems relating to the seating of people around a table are likely
to strike the student as very academic problems in probability.

This book is then an attempt to present the basic statistical concepts and tools which the genetic research worker needs, with examples from genetics. The first ten chapters are intended to be of
this nature.

Because of personal interest and the problems with which I have
been presented, the use of statistics in the understanding of quantitative inheritance is presented in considerable detail. The statistical
techniques here are the simple ones of evaluating and examining means,
variances, and covariances. It is a part of the general outlook of the
author that the analysis of variance is not a tool to be used blindly
with the picking of linear models "out of thin air." The inputs for
the interpretation of the analysis of variance must if possible be based
on genetic theory. A considerable part of the book is devoted therefore to the elementary genetic theory of quantitative inheritance. Perhaps the greatest tragedy in the study of quantitative inheritance has
been the fact that the now famous 1918 paper of R. A. Fisher and the
1921 papers by Sewall Wright have been so long buried in the literature. The work by Sewall Wright has been used quite widely in the

United States, primarily under the influence of J. L. Lush and his coworkers and students, but has not been used extensively elsewhere. The 1918 paper of R. A. Fisher appears to have been largely neglected until the past ten or so years. This is not surprising in view of the extremely condensed style of writing and mathematics used, but is nevertheless regrettable. It is hoped that most of the tremendous amount of material in this paper is given herein in a more accessible form.

The reader will be able to follow the sequence of ideas in the latter part of the book. The publication of the book has been held up by the necessity of filling in gaps in knowledge which would be glaring in a purported complete introductory account of the subject. The book contains a certain amount of work which is original, though other workers have been working on some of the problems contemporaneously. It is probably desirable to list these topics explicitly because of the tendency of uncritical readers to regard either the whole of a book as new, or none of it, both of these possibilities being embarrassing to the author. The specific topics, most of which have been given in recent journals, are: some of the theory of inbreeding (Chapters 5 and 6), some theory on the effect of selection in non-random mating single-locus populations (Chapter 16), the general theory of random mating populations diploid and polyploid in the absence of linkage and selection (Chapters 18, 19), some beginnings of the theory of correlations between relatives under inbreeding (Chapters 17, 20), some theory on diallel crosses which is related to the concepts of general and specific combining ability (Chapters 17, 20), the theory of selfing with epistacy (Chapter 17).

There are many fascinating problems that remain, and I would have liked to have solved these. However, the solutions might suggest themselves in the next few weeks, or perhaps not for several years.

I have taken as an aim, that a person who assimilates the contents of this book will be able to read with some facility the basic writings of Fisher, Wright, Haldane, and Malécot, and the current literature.

Some comment is probably necessary on the absence of certain topics. The theory of natural selection, especially with regard to Fisher's fundamental theorem of natural selection, has been discussed to only a slight extent, for the reason that it is impossible for me to emulate Fisher's own writings on this topic. The theory of assortative mating given by Sewall Wright in 1921 is not presented because it strikes me as being based on assumptions that are insufficiently realistic, and the introduction of more realism has so far been beyond my powers. This work is however remarkably elegant as far as it goes.

It is probably also desirable that I comment, particularly for American readers, on the relative absence of treatment of problems by the method of path coefficients. This tool was extremely powerful in the hands of its inventor, Sewall Wright, and it is hoped that an adequate description of it is given. It has been my experience, however, that it is not necessary for the solution of many problems which were solved first by its use, and it is hoped that the alternative presentations which were chosen deliberately after considerable thought will be intelligible to the reader. My experience in contact with students is that real understanding of the method of path coefficients is difficult to attain. If other procedures which are pedagogically more successful and possibly more intrinsic to the nature of things are available, there seems little point in giving extensive accounts of the use of the method. The general ideas of path analysis are, however, included, because I feel that they are at the root of many inferential problems and procedures.

The prerequisites for the book are essentially nil if we assume that all readers will have had high school algebra. Certain sections require the differentiation of quadratic forms, and a few sections (marked with an asterisk) require what may be termed intermediate mathematics. The amount of statistical knowledge that is assumed is also nil, though the book may be rather heavy going in spots for someone unacquainted with statistical methods. It is probable that anyone interested in the general topic will have read a standard book on statistical methods such as Snedecor's or Goulden's. Notwithstanding, the essential elementary statistical methods have been included to give completeness and continuity.

It is possibly of use to suggest how the material of the book may be used in courses. It has been used for a one-quarter course of about 30 lectures and the material given is as follows: Chapters 1, 2, 5, 6, 7, 8, 9, 15, 19. This was possible because all the students have had at least a two-quarter course based on Snedecor's *Statistical Methods*. For a one-semester course one would, it is thought, wish to include material on inbreeding in relation to quantitative inheritance, and Chapter 14 on regression.

Some problems are given for all chapters except those which do not lend themselves to classwork problems.

My basic debt with regard to the whole book is to Sir Ronald A. Fisher. There is hardly a page, even less a chapter, which does not contain the results of Fisher and extensions of Fisher's results. The writings of Fisher have been a tremendous inspiration to me, and led not only to my becoming interested in genetics but also to an appreciation of the mathematical beauty of the Mendelian mechanism. Essentially all the statistical methodology given in the book traces back to Fisher's work, and the theory of quantitative inheritance presented traces back to his 1918 paper.

I am indebted to Sewall Wright for extensive helpful correspondence on several matters. The book itself is highly indebted to Wright for his work on inbreeding and population genetics. I have attempted to include an introduction to all the basic work on population genetics of Wright, even though his mode of presentation by method of path coefficients is not given when other methods seemed preferable.

It is appropriate also to mention that I used Hogben's book *Introduction to Mathematical Genetics* and Li's book *Population Genetics* as a guide on the early chapters. I was also highly stimulated by mimeographed notes on population genetics by J. L. Lush.

The present book is not a book on breeding theory and procedures, and defers to the famous book *Animal Breeding Plans* of J. L. Lush on all such matters.

I wish to acknowledge the influence of the environment at Ames and in particular J. L. Lush, J. W. Gowen, G. F. Sprague, L. N. Hazel, A. W. Nordskog, Bruce Griffing, T. W. Horner, J. G. O'Mara, who have talked at length with me about problems and have provided stimulation by forceful but friendly argumentation. J. F. Crow of Wisconsin has also been of great help. Without these forces this book would never have been written. I am highly indebted to M. Kimura for detailed reading and many suggestions. My thanks go to Jauvanta Walker for very careful preparation of an index, and to Neeti Bohidar and Melvin Hogsett for reading much of the proofs.

Finally, I am very grateful for sterling secretarial work by Mrs. Margaret Kirwin and Mrs. Betty Brendemuehl.

OSCAR KEMPTHORNE

August 1957

Contents

CHAPTER 1

Elementary Probability

1.1 INTRODUCTION

The starting point of genetics as we know the subject at the present time was the discovery by Mendel that the frequencies of types of offspring from hybrid matings were statistical frequencies. By this we mean that, say, if there were two types of offspring and 100 progeny, we would observe a number n_1 of one type and $100 - n_1$ of the other type, which numbers n_1 and $100 - n_1$ would vary from trial to trial in a manner not at all haphazard. It would be found that in a nonstrict sense, for example, values of n_1 near 50 would occur more frequently than values away from 50. It would be found in many instances that the proportions of the various types would, with a large number of offspring, appear to be close to simple fractions such as $\frac{1}{2}$, or $\frac{1}{4}$ or $\frac{9}{16}$. Part of the genius of Mendel consisted in recognizing that these phenomena bore a striking resemblance to the tossing of coins or dice. If we toss 100 pennies and count the number which fall heads up and the number which fall tails up, we shall not find exactly 50 of each. Or, to take a more simple example, we are not very surprised if when we toss a penny twice we find two heads. We would, however, be somewhat sceptical if we found say 100 heads in 1000 tosses of a penny.

The recognition that the frequencies of types of offspring are much like what one would expect with frequencies of tossing pennies or outcomes with some other gambling device led to the model of the particulate nature of the inheritance of characteristics in which parents each contribute a "particle" of the stuff of inheritance to the offspring. The "particle" or gene which a particular parent hands on to an offspring is a random one of the two genes which he (or she) possesses.

We have used the term "random" and should attempt a definition of it. As with all primitive concepts, exact definition is not easy. For example, we are all used to the concept of a point; we say that a point is a conceptual entity which can never be realized completely. We can envisage a series of pencils whose marking ends become smaller and smaller, and we can envisage a series of marks made on a piece of paper

1

by these pencils. A point may then be defined as the limit of this series of marks, as the end of the pencil gets smaller. We are in somewhat the same situation in attempting to define "random." Possibly we can best make the intuitive definition. Consider any observable ordering of the gene handed on by the parent, for example the gene handed on to the first offspring, to the second offspring, and so on. We shall get a sequence of symbols say

$$A\,a\,a\,a\,A\,A\,a\,a \cdot\,\cdot\,\cdot$$

Then this sequence is random if we are unable to find any system for predicting exactly the symbol at any place in the sequence from the previous members of the sequence. It is clear that random is here a statement of ignorance. We may illustrate this point by noting that it might be possible to predict exactly how a tossed penny would fall if the tossing were done in a specified way with no variations in technique of tossing, and if there were no external forces to affect the process. One might therefore say that we should not incorporate our ignorance in our model or picture of the real world phenomenon, but should strive to remove or alleviate the state of ignorance. It is a tribute to Mendel that he was the first to realize that it would be wiser to accept the state of ignorance, and to determine whether there were some regularity in the "tossing." The tremendous development of genetics in the past fifty or so years is good evidence that this was a wise decision. For it is difficult to imagine how progress could have been made in the study of an ideal tossing mechanism of magnitude perhaps molecular. It is true that cytology has been examining this mechanism and has pushed our state of ignorance to a level much more primitive than that existing fifty years ago, and this progress will no doubt continue.

What we have said above indicates clearly that our first job is to obtain an understanding of tossing mechanisms, or rather of the results produced by tossing mechanisms. We are therefore led to the elementary theory of probability.

1.2 THE LAWS OF PROBABILITY

We consider events, such as the result of the tossing of a penny or of a die, and we suppose that an event E can occur in mutually exclusive forms, $E_1, E_2, \cdot\,\cdot\,\cdot, E_n$. In the case of the tossing of a penny, E_1 could be the occurrence of heads and E_2 of tails. In the case of a die, we would have E_1 as the occurrence of "1," E_2 as the occurrence of "2," and so on. We shall attach numbers $P(E)$, $P(E_1)$, $P(E_2)$, etc., to the event E and to its possible forms of occurrence, in such a way that

$$P(E) = P(E_1) + P(E_2) + P(E_3) + \cdot\,\cdot\,\cdot + P(E_n) \tag{1}$$

For example let E be the event that the tossing of a die produces an even number: i.e. 2 or 4 or 6. Then

$$P(2 \text{ or } 4 \text{ or } 6) = P(2) + P(4) + P(6)$$

We must be careful to see that the decomposition of the event E into the forms $E_1, E_2, \cdots, E_n$ is such that $E_1, E_2, \cdots$, and E_n are mutually exclusive; that is, e.g. that, if E_1 occurs, then none of E_2 to E_n can occur. For example, we might ask "what is the probability that a toss of a die will give us a number which is even or divisible by 3." If we made the mistake of saying that being "even" and "divisible by 3" are mutually exclusive, we would say

$$P(\text{even or divisible by 3}) = P(\text{even}) + P(\text{divisible by 3}) \qquad (2)$$

We would then say the number given by the toss is even if we get E_2, E_4, or E_6, which are mutually exclusive, so that

$$P(\text{even}) = P(E_2) + P(E_4) + P(E_6) \qquad (3)$$

We would also say that the number given by the toss is divisible by 3 if we get E_3 or E_6, which are mutually exclusive, so that

$$P(\text{divisible by 3}) = P(E_3) + P(E_6) \qquad (4)$$

Putting together (3) and (4) in (2) we get

$$P(\text{even or divisible by 3}) = P(E_2) + P(E_3) + P(E_4) + 2P(E_6) \qquad (5)$$

which is clearly fallacious since the possible outcomes or forms which are even or divisible by 3 are E_2, E_3, E_4, and E_6, and these are mutually exclusive. In fact, therefore,

$$P(\text{even or divisible by 3}) = P(E_2) + P(E_3) + P(E_4) + P(E_6) \qquad (6)$$

In a sense the rule we have given, which is usually stated formally as the
   Theorem of Total Probability: The probability of an event E is the sum of the probabilities of its mutually exclusive forms
is nothing more than a rule which enables us to calculate the probability of an event E which is not simple from the probabilities of simpler exclusive forms which make up the entire event E.

A simple genetic example of the use of this law is the following. Suppose we can have the three possibilities

Form or Possibility	*AA*	*Aa*	*aa*
Probability	P	$2Q$	R

and that we have complete dominance. Then the probability of drawing an individual showing the dominant character is $(P + 2Q)$:

$$P(\text{dominant}) = P(AA \text{ or } Aa) = P + 2Q$$

We shall relate probabilities to relative frequencies. In the present instance we can imagine that we have a very large population of N individuals and that PN of them are AA, $2QN$ are Aa, and RN are aa. Now, if we pick out an AA individual from the total of N without any prejudice (overt or covert), we can get AA in PN ways so that in a proportion P of cases we shall get AA; similarly in a proportion $2Q$ of cases we shall get Aa. Now the number of cases in which we shall get AA or Aa is $PN + 2QN$ which equals $(P + 2Q)N$, so that the proportion of cases in which we get AA or Aa is $(P + 2Q)$.

So we have

Proportion of cases with AA $= P$

Proportion of cases with Aa $= 2Q$

Proportion of cases with AA or $Aa = P + 2Q$

In all cases we shall then interpret the probability P of an event E as the proportion of an indefinitely large number of trials which will result in E.

We now go on to consider the case when the forms of the event have two aspects: for instance we might wish to know the probability that the result of a toss of a die is both divisible by 2 and divisible by 3: or for example that a person drawn at random from the United States has blood type O and is also a male. In the first case we might guess $P(\text{divisible by 2 and divisible by 3}) = P(\text{divisible by 2}) P(\text{divisible by 3})$, and, if $P(E_1) = P(E_2) = \cdots = P(E_6) = \frac{1}{6}$, this relationship holds. For

$P(\text{divisible by 2 and divisible by 3}) = P(E_6) = \frac{1}{6}$

$P(\text{divisible by 2}) = P(E_2 \text{ or } E_4 \text{ or } E_6) = P(E_2) + P(E_4) + P(E_6) = \frac{3}{6} = \frac{1}{2}$

and

$P(\text{divisible by 3}) = P(E_3 \text{ or } E_6) = P(E_3) + P(E_6) = \frac{2}{6} = \frac{1}{3}$ and $\frac{1}{6} = \frac{1}{2} \times \frac{1}{3}$

However, this is not generally true. For suppose the die is loaded so that $P(E_1) = P(E_2) = P(E_3) = 0$, and $P(E_4) = P(E_5) = P(E_6) = \frac{1}{3}$. Then we would have

$P(\text{divisible by 2}) = P(E_2) + P(E_4) + P(E_6) = \frac{2}{3}$

$P(\text{divisible by 3}) = P(E_3) + P(E_6) = \frac{1}{3}$

but $P(\text{divisible by 2 and divisible by 3}) = P(E_6) = \frac{1}{3}$

which is certainly not equal to $\frac{2}{3} \times \frac{1}{3}$.

To facilitate presentation, we shall need the term conditional probability and shall use the symbol $P(A/B)$ which we shall read as the probability of A happening, given that B has happened, or more shortly given B. We can then write down the *Theorem of Compound Probability*.

The probability of the compound event A and B is the probability of A times the conditional probability of B given A, which is equal to the probability of B times the probability of A given B.

In symbols:

$$P(A \text{ and } B) = P(A) P(B/A)$$
$$= P(B) P(A/B)$$

In a sense, this is strictly a rule for writing down conditional probabilities

$$P(A/B) = P(A \text{ and } B)/P(B)$$

and

$$P(B/A) = P(A \text{ and } B)/P(A)$$

We state that $P(A/B)$ exists only if $P(B)$ is not zero, and $P(B/A)$ exists only if $P(A)$ is not zero.

This law is really a definition of conditional probability. We can motivate the definition in the following way. Suppose we consider a large number N of trials, and suppose that n_A lead to event A, n_B lead to event B, and n_{AB} lead to event A and B. Then the relative frequencies are, using f with subscripts to denote these frequencies,

$$f_A = n_A/N, \quad f_B = n_B/N, \quad f_{AB} = n_{AB}/N$$

Now consider the trials which lead to A. There are n_A such trials, and, of these n_A trials, a portion n_{AB} lead to B so we can say

$$f_{B/A} = \frac{n_{AB}}{n_A}$$

where $f_{B/A}$ is the frequency of B in the totality of events A. But

$$f_{AB} = \frac{n_{AB}}{N} = \frac{n_A n_{AB}}{N n_A} = f_A f_{B/A}$$

If we set up a correspondence between frequencies and probabilities, we then have

$$P(AB) = P(A) P(B/A)$$

Similarly we can get

$$P(AB) = P(B) P(A/B)$$

This formula or law may be extended indefinitely in a more or less obvious way, namely,

$$P(ABCD \cdots) = P(A) P(B/A) P(C/AB) P(D/ABC) \cdots$$

We are now in a position to consider the concept of independence of events. The event B is said to be independent of the event A if

$$P(B/A) = P(B)$$

We can utilize this in the law of compound probabilities to give the law: If $A, B, C, D, \cdots$ are independent, then

$$P(ABCD \cdots) = P(A) P(B) P(C) P(D) \cdots$$

An example of the use of this law is the derivation of simple Mendelian probabilities. The principle of independent segregation states that the parent transmits to the offspring a random one of its two genes. Thus in the mating $Aa \times Aa$ the probability that the sire transmits A to the offspring is $\frac{1}{2}$ and the probability that the dam transmits A is $\frac{1}{2}$, so that the probability that the offspring is AA is $\frac{1}{4}$: formally

$$P(\text{offspring is } AA) = P(\text{sire transmits } A) P(\text{dam transmits } A)$$
$$= \tfrac{1}{2} \times \tfrac{1}{2} = \tfrac{1}{4}$$

The same probability obviously holds in the selfing of an Aa individual. The law is useful because the conditional probabilities may be easy to get. For example, suppose we are given the population

AA	Aa	aa
P	2Q	R

and we pick an individual at random and self it. What is the probability of the compound event that the mating is $Aa \times Aa$ and the offspring is AA? Here the event that the mating is $Aa \times Aa$ can be regarded as attribute A, and that the offspring is AA as attribute B. Then

$$P(AB) = P(A) P(B/A)$$

But $P(A)$ is equal to $2Q$. We know that the probability that $Aa \times Aa$ produces AA is $\frac{1}{4}$; in other words $P(B/A) = \frac{1}{4}$. So we have

$$P(AB) = \frac{Q}{2}$$

Now let us consider a problem which requires the use of both of the theorems of probability. Consider again the population given above, and suppose there is random mating. What is the probability that an offspring is AA? This is a fairly complex event, and we first say that the AA offspring must come from one of the matings, so we have

P(offspring is AA) $= P$(mating is $AA \times AA$ and offspring is AA)

$\qquad + P$(mating is $AA \times Aa$ and offspring is AA)

$\qquad + P$(mating is $AA \times aa$ and offspring is AA)

$\qquad + P$(mating is $Aa \times AA$ and offspring is AA)

$\qquad + P$(mating is $Aa \times Aa$ and offspring is AA)

$\qquad + P$(mating is $Aa \times aa$ and offspring is AA)

$\qquad + P$(mating is $aa \times AA$ and offspring is AA)

$\qquad + P$(mating is $aa \times Aa$ and offspring is AA)

$\qquad + P$(mating is $aa \times aa$ and offspring is AA)

Here we have used the law of total probability. We have broken the event that the offspring is AA into nine exclusive forms based on the type of mating that can possibly give rise to it (actually some with probability zero). We can now say that

P(mating is $AA \times AA$ and offspring is AA) $= P$(mating is $AA \times AA$) $\times$

$\qquad P$(offspring is AA, given that the mating is $AA \times AA$)

and

P(mating is $AA \times Aa$ and offspring is AA) $= P$(mating is $AA \times Aa$) $\times$

$\qquad P$(offspring is AA, given that the mating is $AA \times Aa$)

and so on. It is now a simple matter to perform the necessary computations, and we may summarize them in Table 1.1, where we have for completeness given the data for the computation of the three possible types of offspring.

TABLE 1.1

COMPUTATION OF PROBABILITY

Mating	Probability of Mating	Conditional Probabilities of		
		AA	Aa	aa
$AA \times AA$	P^2	1	0	0
$AA \times Aa$	$2PQ$	$\frac{1}{2}$	$\frac{1}{2}$	0
$AA \times aa$	PR	0	1	0
$Aa \times AA$	$2PQ$	$\frac{1}{2}$	$\frac{1}{2}$	0
$Aa \times Aa$	$4Q^2$	$\frac{1}{4}$	$\frac{1}{2}$	$\frac{1}{4}$
$Aa \times aa$	$2QR$	0	$\frac{1}{2}$	$\frac{1}{2}$
$aa \times AA$	PR	0	1	0
$aa \times Aa$	$2QR$	0	$\frac{1}{2}$	$\frac{1}{2}$
$aa \times aa$	R^2	0	0	1

All we need to do now is to take the sum of products of the probabilities of mating by the conditional probabilities of the type of offspring, and we get

$$P(AA) = P^2 + PQ + PQ + Q^2$$
$$= P^2 + 2PQ + Q^2$$

Also we get

$$P(Aa) = 2PQ + 2Q^2 + 2PR + 2QR$$

and

$$P(aa) = Q^2 + 2QR + R^2$$

While we are considering this situation, we may as well verify the Hardy–Weinberg law. This law states that, if $P = p^2$, $Q = pq$, $R = q^2$, where $p + q = 1$, then the population $PAA + 2QAa + Raa$ is in equilibrium. If we put P, Q, and R in terms of p and q, we get

$$P(AA) = p^4 + 2p^3q + p^2q^2$$
$$= p^2(p^2 + 2pq + q^2)$$
$$= p^2(p + q)^2$$
$$= p^2$$
$$P(Aa) = 2p^3q + 2p^2q^2 + 2p^2q^2 + 2pq^3$$
$$= 2pq(p^2 + 2pq + q^2)$$
$$= 2pq$$

and

$$P(aa) = p^2q^2 + 2pq^3 + q^4$$
$$= q^2(p^2 + 2pq + q^2)$$
$$= q^2$$

Thus we find that the probability of an offspring having a particular genotype is equal to the probability of a parent being of that genotype. If then we have a very large population so that our probabilities correspond to frequencies, we can say that a population of which p^2 are AA, $2pq$ are Aa, and q^2 are aa will produce on random mating a population of exactly the same structure.

1.3 ANOTHER EXAMPLE OF USE OF LAWS OF PROBABILITY

Suppose we have a very large population composed of P AA's, $2Q$ Aa's, and R aa's and that there is complete dominance. Now suppose that we make a random mating of two dominants, what is the probability that an offspring is recessive?

Since we are mating only dominants, the probabilities of achieving parenthood are

$$\frac{P}{P + 2Q} \text{ for the } AA\text{'s}$$

$$\frac{2Q}{P + 2Q} \text{ for the } Aa\text{'s}$$

These are both conditional probabilities: that is, probabilities conditional on the parents being dominants. The event of an offspring being aa, say E, can be broken down into parts as follows:

E_1 that the mating is $AA \times AA$ and yields an aa
E_2 that the mating is $AA \times Aa$ and yields an aa
E_3 that the mating is $Aa \times AA$ and yields an aa
E_4 that the mating is $Aa \times Aa$ and yields an aa

Then, since these are exclusive forms

$$P(E) = P(E_1) + P(E_2) + P(E_3) + P(E_4)$$

But

$$P(E_1) = P(\text{mating is } AA \times AA) \times P(\text{offspring is } aa, \text{ given that}$$
$$\text{mating is } AA \times AA)$$

$$= \frac{P^2}{(P + 2Q)^2} \times 0$$

$$= 0$$

Similarly $P(E_2)$, $P(E_3)$, and $P(E_4)$ can be obtained by the use of conditional probabilities, and we find that

$$P(E) = \frac{Q^2}{(P + 2Q)^2}$$

If in fact the population is a random mating one so that $P = p^2$, $Q = pq$, we have

$$P(E) = \frac{p^2 q^2}{(p^2 + 2pq)^2} = \frac{q^2}{(p + 2q)^2} = \frac{q^2}{(1 + q)^2} = \left(\frac{q}{1 + q}\right)^2$$

This suggests a method by which we could estimate q in a population if we can make the necessary assumptions, by observing the proportion of *aa* offspring in dominant × dominant matings, say p_{aa}. Then we may estimate q by

$$\frac{\hat{q}}{1 + \hat{q}} = \sqrt{p_{aa}}$$

or

$$\hat{q} = \frac{\sqrt{p_{aa}}}{1 - \sqrt{p_{aa}}}$$

This method is due to Snyder. We shall be considering the problems of estimation of gene frequency in later chapters.

1.4 PERMUTATIONS AND COMBINATIONS

This topic is necessary to the subject of statistical methods in genetics almost only insofar as it is useful in the derivation of the binomial and multinomial theorems. We have so far been concerned with the calculation of probabilities, and for instance we found that the probability of the offspring of a mating dominant × dominant in a random mating population being recessive is

$$\frac{q^2}{(1 + q)^2}$$

Given this result, what can we say about a family of say six offspring? How many of them will be recessive? Suppose the family is a human family and the recessive in fact dies soon after birth, what can one say about the number of pregnancies which will be necessary before an offspring which will not die is obtained? These are all questions of evaluating probabilities, but we may shorten the process by obtaining the binomial and multinomial theorems.

We first define a permutation of n symbols or objects r at a time. Consider n objects, say $a, b, c, d, \cdots$, and let us ask the question: In how many ways may we make an ordered selection of r of these objects? Note that we say "ordered selection," by which we mean that two selections involving the same objects are not the same "ordered selection" unless objects occur in the same order. Thus ab and ba are different ordered selections, but contain the same objects. The answer to our question is easily seen, for we may choose the first object in n ways, the second in $(n-1)$ ways, since we will have removed one object in our first choice, the third in $(n-2)$ ways, and so on. The number of selections will then be

$$n(n - 1)(n - 2) \cdots (n - r + 1)$$

This number is usually denoted by $_nP_r$, and to shorten the formula we use another piece of shorthand, namely that

$$n(n-1)(n-2)\cdots 2.1$$

is denoted by $n!$ which is read as "n factorial." The symbol $0!$ is conventionally taken to be unity since this is consistent with the formula

$$(n-1)! = n!/n \quad \text{with} \quad n = 1$$

It is then easy to see that

$$_nP_r = \frac{n!}{(n-r)!}$$

We now consider the number of selections of r objects which can be made from n objects, where no account is taken of the order of occurrence, and in fact such an order may not exist. This is called the number of combinations of n objects r at a time and is denoted by $_nC_r$. The best way to get the formula for $_nC_r$ is to utilize the information about permutations we have already obtained. Consider a particular combination of r objects. This combination can be arranged in $r!$ ordered ways, which is of course the number of permutations of r objects r at a time. Therefore, in picking out the permutations of n objects r at a time, each combination of n objects r at a time is represented $r!$ times. The number of combinations of n objects r at a time is therefore

$$_nC_r = \frac{1}{r!}\,_nP_r = \frac{n!}{r!(n-r)!}$$

and this is also frequently denoted by $\binom{n}{r}$.

We are now in a position to answer the following question. Suppose the probability of an event on one trial is p, what is the probability of r events in n independent trials? Suppose that n equals 3 and r equals 2. This result can arise in the following ways, where e denotes the event, and $\bar{e}$ the non-occurrence of the event,

$$ee\bar{e}, \quad e\bar{e}e, \quad \text{and} \quad \bar{e}ee$$

If we now consider the general case of r events in n trials, we have all possible distinct ways of writing r e's and $(n-r)$ $\bar{e}$'s in order. We can put the r e's in the n spaces in $_nC_r$ different ways, for all we have to do to get a particular order of e's and $\bar{e}$'s is to pick r objects out of n or r spaces out of n spaces for the e's. Furthermore the probability of any one order of e's and $\bar{e}$'s is $p^r(1 - p)^{n-r}$. We have therefore obtained the probability as

$$P(r \text{ successes in } n \text{ trials}) = {}_nC_r p^r q^{n-r} = \frac{n!}{r!(n-r)!} p^r q^{n-r}$$

where $q = 1 - p$.

When we make n trials, we can and must obtain a number of successes which is between 0 and n, so that the probability of 0, 1, 2, $\cdots$, $n-1$ or n successes is unity. We therefore have, with $q = 1 - p$ as before,

$$p^n + \frac{n!}{1!(n-1)!} p^{n-1}q + \frac{n!}{2!(n-2)!} p^{n-2}q^2 + \cdots$$

$$+ \frac{n!}{r!(n-r)!} p^r q^{n-r} + \cdots + q^n = 1$$

which holds for any positive integer n, since the probabilities of the separate possibilities must add to unity. This corresponds to the binomial equation

$$(p + q)^n = p^n + \frac{n!}{1!(n-1)!} p^{n-1}q + \cdots + \frac{n!}{r!(n-r)!} p^r q^{n-r} + \cdots + q^n$$

A variable which can take integral values between 0 and n, with probability of being r equal to $\dfrac{n!}{r!(n-r)!} p^r(1 - p)^{n-r}$ is said to be a binomial random variable and is said to follow the binomial distribution.

1.5 NOTES ON THE BINOMIAL EXPANSION

There is a simple diagrammatic way in which the coefficients ${}_nC_r$ or $\dfrac{n!}{r!(n-r)!}$, which are called the binomial coefficients, can be obtained. Consider the sum of ${}_nC_r$ and ${}_nC_{r-1}$. We have

$$\begin{aligned}
{}_nC_r + {}_nC_{r-1} &= \frac{n!}{r!(n-r)!} + \frac{n!}{(r-1)!(n-r+1)!} \\[2mm]
&= n! \frac{(n-r+1)+r}{r!(n-r+1)!} = \frac{n!(n+1)}{r!(n-r+1)!} \\[2mm]
&= \frac{(n+1)!}{r!(n+1-r)!} = {}_{n+1}C_r
\end{aligned}$$

Also $_nC_n = {}_nC_0 = 1$. We therefore construct Table 1.2.

TABLE 1.2

SCHEME FOR GETTING BINOMIAL COEFFICIENTS

n	0	1	2	3	4	5	6												
													1						
1	1	1												1		1			
2	1	2	1									1		2		1			
3	1	3	3	1							1		3		3		1		
4	1	4	6	4	1			or		1		4		6		4		1	
5	1	5	10	10	5	1			1		5		10		10		5		1
6	1	6	15	20	15	6	1	1		6		15		20		15		6	1

The process is to start with the first row which is obvious. In any succeeding row of the left-hand part of Table 1.2 the first and last figures are both unity, and any intermediately placed figure is obtained by forming the sum of the figure directly above and the one to its left. In the right-hand part of Table 1.2, the computations are arranged in the form of a triangle.

It is occasionally desirable to obtain a good approximation to the probability of r successes in n trials with specified p, when n and r are sufficiently large to make direct computation tedious. An approximation is easily obtained by use of logarithms and Stirling's formula which states that

$$\log_e n! = \log_e \sqrt{2\pi} - n + \left(n + \frac{1}{2}\right) \log_e n + \frac{1}{12n}$$

where $\log_e n$ is the natural logarithm of n. This calculation is further eased by the existence of tables of logarithms of factorials.

1.6 PROPERTIES OF THE BINOMIAL DISTRIBUTION

Suppose we have six offspring and the probability of an individual of specified nature, e.g. recessive is $\frac{1}{4}$, then the probabilities of 0, 1, 2, $\cdots$, 6 recessive are

No.	Probability
6	$(\frac{1}{4})^6$
5	$6(\frac{3}{4})(\frac{1}{4})^5$
4	$15(\frac{3}{4})^2(\frac{1}{4})^4$
3	$20(\frac{3}{4})^3(\frac{1}{4})^3$
2	$15(\frac{3}{4})^4(\frac{1}{4})^2$
1	$6(\frac{3}{4})^5(\frac{1}{4})$
0	$(\frac{3}{4})^6$

We can now ask various questions, for example, what is the most probable number of recessives? or what is the average number of recessives? and so on. Actually we are rarely interested only in the most probable number in genetic research. The above properties are said to be properties of the corresponding distribution. For example, the most probable number is called the mode of the distribution in general statistical writing.

An important concept in the description and understanding of distributions is that of expectation. Let x be a random variable, and let $f(x)$ be a function of x, such as $x - \mu$, or x^2. Then the expectation of $f(x)$ is the average value which $f(x)$ would take with infinitely many repetitions of the sampling. In the case when x takes the values 0, 1, 2, $\cdots$ with probabilities P_0, P_1, P_2, $\cdots$, the expectation of $f(x)$, denoted by $E[f(x)]$, is given by

$$E[f(x)] = f(0)\,P_0 + f(1)\,P_1 + f(2)\,P_2 + \cdots$$
$$= \sum_x f(x)\,P_x$$

If x can take a continuum of values, the summation is replaced by integration. The expectation of $f(x)$ is also the true or population mean of $f(x)$. Sometimes, for brevity, one says merely "the mean of $f(x)$." It is of course essential to be clear whether the sample or population mean is referred to in any particular context. The context is usually clearly indicative because a sample mean is a random variable, whereas a population mean is a function of the fixed parameters of the distribution, that is, the quantities which must be known before the array of probabilities can be written down numerically.

For most statistical purposes we wish to know the moments of the distribution, which we shall now define in general. The first moment is more generally called the mean of the distribution or the expectation of the number of recessives (or successes as the case may be). It is usually denoted by μ, and by definition

$$\mu = nP_n + (n-1)P_{n-1} + (n-2)P_{n-2} + \cdots + 1P_1 + 0P_0$$

where $\quad P_0$ is the probability of 0 successes

$\qquad\quad P_1$ is the probability of 1 success

$\qquad\quad P_2$ is the probability of 2 successes and so on

We write this as $\displaystyle\sum_{r=0}^{n} rP_r$.

The reason why we are interested in the mean μ of the distribution is that, if we in fact did a large number of sets of n trials (or had a large number of sets of n offspring where the probability is the same), we would expect to get a mean number of successes close to μ. Let us then find μ. In fact,

$$\mu = np^n + (n-1)\frac{n!}{1!(n-1)!}p^{n-1}q + (n-2)\frac{n!}{2!(n-2)!}p^{n-2}q^2$$

$$+ \cdots + (n-r)\frac{n!}{r!(n-r)!}p^{n-r}q^r + \cdots$$

$$= np^n + \frac{n!}{1!(n-2)!}p^{n-1}q + \frac{n!}{2!(n-3)!}p^{n-2}q^2 + \cdots$$

$$+ \frac{n!}{r!(n-r-1)!}p^{n-r}q^r + \cdots$$

$$= np\left[p^{n-1} + \frac{(n-1)!}{1!(n-2)!}p^{n-2}q + \frac{(n-1)!}{2!(n-3)!}p^{n-3}q^2 + \cdots\right.$$

$$\left. + \frac{(n-1)!}{r!(n-r-1)!}p^{n-r-1}q^r + \cdots\right]$$

$$= np(p+q)^{n-1}$$

$$= np$$

Thus the mean of the binomial distribution is np. A further property of considerable utility is the variance or second moment about the mean, which is the average value or expectation of $(r - np)^2$. For example, the probability of r successes is P_r, and on the average we would get np observations; so the deviation from the mean is $r - np$. The variance is then

$$\sum_r P_r(r - np)^2$$

In general for a variable x with mean μ the variance is the average of $(x - \mu)^2$. It is simpler frequently to get this and other moments indirectly as in the following way. We have

$$\sum_r P_r(r - np)^2 = \sum_r P_r(r^2 - 2rnp + n^2p^2)$$

$$= \sum_r r^2 P_r - 2np\sum_r rP_r + n^2p^2\sum_r P_r$$

$$= \sum_r r^2 P_r - 2(np)(np) + n^2p^2$$

$$= \sum_r r^2 P_r - n^2p^2$$

So we shall find $\sum r^2 P_r$. Even this job can be simplified by noting that

$$\sum_r r^2 P_r = \sum_r [r(r-1) + r]P_r = \sum_r r(r-1)P_r + \sum_r rP_r$$

We have already found $\sum_r rP_r$ to be np; so we proceed to find

$$\sum_r r(r-1)P_r$$

$$\sum_r r(r-1)P_r = n(n-1)p^n + (n-1)(n-2)\frac{n!}{1!(n-1)!}p^{n-1}q$$

$$+ (n-2)(n-3)\frac{n!}{2!(n-2)!}p^{n-2}q^2 + \cdots$$

$$+ (n-r)(n-r-1)\frac{n!}{r!(n-r)!}p^{n-r}q^r + \cdots$$

$$= n(n-1)p^n + \frac{n!}{1!(n-3)!}p^{n-1}q + \frac{n!}{2!(n-4)!}p^{n-2}q^2$$

$$+ \cdots + \frac{n!}{r!(n-r-2)!}p^{n-r}q^r + \cdots$$

$$= n(n-1)p^2\left[p^{n-2} + \frac{(n-2)!}{1!(n-3)!}p^{n-3}q + \frac{(n-2)!}{2!(n-4)!}p^{n-4}q^2\right.$$

$$\left. + \cdots + \frac{(n-2)!}{r!(n-2-r)!}p^{n-2-r}q^r + \cdots\right]$$

$$= n(n-1)p^2$$

Therefore $\sum_r r^2 P_r = n(n-1)p^2 + np$, and

$$\sum_r (r-np)^2 P_r = n(n-1)p^2 + np - n^2p^2$$

$$= n^2p^2 - np^2 + np - n^2p^2$$

$$= np - np^2$$

$$= np(1-p)$$

$$= npq$$

We have then obtained the well-known formula for the binomial variance. It should be noted that we have obtained the variance of the number of successes. Frequently one wishes to think not in terms of the *number* of successes but in terms of the *proportion* of successes. The proportion of successes when we observe r successes is clearly r/n. Let us now find the mean and variance of the proportion of successes. In fact

$$\text{Mean proportion} = \sum_r \frac{r}{n} P_r = \frac{1}{n} \sum_r r P_r = \frac{1}{n} \cdot np = p$$

$$\text{Variance of proportion} = \sum_r \left(\frac{r}{n} - p\right)^2 P_r = \frac{1}{n^2} \sum_r (r - np)^2 P_r$$

$$= \frac{1}{n^2} npq = \frac{pq}{n}$$

The third moment about the mean is the expectation of $(r - np)^3$, and the fourth moment is the expectation of $(r - np)^4$. These can be calculated directly in the same way as were the first and second moments. We shall merely state the results here: namely

3rd moment about mean $= np(1 - p)(1 - 2p)$

4th moment about mean $= 3n^2p^2q^2 + npq(1 - 6pq)$.

1.7 THE NORMAL CURVE OF ERROR

For reasons to be described later, the distribution known as the normal or Gaussian distribution is of fundamental importance in the whole of statistical theory and application. Unlike the binomial distribution which has already been described, this distribution is a continuous one. The binomial distribution is called a discrete distribution because all the probability is concentrated at the positive integers, and all discrete distributions have the property that the probability is concentrated at points between which there is no probability. (We cannot, for example, have 2.45 successes in 6 trials.) The formula for the normal distribution is

$$y = \frac{1}{(2\pi)^{1/2}\sigma} \exp\left[-\frac{1}{2\sigma^2}(x - \mu)^2\right]$$

and this curve is pictured in Figure 1.1, with some points of particular practical importance.

The area under the whole curve is unity corresponding to the fact that a random variable must be somewhere between minus infinity and plus infinity. The mean of the distribution is μ, and the variance is σ^2, and the probability that the random variable takes a value less than x is equal to the area under the curve to the left of an ordinate erected at x. There are numerous sets of tables which give the ordinates for various x and the area to the left of x for a series of values of x. This distribution is important for at least two reasons:

1. Many populations in the real world appear to have a distribution with respect to some characteristics which is closely approximated by the normal distribution.

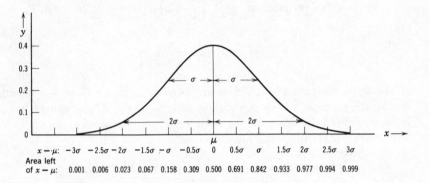

FIGURE 1.1.   The normal curve with areas to left of various ordinates.

2. It can be shown that in a certain mathematical sense (which is of practical utility) most distributions tend in form to a normal distribution as some parameters get large. In addition, it can be shown that, if a quantity x is the sum of a large number of independent small quantities with reasonable properties (actually finite variance), then x tends to be normally distributed. We shall state below the way in which the binomial distribution tends to have normal form or in other words tends to normality as n, the size of sample, gets large.

It can be shown that the probability that in n trials there will be a number of successes equal to or greater than r_1 and less than or equal to r_2 is equal approximately to the probability that a normal variable with mean zero and unit variance lies between

$$\frac{r_1 - np}{(npq)^{1/2}} \quad \text{and} \quad \frac{r_2 - np}{(npq)^{1/2}}$$

In other words

$$\frac{r - np}{(npq)^{1/2}}$$

is approximately normally distributed. By including the "correction for continuity" the approximation is improved by calculating the probability that the normal deviate lies between

$$\frac{r_1 - np - \frac{1}{2}}{(npq)^{1/2}} \quad \text{and} \quad \frac{r_2 - np + \frac{1}{2}}{(npq)^{1/2}}$$

For example, from the tables of the incomplete beta function we know that, with $n = 50$ and $p = 0.3$, the probability of a number of successes between 10 and 22 is 0.9475. Without the continuity correction we find the approximate probability to be 0.9232, and with the correction it is 0.9449.

The approximation of the binomial by the normal distribution is not uniformly good. We see for instance that the normal distribution is completely symmetrical about the mean whereas the binomial distribution is not, unless $p = q$, or n is large. See Feller (1950) for a definitive account of all such matters.

1.8 THE POISSON DISTRIBUTION

It can be shown that the binomial distribution tends to a distribution called the Poisson distribution under some circumstances. The mathematical fact is that the probability of r successes in n trials, which is

$$\frac{n!}{r!(n-r)!} p^r q^{n-r}$$

tends to

$$e^{-np} \frac{(np)^r}{r!}$$

if n tends to infinity and p tends to zero, in such a way that np stays constant. A random variable x with expectation m is said to have the Poisson distribution if

$$P(x=r) = e^{-m} \frac{m^r}{r!}$$

so that the binomial distribution tends to the Poisson distribution with mean m. It can be shown that the expected value of r is equal to m and that the variance of r is also m. This distribution tends to the normal distribution as m gets large in essentially the same sense as the binomial distribution tends to normality.

The Poisson law is useful in getting quick approximations to binomial probabilities.

1.9 THE MULTINOMIAL DISTRIBUTION

Let us take the simple situation of selfing an Aa individual and obtaining ten offspring. We know that on the average we will get $2\frac{1}{2}$ AA's, $2\frac{1}{2}$ aa's, and 5 Aa's. Clearly we will not get these numbers at one trial but shall get some numbers distributed in some way around their expectations. To consider the general situation we suppose we make n trials and that there are t possible results, say $a_1, a_2, \cdots, a_t$ with probabilities $P_1, P_2, P_3, \cdots, P_t$. What is the probability that we shall get n_1 a_1's, n_2 a_2's, and so on? Again the matter is solved by permutations and combinations, for any possible arrangement of n_1 a_1's, n_2 a_2's and so on has probability

$$P_1^{n_1} P_2^{n_2} \cdots P_t^{n_t}$$

and we have to find out in how many ways this result can arise. Now we can choose n_1 of the individuals to be a_1's in $n!/(n - n_1)!$ ways; we can then choose n_2 of the individuals to be a_2's in $(n - n_1)!/(n - n_1 - n_2)!$ ways, and so on. So the total number of ways in which we can pick out n_1 a_1's, n_2 a_2's, and so on is

$$\frac{n!}{(n - n_1)!} \frac{(n - n_1)!}{(n - n_1 - n_2)!} \frac{(n - n_1 - n_2)!}{(n - n_1 - n_2 - n_3)!} \cdots$$

But we have obtained the number of permutations and we want the number of combinations. The n_1 a_1's can be permuted in $n_1!$ ways and therefore in our count we shall have counted each combination of n_1 a_1's $n_1!$ times. Similarly for the other a_i's. So the number of distinct ways of picking out n_1 a_1's, n_2 a_2's, etc. is

$$\frac{n!}{n_1! \, n_2! \, n_3! \cdots n_t!}$$

and the probability of getting n_1 a_1's, n_2 a_2's, etc. is

$$\frac{n!}{n_1! \, n_2! \cdots n_t!} P_1^{n_1} P_2^{n_2} \cdots P_t^{n_t}$$

In our initial example we can say that the probability of 3 AA's, 5 Aa's, and 2 aa's is

$$\frac{10!}{3! \, 5! \, 2!} \left(\frac{1}{4}\right)^3 \left(\frac{2}{4}\right)^5 \left(\frac{1}{4}\right)^2$$

A more complex example is the case of the O, A, B blood groups. We shall use some knowledge to be covered in Chapter 2, and merely state that, if the gene frequencies for the A, B, O alleles are p, q, and r, respectively, with $p + q + r = 1$, then the probabilities for the various types under panmixia are

Phenotype	Probability
O	r^2
A	$p^2 + 2pr$
B	$q^2 + 2qr$
AB	$2pq$

If we observe a sample of n individuals then, we can say that the probability of n_1 O individuals, n_2 A individuals, n_3 B individuals, and n_4 AB individuals, is

$$\frac{n!}{n_1!\,n_2!\,n_3!\,n_4!}\,(r^2)^{n_1}(p^2 + 2pr)^{n_2}(q^2 + 2qr)^{n_3}(2pq)^{n_4}$$

As we shall see later, knowledge of this probability is necessary for the estimation of the gene frequencies p, q, and r, given a random sample of a population.

1.10 PROPERTIES OF THE MULTINOMIAL DISTRIBUTION

We shall review only the properties essential for elementary genetic analysis. First we would like to know the expectation of the number of a_1's, of a_2's, and so on. This follows immediately from the binomial case. Consider the a_1's, and lump together all the other classes into say the $\bar{a}_1$ class. Then n_1 and $\bar{n}_1$, the numbers in these two classes, follow the binomial distribution

$$[P_1 + (1 - P_1)]^n$$

and the expectation of n_1 is nP_1, and its variance is $n\,P_1(1 - P_1)$. Similarly $E(n_i) = nP_i$, and $V(n_i) = n\,P_i(1 - P_i)$, where E stands for expectation and V for variance.

Finally we have to consider the way $n_1, n_2, \cdots, n_t$ vary together. If for example n_1 equals n, then $n_2, n_3, \cdots, n_t$ must all be zero, so that there is some tendency for the n_i's to vary in opposition to each other. Consider two new classes, say c_1 and c_2, where individuals fall into class c_1 if they are a_1 or a_2 individuals and into c_2 otherwise. The observed number in class c_1 is $(n_1 + n_2)$, and we know that this number and $(n - n_1 - n_2)$ are binomially distributed, so that

$$V(n_1 + n_2) = n(P_1 + P_2)(1 - P_1 - P_2)$$

Now we know $V(n_1)$, $V(n_2)$, and $V(n_1 + n_2)$, and we have to find how n_1 and n_2 tend to vary together. This is measured by the covariance. In general terms the covariance of two random variables x and y with expectations μ_x and μ_y is

$$E(x - \mu_x)(y - \mu_y) = \text{Cov}\,(x, y)$$

in other words, the average product of deviations from the respective means.

Now

$$(n_1 - nP_1 + n_2 - nP_2)^2 = (n_1 - nP_1)^2 + (n_2 - nP_2)^2$$
$$+ 2(n_1 - nP_1)(n_2 - nP_2)$$

so

$$V(n_1 + n_2) = V(n_1) + V(n_2) + 2\,\text{Cov}\,(n_1, n_2)$$

Therefore

$$2\,\text{Cov}\,(n_1, n_2) = n(P_1 + P_2)(1 - P_1 - P_2) - n\,P_1(1 - P_1) - n\,P_2(1 - P_2)$$
$$= nP_1 + nP_2 - nP_1^2 - nP_2^2 - 2nP_1P_2 - nP_1 + nP_1^2$$
$$- nP_2 + nP_2^2$$
$$= -2nP_1P_2$$

So that

$$\text{Cov}\,(n_1, n_2) = -nP_1P_2$$

Finally, if we denote the observed *proportions* by $p_1, p_2, \ldots, p_t$, we have

$$E(p_i) = P_i$$

$$V(p_i) = \frac{P_i(1 - P_i)}{n}, \qquad \text{Cov}\,(p_i, p_j) = -\frac{P_iP_j}{n}.$$

1.11* MOMENT GENERATING FUNCTIONS

There is a mathematical device which is of considerable utility in finding the moments of distributions. Consider for illustration a distribution of a random variable x which is discrete and such that

$$P(x=0) = P_0, \quad P(x=1) = P_1, \quad \text{etc.}$$

Now consider the expectation of the quantity e^{tx}, where e is the base of natural logarithms. By definition this is equal to

$$e^0 P_0 + e^t P_1 + e^{2t} P_2 + \cdots$$

or, more simply,

$$\sum_x e^{tx} P_x$$

* Not necessary for continuity.

This is a function of t only, say $M(t)$. But we have

$$e^{tx} = 1 + tx + \frac{(tx)^2}{2!} + \cdots + \frac{(tx)^r}{r!} + \cdots$$

so

$$M(t) = \sum_x e^{tx} P_x = (\sum P_x) + t(\sum x P_x) + \frac{t^2}{2!} \sum x^2 P_x + \cdots$$

$$+ \frac{t^r}{r!} \sum x^r P_x + \cdots$$

Since

$$\mu_1' = \sum x P_x = \text{mean or first moment}$$
$$\mu_2' = \sum x^2 P_x = \text{expectation of } x^2 = \text{2nd moment about origin, etc.}$$
$$\mu_r' = \sum x^r P_x = r\text{th moment about origin}$$

we have

$$M(t) = 1 + t\mu_1' + \frac{t^2}{2!} \mu_2' + \cdots + \frac{t^r}{r!} \mu_r' + \cdots$$

If therefore we can find $M(t)$ and then expand it in powers of t, we can read off the moments immediately.

A simple example is the binomial distribution for which

$$P_x = \frac{n!}{x!(n-x)!} p^x q^{n-x}$$

so that

$$\sum_x e^{tx} P_x = \sum \frac{n!}{x!(n-x)!} e^{tx} p^x q^{n-x}$$

$$= \sum \frac{n!}{x!(n-x)!} (pe^t)^x q^{n-x}$$

$$= (pe^t + q)^n$$

$$= \left(1 + pt + p\frac{t^2}{2!} + \cdots + p\frac{t^r}{r!} + \cdots\right)^n$$

If in addition one has knowledge of the differential calculus, one knows that the rth moment about the origin $E(x^r)$ usually denoted by μ_r' is given by

$$\mu_r' = \frac{\partial r}{\partial t^r} [M(t)] \Big|_{t=0}$$

the rth derivative of $M(t)$ evaluated at $t = 0$.

To get "moments about the mean" or moments about the expectation we may take

$$\sum_x e^{t(x-\mu)}P_x = M_\mu(t) = M(t)e^{-t\mu}$$

and then read off the rth moment as the coefficient of $t^r/r!$ in $M_\mu(t)$.

The idea of moment generating functions can be extended to the case of the joint distribution of several variables, but there are more pressing matters which require our attention.

REFERENCE

Feller, W. 1950. *An introduction to probability theory and its applications.* John Wiley & Sons, New York.

PROBLEMS

1. What are the probabilities of 0, 1, 2, 3, 4, 5, 6, 7, 8, 9, 10 heads with 10 tosses of a penny?

2. What is the probability that 3 tosses of a penny will give (a) exactly 2 heads, (b) 2 or more heads?

3. In how many different orders can a family of 3 boys and 2 girls arise?

4. What is the probability that 2 tosses of a die will give a total of 7?

5. What is the probability of a family of six containing at least one boy and one girl?

6. If one wishes to have a family that contains at least one boy, how many children should one have?

7. Suppose one obtains 100 progeny from the cross $Aa \times aa$. What is the probability that the number of Aa progeny is 50?

8. With the same conditions as question 7, what is the probability that the number of Aa progeny will be between 40 and 60? What is the probability that the number of Aa progeny will be less than 20.

9. What is the probability that the total of the results of two tosses of a die will be (a) even, (b) divisible by 3, (c) both even and divisible by 3?

10. Suppose we have the population

$$\tfrac{1}{4}AA + \tfrac{1}{2}Aa + \tfrac{1}{4}aa$$

and there is complete dominance, so that AA and Aa are indistinguishable. We then mate two random dominant individuals. What is the probability that one offspring will be AA? What is the probability that two offspring of such a mating will be both AA?

11. Suppose we have the population

$$p^2\,AA + 2pq\,Aa + q^2\,aa$$

and mating is at random. What is the conditional probability that an offspring is aa, given that the sire is Aa?

12. Evaluate numerically the mean and variance of the binomial population for which $n = 8$ and $p = \frac{1}{2}$.

13. Given a mating $Aa \times aa$, what is the probability that r offspring out of a total of n are aa, given that at least one offspring is aa?

14. Given that an event has probability 0.0001, what is the probability that the event will not happen in (a) 100 trials, (b) 1000 trials?

15. Prove that the expected value of the random variable r in the Poisson distribution

$$P_r = e^{-m} \frac{m^r}{r!}$$

is equal to m.

16. Prove that the variance of r in question 15 is m.

17. Evaluate the probabilities in question 14 by means of the Poisson distribution.

18. Given a mating of 2 A-type individuals in a random mating population, what is the probability that an offspring will be of O type.

19. Given a mating of 2 A-type individuals, what is the probability that two offspring will be of O type?

20. What is the probability that four progeny of a mating of an A-type individual with a B-type individual will contain one of each of the 4 types?

21. Show that, if $f(z) = E(z^t)$, then the mean μ and variance μ_2 of t are given by

$$\mu = \left. \frac{d \log f(z)}{d \log z} \right|_{z=1}$$

$$\mu_2 = \left. \frac{d^2 \log f(z)}{d (\log z)^2} \right|_{z=1}$$

Apply these formulas to the binomial distribution.

22. Show that with $f(z)$ as in problem 21, the mean μ and $\mu_2' - \mu_1$ are given by

$$\mu = \left. \frac{df(z)}{dz} \right|_{z=1}$$

$$\mu_2' - \mu = \left. \frac{d^2 f(z)}{dz^2} \right|_{z=1}$$

CHAPTER 2

Random Mating Populations

Our aim in this chapter is to illustrate the uses of probability theory in examining some simple problems in population dynamics: that is, in how populations under a particular set of conditions change from generation to generation. For example, we may ask how a population started by the mating

$$\frac{AB}{ab} \times \frac{AB}{ab}$$

will change in successive generations. In the mating which we can regard as the zeroth generation, the proportion of individuals in the coupling phase is 100 per cent. We may ask what the proportion of coupling double heterozygotes will be in 10 generations, in 100 generations, or 1000 generations. The ability to answer questions of this sort is crucial to an understanding of quantitative inheritance and evolutionary theory. It may perhaps be remarked that such problems are more mathematical than statistical, and this is true insofar as the theory of probability is a branch of mathematics. However, it is necessary for our purposes to cover the laws of probability, and we regard the particular problems in population dynamics reviewed here as excellent exercises in the application of simple probability theory. We shall be concerned almost entirely with diploid individuals, though we shall touch on the case of tetraploids. We shall first review the notion of gene frequency and then consider the progress of populations under random mating.

2.1 THE CONCEPT OF GENE FREQUENCY

Suppose we have two alleles at a locus, the three possible genotypes are distinguishable, and we have a count made of each genotype on a population. So for example we have

Genotype	Number	Proportion
AA	N_2	$P = N_2/N$
Aa	N_1	$2Q = N_1/N$
aa	N_0	$R = N_0/N$
Total	N	

Of the total number $2N$ of genes in the population, $2N_2+N_1$ are A's and N_1+2N_0 are a's, so that the proportion of A genes, or the gene frequency P_A of A, is given by

$$P_A = \frac{2N_2 + N_1}{2N} = P + Q$$

Similarly

$$P_a = Q + R$$

We shall not deal extensively in this chapter with the estimation of gene frequencies, but we may consider the following question since we have already acquired the necessary knowledge. Suppose we observe a random sample of size n of a population, observing proportions p_s, $2q_s$, r_s of AA, Aa, and aa. We shall estimate P_A by

$$\hat{P}_A = p_s + q_s$$

where we adopt the standard procedure of distinguishing between a population attribute P_A and the estimate based on a sample $\hat{P}_A$, by the presence of a "hat." (This is read as P_A hat.) What is the variance of $\hat{P}_A$? We know that

$$V(p_s) = P\frac{1 - P}{n}, \qquad V(2q_s) = 2Q\frac{1 - 2Q}{n}, \qquad \text{Cov}(p_s, 2q_s) = \frac{-2PQ}{n}$$

so, since

$$V(p_s + q_s) = V(p_s) + V(q_s) + 2\,\text{Cov}(p_s, q_s)$$

and

$$V(q_s) = \tfrac{1}{4}V(2q_s), \qquad \text{Cov}(pq) = \tfrac{1}{2}\,\text{Cov}(p_s, 2q_s)$$

we have

$$V(\hat{P}_A) = P\frac{1 - P}{n} + \tfrac{1}{2}Q\frac{1 - 2Q}{n} - 2\frac{PQ}{n}$$

so that

$$V(\hat{P}_A) = (P - P^2 + Q/2 - Q^2 - 2PQ)/n$$
$$= (P + Q/2 - (P + Q)^2)/n$$

It may be noted that this is *not* $(P + Q)(1 - \overline{P + Q})/n$. It may, however, be noted that, if $P = p^2$, $Q = pq$, and $R = q^2$, then the genes are combined with the same frequencies as under random mating, and we find

$$V(\hat{P}_A) = (p^2 + \tfrac{1}{2}pq - p^2)/n = pq/2n$$

as we would expect.

2.2 RANDOM MATING

We shall now apply the laws of probability to the study of the progress of populations as regards gene frequency, genotypic frequencies, and so on. We shall first establish a general rule or theorem, which shortens the process considerably. This theorem may be stated as follows:

The genotypic array of a population produced by random mating is the square of the gametic array in the initial population, when each parent contributes equally to the offspring. We shall prove this theorem for a quite general situation. If a population contains a proportion P_1 individuals of type A_1, say, P_2 individuals of type A_2, and so on, then

$$\sum P_i A_i$$

is called the array of the population. In our present connection we need both the gametic array and the genotypic array.

Suppose we have in the initial population g genotypes $G_1, G_2, \cdot \cdot \cdot, G_g$ say in the proportions $P_1, P_2, \cdot \cdot \cdot, P_g$ and that an individual of the ith genotype produces gametes $\alpha_1, \alpha_2, \cdot \cdot \cdot, \alpha_s$ in the proportions $p_{i1}, p_{i2}, \cdot \cdot \cdot, p_{is}$. Then the proportion of matings $G_i \times G_j$ will be $P_i P_j$, and the probability of gametes α_m and α_n coming together in a mating of this type is $p_{im} p_{jn}$. Hence the total genotypic array in the resulting population is

$$\sum_{ij} P_i P_j \sum_{mn} p_{im} p_{jn} \alpha_m \alpha_n$$

where $P_i P_j p_{im} p_{jn}$ is the contribution of individuals with genotype $\alpha_m \alpha_n$ from matings $G_i \times G_j$. But

$$\sum_{ij} P_i P_j \sum_{mn} p_{im} p_{jn} \alpha_m \alpha_n = \sum_{mn} \left(\sum_i P_i p_{im} \alpha_m \right) \left(\sum_j P_j p_{jn} \alpha_n \right)$$

$$= \left(\sum_m \sum_i P_i p_{im} \alpha_m \right)^2$$

But $\sum_m \sum_i P_i p_{im} \alpha_m$ is the gametic array of the initial generation, because the proportion of gametes α_m produced is $\sum_i P_i p_{im}$, since each individual of genotype G_i produces a proportion p_{im} of gametes α_m.

It should be noted that the term random mating is used not merely to describe the situation when matings are made at random, but also includes the requirement which is made tacitly in our theorem that all matings produce the same number of offspring. The situation when there are different numbers of offspring is generally treated as a problem in which selection is operative. In applying our theorem it is essential to realize all the assumptions on which it is based.

Applications of the Theorem

Consider a population consisting of the following:

$$AA \qquad Aa \qquad aa$$
$$P \qquad 2Q \qquad R$$

Then the gametic array is

$$(P + Q)A + (Q + R)a$$

Therefore under random mating the genotypic array in the next generation is

$$[(P + Q)A + (Q + R)a]^2 = (P + Q)^2 AA + 2(P + Q)(Q + R)Aa$$
$$+ (Q + R)^2 aa$$

It is obvious that this population is in equilibrium under random mating because its gametic array is

$$[(P + Q)^2 + (P + Q)(Q + R)]A + [(P + Q)(Q + R) + (Q + R)^2]a$$

which, since $P + 2Q + R = 1$, is

$$(P + Q)A + (Q + R)a$$

and the second generation is, therefore, identical in structure with the first. Hence we have the statement that any population will attain equilibrium for one locus as regards random mating in one generation. The proof of this statement for the case of arbitrary number of alleles is left to the reader.

Consequences of the Theorem in Particular Cases

2 alleles. The population

$$p^2 AA + 2pq Aa + q^2 aa$$

with $p + q = 1$ is in equilibrium under random mating.

3 alleles. The population

$$r^2 aa + p^2 AA + q^2 BB + 2pr Aa + 2qr Ba + 2pq AB$$

with $p + q + r = 1$, is in equilibrium under random mating.

General. With m alleles $A_1, A_2, \cdots, A_m$ the following population is in equilibrium:

$$\left(\sum_i p_i A_i \right)^2 = \sum_i p_i^2 A_i A_i + 2 \sum_{i<j} p_i p_j A_i A_j$$

Generalization of Theorem

It is easily seen that, with random mating, the genotypic array of the offspring is equal to the product of the possible gametic array of the males and the possible gametic array of the females.

2.3 SEX-LINKED GENES

In the case of sex-linked genes, the parents do not contribute equally to all offspring. We shall speak of the female sex as being the homogametic sex, so that females have two X chromosomes. The males will then be heterogametic and will have one X and one Y chromosome. The general structure of transmission to offspring is that the male transmits the X chromosome to his daughters and the Y chromosome to his sons. The female transmits a random sex chromosome to her offspring regardless of their sex. A sex-linked gene is a gene carried on the X chromosome. If the male sex is homogametic, the words male and female or son and daughter must be interchanged in what follows.

As far as such genes are concerned, the male can have possibilities say $A_1, A_2, A_3, \cdots$, while the females will, of course, be diploid with respect to the gene and can have a genotype which is any of the full range, A_1A_1, A_1A_2, A_1A_3, A_2A_2, etc.

In view of the fact that a son receives his X chromosome from the mother, it is obvious that under random mating his genotypic array is the gametic array of the mother. Since the daughters have equal inheritance from both mother and father, their genotypic array under random mating is the product of the gametic array of the father and the gametic array of the mother. To illustrate these points suppose we start with a population and a locus with two alleles, consisting of

Females	AA	Aa	aa
Proportions	r_0	$2s_0$	t_0

with $r_0 + 2s_0 + t_0 = 1$

Males	A	a
Proportions	p_0	q_0

with $p_0 + q_0 = 1$

We attach the suffix 0 to the proportions to denote the fact that these are the proportions in the zeroth generation. Our problem is to calculate the proportions in generations 1, 2, and so on, under random mating.

The gametic array of the females is

$$(r_0 + s_0)A + (s_0 + t_0)a$$

and of the males is

$$p_0A + q_0a$$

so that the genotypic array of the females in generation 1 is

$$[(r_0 + s_0)A + (s_0 + t_0)a](p_0A + q_0a)$$
$$= (r_0 + s_0)p_0AA + [p_0(s_0 + t_0) + q_0(r_0 + s_0)]Aa + q_0(s_0 + t_0)aa$$
$$= r_1AA + 2s_1Aa + t_1aa$$

The genotypic array in generation 1 for the males is the gametic array for the females in generation 0, i.e.,

$$(r_0 + s_0)A + (s_0 + t_0)a = p_1A + q_1a$$

In this way we have expressed the proportions in generation 1 in terms of the proportions in generation 0. Our problem is now to express the proportions in generation 2 in terms of generation 1, which is done, of course, by advancing all subscripts by unity, and then to express these in terms of the frequencies in generation 0.

In fact we have

$$r_{n+1} = p_n(r_n + s_n)$$
$$2s_{n+1} = p_n(s_n + t_n) + q_n(r_n + s_n)$$
$$t_{n+1} = q_n(s_n + t_n)$$

and

$$p_{n+1} = r_n + s_n$$
$$q_{n+1} = s_n + t_n$$

It follows that

$$r_{n+1} = p_n p_{n+1}$$
$$2s_{n+1} = p_n q_{n+1} + q_n p_{n+1}$$
$$t_{n+1} = q_n q_{n+1}$$

Let us construct a table showing the progress of a specified population (the frequencies are not chosen with any real genetic situation in mind).

TABLE 2.1

Generation	r	$2s$	t	p	q
0	0.5	0.2	0.3	0.4	0.6
1	0.24	0.52	0.24	0.6	0.4
2	0.3	0.5	0.2	0.5	0.5
3	0.275	0.5	0.225	0.55	0.45
4	0.289	0.4975	0.2138	0.525	0.475
5	0.282	0.4981	0.2197	0.5375	0.4625
6	0.286	0.4976	0.2168	0.53125	0.46875

We see that gradually the differences in genotypic frequencies from generation to generation tend to decrease. Let us attempt to find how p and q behave.

We have

$$2r_{n+1} + 2s_{n+1} = 2p_n(r_n + s_n) + p_n(s_n + t_n) + q_n(r_n + s_n)$$
$$= p_n + (r_n + s_n)$$

or

$$2p_{n+2} = p_n + p_{n+1}$$

or

$$p_{n+2} - p_{n+1} = (-\tfrac{1}{2})(p_{n+1} - p_n)$$

If then we let

$$p_{n+1} - p_n = \Delta_n$$
$$\Delta_{n+1} = -\tfrac{1}{2}\Delta_n$$
$$\Delta_n = -\tfrac{1}{2}\Delta_{n-1}$$
$$\text{etc.}$$

we have

$$\Delta_{n+1} = (-\tfrac{1}{2})^{n+1}\Delta_0$$

and, when n becomes very large, Δ_n becomes small, tending to zero.

We have therefore

$$p_n = p_0 + (p_1 - p_0) + (p_2 - p_1) + \cdots + (p_n - p_{n-1})$$
$$= p_0 + \Delta_0 + (-\tfrac{1}{2})\Delta_0 + (-\tfrac{1}{2})^2\Delta_0 + \cdots + (-\tfrac{1}{2})^{n-1}\Delta_0$$
$$= p_0 + \Delta_0[1 + (-\tfrac{1}{2}) + (-\tfrac{1}{2})^2 + \cdots + (-\tfrac{1}{2})^{n-1}]$$

We now note that

$$1 + x + x^2 + \cdots + x^{n-1} = \frac{1 - x^n}{1 - x}$$

so putting $x = -\tfrac{1}{2}$

$$p_n = p_0 + \frac{1 - (-\tfrac{1}{2})^n}{\tfrac{3}{2}}\Delta_0$$

We see that, as n gets large, p_n tends to

$$p_0 + \tfrac{2}{3}\Delta_0$$

i.e., to $p_0 + \tfrac{2}{3}(p_1 - p_0) = \tfrac{1}{3}p_0 + \tfrac{2}{3}p_1 = p_\infty$ say

In view of the relationships

$$r_{n+1} = p_n p_{n+1}$$
$$t_{n+1} = q_n q_{n+1}$$

it is obvious that r_n tends to p_∞^2 and t_n tends to q_∞^2 where $q_\infty = 1 - p_\infty$, and s_n tends to $p_\infty q_\infty$.

The treatment here can be generalized immediately to the case of m alleles, m being greater than two. Suppose we denote the alleles by A_i where i takes the values 1, 2, $\cdots$, m. Then the genotypic array for the females in generation zero can be written

$$\sum_{\text{all } i \text{ and } j} P_{ij}^{(0)} A_i A_j$$

where $P_{ij}^{(0)}$ is the frequency of individuals of genotype $A_i A_j$ in the zeroth generation, and $P_{ij}^{(0)} = P_{ji}^{(0)}$. The gametic array of the females is clearly

$$\sum_i \left[\sum_j P_{ij}^{(0)} \right] A_i = \sum_i P_i^{(0)} A_i, \quad \text{say}$$

The genotypic and gametic arrays for the males are identical, being say

$$\sum_i M_i^{(0)} A_i$$

It is left as an exercise to the reader to show that

$$M_i^{(n+1)} = P_i^{(n)}$$
$$2P_{ij}^{(n+1)} = P_i^{(n)} M_j^{(n)} + P_j^{(n)} M_i^{(n)}$$
$$= P_i^{(n)} P_j^{(n-1)} + P_j^{(n)} P_i^{(n-1)}$$

Now, using

$$2 \sum_j P_{ij}^{(n+1)} = 2M_i^{(n+2)}$$

we get

$$2M_i^{(n+2)} = M_i^{(n+1)} + M_i^{(n)}$$

which is the same relation as held in the case of two alleles.

Note on Practical Interest of Above Results

We have seen that the equilibrium for a sex-linked locus is

AA	Aa	aa
p_∞^2	$2p_\infty q_\infty$	q_∞^2

for the homogametic sex, and

A	a
p_∞	q_∞

for the heterogametic sex, where p_∞ is equal to $(p_0 + 2p_1)/3$, and p_0 and p_1 are the frequencies of A in the heterogametic sex in generations 0 and 1.

Suppose that a locus in fact gives rise to a rare recessive sex-linked trait. Then the frequency of the trait in the homogametic sex will be q_∞^2 and in the heterogametic sex will be q_∞.   Therefore the trait will be less frequent in the ratio q_∞ to 1 in the homogametic sex than in the heterogametic sex. Some examples of characters arising in this way are red–green color blindness and pseudohypertropic muscular dystrophy, and hemophilia.

2.4 NOTES ON THE SOLUTION OF RECURRENCE RELATIONS

The equation

$$2p_{n+1} = p_n + p_{n-1}$$

is an example of a class of equations known in mathematics as recurrence relations.   The general form of such a relationship is

$$p_{n+r} + \alpha_{r-1}p_{n+r-1} + \cdots + \alpha_0 p_n = 0$$

which is understood to mean that there is a linear relation between the functions p_n for integral values of n and r.   This type of equation is of fairly frequent occurrence in population dynamics, so that it is desirable to record the general solution.

Consider the equation in E

$$E^r + \alpha_{r-1}E^{r-1} + \cdots + \alpha_1 E + \alpha_0 = 0$$

This equation will have roots $\lambda_1, \lambda_2, \cdots, \lambda_r$, and we can say that

$$p_n = \beta_1 \lambda_1^n + \beta_2 \lambda_2^n + \cdots + \beta_r \lambda_r^n$$

where the values of $\beta_1, \beta_2, \cdots, \beta_r$ are determined from the values $p_0, p_1, \cdots, p_{n-1}$, which must be given in the problem in order that a particular solution may be written down.

This result is special in that all the roots may not be different.   The general result with real roots is that the solution p_n consists additively of a part corresponding to each distinct root, and, if a root λ_i say occurs r times so that $(E - \lambda_i)^r$ is a factor of the left-hand side of the equation in E, then the part deriving from this root is of the form

$$(\beta_{i0} + \beta_{i1}n + \beta_{i2}n^2 + \cdots + \beta_{i(r-1)}n^{r-1})\lambda_i^n$$

The case when some of the roots are not real requires the use of complex numbers and will not be given.   As examples of the procedure, the case

$$p_{n+2} - \tfrac{1}{2}p_{n+1} - \tfrac{1}{2}p_n = 0$$

gives the equation

$$E^2 - \tfrac{1}{2}E - \tfrac{1}{2} = 0$$

with roots 1 and $-\tfrac{1}{2}$, so that

$$p_n = \beta_1 + \beta_2(-\tfrac{1}{2})^n$$

Also, since

$$p_0 = \beta_1 + \beta_2$$
$$p_1 = \beta_1 - \tfrac{1}{2}\beta_2$$
$$p_n = \frac{p_0 + 2p_1}{3} - \frac{2}{3}(-\tfrac{1}{2})^n(p_1 - p_0)$$

As an example of the case of multiple roots the equation

$$p_{n+2} - p_{n+1} + \tfrac{1}{4}p_n = 0$$

leads to

$$p_n = (\beta_{10} + \beta_{11}n)(\tfrac{1}{2})^n$$

2.5 SELF-STERILITY GENES

This case is interesting because the probability argument is rather simple in the case of three alleles. Let the series of alleles at a locus be S_1, S_2, S_3. Then pollen grains containing allele S_i cannot function on plants which contain this allele. There are therefore no homozygous individuals in the population. A plant with genotype S_1S_2 can be fertilized only by S_3 pollen and produces S_1S_3 and S_2S_3 individuals in equal numbers.

Let the initial population genotypic array be

$$x_0 S_1 S_2 + y_0 S_1 S_3 + z_0 S_2 S_3$$

The resulting population is therefore

$$\tfrac{1}{2}x_0(S_1S_3 + S_2S_3) + \tfrac{1}{2}y_0(S_1S_2 + S_2S_3) + \tfrac{1}{2}z_0(S_1S_2 + S_1S_3)$$
$$= \tfrac{1}{2}(y_0 + z_0)S_1S_2 + \tfrac{1}{2}(x_0 + z_0)S_1S_3 + \tfrac{1}{2}(x_0 + y_0)S_2S_3$$
$$= x_1 S_1 S_2 + y_1 S_1 S_3 + z_1 S_2 S_3$$

Here we have

$$x_1 = \tfrac{1}{2}(y_0 + z_0) = \tfrac{1}{2}(1 - x_0)$$

Recurrence relations of this type or specifically those in which a constant appears can be handled by introducing a new variate say

$$X = x + k$$

where k is a constant, and then choosing k so that we get a recurrence relation involving X's only. In this case

$$X_1 - k = \tfrac{1}{2}(1 - X_0 + k)$$

so, if $-k = \frac{1}{2}(1 + k)$, or $k = -\frac{1}{3}$, we have

$$X_1 = -\frac{1}{2}X_0$$

and

$$X_n = (-\frac{1}{2})^n X_0$$

Hence

$$x_n = X_n - k$$
$$= (-\frac{1}{2})^n(x_0 + k) - k$$
$$= \frac{1}{3}[1 - (-\frac{1}{2})^n] + (-\frac{1}{2})^n x_0$$

which is the desired general result.

The same argument applies to y and z. In this particular case then the genotypic frequencies tend to $\frac{1}{3}$ in an oscillatory way.

The general case with more than three alleles is not easy to work out, but presumably the equilibrium population is one in which all genotypes are equally frequent.

2.6 AUTOTETRAPLOIDS

The basic probabilistic facts about autotetraploids in the absence of double reduction are that they have four genes at a locus, say a, b, c, and d, and that a parent passes on to an offspring one of the six possible pairs of genes at random: i.e. one of ab, ac, ad, bc, bd, cd. Hence any one gene is passed on with a probability of $\frac{1}{2}$. If there are two alleles, there

Genotype	Gametes
$AAAA = A^4$	AA
$AAAa = A^3a$	$\frac{1}{2}AA + \frac{1}{2}Aa$
$AAaa = A^2a^2$	$\frac{1}{6}AA + \frac{4}{6}Aa + \frac{1}{6}aa$
$Aaaa = Aa^3$	$\frac{1}{2}Aa + \frac{1}{2}aa$
$aaaa = a^4$	aa

are five genotypes which produce gametes as shown in the table. Consider an initial population mating at random for which the gametic array is

$$x_0 AA + 2y_0 Aa + z_0 aa$$

so that the population in generation 1 is

$$(x_0 AA + 2y_0 Aa + z_0 aa)^2$$

The gametic array in generation 1 is easily found to be

$$(x_0^2 + 2x_0 y_0 + \frac{2}{3}y_0^2 + \frac{1}{3}x_0 z_0)AA + 2(x_0 y_0 + \frac{4}{3}y_0^2 + \frac{2}{3}x_0 z_0 + y_0 z_0)Aa$$
$$+ (\frac{2}{3}y_0^2 + \frac{1}{3}x_0 z_0 + 2y_0 z_0 + z_0^2)aa$$

Hence, if the gametic array in generation 1 is denoted by

$$x_1 AA + 2y_1 Aa + z_1 aa$$

we have

$$x_1 = x_0^2 + 2x_0 y_0 + \tfrac{2}{3}y_0^2 + \tfrac{1}{3}x_0 z_0$$
$$y_1 = x_0 y_0 + \tfrac{1}{3}y_0^2 + \tfrac{2}{3}x_0 z_0 + y_0 z_0$$
$$z_1 = \tfrac{2}{3}y_0^2 + \tfrac{1}{3}x_0 z_0 + 2y_0 z_0 + z_0^2$$

It is easy to verify that gene frequency does not change, and this is, of course, obvious from general considerations. Therefore, let

$$x_0 + y_0 = p = x_1 + y_1$$
$$y_0 + z_0 = q = y_1 + z_1$$

Now consider the quantity $(x_1 - p^2)$. We have

$$x_1 - p^2 = x_0^2 + 2x_0 y_0 + \tfrac{2}{3}y_0^2 + \tfrac{1}{3}x_0 z_0 - (x_0 + y_0)^2$$
$$= \tfrac{1}{3}(x_0 z_0 - y_0^2)$$

Similarly

$$y_1 - pq = -\tfrac{1}{3}(x_0 z_0 - y_0^2)$$

and

$$z_1 - q^2 = \tfrac{1}{3}(x_0 z_0 - y_0^2)$$

The quantity $(xz - y^2)$ is clearly a quantity of intrinsic importance; so let us denote it by Δ, with subscripts to denote the generation. We have

$$x_1 = p^2 + \tfrac{1}{3}\Delta_0$$
$$y_1 = pq - \tfrac{1}{3}\Delta_0$$
$$z_1 = q^2 + \tfrac{1}{3}\Delta_0$$

so that

$$\Delta_1 = (x_1 z_1 - y_1^2) = (p^2 + \tfrac{1}{3}\Delta_0)(q^2 + \tfrac{1}{3}\Delta_0) - (pq - \tfrac{1}{3}\Delta_0)^2$$
$$= p^2 q^2 + \tfrac{1}{3}p^2 \Delta_0 + \tfrac{1}{3}q^2 \Delta_0 + \tfrac{1}{9}\Delta_0^2 - p^2 q^2 + \tfrac{2}{3}pq\Delta_0 - \tfrac{1}{9}\Delta_0^2$$
$$= \tfrac{1}{3}(p^2 + 2pq + q^2)\Delta_0$$
$$= \tfrac{1}{3}\Delta_0$$

Therefore,

$$x_n = p^2 + (\tfrac{1}{3})^n \Delta_0$$
$$y_n = pq - (\tfrac{1}{3})^n \Delta_0$$
$$z_n = q^2 + (\tfrac{1}{3})^n \Delta_0$$

and the genotypic array of the population in generation $n + 1$ is equal to

$$\{[p^2 + (\tfrac{1}{3})^n \Delta_0]AA + 2[pq - (\tfrac{1}{3})^n \Delta_0]Aa + [q^2 + (\tfrac{1}{3})^n \Delta_0]aa\}^2$$

In the limit as n gets indefinitely large the population genotypic array tends to

$$(p^2AA + 2pqAa + q^2aa)^2$$

or more succinctly

$$(pA + qa)^4$$

The equilibrium is reached only asymptotically unless Δ_0 is zero initially, when it is already in equilibrium under random mating.

The derivation given above for the case of 2 alleles can be extended readily to the case of an arbitrary number of alleles.

2.7 TWO LOCI WITH TWO ALLELES PER LOCUS

As soon as we consider two loci, we have to take account of the fact that these loci may be linked. The statistical and probability treatment of the problems may be dealt with by using the two rules:

1. An individual of type AB/ab produces gametes in the following proportions, or with the following probabilities:

AB	Ab	aB	ab
$\frac{1}{2}(1-r)$	$r/2$	$r/2$	$\frac{1}{2}(1-r)$

2. An individual of type Ab/aB produces gametes in the following proportions:

AB	Ab	aB	ab
$r/2$	$\frac{1}{2}(1-r)$	$\frac{1}{2}(1-r)$	$r/2$

The number r is called the recombination value, and is the proportion of cross-over gametes. There are in all nine genotypes with two loci and two alleles per locus, but because of the differences in gamete production between the two types of double heterozygote, there are in fact ten classes of individuals as regards breeding behavior. To facilitate the presentation we shall specify the genotypes in the usual way; the coupling heterozygote by AB/ab and the repulsion heterozygote by Ab/aB. We shall denote the frequencies of the genotypes in the nth generation by $f_{ij}^{(n)}$, where i equals 0, 1, or 2 depending on the number of A genes present, and j equals 0, 1, or 2 likewise. Thus the frequency of $Aabb$ in the nth generation will be denoted by $f_{10}^{(n)}$. For the frequency of coupling and repulsion heterozygotes we shall use $f_{11c}^{(n)}$ and $f_{11r}^{(n)}$, respectively.

The examination of the progress through generations of a random mating population is eased considerably by our general theorem that the genotypic array in generation n is the square of the gametic array in generation $(n-1)$.   In Table 2.2 we list the ten genotypes, their frequencies at generation 0, and the gametes produced by this population.

TABLE 2.2

GAMETE PRODUCTION OF POPULATION

Genotype	Frequency in Generation Zero	Frequency of gametes produced			
		AB	Ab	aB	ab
$AABB$	$f_{22}^{(0)}$	1	0	0	0
$AABb$	$f_{21}^{(0)}$	$\frac{1}{2}$	$\frac{1}{2}$	0	0
$AAbb$	$f_{20}^{(0)}$	0	1	0	0
$AaBB$	$f_{12}^{(0)}$	$\frac{1}{2}$	0	$\frac{1}{2}$	0
AB/ab	$f_{11c}^{(0)}$	$\frac{1}{2}(1-r)$	$\frac{1}{2}r$	$\frac{1}{2}r$	$\frac{1}{2}(1-r)$
Ab/aB	$f_{11r}^{(0)}$	$\frac{1}{2}r$	$\frac{1}{2}(1-r)$	$\frac{1}{2}(1-r)$	$\frac{1}{2}r$
$Aabb$	$f_{10}^{(0)}$	0	$\frac{1}{2}$	0	$\frac{1}{2}$
$aaBB$	$f_{02}^{(0)}$	0	0	1	0
$aaBb$	$f_{01}^{(0)}$	0	0	$\frac{1}{2}$	$\frac{1}{2}$
$aabb$	$f_{00}^{(0)}$	0	0	0	1

The gametic array of the population is therefore

$$[f_{22}^{(0)} + \tfrac{1}{2}f_{21}^{(0)} + \tfrac{1}{2}f_{12}^{(0)} + \tfrac{1}{2}(1 - r)f_{11c}^{(0)} + \tfrac{1}{2}rf_{11r}^{(0)}]AB$$

$$+ [\tfrac{1}{2}f_{21}^{(0)} + f_{20}^{(0)} + \tfrac{1}{2}rf_{11c}^{(0)} + \tfrac{1}{2}(1 - r)f_{11r}^{(0)} + \tfrac{1}{2}f_{10}^{(0)}]Ab$$

$$+ [\tfrac{1}{2}f_{12}^{(0)} + \tfrac{1}{2}rf_{11c}^{(0)} + \tfrac{1}{2}(1 - r)f_{11r}^{(0)} + f_{02}^{(0)} + \tfrac{1}{2}f_{01}^{(0)}]aB$$

$$+ [\tfrac{1}{2}(1 - r)f_{11c}^{(0)} + \tfrac{1}{2}rf_{11r}^{(0)} + \tfrac{1}{2}f_{10}^{(0)} + \tfrac{1}{2}f_{01}^{(0)} + f_{00}^{(0)}]ab$$

which we may write as

$$P_{11}^{(0)}AB + P_{10}^{(0)}Ab + P_{01}^{(0)}aB + P_{00}^{(0)}ab$$

As we have already seen, the population will be at equilibrium for the two loci separately after one generation of random mating.

Given the gametic array, we can write down the frequencies of the genotypes in generation 1 and hence the gametic array for generation 1. For example the frequency of individuals with $AABB$ will be $[P_{11}^{(0)}]^2$, of AB/ab will be $2P_{11}^{(0)}P_{00}^{(0)}$, and so on.   The frequency of AB gametes is seen to be

$$[P_{11}^{(0)^2} + P_{11}^{(0)}P_{10}^{(0)} + P_{11}^{(0)}P_{01}^{(0)} + P_{11}^{(0)}P_{00}^{(0)}(1 - r) + rP_{10}^{(0)}P_{01}^{(0)}]$$

which, since

$$P_{11}^{(0)} + P_{10}^{(0)} + P_{01}^{(0)} + P_{00}^{(0)} = 1$$

is equal to

$$P_{11}^{(0)} - r[P_{11}^{(0)}P_{00}^{(0)} - P_{01}^{(0)}P_{10}^{(0)}] = P_{11}^{(0)} - r\Delta^{(0)}$$

where

$$\Delta^{(0)} = P_{11}^{(0)}P_{00}^{(0)} - P_{01}^{(0)}P_{10}^{(0)}$$

Putting together similar calculations for the other gametes, we find the gametic array for generation 1 to be

$$P_{11}^{(1)}AB + P_{10}^{(1)}Ab + P_{01}^{(1)}aB + P_{00}^{(1)}ab$$

where

$$P_{11}^{(1)} = P_{11}^{(0)} - r\Delta^{(0)}$$

$$P_{10}^{(1)} = P_{10}^{(0)} + r\Delta^{(0)}$$

$$P_{01}^{(1)} = P_{01}^{(0)} + r\Delta^{(0)}$$

$$P_{00}^{(1)} = P_{00}^{(0)} - r\Delta^{(0)}$$

Now let us find

$$\Delta^{(1)} = P_{11}^{(1)}P_{00}^{(1)} - P_{01}^{(1)}P_{10}^{(1)}$$

In fact,

$$\Delta^{(1)} = [P_{11}^{(0)} - r\Delta^{(0)}][P_{00}^{(0)} - r\Delta^{(0)}] - [P_{01}^{(0)} + r\Delta^{(0)}][P_{10}^{(0)} + r\Delta^{(0)}]$$

$$= [P_{11}^{(0)}P_{00}^{(0)} - P_{01}^{(0)}P_{10}^{(0)}] - r\Delta^{(0)}[P_{11}^{(0)} + P_{10}^{(0)} + P_{01}^{(0)} + P_{00}^{(0)}]$$
$$+ r^2\Delta^{(0)^2} - r^2\Delta^{(0)^2}$$

which since

$$P_{11}^{(0)} + P_{10}^{(0)} + P_{01}^{(0)} + P_{00}^{(0)} = 1$$

is equal to

$$\Delta^{(0)} - r\Delta^{(0)}$$

so

$$\Delta^{(1)} = (1 - r)\Delta^{(0)}$$

Similarly,

$$\Delta^{(2)} = (1 - r)\Delta^{(1)} \quad \text{and so on}$$

so that

$$\Delta^{(n)} = (1 - r)^n\Delta^{(0)}$$

Hence, as n tends to infinity, and since r is between zero and unity, $\Delta^{(n)}$ tends to zero.

Now let us find $P_{11}^{(n)}$. We have

$$P_{11}^{(n)} - P_{11}^{(n-1)} = -r\Delta^{(n-1)}$$

$$P_{11}^{(n-1)} - P_{11}^{(n-2)} = -r\Delta^{(n-2)}$$

$$\cdot \quad \cdot \quad \cdot \quad \cdot \quad \cdot \quad \cdot \quad \cdot \quad \cdot \quad \cdot \quad \cdot \quad \cdot$$

$$P_{11}^{(1)} - P_{11}^{(0)} = -r\Delta^{(0)}$$

So, adding, we get

$$P_{11}^{(n)} - P_{11}^{(0)} = -r[\Delta^{(0)} + \Delta^{(1)} + \cdots \Delta^{(n-1)}]$$

$$= -r\Delta^{(0)}[1 + (1 - r) + (1 - r)^2 + \cdots + (1 - r)^{n-1}]$$

$$= -r\Delta^{(0)} \frac{1 - (1 - r)^n}{1 - (1 - r)}$$

$$= -\Delta^{(0)}[1 - (1 - r)^n]$$

We therefore have the result that

$$P_{11}^{(n)} \text{ tends to } P_{11}^{(0)} - \Delta^{(0)} = P_{11}, \quad \text{say}$$

Similarly

$$P_{10}^{(n)} \text{ tends to } P_{10}^{(0)} + \Delta^{(0)} = P_{10}, \quad \text{say}$$

$$P_{01}^{(n)} \text{ tends to } P_{01}^{(0)} + \Delta^{(0)} = P_{01}, \quad \text{say}$$

$$P_{00}^{(n)} \text{ tends to } P_{00}^{(0)} - \Delta^{(0)} = P_{00}, \quad \text{say}$$

The difference between the frequencies of coupling and repulsion hetero-zygotes is seen to be

$$2[P_{11}^{(n)}P_{00}^{(n)} - P_{10}^{(n)}P_{01}^{(n)}] = 2\Delta^{(n)}$$

and we have found that $\Delta^{(n)}$ tends to zero, so that in the equilibrium state, which is approached as n gets large, the coupling and repulsion heterozygotes are equal in frequency.

Furthermore the equilibrium genotypic array is given by

$$(P_{11}AB + P_{10}Ab + P_{01}aB + P_{00}ab)^2$$

Since

$$P_{11}P_{00} - P_{10}P_{01} = 0$$

$$P_{11} = f_A f_B, \qquad P_{10} = f_A f_b, \qquad P_{01} = f_a f_B, \qquad P_{00} = f_a f_b$$

where the f's are the gene frequencies.

Hence we have the total result, that a randomly mating population with two loci tends to a population in which the genotypic frequencies are given by

$$[(f_A A + f_a a)(f_B B + f_b b)]^2$$

where f_A, f_a, f_B, f_b are the original gene frequencies.

2.8 GENERAL TREATMENT OF TWO LINKED LOCI

We shall now give a general result for the case when the number of alleles is arbitrary for each locus and not necessarily the same for both loci. The main purpose of this section is to familiarize the reader with handling summations, and not to provide a short proof of the result.

It is clear from our general theorem on random mating that the only effect an initial generation can have on its succeeding generation is through the gametic array. We shall use the letter A with subscripts i (i_1 or i_2) for the alleles at that one locus and the letter B with subscripts j (j_1 and j_2) for the alleles at the other locus. A genotype will be denoted by $A_{i_1}A_{i_2}B_{j_1}B_{j_2}$ where it is supposed that the individual with this genotype has received genes A_{i_1} and B_{j_1} from the sire and genes $A_{i_2}B_{j_2}$ from the dam. Linkage will then produce the following segregation

$$A_{i_1}B_{j_1} \qquad A_{i_2}B_{j_1} \qquad A_{i_1}B_{j_2} \qquad A_{i_2}B_{j_2}$$
$$\tfrac{1}{2}(1-r) \qquad \tfrac{1}{2}r \qquad \tfrac{1}{2}r \qquad \tfrac{1}{2}(1-r)$$

Note that, if in fact $i_1 = i_2 = i$ say, only two gametes are formed since then $A_{i_1}B_{j_1}$ and $A_{i_2}B_{j_1}$ would be the same as would $A_{i_1}B_{j_2}$ and $A_{i_2}B_{j_2}$, and that these would be produced in equal numbers. We shall write the gametic array in generation 0 as

$$\sum_{ij} P_{ij}A_iB_j$$

The next generation will therefore have a genotypic array

$$\left(\sum_{i_1j_1} P_{i_1j_1}A_{i_1}B_{j_1}\right)\left(\sum_{i_2j_2} P_{i_2j_2}A_{i_2}B_{j_2}\right)$$

corresponding to the fact that an individual in this generation has received a random gamete from the sire and a random one from the dam. This can be written as

$$\sum_{i_1i_2j_1j_2} P_{i_1j_1}P_{i_2j_2}A_{i_1}B_{j_1}A_{i_2}B_{j_2}$$

Now, if we use the above statement about segregation, we see that the gametic array of generation 1 is

$$\sum_{i_1i_2j_1j_2} P_{i_1j_1}P_{i_2j_2}[\tfrac{1}{2}(1-r)A_{i_1}B_{j_1} + \tfrac{1}{2}rA_{i_2}B_{j_1} + \tfrac{1}{2}rA_{i_1}B_{j_2} + \tfrac{1}{2}(1-r)A_{i_2}B_{j_2}]$$

$$= \tfrac{1}{2}(1-r)\sum_{i_1i_2j_1j_2} P_{i_1j_1}P_{i_2j_2}A_{i_1}B_{j_1} + \tfrac{1}{2}r\sum_{i_1i_2j_1j_2} P_{i_1j_1}P_{i_2j_2}A_{i_2}B_{j_1}$$

$$+ \tfrac{1}{2}r\sum_{i_1i_2j_1j_2} P_{i_1j_1}P_{i_2j_2}A_{i_1}B_{j_2} + \tfrac{1}{2}(1-r)\sum_{i_1i_2j_1j_2} P_{i_1j_1}P_{i_2j_2}A_{i_2}B_{j_2}$$

Now in any finite sum such as

$$\sum_{i_1i_2j_1j_2} f(i_1, i_2, j_1, j_2)$$

where the range of summation is independent for each variable (i.e., i_1, i_2, j_1, j_2), we may interchange the symbols as we please. The first term we leave as it stands. The second can be written

$$\tfrac{1}{2}r \sum_{i_1 i_2 j_1 j_2} P_{i_2 j_1} P_{i_1 j_2} A_{i_1} B_{j_1} \quad (i_1 \text{ and } i_2 \text{ interchanged throughout})$$

and the third as

$$\tfrac{1}{2}r \sum_{i_1 i_2 j_1 j_2} P_{i_1 j_2} P_{i_2 j_1} A_{i_1} B_{j_1} \quad (j_1 \text{ and } j_2 \text{ interchanged throughout})$$

and the fourth as

$$\tfrac{1}{2}(1 - r) \sum_{i_1 i_2 j_1 j_2} P_{i_2 j_2} P_{i_1 j_1} A_{i_1} B_{j_1} \quad \begin{array}{l}(i_1 \text{ and } i_2 \text{ interchanged and } j_1 \text{ and } j_2 \\ \qquad \text{interchanged throughout})\end{array}$$

So we find the gametic array in generation 1 to be

$$\sum_{i_1 j_1} \sum_{i_2 j_2} [\tfrac{1}{2}(1 - r)P_{i_1 j_1}P_{i_2 j_2} + \tfrac{1}{2}rP_{i_2 j_1}P_{i_1 j_2} + \tfrac{1}{2}rP_{i_1 j_2}P_{i_2 j_1}$$
$$+ \tfrac{1}{2}(1 - r)P_{i_2 j_2}P_{i_1 j_1}]A_{i_1} B_{j_1}$$
$$= \sum_{i_1 j_1} P'_{i_1 j_1} A_{i_1} B_{j_1}, \quad \text{say}$$

What in fact is $P'_{i_1 j_1} \cdots$? We note first that

$$\sum_{i_2 j_2} P_{i_2 j_2} = 1$$

$$\sum_{i_2} P_{i_2 j_1} = G_{j_1}$$

$$\sum_{j_2} P_{i_1 j_2} = F_{i_1}$$

and so on, where G_{j_1} is the frequency for gene B_{j_1} at the B locus and F_{i_1} is the frequency of gene A_{i_1} at the A locus. So we have

$$P'_{i_1 j_1} = \tfrac{1}{2}(1 - r)P_{i_1 j_1} + \tfrac{1}{2}rG_{j_1}F_{i_1} + \tfrac{1}{2}rF_{i_1}G_{j_1} + \tfrac{1}{2}(1 - r)P_{i_1 j_1}$$
$$= (1 - r)P_{i_1 j_1} + rF_{i_1}G_{j_1}$$
$$= P_{i_1 j_1} + r(F_{i_1}G_{j_1} - P_{i_1 j_1}) \qquad \text{(A)}$$

Now we verify the well-known fact that gene frequency does not change from generation to generation under random mating. In fact, using primes for generation 1, we have

$$F'_{i_1} = \sum_{j_1} P'_{i_1 j_1} = F_{i_1} + r(F_{i_1} - F_{i_1}) = F_{i_1}$$

and similarly $G'_{j_1} = G_{j_1}$.

If we subtract $F'_{i_1}G'_{j_1}$ from the left-hand side of (A) and $F_{i_1}G_{j_1}$ from the right-hand side, we still have an equality: i.e.,

$$P'_{i_1j_1} - F'_{i_1}G'_{j_1} = P_{i_1j_1} + r(F_{i_1}G_{j_1} - P_{i_1j_1}) - F_{i_1}G_{j_1}$$
$$= (1 - r)P_{i_1j_1} - (1 - r)F_{i_1}G_{j_1}$$
$$= (1 - r)(P_{i_1j_1} - F_{i_1}G_{j_1})$$

We now denote the quantity

$$P_{i_1j_1} - F_{i_1}G_{j_1}$$

by Δ_{ij} and use a prime for the same quantity in generation 1. In this way we have the simple equation $\Delta'_{ij} = (1 - r)\Delta_{ij}$. Thus we say that Δ_{ij} decreases in the ratio of $(1 - r)$ for each generation. If we return to the notation as regards generations used in the previous section, we have

$$\Delta_{ij}^{(n)} = (1 - r)^n \Delta_{ij}^{(0)}$$

and we can write down immediately

$$P_{ij}^{(n)} = F_iG_j + (1 - r)^n \Delta_{ij}^{(0)}$$

from which we can calculate the genotypic array for any generation.

Since r is between zero and unity, $\Delta^{(n)}$ tends to zero as n gets large, and the gametic array tends to

$$\sum_{ij} F_iG_jA_iB_j$$

which equals

$$\left(\sum_i F_iA_i\right)\left(\sum_j G_jB_j\right)$$

which is the gametic array of a population with array

$$\sum_{ijmn} F_iF_jG_mG_nA_iA_jB_mB_n$$

or a population in which all genes are combined strictly at random according to their frequencies.

Finally we may note that essentially r is restricted to be between 0 and $\frac{1}{2}$ (see, however, Fisher, 1948). If r is equal to $\frac{1}{2}$, we have the result obtained previously for two unlinked loci. If the linkage is moderately close, that is, the proportion of recombinants r is near zero, the rate at which the population reaches equilibrium is slow. The population of an F_2 generation will be not at all near equilibrium with respect to closely linked genes for example, and the disequilibrium measured by Δ will decrease very slowly unless r is close to $\frac{1}{2}$, i.e., the loci are essentially unlinked.

REFERENCE

Fisher, R. A. 1948. A quantitative theory of genetic recombination and chiasma formation. *Biometrics*, **4**, 1–8.

FURTHER READING

Bennett, J. H. On the theory of random mating. *Ann. Eugen. Lond.*, **18**, 311–317.

Geiringer, H. 1944. On the probability theory of linkage in Mendelian heredity. *Ann math. Statist.*, **15**, 25–27.

Geiringer, H. 1945. Further remarks on linkage theory in Mendelian heredity. *Ann. math. Statist.*, **16**, 390–393.

Geiringer, H. 1948. On the mathematics of random mating in case of different recombination values for males and females. *Genetics*, **33**, 548–564.

Geiringer, H. 1949. Chromatid segregation of tetraploids and hexaploids. *Genetics*. **34**, 665–684.

Geiringer, H. 1949. Contribution to the linkage theory of autopolyploids. *Bull. math. Biophys.*, **2**, 59–82.

Geiringer, H. 1949. Contribution to the linkage theory of autopolyploids. *Bull. math. Biophys.*, **2**, 197–219.

Geiringer, H. 1949. On some mathematical problems arising in the development of Mendelian genetics. *J. Amer. Statist. Ass.*, **44**, 526–547.

Haldane, J. B. S. 1954. An exact test for randomness of mating. *J. Genet.*, **52**, 631–635.

Hardy, G. H. 1908. Mendelian proportions in a mixed population. *Science*, **28**, 49–50.

Owen, A. R. G. 1949. The theory of genetical recombination. I. Long-chromosome arms. *Proc. roy. Soc. Lond. B.*, **136**, 67–94.

Owen, A. R. G. 1950. The theory of genetical recombination. *Advanc. Genet.* **3**, 117–157.

Owen, A. R. G. 1953. A genetical system admitting of two distinct stable equilibria under natural selection. *Heredity*, **7**, 97–102.

Robbins, R. B. 1917. Applications of mathematics to breeding problems. *Genetics*, **2**, 489–504.

Robbins, R. B. 1918. Applications of mathematics to breeding problems. II. *Genetics*, **3**, 73–92.

Robbins, R. B. 1918. Some applications of mathematics to breeding problems. III. *Genetics*, **3**, 375–379.

PROBLEMS

1. The gene frequency for M in the MN system is 0.63. What are the frequencies of M, N, and MN types if mating is random?

2. Suppose we take a sample of 10 plants from an F_2 arising by crossing AA and aa. What is the expected value of the frequency of gene A in the sample, and what is its variance? Would you regard this size of sample as adequate?

3. The frequencies of genes O, A, B in a population are respectively 0.72, 0.25, and 0.03. What is the genotypic array of the population under random mating?

4. In question 3 what is the probability that an individual of type A is homozygous? What is the probability that an offspring resulting from the mating of two type-A individuals is homozygous?

5. Specify the progress under random mating of a population with respect to a sex-linked factor with the following initial genotypic frequencies:

$$\text{Male} \qquad 0.4A + 0.6a$$
$$\text{Female} \qquad 0.3AA + 0.5Aa + 0.2aa$$

6. Suppose we make crosses between two populations

$$\text{I} \qquad 0.25AA + 0.5Aa + 0.25aa$$
$$\text{II} \qquad 0.16AA + 0.48Aa + 0.36aa$$

the males coming from I and the females from II, what is the resulting population? What populations would follow under random mating and when would equilibrium be reached?

7. Suppose we have a quantity x which takes values $x_0, x_1, x_2, \cdot \cdot \cdot$, in generation 0, 1, 2, $\cdot \cdot \cdot$, respectively. Suppose also that we can prove that

$$x_n - \tfrac{1}{2}x_{n-1} - \tfrac{1}{4}x_{n-2} = 0$$

what is the general formula for x_n?

8. Suppose under the same conditions as question 7

$$x_{n+3} - \tfrac{7}{4}x_{n+2} + \tfrac{7}{8}x_{n+1} - \tfrac{1}{8}x_n = 0$$

What is the general formula for x_n in terms of n?

9. Suppose we self an individual AB/ab and then mate at random in succeeding generations, what is the genotypic array of the population resulting from random mating for 5 generations?

10. In the same conditions as question (9) get a general formula for the ratio of coupling double heterozygotes to repulsion double heterozygotes, and make a graph of this ratio.

11. Suppose we mate at random and start with the population

$$\tfrac{1}{2}S_1S_2 + \tfrac{1}{3}S_1S_3 + \tfrac{1}{6}S_2S_3$$

where S_1, S_2, and S_3 are self-sterility genes, what are the proportions of S_1S_2 individuals in generation 5, 10, 50, 100, 1000?

12. Suppose we start with a population consisting entirely of A^2a^2 individuals and mate at random. What are the proportions of A^4 individuals in successive generations?

13. Prove that the autotetraploid population

$$\left(\sum_{i=1}^{n} p_iA_i \right)^4$$

is in equilibrium under random mating.

CHAPTER 3

Elementary Selection Problems

We have examined some simple instances of population dynamics under "random mating." The term "random mating" includes other restrictions in addition to the obvious one that individuals mate at random in the population. The most important of the restrictions for an isolated population are that the mortality is constant over all genotypes, that is, the genotypes have the same life table and that each individual and mating are equally effective in producing offspring.* In contradistinction to this, we can, for example, imagine a situation in a human population where matings $AA \times AA$ produce a certain number of offspring on the average, whereas another mating such as $Aa \times aa$ produces only half that number of offspring on the average. As another example consider a field of corn that contains a mixture of inbred lines or pure stocks. Frequently it is hoped that open pollination results in random mating. This will not happen, however, unless all lines produce essentially the same amount of pollen, which is moved around by air currents (or whatever other forces may be operative) equally over all lines and, of course, are producing pollen over the same period of time. It is not our aim here to attempt anything like a complete coverage of these matters. We shall consider only a few of the simpler instances of selection.

3.1 SELECTION BASED ON GENOTYPE

Consider the case when the generations do not overlap. There are various possibilities which can arise, but they lead to essentially the same type of mathematical argument. For instance, we may have artificial selection in which the breeder introduces a non-random mating structure based on genotypes, or we may have the situation in which there is random mating of individuals but the reproductive capacities of individuals vary with genotype.

We take the case when individuals have different survival rates to the

---

* It is probably because of these facts and possibly others that the term "panmixia," which includes all the restrictions, is used frequently.

reproductive phase, depending on genotype. Let the initial population at birth be

$$p^2AA + 2pqAa + q^2aa$$

and let the survival rates be in the ratios

$$1-S:1:1-s$$

for the genotypes AA, Aa, and aa, respectively. Then the population which mates consists of

$$\frac{(1 - S)p^2AA + 2pqAa + (1 - s)q^2aa}{1 - Sp^2 - sq^2}$$

The gametic output of the population is

$$\frac{(p - Sp^2)A + (q - sq^2)a}{1 - Sp^2 - sq^2}$$

and the gene frequency for A at birth in the next generation is

$$\frac{p - Sp^2}{1 - Sp^2 - sq^2} = p^{(1)} \quad \text{say}$$

Hence

$$p^{(1)} - p = \frac{-pq(Sp - sq)}{1 - Sp^2 - sq^2} = -pq\left[\frac{S - (S + s)q}{1 - Sp^2 - sq^2}\right]$$

so that equilibrium exists and is stable when

$$q = \frac{S}{S + s}$$

if S and s are both in the range 0 to 1.

With the general formulation above we may proceed to examine particular instances in detail. One case of some interest to breeders and eugenists is the case when $S = 0$ and $s = 1$: that is, when the homozygous dominant and the heterozygote have the same mortality and the same reproductive value (as measured by expected number of offspring) and the recessive is eliminated or sterilized. In that case we have

$$p^{(1)} = \frac{p}{1 - q^2} = \frac{p}{(1 - q)(1 + q)} = \frac{1}{1 + q}$$

or

$$q^{(1)} = 1 - p^{(1)} = 1 - \frac{1}{1 + q} = \frac{q}{1 + q}$$

It is easy to trace the development of the population under this system of selection for we have

$$\frac{1}{q^{(1)}} = \frac{1+q}{q} = \frac{1}{q} + 1$$

which leads clearly to

$$\frac{1}{q^{(n)}} = \frac{1}{q} + n$$

where $q^{(n)}$ is the frequency for a in the nth generation. The direct formula for $q^{(n)}$ is

$$q^{(n)} = \frac{q}{1 + nq}$$

and of course $q^{(n)}$ tends to zero but rather slowly when q is small.

It is perhaps of some interest (academic if no other) to examine the situation where the heterozygote is selected against completely as regards reproduction.

Suppose our initial adult population consists of

$$AA \qquad aa$$
$$P \qquad R \qquad P + R = 1$$

We shall obtain a genotypic array of individuals at birth in generation 1 of

$$P^2 AA + 2PRAa + R^2 aa$$

and of adults

$$\frac{P^2 AA + R^2 aa}{P^2 + R^2}$$

This will give a genotypic array of adults in generation 2 of

$$\frac{P^4 AA + R^4 aa}{(P^2 + R^2)^2 [1 - 2P^2 R^2/(P^2 + R^2)^2]}$$

and so on.

The gene frequency for a at birth is as follows:

Generation	Frequency
0	R
1	$\dfrac{R^2}{P^2 + R^2}$
2	$\dfrac{R^4}{(P^2 + R^2)^2} \Big/ \left[1 - \dfrac{2P^2 R^2}{(P^2 + R^2)^2} \right]$

so that, if $q^{(i)}$ denotes the gene frequency for a in generation i, we have

$$q^{(i+1)} = \frac{[q^{(i)}]^2}{1 - 2q^{(i)} + 2[q^{(i)}]^2}$$

This gives

$$\frac{1}{q^{(i+1)}} = \frac{1}{[q^{(i)}]^2} - \frac{2}{q^{(i)}} + 2$$

or

$$\left[\frac{1}{q^{(i+1)}} - 1 \right] = \frac{1}{[q^{(i)}]^2} - \frac{2}{q^{(i)}} + 1 = \left[\frac{1}{q^{(i)}} - 1 \right]^2$$

Hence in general we have

$$\left[\frac{1}{q^{(n)}} - 1 \right] = \left[\frac{1}{q^{(0)}} - 1 \right]^{2^n}$$

or

$$q^{(n)} = \frac{[q^{(0)}]^{2^n}}{[p^{(0)}]^{2^n} + [q^{(0)}]^{2^n}}$$

We may examine the limiting behavior as n tends to infinity by the relation

$$\log \left[\frac{1 - q^{(n)}}{q^{(n)}} \right] = 2^n \log \left[\frac{1 - q^{(0)}}{q^{(0)}} \right]$$

If $q^{(0)}$ is less than $\frac{1}{2}$, then $[1 - q^{(0)}]/q^{(0)}$ is greater than unity, so that

$$\log \left[\frac{1 - q^{(n)}}{q^{(n)}} \right] \rightarrow \infty$$

which can happen if and only if $q^{(n)}$ tends to zero. If $q^{(0)}$ is greater than $\frac{1}{2}$, then $[1 - q^{(0)}]/q^{(0)}$ is less than unity,

$$\log \left[\frac{1 - q^{(0)}}{q^{(0)}} \right] \text{ is negative}$$

and

$$\log \left[\frac{1 - q^{(n)}}{q^{(n)}} \right] \rightarrow -\infty$$

or $q^{(n)}$ tends to unity. Hence under this system of selection the more prevalent gene initially eventually comprises the whole population. When $q^{(0)}$ is exactly $\frac{1}{2}$, q does not change from generation to generation, but the above argument shows that any deviation from this equilibrium situation will result in the population moving in the direction of deviation. Hence the equilibrium at $q^{(0)} = \frac{1}{2}$ is an unstable equilibrium.

3.2 SEX-LIMITED SELECTION

Here, as an example, we consider selection for an autosomal gene, when selection can be practiced only in the males. As one example of the situation, suppose the recessive males can be removed completely. Let the gametic output of males in generation n be

$$u_n A + (1 - u_n)a$$

and for females be

$$v_n A + (1 - v_n)a$$

Then the generation $(n+1)$ at birth consists of $u_n v_n AA + [u_n(1 - v_n) + v_n(1 - u_n)]Aa + (1 - u_n)(1 - v_n)aa$. The reproducing part of the male population consists of

$$\{u_n v_n AA + [u_n(1 - v_n) + v_n(1 - u_n)]Aa\}/[1 - (1 - u_n)(1 - v_n)]$$

with gametic array

$$\left[\left(\frac{u_n + v_n}{2} \right) A + \left(\frac{u_n(1 - v_n) + v_n(1 - u_n)}{2} \right) a \right] \bigg/ [1 - (1 - u_n)(1 - v_n)]$$

The females give a gametic array

$$\left(\frac{u_n + v_n}{2} \right) A + \left(\frac{2 - u_n - v_n}{2} \right) a$$

Hence we have

$$v_{n+1} = \frac{u_n + v_n}{2}, \qquad u_{n+1} = \left(\frac{u_n + v_n}{2} \right) \left[\frac{1}{1 - (1 - u_n)(1 - v_n)} \right]$$

$$v_{n+2} = \frac{u_{n+1} + v_{n+1}}{2} = \frac{(u_n + v_n)}{4} \left[1 + \frac{1}{1 - (1 - u_n)(1 - v_n)} \right]$$

so

$$v_{n+2} = \tfrac{1}{2} v_{n+1} \left[1 + \frac{1}{1 - (1 - v_n)(1 + v_n - 2v_{n+1})} \right]$$

which is a recurrence relation for the frequency of the gene A in the female population. This recurrence relation is non-linear, and a simple general solution does not appear to exist. Our treatment here is admittedly inconclusive, and the sole purpose of the example is to illustrate the type of selection.

3.3 SELECTION FOR A SEX-LINKED GENE

In this case the number of possibilities is large. As an example of the working out of cases, consider the case when all recessives are rejected. Let the initial population at birth be as follows:

	Females			Males	
AA	Aa	aa		A	a
$r^{(0)}$	$2s^{(0)}$	$t^{(0)}$		$u^{(0)}$	$v^{(0)}$

Then, with complete rejection of recessives, the gametic output of females is

$$[(r^{(0)} + s^{(0)})A + s^{(0)}a]/(1 - t^{(0)})$$

and for males is A only. Hence in the next generation

$$u^{(1)} = \frac{r^{(0)} + s^{(0)}}{1 - t^{(0)}}, \qquad v^{(1)} = \frac{s^{(0)}}{1 - t^{(0)}}$$

and

$$r^{(1)} = \frac{r^{(0)} + s^{(0)}}{1 - t^{(0)}}, \qquad 2s^{(1)} = \frac{s^{(0)}}{1 - t^{(0)}}, \qquad t^{(1)} = 0$$

Continuing in the same fashion, we have

$$u^{(2)} = r^{(1)} + s^{(1)}, \qquad v^{(2)} = s^{(1)}$$

$$r^{(2)} = r^{(1)} + s^{(1)}, \qquad 2s^{(2)} = s^{(1)}, \qquad t^{(2)} = 0$$

Hence the recessive females are eliminated in one generation, and after one generation heterozygous females are reduced by one half in each generation. When the selection is sex-limited, so that only recessive males are rejected, we find that the gametic output of females in generation 0 consists of

$$[r^{(0)} + s^{(0)}]A + [s^{(0)} + t^{(0)}]a$$

and of males is A entirely. Hence the population of females in generation 1 consists of

$$[r^{(0)} + s^{(0)}]AA + [s^{(0)} + t^{(0)}]Aa$$

and of males at birth consists of

$$[r^{(0)} + s^{(0)}]A + [s^{(0)} + t^{(0)}]a$$

If we let $p^{(i)} = r^{(i)} + s^{(i)}$ and $q^{(i)} = 1 - p^{(i)}$, we have

$$p^{(1)} = r^{(0)} + s^{(0)} + \tfrac{1}{2}[s^{(0)} + t^{(0)}]$$
$$= p^{(0)} + \tfrac{1}{2}q^{(0)}$$
$$= p^{(0)} + \tfrac{1}{2}[1 - p^{(0)}]$$
$$= \tfrac{1}{2} + \tfrac{1}{2}p^{(0)}$$

and

$$q^{(1)} = \tfrac{1}{2}q^{(0)}$$

so

$$q^{(n)} = (\tfrac{1}{2})^n q^{(0)}$$

The frequency of heterozygous females is $2q^{(n)}$ which therefore decreases by one half in each generation.

3.4 OTHER CASES

There is really no limit to the number of possible cases which may be relevant. The reader is referred to the sequence of papers by Haldane (1923–1927) for many cases.

It is of a little interest to describe lines on which such deductive work might proceed. The cases so far dealt with have the property that selection takes place among individuals on the basis of their genotype. Haldane (1923–1927) proposed another type of selection, which he called familial selection. Here the selection is among members of the same family, the family having one or both parents in common. A simple case can be visualized when there is enough food for 10 embryos but 20 embryos are produced, and there are differences between embryos, related to genotype, with respect to ability to survive in the competitive situation.

Another type of selection which is of considerable interest in humans, with respect to the Rhesus factor, results when the ability of an individual to survive depends on the relation of its genotype to its mother's genotype. More generally, we could envisage the case in which every distinct kind of mating, as specified by the genotypes of the parents, has its characteristic distribution of offspring with respect to number and genotype.

The particular case of the Rh factor was examined by Haldane (1941). Consider a population in which the survivors in one generation have the array

$$uRR + 2vRr + wrr$$

and suppose mating is at random. The frequency of Rr children from rr mothers will be

$$uw + vw = (u + v)w$$

Let a proportion k of these die.   Then the following generation consists of

$$(u + v)^2 RR + 2(u + v)(v + w)Rr + (v + w)^2 rr$$

minus

$$(u + v)wkRr$$

or

$$\frac{(u + v)^2 RR + (u + v)(2v + 2w - kw)Rr + (v + w)^2 rr}{1 - k(u + v)w}$$

Let p equal the frequency of r genes: i.e., $p = v + w$.   Then the frequency in the succeeding generation p' is given by

$$p' = \frac{p - \tfrac{1}{2}kw(1 - p)}{1 - kw(1 - p)}$$

so

$$\Delta p = p' - p = \frac{kw(1 - p)}{1 - kw(1 - p)}\left(p - \frac{1}{2}\right)$$

Hence, if p is greater than $\tfrac{1}{2}$, it increases, and, if less than $\tfrac{1}{2}$, it decreases. The reader is referred to Haldane (1941) for extensive discussion of the situation.   The general result is similar to that given earlier for selection against the heterozygote per se.

3.5 FURTHER NOTES

The situations we have described are the simple textbook situations. The most important problem from the point of view of evolutionary theory is the survival of mutations which have some selective advantage. For this the reader is referred to the work of Fisher contained in Chapters IV and V of *The Genetical Theory of Natural Selection* (1930), of which the elementary mathematical parts are given in the following chapter, the work of Haldane (1923–1927), and the work of Sewall Wright (1931, 1951).   This area has been characterized by considerable controversy and disagreement, and the reader should attempt to form his own judgment on the situation, because it appears that the deductive theory has not been developed to the extent that it can be relied on to resolve the problems.

REFERENCES

Fisher, R. A.   1930.   *The genetical theory of natural selection*.   Clarendon Press, Oxford.

Haldane, J. B. S.   1923 and later.   A mathematical theory of natural and artificial selections: I. *Trans. Camb. phil. Soc.*, **23**, 19–42, 1923.   III. *Proc. Camb. phil. Soc.*, **23**, 363–372, 1925–7.   IV. *Ibid.*, **23**, 607–615, 1925–7.   V. *Ibid.*, **23**, 838–844, 1925–7.

Haldane, J. B. S.   1941.   Selection against heterozygosis in man.   *Ann. Eugen. Lond.*, **11**, 333–340.

Wright, Sewall.   1931.   Evolution in Mendelian populations.   *Genetics*, **16**, 97–159.

Wright, Sewall.   1951.   The genetical structure of populations.   *Ann. Eugen. Lond.*, **15**, 323–354.

FURTHER READING

Fisher, R. A.   1941.   The theoretical consequences of polyploid inheritance for the Mid style form of *Lythrum salicaria*.   *Ann. Eugen. Lond.*, **11**, 31–38.

PROBLEMS

1. Consider the case of a simple Mendelian character in which the genotypic array in generation n is

$$p_n^2 AA + 2p_n q_n Aa + q_n^2 aa$$

and suppose that only $(1-k)$ of the recessives survive to reproduce, but otherwise there is no selection.

Prove from the beginning the relation

$$u_{n+1} = \frac{u_n(1 + u_n)}{1 + u_n - k}$$

where

$$p = \frac{u}{1 + u}$$

Hence, if k is small

$$\Delta u_n = u_{n+1} - u_n = \frac{ku_n}{1 + u_n}$$

and approximately

$$kn = u_n - u_0 + \log_e \left(\frac{u_n}{u_0}\right) \qquad\qquad (Haldane)$$

2. Consider a character which is dominant in the male sex and recessive in the female sex, and suppose that none of the individuals exhibiting the character are allowed to breed.   Describe the progress of the population.

3. Under the same circumstances as question 2, let a proportion k of the individuals not exhibiting the character be rejected, and suppose the gametic arrays in generation n are:

$$\male (u_n A + 1a)/(1 + u_n)$$
$$\female (v_n A + 1a)/(1 + v_n)$$

Prove that, when k is small,

$$v_{n+1} - u_{n+1} = \frac{ku_n(u_n - 1)}{1 + u_n}, \quad \text{approximately}$$

and that

$$kn = 2 \log_e u_n \qquad\qquad (Haldane)$$

4. Consider a sex-linked character in which selection is practiced only in the homogametic sex, and suppose a proportion k of the recessives are discarded. Evaluate the progress of the population.

5. Suppose a recessive trait occurs in 1 in 1000 of a random mating population.   How many generations of complete selection against the recessive individuals would be necessary to reduce the proportion to 1 in 1,000,000?

CHAPTER 4

The Elementary Stochastic
Theory of Genetic Populations*

4.1 STOCHASTIC PROBLEMS

The problem that will be dealt with in this chapter is the probable state of a genetic population through time under particular circumstances. To take a simple example suppose that we start with an F_2 population in which gene frequency is one half and there is no mutation or selection and the population maintains a specified size N of individuals. The expectations that have been worked out tell us what would happen with an indefinitely large population reproducing itself. However, as soon as the finiteness of the population is taken into account, the genes in a generation are a random sample of the genes of the previous generation, this random sample arising definitely from Mendelian segregation of crosses and also by selection in that some individuals do not become parents. The particular forces will be operating in every generation, so that the final outcome is the result of several steps, with random variation entering at every step.

If again we have a population of Aa individuals, for example, the expectation of the progeny is $\frac{1}{4}AA + \frac{1}{2}Aa + \frac{1}{4}aa$. However, there is some definite probability that say only AA types will be represented in the progeny, and in this case the population is fixed immediately, of course. The progress of a population through time is a result of a process in which random sampling occurs at each stage or step. The progress over two generations is a compound of random sampling in the first generation and then random sampling of the *result* of the sampling giving the first generation to give the second generation.

Any process which can be visualized as consisting of steps at each of which the movement made is random according to some distribution is called a *stochastic* process. A question involving the understanding of a stochastic process which was posed at the end of the last century by Galton was the probability of extinction of family surnames. In this

* This chapter is not elementary. It may be skipped without losing continuity.

case it is supposed that an individual has n sons, where n is a random variable following a particular distribution.   It turns out that, if the mean number of sons is less than or equal to unity, extinction is certain (see e.g. Bartlett, 1955, p. 41).   Lotka (1931) found that for the U.S. white population the chance of extinction is 0.9.   We note also that the variance of the probability of homozygosity under inbreeding (Chapter 5) will be determined by sampling variance introduced in every crossing.

Stochastic processes clearly have relevance to all aspects of genetic populations, and quite probably the most important aspect economically is the theory of breeding systems.   The choice between systems appears largely up to now if not entirely to be based on deterministic theories (or none at all) in which random variation is assumed negligible.   It is clear that the size of population possible in the operation of a breeding system will be such as to make random sampling and other variation important.

The theory worked out so far has been aimed mainly at an understanding of the evolutionary process, and it is this aspect which will be discussed in this chapter.   The history of the work is as follows.   The problems were first discussed by Fisher in 1918 and 1922.   They were later discussed in considerable detail by Wright (1931) and by Fisher (1930a, b), essentially the same results being reached after adjustment for a few errors which are of little importance from the point of view of methodology but do affect the results.   The methodologies followed by Fisher and Wright are rather different, though intrinsically they amount to the same thing.   The type of problem which led to stochastic process theory arose initially in physics in connection with the random walk problem first explicitly formulated by Karl Pearson (1905) and dealt with by various physicists.   The problem was taken up by Markoff (1912) whose name is now so frequently associated with least squares.   (Just why is somewhat of a moot point.)   The random walk problem in its simplest form concerns an individual walking along a straight line in a series of steps of equal length, each step being taken in a forward or backward direction with certain probabilities, in the simple case both equal to one half, the question being what is the probability of the individual reaching a prechosen point after a specified number of steps.   This problem can clearly be extended to three or more dimensions, and it is easy to visualize how the theory of Brownian movement would be a natural problem for consideration within the framework.   A particle undergoing Brownian movement makes about 10^{21} collisions with other particles per second, each collision producing a kink in the path of the particle.   The pursuit of various problems in statistical mechanics led to the Fokker–Planck equation (Fokker, 1914, and Planck, 1917), which is applicable to the study of Brownian movement. The mathematical theory of stochastic processes is generally regarded as stemming from the basic work of Kolmogorov (1931), who himself worked on the problem of a large population consisting of subgroups of size n, each of which receives a number of immigrants from the general population but otherwise breeds within itself, with regard to the change of gene frequency (Kolmogorov, 1935). It is perhaps of interest to note that Fisher's methodology is essentially that of the mathematical physicist, and he introduces physical analogies such as flux and diffusion. Wright's early methodology (1931, 1937, 1938, 1942) is unique to Wright and much related to his early (1921) treatment of inbreeding. His later papers (1945, 1951) have been based on the Fokker–Planck equation. For a long discussion of stochastic problems in physics, the reader may refer to Chandrasekar (1943), and the book on stochastic processes by Bartlett (1955) in which problems arising from many fields of science are discussed.

The general problem which will be discussed in this chapter is the distribution of gene frequencies in a population subjected to particular forces such as random survival of genes, mutation, selection, and immigration. The basic point is that, after a particular time t, the gene frequency will not be a definite number between 0 and 1 but will be a random variable which will follow some distribution. If the density function of this distribution is $g(p, t)$ say, then

$$\text{Prob } (p \le P \text{ at time } t) = \int_0^P g(p, t) \, dp$$

and the problem is to determine $g(p, t)$ under particular circumstances. However, before taking up this problem, we shall describe some work by Fisher (1922) on the survival of individual genes.

4.2 THE SURVIVAL OF AN INDIVIDUAL GENE

The validity of the following results depends on the population size being infinite and the number of mutant genes being small.

Consider a particular gene in a particular generation, and suppose that the probabilities of this gene occurring in the next generation in 0, 1, 2, $\cdots$ individuals are p_0, p_1, p_2, etc. with, of course,

$$p_0 + p_1 + p_2 + \cdots = 1$$

We suppose that these probabilities, which are the probabilities of an individual passing on a gene he possesses to 0, 1, 2, etc. individuals in the next generation, are the same in all generations. We now want to find the probability that this gene will occur in $0, 1, 2, \cdots$ individuals in the second generation, which we may denote by $p_0^{(2)}, p_1^{(2)}, p_2^{(2)}, \cdots$. Clearly

$$p_0^{(2)} = p_0 + p_1 p_0 + p_2 (p_0)^2 + p_3 (p_0)^3 + \cdots$$

$$p_1^{(2)} = p_1 p_1 + p_2 2 p_0 p_1 + p_3 3 (p_0)^2 p_1 + \cdots$$

$$p_2^{(2)} = p_1 p_2 + p_2 [2 p_0 p_2 + (p_1)^2] + \cdots \tag{A}$$

The neat formulation given by Fisher (1922) is to note that, if

$$f(z) = p_0 + p_1 z + p_2 z^2 + \cdots$$

and

$$f^{(2)}(z) = p_0^{(2)} + p_1^{(2)} z + p_2^{(2)} z^2 + \cdots$$

so that these are probability generating functions or, if one likes population arrays, in which the coefficient of z^r is the probability that the gene occurs r times, then

$$f^{(2)}(z) = f[f(z)]$$

We have

$$
\begin{aligned}
p_0^{(2)} + p_1^{(2)} z + p_2^{(2)} z^2 + \cdots = {}& p_0 \\
& + p_1 (p_0 + p_1 z + p_2 z^2 + \cdots) \\
& + p_2 (p_0 + p_1 z + p_2 z^2 + \cdots)^2 \\
& + p_3 (p_0 + p_1 z + p_2 z^2 + \cdots)^3 \\
& + \text{etc.} \tag{B}
\end{aligned}
$$

Note that the easily seen relationships (A) can be derived from (B). It follows therefore that

$$f^{(3)}(z) = f[f(fz)]$$

and in general

$$f^{(n)}(z) = f \cdot f \cdot f \cdot \cdots \cdot f(z)$$

in which the dot $\cdot$ means "insert as the argument of f" and there are a total of n f's in the string.

The function $f(x)$ will vary from species to species and from environment to environment but is assumed in the present argument to stay constant. We may first note that, since

$$\frac{dz^i}{d(\log z)} = i z^i$$

if

$$F(z) = p_0 + p_1 z + p_2 z^2 + \cdots$$

is a probability generating function, then

$$\frac{d \log F(z)}{d \log z}\bigg|_{z=1} = \left[\frac{1}{F(z)}\sum_i p_i i z^i\right]_{z=1} = \sum_i p_i i = \text{mean}$$

and similarly

$$\frac{d^2 \log F(z)}{d (\log z)^2}\bigg|_{z=1} = \text{variance}$$

The mean and variance of the distribution are not the crucial aspects but are included to give some idea of the general shape of the distribution. Hence,* since

$$f^{(n)}(z) = f[f^{(n-1)}(z)]$$

we have

$$\frac{d \log f^{(n)}z}{d \log z} = \frac{d \log f[f^{(n-1)}(z)]}{d \log f(z)}\frac{d \log f(z)}{d \log z}$$

and

$$\frac{d^2 \log f^{(n)}(z)}{d (\log z)^2} = \frac{d^2 \log f[f^{(n-1)}(z)]}{d (\log f(z))^2}\left[\frac{d \log f(z)}{d \log z}\right]^2$$

$$+ \frac{d \log f[f^{(n-1)}(z)]}{d \log f(z)}\frac{d^2 \log f(z)}{d (\log z)^2}$$

and since

$$\frac{d^r \log f[f^{(n-1)}(z)]}{d [\log f(z)]^r} = \frac{d^r \log f[f^{(n-2)}(u)]}{d (\log u)^r} \quad \text{with} \quad u = f(z)$$

we have, following Bartlett (1955), that $\mu^{(n)}$, the mean in generation n, and $\mu_2^{(n)}$, the variance in generation n, are given by

$$\mu^{(n)} = \mu\mu^{(n-1)}$$
$$\mu_2^{(n)} = (\mu)^2\mu_2^{(n-1)} + \mu^{(n-1)}\mu_2$$

Hence, with an arbitrary initial generation whose mean is $\mu^{(0)}$ and variance is $\mu_2^{(0)}$,

$$\mu^{(n)} = \mu^n\mu^{(0)}$$

$$\mu_2^{(n)} = \mu^{2n}\mu_2^{(0)} + \frac{\mu^{n-1}(1 - \mu^n)\,\mu^{(0)}\mu_2}{(1 - \mu)}$$

with

$$\mu_2^{(n)} = \mu_2^{(0)} + n\mu^{(0)}\mu_2 \quad \text{for} \quad \mu = 1$$

* The following argument leads directly to the variance. Alternatively one may note that $\dfrac{dF}{dz}\bigg|_{z=1} = \text{mean}$ and $\dfrac{d^2F}{dz^2}\bigg|_{z=1} = \text{variance} + \text{mean}^2 - \text{mean}$.

Fisher (1922) notes that, if the population number is essentially constant, μ must equal unity, and, if the population is large so that each individual gene has a small chance of surviving, the function of z used above, $f(z)$, must be approximately e^{z-1}, giving p_0, p_1, p_2, p_3, $\cdots$ as the Poisson probabilities

$$e^{-1}, e^{-1}, \frac{e^{-1}}{2!}, \frac{e^{-1}}{3!}, \cdots$$

If on the other hand the population number is increasing in the ratio μ to 1 per generation, it will be reasonable to take

$$f(z) = e^{\mu(z-1)}$$

for which, for example, p_0, the chance of extinction over one generation is $e^{-\mu}$, and the mean number of progeny containing the individual gene is μ, which is also the variance.*

In the particular case μ equal to unity, we see that

$$\mu^{(n)} = \mu^{(0)}$$
$$\mu_2^{(n)} = \mu_2^{(0)} + n\mu^{(0)}$$

Some probabilities of survival based on the calculations of Fisher (1930) are given in Table 4.1.

TABLE 4.1

No. of Generations	Probability of survival	
	$\mu = 1.0$	$\mu = 1.01$
1	0.6321	0.6358
3	0.3741	0.3803
7	0.2095	0.2175
15	0.1127	0.1217
31	0.0589	0.0687
63	0.0302	0.0409
127	0.0153	0.0271
∞	0	0.0197

Bartlett (1955) shows that the probability of extinction is approximately $\exp\left(-2(\mu - 1)/\mu_2\right)$.† For the Poisson distribution with mean μ and

* It is clear that μ here should refer to the particular mutual gene under consideration and not the reproductive value of individuals in the general population, so that even for a stationary population μ need not be near unity (Kimura, personal communication).

† This formula gives a good approximation only for $(\mu - 1)$ equal to a small positive quantity (Kimura, personal communication).

variance μ, the probability is approximately $\exp[-2(\mu - 1)/\mu]$. The values of the probability of survival for various values of μ are given in Table 4.2.

TABLE 4.2

PROBABILITY OF SURVIVAL OF GENE

Selective Advantage $(\mu - 1)$	Probability
0	0
0.001	0.002
0.005	0.009
0.01	0.020
0.02	0.038
0.05	0.256

Note that for small positive selective advantage ϵ, the chance of survival is about 2ϵ.

The reader is referred to Chapter IV of Fisher's *The Genetical Theory of Natural Selection* for a detailed discussion of the significance of the above results. It may be noted, however, that, if the population number is 10^6 and the mutation rate is 1 in 10^5, about 10 mutations will appear in each generation, and the chance of survival of at least one of these is $1 - (0.980)^{10}$ if the mutation has a 1 per cent selective advantage. This works out to be about 0.18. The probability of this mutation pervading the population is therefore not at all inappreciable and would with a population of this size become a certainty over a large number of generations.

Fisher (1930b) shows that the chance of survival of a gene with no selective advantage is after n generations approximately $2/n$ and concludes that the gene will be represented in $n/2$ individuals *on the average*. The actual distribution of the number of individuals possessing the gene is given by the fact that the probability that the number of individuals is greater than x is $\exp(-2x/n)$, approximately. If the gene has a small selective advantage δ, the probability that it is represented in more than x individuals after n generations is deduced by Fisher (1930b) to be

$$\exp[-2\delta x/(1 + \delta)^n]$$

4.3 THE DISTRIBUTION OF GENE FREQUENCIES

There are two aspects of this problem, the first being the specification of the distribution in its central parts and the other the specification of the distribution in its terminal parts, where the discontinuity of possible gene frequencies makes a special type of attack necessary. We shall describe only the former.

For the specification of the central part of the distribution we shall base the description on the Fokker–Planck equation in its one-dimensional form. We shall give a non-rigorous derivation of the equation, as this should be of some interest and possible utility.

Let $f(p, t)\, dp$ be the probability that the gene frequency lies in the range $p, p + dp$ at time t. Now suppose that in the time interval Δt, the probability that the change in p is between Δp and $\Delta p + d(\Delta p)$ (given that the frequency is p at time t) be denoted by

$$g(p, \Delta p)\, d(\Delta p)$$

Then it follows that

$$f(p, t + \Delta t) = \int f(p - \Delta p, t)\, g(p - \Delta p, \Delta p)\, d(\Delta p)$$

since in order for the frequency to be p at time $(t + \Delta t)$ it must have been at $p - \Delta p$ at time t and changed by Δp in the interval t to $t + \Delta t$. Now we note that

$$f(p - \Delta p, t) = f(p, t) - \Delta p \frac{\partial f}{\partial p}(p, t) + \left(\frac{\Delta p^2}{2}\right) \frac{\partial^2 f}{\partial p^2}(p, t)$$
$$+ \text{remainder}$$

$$g(p - \Delta p, \Delta p) = g(p, \Delta p) - \Delta p \frac{\partial g}{\partial p}(p, \Delta p) + \left(\frac{\Delta p^2}{2!}\right) \frac{\partial^2 g}{\partial p^2}(p, \Delta p)$$
$$+ \text{remainder}$$

Inserting these in the integral after ignoring the remainders and terms involving $(\Delta p)^3$, we have

$$f(p, t + \Delta t) = \int f(p, t)\, g(p, \Delta p)\, d(\Delta p) - \int \frac{\partial f}{\partial p}(p, t)\, g(p, \Delta p)\, \Delta p\, d(\Delta p)$$

$$- \int f(p, t) \frac{\partial g}{\partial p}(p, \Delta p)\, \Delta p\, d(\Delta p) + \int f(p, t) \frac{\partial^2 g}{\partial p^2}(p, \Delta p) \left(\frac{\Delta p^2}{2!}\right) d(\Delta p)$$

$$+ \int \frac{\partial f}{\partial p}(p, t) \frac{\partial g}{\partial p}(p, \Delta p)(\Delta p)^2\, d(\Delta p) + \int \frac{\partial^2 f}{\partial p^2}(p, t)\, g(p, \Delta p) \left(\frac{\Delta p^2}{2!}\right) d(\Delta p)$$

Now we note that

$$\int g(p, \Delta p)\, d(\Delta p) = 1$$

$$\int g(p, \Delta p)\, \Delta p\, d(\Delta p) = M_\Delta, \quad \text{the mean change}$$

$$\int g(p, \Delta p)\, (\Delta p)^2\, d(\Delta p) = V_\Delta, \quad \text{the mean squared change}$$

and that the operation of taking derivatives may be used freely. Then we have

$$f(p, t + \Delta t) = f(p, t) - \frac{\partial f}{\partial p}(p, t) M_\Delta - f(p, t) \frac{\partial M_\Delta}{\partial p}$$

$$+ f(p, t) \frac{\partial^2 V_\Delta}{2! \, \partial p^2} + \frac{\partial f}{\partial p}(p, t) \frac{\partial V_\Delta}{\partial p} + \frac{\partial^2 f}{2! \, \partial p^2}(p, t) V_\Delta$$

or dropping the arguments p, t of the function f and noting that

$$\frac{\partial}{\partial p}(fM_\Delta) = \frac{\partial f}{\partial p} M_\Delta + f \frac{\partial M_\Delta}{\partial p}$$

$$\frac{\partial^2}{\partial p^2}(fV_\Delta) = \frac{\partial^2 f}{\partial p^2} V_\Delta + 2 \frac{\partial f}{\partial p} \frac{\partial V_\Delta}{\partial p} + f \frac{\partial^2 V_\Delta}{\partial p^2}$$

and

$$f(p, t + \Delta t) = f(p, t) + \frac{\partial f}{\partial t} \Delta t \quad \text{approximately}$$

we have

$$\frac{\partial f}{\partial t} \Delta t = - \frac{\partial}{\partial p}(fM_\Delta) + \frac{1}{2} \frac{\partial^2}{\partial p^2}(fV_\Delta)$$

This is the most general form of the one-dimensional Fokker–Planck differential equation, and we shall now apply it to certain theoretical situations in genetics. The solution of new problems would, of course, involve the solution of differential equations which is a purely mathematical process. The equations are, however, of singular type (Feller 1951, 1952), and this introduces difficulties of considerable magnitude.

4.4 THE SOLUTION FOR STEADY DECAY

In this case the only change occurs through random sampling of genes for representation in the next generation, and we may write

$$M_\Delta(p) = 0$$

$$V_\Delta(p) = \frac{pq}{2n} \Delta t$$

where n is the population number. This gives the differential equation

$$\frac{\partial f}{\partial t} = \frac{1}{4n} \frac{\partial^2}{\partial p^2} [p(1 - p)f]$$

It may be verified easily that the function

$$f(p, t) = C \exp(-t/2n)$$

satisfies the differential equation, C being a constant.*

It is of interest to note here that Fisher's solution presented first in 1922 and modified because of an error in 1930 was to obtain the distribution of θ where

$$\cos \theta = 1 - 2p$$

This appears to be the first use of the well-known angular transformation to make sampling variance constant. The distribution for θ, say $g(\theta, t)$, will be related to $f(p, t)$ by the equation

$$g(\theta, t) = f(\theta, t) \frac{dp}{d\theta}$$

$$= f(\theta, t) \frac{\sin \theta}{2}$$

Fisher's (1930a, b) modified equation in our notation is obtained by noting that

$$M_\Delta(\theta) = -\frac{1}{4n} \cot \theta \, \Delta t$$

$$V_\Delta(\theta) = \frac{1}{2n} \Delta t \quad \left(\text{to order } \frac{1}{n}\right)$$

so that the equation to be satisfied is

$$\frac{\partial g}{\partial t} = \frac{1}{4n} \frac{\partial}{\partial \theta} (g \cot \theta) + \frac{1}{4n} \frac{\partial^2 g}{\partial \theta^2}$$

The solution given by Fisher is

$$g(\theta, t) = A \sin \theta \exp(-t/2n)$$

4.5 VARIABILITY MAINTAINED CONSTANT BY MUTATIONS WITH NO SELECTION

In this case we have

$$\frac{\partial f}{\partial t} = 0$$

so that

$$\frac{\partial^2}{\partial p^2} [p(1 - p)f] = 0$$

* Kimura (1955b) has shown that this is only one of an infinite set of solutions.

for which

$$f = \frac{\beta}{1 - p} + \frac{\gamma}{p(1 - p)}$$

This function for the distribution will of course hold only in the central part of the distribution.

Fisher gives the solution in the form

$$g(\theta, t) = g(\theta) = A \cosec \theta + 4nB \cot \theta$$

with

$$g = A \cosec \theta$$

if mutations are being supplied with equal frequencies at $\theta = 0(p = 0)$ and $\theta = \pi(p = 1)$ and

$$g = 4nB (\cosec \theta + \cot \theta)$$

if mutations occur at $\theta = 0$.

In this connection Fisher (1930a) used the transformation

$$z = \log (p/q)$$

which he first used in his famous 1918 paper and is now generally known as the logit transformation and found that

$$f(z) \, dz = \frac{4nB}{1 + e^z} \, dz$$

for the case of unidirectional mutation.

4.6 SMALL SELECTIVE ADVANTAGE OR DISADVANTAGE

Fisher (1922) gave the definitions of two types of selection. Suppose that the relative fitnesses of the classes AA, Aa, aa are, respectively, a, b, and c. As we have seen [in the extreme case, and the other cases can be worked out (Fisher, 1930a, pp. 100–101)], if b is less than a or c, the only stable equilibrium is with one allele at unit frequency and the other absent, and, only when b exceeds both a and c, does there exist a stable equilibrium under random mating of unselected individuals. The two cases put forward by Fisher (1922) as meriting consideration are:

1. In which $b^2 = ac$, and the selection merely affects the proportions of the genes: this is called uniform genetic selection by Fisher.
2. In which b equals a, so that there is complete dominance as regards selective value, and this is called uniform genotypic selection.

In uniform slow selection we may suppose that

$$c = 1, \qquad b = 1 + s, \qquad a = 1 + 2s$$

ignoring s^2, so that the change in p in one generation is Δp, where

$$\Delta p = \frac{p^2 + 2p^2 s + pq + spq}{1 + 2sp^2 + 2spq} - p$$

$$= spq$$

again ignoring s^2.

Hence the change in $\log p/q$ is

$$\log \left(\frac{p + \Delta p}{q - \Delta p}\right) - \log \left(\frac{p}{q}\right) = \log \left(1 + \frac{\Delta p}{p}\right) - \log \left(1 - \frac{\Delta p}{q}\right) = \frac{\Delta p}{pq}$$

Hence under uniform slow selection $\log (p/q)$ changes by s in each generation or

$$\frac{p_n}{q_n} = r^n \frac{p_0}{q_0}$$

where the suffixes denote generations n and zero and r equals e^s which to the order of magnitude considered is $1 + s$ or equal to both a/b and b/c.

In this case we insert in the Fokker–Planck equation

$$M_\Delta = s\, p(1 - p)\, \Delta t$$

$$V_\Delta = \frac{p(1 - p)}{2n}\, \Delta t, \quad \text{ignoring terms in } (\Delta t)^2$$

so that the differential equation to be solved is

$$\frac{\partial f}{\partial t} = -\frac{d}{dp}\left[s\, p(1 - p)f\right] + \frac{1}{2}\frac{\partial^2}{\partial p^2}\left[\frac{p(1 - p)}{2n}f\right]$$

The solution given by Wright (1945) to this equation is

$$f = \frac{\exp (4nsp)}{p(1 - p)}\left[C - 2D \int \exp (-4nsq)\, dq\right]$$

where C and D are constants to be fixed by the initial conditions. Fisher (1930a) again worked in terms of θ where $2p = 1 - \cos \theta$ and obtained

$$y = \operatorname{cosec} \theta\, [2A + B \exp (-2sn \cos \theta)]$$

At p equals unity there will be no mutations so that $1 - y \sin \theta$ equals zero at θ equals π, giving

$$y = 2A \operatorname{cosec} \theta\{1 - \exp [-2sn(1 + \cos \theta)]\}$$

and, if there is one mutation per generation at $\theta = 0$

$$A = \frac{2}{1 - \exp(-4sn)}$$

giving

$$y = 4 \csc \theta \, \frac{\{1 - \exp[-2sn(1 + \cos \theta)]\}}{1 - \exp(-4sn)}$$

as the density function for the distribution of θ. The solution given by Fisher and Wright is a steady-flux solution. The general solution for a finite population was first given by Kimura (1955a).

4.7 THE STEADY-STATE SOLUTION

Wright (1938a) has given a general steady-state solution for the case of mutation rate equal to v, back-mutation rate of u, immigration rate equal to $m(q - q_i)$, selective change rate equal to $q(1 - q)(s + tq)$, and variance equal to $q(1 - q)/2n$ as

$$f(p) = C \exp(4nsp + 2ntp^2) \, p^{4n(mq_i+v)-1}(1 - q)^{4n[m(1-q_i)+u]-1}$$

This solution is in fact a special case even for a steady-state solution, and differs from that in the previous section which is a steady-flux solution (Kimura, personal communication).

4.8 CONCLUSION

It would take us too far afield to describe the position as known at present and discuss the biological implications of the equations given above. Any deep understanding of evolution must be based to a considerable extent on the form of the equations. That they are based on assumptions which are unrealistically simple is not an argument intrinsically against them but an argument for more theoretical work on more realistic models. The understanding of the consequences of a simple model including mutation, immigration, and slow selection and random sampling must be based on the equations presented, because it is impossible for the human mind to comprehend the development of a population except by the equations. An understanding of more complex situations will presumably lead to more complex equations, unless a different mathematical formulation should be discovered.

The reader is referred to Fisher's book (1930a), and the papers cited in the references, particularly for his beautiful treatment of the terminal parts of the distribution. For Wright's approach which leads to the same results and which in later papers is based on the Fokker–Planck equation, there are a considerable number of papers listed. Wright's work has been more extensive than Fisher's with regard to mutation, reverse mutation, selection, and immigration, and on its own would give Wright a leading position in the development of mathematical genetics. Fisher appears to have written only two papers since his 1930 work, one on a steadily advancing wave of advantageous genes with a constant selective advantage (1937), and a second paper (1950) dealing with the case of diffusion of genes through a population in the presence of a selection gradient. Malécot (1948) has studied migration and the decrease of correlation with distance, as also has Lamotte (1952). The student of this aspect of genetics should also examine the work of Haldane, in particular the 1948 reference. A more recent extensive contributor is Kimura (1954, 1955a, 1955b, 1955c, 1956) whose work should be referred to for definitive knowledge.

REFERENCES

Bartlett, M. S. 1955. *An introduction to stochastic processes.* University Press, Cambridge.

Chandrasekhar, S. 1943. Stochastic problems in physics and astronomy. *Rev. Mod. Phys.*, **15**, 1–90.

Crow, J. F., and M. Kimura. 1955. Some genetic problems in natural populations. *Proc. 3rd Berkeley Symp. math. Statist. Prob.*, **4**, 1–22.

Feller, W. 1951. Diffusion problems in genetics. *Proc. 2nd Berkeley Symp. math. Statist. Prob.*, 226–247.

Feller, W. 1952. The parabolic differential equations and the associated semi-groups of transformations. *Ann. Math. Princeton*, **55**, 468–519.

Fisher, R. A. 1918. The correlations between relatives on the supposition of Mendelian inheritance. *Trans. roy. Soc. Edinb.*, **52**, 399–433.

Fisher, R. A. 1922. On the dominance ratio. *Proc. roy. Soc. Edinb.*, **42**, 321–341.

Fisher, R. A. 1930a. The distribution of gene ratios for rare mutations. *Proc. roy. Soc. Edinb.*, **50**, 205–220.

Fisher, R. A. 1930b. *The genetical theory of natural selection.* Clarendon Press, Oxford.

Fisher, R. A. 1937. The wave of advance of advantageous genes. *Ann. Eugen. Lond.*, **7**, 355–369.

Fisher, R. A. 1950. Gene frequencies in a cline determined by selection and diffusion. *Biometrics*, **6**, 353–361.

Fokker, A. D. 1914. Die mittlere Energie rotierender electrischer Dipole im Strahlungsfeld. *Ann. Phys. Lpz.*, **43**, 810–820.

Haldane, J. B. S. 1939a. The spread of harmful autosomal recessive genes in human populations. *Ann. Eugen. Lond.*, **9**, 232–237.

Haldane, J. B. S. 1939b. The equilibrium between mutation and random extinction. *Ann. Eugen. Lond.*, **9**, 400–405.

Haldane, J. B. S. 1940. The conflict between selection and mutation of harmful recessive genes. *Ann. Eugen. Lond.*, **10**, 417–421.

Haldane, J. B. S. 1948. The theory of a cline. *J. Genet.*, **48**, 277–284.

Haldane, J. B. S. 1949. Some statistical problems arising in genetics. *J. R. statist. Soc. B*, **11**, 1–14.

Kimura, M. 1954. Process leading to quasi-fixation of genes in natural populations due to random fluctuation of selection intensities. *Genetics*, **39**, 280–295.

Kimura, M. 1955a. Solution of a process of random genetic drift with a continuous model. *Proc. nat. Acad. Sci. Wash.*, **41**, 144–149.

Kimura, M. 1955b. Random genetic drift in multi-allelic locus. *Evolution*, **9**, 419–435.

Kimura, M. 1955c. Stochastic processes and distribution of gene frequencies under natural selection. *Proc. XXth Cold Spr. Harb. Symp. Quant. Biol.*, 33–51.

Kimura, M. 1956a. Random genetic drift in a tri-allelic locus; exact solution with a continuous model. *Biometrics*, **12**, 57–66.

Kimura, M. 1956b. Rules for testing stability of a selective polymorphism. *Proc. nat. Acad. Sci.*, **6**, 336–340.

Kimura, M. 1956c. A model of a genetic system leads to closer linkage by natural selection. *Evolution*, **3**, 278–287.

Kolmogoroff, A. 1931. Über die analytischen Methoden in der Wahrscheinlichtkeitsrechnung. *Math. Ann.*, **104**, 415–459.

Kolmogoroff, A. 1935. Deviations from Hardy's formula in partial isolation. *C. R. Acad. Sci. U.R.S.S.*, **3**, 129–132.

Lamotte, M. 1952. Le rôle des fluctuations fortuites dans la diversité des populations naturelles de *Cepaea nemoralis* (*L*), *Heredity*, **6**, 333–344.

Lotka, A. J. 1931. The extinction of families. *J. Wash. Acad. Sci.*, **21**, 377–380, 453–459.

Malécot, G. 1948. *Les mathématiques de l'hérédité*. Masson et Cie, Paris.

Markoff, A. A. 1912. *Wahrscheinlichtkeitsrechnung*. Teubner, Leipzig.

Pearson, K. 1905. The problem of the random walk. *Nature*, **72**, 294, 342.

Planck, M. 1917. Über einen Satz der statischen Dynamik und seine Erweiterung in der Quantentheorie. *S. B. preuss. Akad. Wiss.*, 324–341.

Wright, Sewall. 1921. Systems of mating. *Genetics*, **6**, 111–178.

Wright, Sewall. 1931. Evolution in Mendelian population. *Genetics*, **16**, 97–159.

Wright, Sewall. 1932. The roles of mutation, inbreeding, crossbreeding and selection in evolution. *Proc. 6th int. Congr. Genet.*, 356–366.

Wright, Sewall. 1935. Evolution in populations in approximate equilibrium. *J. Genet.*, **30**, 357–366.

Wright, Sewall. 1937. The distribution of gene frequencies in populations. *Proc. nat. Acad. Sci. Wash.*, **23**, 307–320.

Wright, Sewall. 1938a. The distribution of gene frequencies under irreversible mutation. *Proc. nat. Acad. Sci. Wash.*, **24**, 253–259.

Wright, Sewall. 1938b. The distribution of gene frequencies in populations of polyploids. *Proc. nat. Acad. Sci. Wash.*, **24**, 372–377.

Wright, Sewall. 1939. Statistical genetics in relation to evolution. *Expos. Biomét. statist. biol.*, **802**, 63. Hermann et Cie, editeurs.

Wright, Sewall. 1939. The distribution of self-sterility alleles in populations. *Genetics*, **24**, 538–552.

Wright, Sewall. 1940. Breeding structure of populations in relation to speciation. *Amer. Nat.*, **74**, 232–248.

Wright, Sewall. 1942. Statistical genetics and evolution. *Bull. Amer. math. Soc.*, **48**, 223–246.

Wright, Sewall. 1943. Isolation by distance. *Genetics*, **28**, 114–138.

Wright, Sewall. 1945. The differential equation of the distribution of gene frequencies. *Proc. nat. Acad. Sci. Wash.*, **31**, 382–389.

Wright, Sewall. 1946. Isolation by distance under diverse systems of mating. *Genetics*, **31**, 39–59.

Wright, Sewall. 1948a. On the roles of directed and random changes in gene frequency in the genetics of populations. *Evolution*, **2**, 279–294.

Wright, Sewall. 1948b. Evolution, organic. *Encycl. Brit.*, **8**, 915–929.

Wright, Sewall. 1948c. Genetics of populations. *Encycl. Brit.*, **10**, 111, 111A–D, 112.

Wright, Sewall. 1949a. Adaptation and selection. Chapter 20, pp. 365–389, of *Genetics, paleontology and evolution*, edited by G. L. Jepson, G. G. Simpson, and E. Mayr.

Wright, Sewall. 1949b. Population structure in evolution. *Proc. Amer. phil. Soc.*, **93**, 471–478.

Wright, Sewall. 1951. The genetical structure of populations. *Ann. Eugen. Lond.*, **15**, 323–354.

FURTHER READING

Crow, James F., and Newton E. Morton. 1955. Measurement of gene frequency drift in small populations. *Evolution*, **9**, 202–214.

Fisher, R. A. 1928a. The possible modification of the response of the wild type to recurrent mutations. *Amer. Nat.*, **62**, 115–126.

Fisher, R. A. 1928b. Two further notes on the origin of dominance. *Amer. Nat.*, **62**, 571–574.

Fisher, R. A. 1929. The evolution of dominance: Reply to Professor Sewall Wright. *Amer. Nat.*, **63**, 553–556.

Fisher, R. A. 1931. The evolution of dominance. *Biol. Rev.*, **6**, 345–368.

Fisher, R. A. 1935. Dominance in poultry. *Phil. Trans. B*, **225**, 195–226.

Fisher, R. A. 1939. Selective forces in wild populations of *Parattetix tetanus*. *Ann. Eugen. Lond.*, **9**, 109.

Fisher, R. A. 1952. Statistical methods in genetics. *Heredity*, **6**, 1–12.

Fisher, R. A. 1953. Population genetics. *Proc. roy. Soc. Lond. B*, **141**, 510–523.

Haldane, J. B. S. 1937. The effect of variation on fitness. *Amer. Nat.*, **71**, 337–349.

Haldane, J. B. S. 1947. The dysgenic effect of induced recessive mutations. *Ann. Eugen. Lond.*, **14**, 35–43.

Levy, Paul. 1948. *Processus stochastiques et mouvement Brownien.* Gauthier-Villars, Paris.

Wright, Sewall. 1929a. Fisher's theory of dominance. *Amer. Nat.*, **63**, 274–279.

Wright, Sewall. 1929b. The evolution of dominance. *Amer. Nat.*, **63**, 556–561.

Wright, Sewall. 1950. Genetical structure of populations. *Nature*, **166**, 247–253.

Wright, Sewall, and W. E. Kerr. 1954. Experimental studies of the distribution of gene frequencies in very small populations of *Drosophila melanogaster*. II. Bar. *Evolution*, **8**, 225–240.

CHAPTER 5

Inbreeding

5.1 GENERAL FRAMEWORK

Inbreeding is a generic term for mating systems in which individuals are mated to individuals more closely related to themselves than are random members of the whole population. The notion of the closeness of the relationship between two individuals is easily visualized in simple cases, such as that, for example, father and son are more closely related than grandfather and grandson. Likewise the mating of double first cousins would be regarded by almost anyone with the barest knowledge of genetics as constituting inbreeding. The job before us is to make these notions of inbreeding and degree of relationship precise, so that we have quantitative measures of their intensity which have a strict meaning. The main basis on which this is done goes back to the work of Wright (1921), but the work of Malécot (1948) which resulted in essentially the same formulas as that of Wright lay bare the crucial ideas untrammeled by unnecessary assumptions.

The basic notion in Malécot's presentation is that two genes in the population may be alike for two entirely exclusive reasons:

1. They may be alike because they are copies arising in the reproductive process of one gene occurring previously in the ancestry, or one is a copy of the other. This will be called identical by descent.

2. They may be alike in the sense of being both A: for example, because two genes are drawn at random from the population and both happen to be A. If the gene frequency for A is p, then the probability of two randomly drawn genes being both A is p^2. This will be called identical in state, and not by descent.

Take, for instance, the population

$$p^2AA + 2pqAa + q^2aa$$

and draw two individuals at random from this population, and then take a gene at random from each individual. The probabilities are:

Gene 1A and gene 2A: p^2

Gene 1A and gene 2a: pq

Gene 1a and gene 2A: pq

Gene 1a and gene 2a: q^2

The probability of the genes being alike is equal to $p^2 + q^2$.

Now let the two individuals be mated, and suppose their genotypes are ab and cd, where a, b, c, and d may be A or a independently. Then take two offspring of this mating: Parent ab contributes a copy of gene a one half of the time and a copy of gene b the other half. Likewise parent cd contributes a copy of gene c one half of the time and a copy of gene d the other half of the time. Hence the offspring are ac, ad, bc, and bd, each with probability of $\frac{1}{4}$. Now consider two random offspring. The possible pairs are:

ac and ac with probability $\frac{1}{16}$

ac and ad with probability $\frac{2}{16}$

ac and bc with probability $\frac{2}{16}$

ac and bd with probability $\frac{2}{16}$

ad and ad with probability $\frac{1}{16}$

ad and bc with probability $\frac{2}{16}$

ad and bd with probability $\frac{2}{16}$

bc and bc with probability $\frac{1}{16}$

bc and bd with probability $\frac{2}{16}$

bd and bd with probability $\frac{1}{16}$

In the pair ac and ac, the gene a possessed by each is a copy of the gene a possessed by parent ab. Regardless of what gene a is, the two individuals will possess this gene, and the gene will be identical for the two individuals providing mutation did not occur. Mutation will be ignored entirely in the following discussion of inbreeding, because its effect in disturbing probabilities will be trivial. This is so because mutation rates are commonly agreed to lie between say 10^{-4} and 10^{-6}.

We are now in a position to quantify the degree of relationship between two individuals precisely. Malécot uses the term "coefficient de parenté" for which no English translation appears yet to have been made. The term "coefficient of relationship" has been used by Wright (1922) to denote a quantity which is twice Malécot's "coefficient de parenté" under random mating. To avoid confusion in the minds of readers used to Wright's terminology we shall translate Malécot's term as "coefficient of parentage." This is defined as follows: Consider two individuals X and Y with genotypes ab and cd. Then r_{XY} is defined to be the probability that a random gene from X is identical by descent with a random gene from Y. In other words if we use $P(a=c)$ say to denote the probability that genes a and c are identical by descent then

$$r_{XY} = \tfrac{1}{4}[P(a=c) + P(a=d) + P(b=c) + P(b=d)]$$

In the case of two full-sibs resulting from two random parents in the population, the coefficient of parentage is equal to $\tfrac{1}{4}$, since the probability that a random gene in one full-sib is identical by descent with any one gene in the other full-sib is $\tfrac{1}{4}$, the mean of $\tfrac{1}{2}$ and 0.

The other concept which is to be defined is that of the coefficient of inbreeding of an individual, and that is defined to be the probability that the two genes possessed by that individual at a locus are identical by descent.

We may now very easily determine the rules by which coefficients of parentage and coefficients of inbreeding can be evaluated.

Let X have a coefficient of inbreeding F_X. What is the coefficient of parentage of X with itself? If X has the genotype ab at a locus, then F_X is given by

$$F_X = P(a=b)$$

Now, if we compare X with itself, we find

$$r_{XX} = \tfrac{1}{4}[P(a=a) + P(a=b) + P(b=a) + P(b=b)]$$

so

$$r_{XX} = \tfrac{1}{4}(2 + 2F_X)$$

or

$$r_{XX} = \tfrac{1}{2}(1 + F_X)$$

Hence we have in words:

The coefficient of parentage of X with itself equals unity plus the coefficient of inbreeding of X, all divided by 2.

Next consider an offspring of the mating of two individuals X and Y. Let X be (ab) and Y be (cd). Then

$$r_{XY} = \tfrac{1}{4}[P(a=c) + P(a=d) + P(b=c) + P(b=d)]$$

The inbreeding coefficient of the offspring is obtained by noting that the genotypic array of an offspring is

$$\tfrac{1}{4}(ac) + \tfrac{1}{4}(ad) + \tfrac{1}{4}(bc) + \tfrac{1}{4}(bd)$$

The probability that the two genes of an offspring are identical by descent is therefore

$$[\tfrac{1}{4}P(a{=}c) + \tfrac{1}{4}P(a{=}d) + \tfrac{1}{4}P(b{=}c) + \tfrac{1}{4}P(b{=}d)]$$

which is equal to r_{XY}. Hence we have the equation

$$F_{X \times Y} = r_{XY}$$

The coefficient of parentage of the offspring $X \times Y$ with itself is then equal to

$$\tfrac{1}{2}(1 + r_{XY})$$

Now consider the coefficient of parentage of individual A with the offspring of individuals B and C. Let individuals B and C have genotypes uv and wx, respectively, and individual A the genotype yz. Then

$$B \times C = \tfrac{1}{4}(uw) + \tfrac{1}{4}(ux) + \tfrac{1}{4}(vw) + \tfrac{1}{4}(vx)$$

so

$$
\begin{aligned}
r_{A,\,B \times C} &= \tfrac{1}{4}\{\tfrac{1}{4}[P(y{=}u) + P(y{=}w) + P(z{=}u) + P(z{=}w)] \\
&\quad + \tfrac{1}{4}[P(y{=}u) + P(y{=}x) + P(z{=}u) + P(z{=}x)] \\
&\quad + \tfrac{1}{4}[P(y{=}v) + P(y{=}w) + P(z{=}v) + P(z{=}w)] \\
&\quad + \tfrac{1}{4}[P(y{=}v) + P(y{=}x) + P(z{=}v) + P(z{=}x)]\} \\
&= \tfrac{1}{8}[P(y{=}u) + P(y{=}v) + P(z{=}u) + P(z{=}v) \\
&\quad + P(y{=}w) + P(y{=}x) + P(z{=}w) + P(z{=}x)] \\
&= \tfrac{1}{8}(4r_{AB} + 4r_{AC}) \\
&= \tfrac{1}{2}(r_{AB} + r_{AC})
\end{aligned}
$$

We note that this formula holds in complete generality, the special case which is of considerable use being that when B or C is the same individual as A. It is a consequence of this equation that

$$r_{A,\,A \times B} = \tfrac{1}{2}(r_{AA} + r_{AB})$$

and that

$$r_{A \times B,\,A \times B} = \tfrac{1}{4}(r_{AA} + r_{BB} + 2r_{AB})$$

where $r_{A \times B,\,A \times B}$ is the coefficient of parentage of two independent offspring of the mating $A \times B$. The only point to be watched in applying the formula is that the coefficient of parentage of an offspring of the mating $A \times B$ *with itself* is $\tfrac{1}{2}(1 + r_{AB})$, while the coefficient of parentage of an offspring of the mating $A \times B$ with an independent offspring of the same mating is

$$\tfrac{1}{4}(r_{AA} + r_{BB} + 2r_{AB})$$

The way in which these equations are used will be illustrated with the pedigree shown in Figure 5.1. Here C and D are full-sibs from the

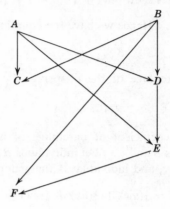

FIGURE 5.1

mating $A \times B$, E is an offspring of the mating $A \times D$, and F is an offspring of the mating $B \times E$. Let us suppose that F_A and F_B are both zero: i.e. that A and B are random members of a population in which there is no inbreeding. The coefficients of parentage are obtained in the way which is most routine by constructing Table 5.1 of coefficients of parentage.

TABLE 5.1

COEFFICIENTS OF PARENTAGE

	A	B	C	D	E	F
A	$\frac{1}{2}$	0	$\frac{1}{4}$	$\frac{1}{4}$	$\frac{3}{8}$	$\frac{3}{16}$
B	0	$\frac{1}{2}$	$\frac{1}{4}$	$\frac{1}{4}$	$\frac{1}{8}$	$\frac{5}{16}$
C	$\frac{1}{4}$	$\frac{1}{4}$	$\frac{1}{2}$	$\frac{1}{4}$	$\frac{1}{4}$	$\frac{1}{4}$
D	$\frac{1}{4}$	$\frac{1}{4}$	$\frac{1}{4}$	$\frac{1}{2}$	$\frac{3}{8}$	$\frac{5}{16}$
E	$\frac{3}{8}$	$\frac{1}{8}$	$\frac{1}{4}$	$\frac{3}{8}$	$\frac{5}{8}$	$\frac{3}{8}$
F	$\frac{3}{16}$	$\frac{5}{16}$	$\frac{1}{4}$	$\frac{5}{16}$	$\frac{3}{8}$	$\frac{9}{16}$

This table was constructed as follows: A and B are not inbred and have zero coefficient of parentage so that $r_{AA} = r_{BB} = \frac{1}{2}$, $r_{AB} = 0$. Individual C is an offspring of $A \times B$ so that

$$r_{AC} = \tfrac{1}{2}(r_{AA} + r_{AB}) = \tfrac{1}{4}$$
$$r_{BC} = \tfrac{1}{2}(r_{BA} + r_{BB}) = \tfrac{1}{4}$$

Individual E is an offspring of $A \times D$ so that

$$r_{AE} = \tfrac{1}{2}(r_{AA} + r_{AD})$$

and so on.

The coefficients of inbreeding of individuals may be obtained from the diagonal elements, using the fact that

$$F_X = 2r_{XX} - 1$$

so that for instance

$$F_F = 2 \times \tfrac{9}{16} - 1 = \tfrac{1}{8}$$

or more simply

$$F_F = F_{B \times E} = r_{BE} = \tfrac{1}{8}$$

It is not necessary to compute the whole of Table 5.1 to get the coefficient of inbreeding of particular individuals. To get the inbreeding coefficient of F we have merely to get the coefficient of parentage of individuals B and E, and this is derived from the coefficients of parentage of A and D with A since E is $A \times D$.

An alternative formula is given by Wright. We note that the only contributions to the coefficient of parentage of two individuals X and Y arise from lines of ancestry leading from X and Y to common ancestors. If we denote by Z a common ancestor which is n_1 steps above X and n_2 steps above Y, then it is clear that the only contribution to the coefficient of parentage arising from the chain of relationship from X to Z to Y is equal to

$$(\tfrac{1}{2})^{n_1+n_2} r_{ZZ}$$

or

$$(\tfrac{1}{2})^{n_1+n_2} \left(\frac{1 + F_Z}{2} \right)$$

Hence Wright's rule is as follows: Let Z be an ancestor of X and Y such that lines of descent to X and Y meet at Z, and the descent from Z to X involves n_1 divisions and from Z to Y involves n_2 divisions; then the contribution to the coefficient of parentage from this chain of relationship is

$$(\tfrac{1}{2})^{n_1+n_2} \left(\frac{1 + F_Z}{2} \right)$$

To get the total coefficient of parentage we merely consider all possible chains of relationship of X and Y which are distinct in that the head of the two lines of descent is distinct, or the chains regarded as a whole are distinct, and add up the contributions.

Thus in the example we have to find the coefficient of parentage of B

and E, of which the only common ancestor is B which is zero steps from B and two steps from E. Also B has zero coefficient of inbreeding so that

$$r_{BE} = (\tfrac{1}{2})^2\tfrac{1}{2}(1 + 0) = \tfrac{1}{8}$$

We shall now give some notes on the two concepts coefficient of parentage and coefficient of inbreeding. We first note that these coefficients are probabilities which bear no relation at all to the effects of the genes. It may turn out, as we shall see later, that the coefficients enter into correlations between relatives with respect to characters which are actually quantitative or translated into quantitative terms from a dichotomous character. Any such usage of the coefficients is to be regarded as an appendage and not to be their real basis. The theory of inbreeding is in its basic aspects purely a theory about probabilities. I found difficulty before reading Malécot's presentation in understanding the true nature of F which was described by Wright as the "correlation between uniting gametes." If such terminology is used, presumably some quantitative attribute is to be assigned to each gamete so that one can consider a correlation. Of course, in the case of two alleles A and a, one can construct a two-by-two table and insert merely frequencies in the cells. We can then attach numbers 1 and 0 to A and a, respectively, and compute the correlation between the numbers for the sire and dam gametes. However, if we should use such a rule as a definition, we clearly get into trouble when we have more than two alleles.

The structure of the present book essentially is that it consists of two parts with respect to genetical theory; the first part deals with formal genetics, i.e., the existence and transmission of genotypes and of qualitative phenotypic characters, and the second part deals with the analysis of quantitative characters. Any uses of the theory of inbreeding with respect to quantitative characters will therefore be given in the latter half of the book, when the results on the probability theory of gene transmission will be used.

It is clear that the coefficients of inbreeding and of parentage are defined in such a way that the number of possible alleles is irrelevant. The coefficients could be calculated if we were dealing with a population which is composed entirely of one homozygous genotype. Of course, their uses under that circumstance would not be at all biological, because all individuals in the population would have the same genotype, always excluding mutations. The coefficient of parentage could, however, be used if there were a law by which an individual passed his possessions at his death to the individual most closely related to him.

It is clear that, in using the coefficients of parentage and of inbreeding, as calculated in a given pedigree, we must make assumptions about the coefficients of parentage and inbreeding of the individuals at the head of the lines of ancestry. Any use of the coefficients to determine the probability that genes are alike in state must be based on assumptions about the probabilities that genes are alike in state at the head of the ancestry. In fact, we can say that two genes are alike in state because either (1) they are identical by descent, i.e. are copies of one particular gene, or (2) are not identical by descent but are copies of different genes which were alike in state. Thus, if we start with the population

$$(\sum p_i A_i)^2$$

and choose individuals at random to enter the pedigree, then it is clear that the probability that any one gene is A_i is p_i. If F is the probability that two genes in an individual are alike by descent, the probability that they are both A_i is Fp_i. The probability that they are unlike by descent is $(1-F)$, and the probability that two ordered original genes are A_i and A_j is $p_i p_j$. Hence we can state that the population which would result from inbreeding the population $(\sum p_i A_i)^2$ to an extent measured by F has the array

$$F(\sum p_i A_i A_i) + (1 - F)(\sum p_i A_i)^2$$

In the case of two alleles A and a, the resulting population genotypic array would, for example, be

$$[Fp + (1 - F)p^2]AA + [2(1 - F)pq]Aa + [Fq + (1 - F)q^2]aa$$

where p and q are the gene frequencies for A and a. Alternatively this may be written

$$[p - (1 - F)pq]AA + [2(1 - F)pq]Aa + [q - (1 - F)pq]aa$$

or as

$$[p^2 + Fpq]AA + [2(1 - F)pq]Aa + [q^2 + Fpq]aa$$

showing that the homozygotic classes are each increased by Fpq which is one half of the loss of heterozygotes resulting from the inbreeding.

It is of interest to examine the proportion of heterozygous individuals in the inbred population compared to the proportion in the original population. In the particular case when the original population is $(\sum p_i A_i)^2$, the original proportion of heterozygotes is $\sum_{i \neq j} p_i p_j$. After inbreeding to the extent measured by F, the proportion is $(1 - F) \sum_{i \neq j} p_i p_j$, so that the proportion of heterozygotes is reduced from the original proportion by a relative amount F. In the general case it is a direct consequence of the preceding derivations that, if an original population leads by consanguineous mating to a population which has a coefficient of inbreeding of F, and the members of the original population contribute equally to the inbred population, then the probability of an individual being heterozygous is $(1-F)$ times the probability that an individual in the original population is heterozygous. It would be erroneous to suppose that a natural population would have the genotypic array

$$F\left(\sum_i p_i A_i A_i\right) + (1 - F)\left(\sum_i p_i A_i\right)^2$$

From the preceding derivations it is clear that this would happen only if the population was derived from an original population which itself arose by random mating, by a process of mating based purely on consanguinity. It seems unlikely that natural populations do mate in this way, the prime example being the human population for which homogamy is important. Here the word homogamy is used to denote some preferential mating based either on the genotype or the phenotype of the individuals. It is therefore difficult to see how the particular inbred population specified above has any special significance in evolutionary theory, except for the case of a population divided into small groups as regards mating.

Finally it may be of interest to consider the coefficient of inbreeding and its relation to the proportion of heterozygous loci contained by an individual. The probability that any one locus contains two genes which are identical by descent is F. This holds for all loci which are segregating independently. The exact effect of linkage on the homozygosity of inbred individuals is an interesting problem which does not appear to have been solved. In the case of selfing with two loci, linkage results in a proportion homozygous by descent with respect to two loci which is greater than F^2 and a proportion heterozygous at both loci which is greater than $(1-F)^2$. In this case then the mean number of heterozygous loci is equal to $2F$ but the variance in the number of heterozygous loci is greater than $2F(1-F)$, which is the value for the case of no linkage. This particular case is probably typical of the general solution, that linkage, which, of course, has no effect on the mean number of heterozygous loci, increases the variance of the number of heterozygous loci.

5.2 REGULAR SYSTEMS OF INBREEDING

We now turn to the consideration of regular systems of inbreeding of which the simple examples are selfing, full-sibbing, and parent–offspring mating. We shall treat these in order.

5.2.1 Selfing

Let the initial individual X be (ab). Then the offspring array is

$$\tfrac{1}{4}(aa) + \tfrac{1}{2}(ab) + \tfrac{1}{4}(bb)$$

Let $F_X = P(a=b)$ and let F_Y be the coefficient of inbreeding of the offspring. We see immediately that

$$F_Y = \tfrac{1}{4}(1 + 2F_X + 1)$$

Alternatively, since

$$F_{A \times B} = r_{AB}$$

$$F_{X \times X} = r_{XX} = \tfrac{1}{2}(1 + F_X)$$

So we have the simple recurrence relation

$$F = \tfrac{1}{2} + \tfrac{1}{2}F'$$

where F denotes the coefficient of inbreeding in a generation and F' denotes the coefficient in the preceding generation. If we let $P = 1 - F$, we have

$$(1 - P) = \tfrac{1}{2} + \tfrac{1}{2}(1 - P')$$

or

$$P = \tfrac{1}{2}P'$$

so

$$P^{(n)} = (\tfrac{1}{2})^n P^{(0)}$$

and

$$F^{(n)} = 1 - (\tfrac{1}{2})^n (1 - F^{(0)})$$

where the superscript in parentheses denote the generation. The quantity P is due to Wright and is called the panmictic index.

5.2.2 Full-Sibbing

Let two full-sibs in generation n be X and Y; so we have the pedigree shown in Figure 5.2. Let the coefficient of inbreeding in generation n be

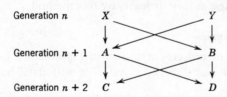

Generation n X Y

Generation $n + 1$ A B

Generation $n + 2$ C D

FIGURE 5.2. Full-sib inbreeding.

F_n and the coefficient of parentage of full-sibs be r_n, so that

$$F_X = F_Y = F_n, \qquad r_n = r_{XY}$$

Then

$$r_{n+1} = \tfrac{1}{4}(r_{XX} + r_{YY} + 2r_{XY})$$
$$= \tfrac{1}{4}[\tfrac{1}{2}(1 + F_n) + \tfrac{1}{2}(1 + F_n) + 2r_n]$$

But

$$r_{n+1} = F_{n+2}, \qquad r_n = F_{n+1}$$

so

$$F_{n+2} = \tfrac{1}{4}(1 + F_n + 2F_{n+1})$$

or, if

$$P = 1 - F$$
$$P_{n+2} = \tfrac{1}{4}(P_n + 2P_{n+1})$$

so

$$P_{n+2} - \tfrac{1}{2}P_{n+1} - \tfrac{1}{4}P_n = 0$$

We now use the theory of recurrence equations to state that

$$P_n = \beta_1 \epsilon^n + \beta_2 \epsilon'^n$$

where ϵ and ϵ' are the roots of the quadratic equation

$$x^2 - \tfrac{1}{2}x - \tfrac{1}{4} = 0$$

i.e.

$$\epsilon = \tfrac{1}{4}(1 + \sqrt{5})$$
$$\epsilon' = \tfrac{1}{4}(1 - \sqrt{5})$$

We may note that P, which equals $1 - F$, is the probability that two genes possessed by an individual are unlike by descent. If the probability that an individual is heterozygous at the founding of the population is H, then the probability that an individual is heterozygous in generation n is equal to $P_n H$. The whole of the above material on full-sibbing is due to Wright (1921), but it is necessary to remark that his derivation used the method of path coefficients, and the generality of the result is obscured to some people (the author at least) by this method.

5.2.3 Parent–Offspring

Here one type of pedigree is shown in Figure 5.3. Let the coefficient of parentage of X and Y be r_{XY} and of X with itself be r_{XX}. Then

$$F_A = r_{XY}$$
$$F_B = r_{XA} = \tfrac{1}{2}(r_{XX} + r_{XY}) = \tfrac{1}{2}(r_{XX} + F_A)$$
$$F_C = r_{XB} = \tfrac{1}{2}(r_{XX} + r_{XA}) = \tfrac{1}{2}(r_{XX} + F_B)$$

so

$$F_B - F_C = \tfrac{1}{2}(F_A - F_B)$$

or if

$$P = 1 - F$$
$$P_C - P_B = \tfrac{1}{2}(P_B - P_A)$$

or

$$P_C - \tfrac{3}{2}P_B + \tfrac{1}{2}P_A = 0$$

In general, denoting the generation by a subscript, we have

$$P_{n+2} - \tfrac{3}{2}P_{n+1} + \tfrac{1}{2}P_n = 0$$

Hence

$$P_n = \beta_1 + \beta_2(\tfrac{1}{2})^n$$

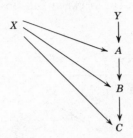

FIGURE 5.3. System of parent–offspring inbreeding.

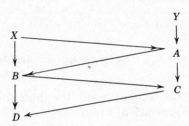

FIGURE 5.4. System of parent–offspring inbreeding.

If, for example, $P_1 = \tfrac{3}{8}$ and $P_2 = \tfrac{5}{16}$, we get the series, $\tfrac{3}{8}, \tfrac{5}{16}, \tfrac{9}{32}, \tfrac{17}{64}$, etc., as given by Wright (1921).   Another type of parent–offspring mating is given in Figure 5.4.   Here using r_{XY} which equals F_A, we get

$$F_A = r_{XY}$$
$$F_B = r_{XA}$$
$$F_C = r_{AB} = \tfrac{1}{2}(r_{AA} + r_{AX}) = \tfrac{1}{2}[\tfrac{1}{2}(1 + F_A) + F_B]$$

so

$$F_C = \tfrac{1}{2}F_B + \tfrac{1}{4}(1 + F_A)$$

or with

$$P = 1 - F$$
$$P_C = \tfrac{1}{2}P_B + \tfrac{1}{4}P_A$$

This is exactly the same recurrence relation as with full-sib mating; so we have, if P_n is the value of P in the nth generation,

$$P_n = \beta_1 \epsilon^n + \beta_2 \epsilon'^n$$

where β_1 and β_2 are determined by P_0 and P_1.

5.2.4 Double First Cousins

Let a segment of a line be as given in Figure 5.5. It is easy to verify that coefficients of parentage between full-sibs will be constant within

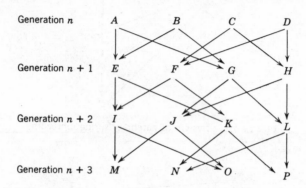

FIGURE 5.5. Double first cousin inbreeding.

any generation after the second as will the inbreeding coefficient of the individuals within a generation. Individuals A, C are full-sibs, as are B and D.

Let

$$F_n = F_A = F_B = F_C = F_D$$
$$F_{n+1} = F_E = F_F = F_G = F_H$$
$$F_{n+2} = F_I = \text{etc.}$$
$$F_{n+3} = F_M = \text{etc.}$$

Then

$$r_{AB} = r_{CD} = F_{n+1}$$

and, letting

$$r_{EF} = \tfrac{1}{4}(r_{AC} + r_{AD} + r_{BC} + r_{BD}) = r_{GH}$$
$$r_{EF} = F_{n+2}$$

Also

$$F_{n+3} = r_{IJ} = \tfrac{1}{4}(r_{EG} + r_{EH} + r_{FG} + r_{FH})$$
$$= \tfrac{1}{2}(r_{EG} + r_{EH})$$

since
$$r_{EG} = r_{FH}, \qquad r_{EH} = r_{FG}$$
So
$$r_{EG} = \tfrac{1}{4}(r_{AA} + r_{BB} + 2r_{AB})$$
$$= \tfrac{1}{4}[\tfrac{1}{2}(1 + F_n) + \tfrac{1}{2}(1 + F_n) + 2F_{n+1}]$$
$$= \tfrac{1}{4}(1 + F_n + 2F_{n+1})$$
$$r_{EH} = r_{EF} = F_{n+2}$$
and
$$F_{n+3} = \tfrac{1}{2}[\tfrac{1}{4}(1 + F_n + 2F_{n+1}) + F_{n+2}]$$
or
$$F_{n+3} = \tfrac{1}{2}F_{n+2} + \tfrac{1}{4}F_{n+1} + \tfrac{1}{8}F_n + \tfrac{1}{8}$$
Putting
$$P = 1 - F$$
we get
$$P_{n+3} = \tfrac{1}{2}P_{n+2} + \tfrac{1}{4}P_{n+1} + \tfrac{1}{8}P_n$$

Hence, given an initial mating or series of matings, we may calculate P_1, P_2, and P_3, hence get P_4 and all succeeding ones.

Other systems of inbreeding may be examined readily by the use of the basic rules given in the previous chapter. No further systems will be pursued herein.

5.2.5 Discussion of Results

It remains only to comment on the results. It should first be emphasized that the formulas give the probability that an individual in generation n is homozygous by descent in terms of the probabilities for previous generations. The results do not tell us anything about the frequencies

TABLE 5.2

EFFECTS OF DIFFERENT REGULAR MATING SYSTEMS

Systems	Recurrence Relation
Selfing	$P_{n+1} = \tfrac{1}{2}P_n$
Full-sibbing	$P_{n+2} = \tfrac{1}{2}P_{n+1} + \tfrac{1}{4}P_n$
Parent–offspring*	$P_{n+2} = \tfrac{1}{2}P_{n+1} + \tfrac{1}{4}P_n$
Double first cousins	$P_{n+3} = \tfrac{1}{2}P_{n+2} + \tfrac{1}{4}P_{n+1} + \tfrac{1}{8}P_n$
Quadruple second cousins†	$P_{n+4} = \tfrac{1}{2}P_{n+3} + \tfrac{1}{4}P_{n+2} + \tfrac{1}{8}P_{n+1} + \tfrac{1}{16}P_n$
Octuple third cousins†	$P_{n+5} = \tfrac{1}{2}P_{n+4} + \tfrac{1}{4}P_{n+3} + \tfrac{1}{8}P_{n+2} + \tfrac{1}{16}P_{n+1} + \tfrac{1}{32}P_n$

* Any parent used only once.

† See Wright (1921).

with which pairs of relatives have particular genotypes. This point is mentioned because a full treatment of the theory of inbreeding should give us the whole story so that we can for example examine correlations between relatives in inbred populations. The results given above can be used for this purpose only under special circumstances which will be discussed later in the book.

The basic formulas for the probabilities of heterozygosity by descent, that is, the probabilities that the two genes possessed by an individual are not descended from a single gene, are given in Table 5.2.

5.3 MIXTURES OF INBREEDING SYSTEMS

The extension of the use of the probability argument to the case of a mixture of inbreeding systems proceeds easily. As an example let us consider the case in which there is a constant probability s of selfing and of $(1-s)$ of mating at random. Then, if a sequence of offspring is denoted by $A, B, C, \cdots$, we have

$$F_B = s\tfrac{1}{2}(1 + F_A)$$
$$F_C = s\tfrac{1}{2}(1 + F_B), \quad \text{etc.}$$

so that, if $F = k + Q$, then

$$k + Q_B - \frac{s}{2} - \frac{s}{2}(k + Q_A) = 0$$

If we take

$$k - \frac{s}{2} - \frac{s}{2}k = 0$$

or

$$k = \frac{s}{2 - s}$$

then

$$Q_B = \frac{s}{2} Q_A$$

and, if a subscript n is used to denote the value in the nth generation,

$$F_n = \frac{s}{2 - s}\left[1 - \left(\frac{s}{2}\right)^n\right] + \left(\frac{s}{2}\right)^n F_0$$

In this case F tends to the value $s/(2 - s)$ as n tends to infinity. This case is interesting in that an equilibrium population with arbitrary F value is possible if s can take out any particular definite value. It is also easily seen that

$$r_{AB} = sr_{AB/S} + (1 - s)r_{AB/R}$$

where

$$r_{AB/S} = r_{AB} \quad \text{if selfing takes place}$$
$$= \tfrac{1}{2}(1 + F_A)$$

and

$$r_{AB/R} = r_{AB} \quad \text{under random mating}$$
$$= \tfrac{1}{4}(1 + F_A)$$

so that

$$r_{AB} = \left(\frac{1 + s}{4}\right)(1 + F_A)$$

It is left as an exercise to the reader to work out the consequences of a full-sib mating system in which there is a probability s say that any offspring of an individual arises by full-sibbing.

5.4 INBREEDING DUE TO FINITE POPULATION SIZE

It is readily apparent that the finiteness of a population will result in inbreeding, or non-zero probability of genes possessed by an individual being identical by descent. The theory of this effect was worked out essentially by Sewall Wright (1921). We shall however follow the mode of presentation of Malécot (1948), because Wright used the method of path coefficients which is in our opinion somewhat confusing and based on somewhat sophisticated (statistically) theory, whereas Malécot's presentation is in the terms of the present chapter and deals with the intrinsic probabilities.

The first case to be considered occurs when there are separate sexes. Suppose the population consists of N_1 males and N_2 females. Let the male population in generation n be denoted by $_1\prod_n$ and the female population by $_2\prod_n$. Then under panmixia the two genes at a locus of an individual in generation n consist of a random gene from the population $_1\prod_{n-1}$ and a random gene from the population $_2\prod_{n-1}$, the assumption of panmixia amounting to the assumption that the N_1 paternal genes possessed by males in a generation are a random sample with replacement of the $2N_1$ genes possessed by the N_1 males in the previous generation and so on. The probability that the two genes of an individual in generation n come from a single individual in generation $(n-2)$ is equal to

$$\frac{1}{4}\frac{1}{N_1} + \frac{1}{4}\frac{1}{N_2}$$

because the probability that the two genes both occur as paternal genes in generation $(n-1)$ is $\tfrac{1}{4}$; and, given that the paternal gene in one individual arises from a particular individual in generation $(n-2)$, the probability that the other paternal gene arises from the same individual is $1/N_1$, with a similar argument for the case when the two genes both occur as maternal genes in generation $(n-1)$. Let

$$\frac{1}{4N_1} + \frac{1}{4N_2} = \frac{1}{N}$$

the quantity N being called the effective size of the population.* The probability that the two genes in an individual in generation n arise from different individuals in generation $(n-2)$ is therefore $(1 - 1/N)$. In case the two genes arise from the same individual in generation $(n-2)$, the probability that they are identical by descent is $(1 + F_{n-2})/2$. In case they arise from different individuals, the probability that they are identical by descent is F_{n-1}, because this is the probability that the genes from two different individuals in generation $(n-2)$ are identical by descent. Hence

$$F_n = \frac{1}{N}\left(\frac{1 + F_{n-2}}{2}\right) + \left(1 - \frac{1}{N}\right)F_{n-1}$$

Another way of getting the result which is possibly more revealing in some ways is as follows. Let the sire genes of any individual be those genes contributed by the sire of the individual and so on. Then let S_1 be the probability that two random sire genes in generation 1 are identical by descent and D_1 the corresponding probability for dam genes. Let F_1 be the probability that the sire gene and dam gene of an individual are identical by descent or indeed that any sire gene is identical by descent with any dam gene. Then

$$F_2 = \tfrac{1}{4}(S_1 + D_1 + 2F_1)$$

Also

$$S_2 = \frac{1}{2N_1} + \tfrac{1}{4}(S_1 + D_1) - \frac{1}{4N_1}(S_1 + D_1) + \tfrac{1}{2}F_1$$

$$D_2 = \frac{1}{2N_2} + \tfrac{1}{4}(S_1 + D_1) - \frac{1}{4N_2}(S_1 + D_1) + \tfrac{1}{2}F_1$$

and

$$F_3 = \tfrac{1}{4}(S_2 + D_2 + 2F_2)$$

These equations lead to

$$F_3 = \frac{1}{2N} + \frac{F_1}{2N} + \left(1 - \frac{1}{N}\right)F_2$$

Let

$$P = 1 - F$$

then

$$P_n = \left(1 - \frac{1}{N}\right)P_{n-1} + \frac{1}{2N}P_{n-2}$$

* Note that, if the sexes are equally frequent, N is the population size.

Hence

$$P = \beta_1 \lambda_1^n + \beta_2 \lambda_2^n$$

where λ_1 and λ_2 are the roots of

$$x^2 - \left(1 - \frac{1}{N}\right) x - \frac{1}{2N} = 0$$

We therefore have

$$P_n = \beta_1 \left[\frac{1}{2}\left(1 - \frac{1}{N}\right) + \frac{1}{2}\left(1 + \frac{1}{N^2}\right)^{1/2}\right]^n$$
$$+ \beta_2 \left[\frac{1}{2}\left(1 - \frac{1}{N}\right) - \frac{1}{2}\left(1 + \frac{1}{N^2}\right)^{1/2}\right]^n$$

the values of β_1 and β_2 being determined by the initial condition of the population.

In the case when $N = 2$, which is of course full-sib mating we have

$$P_n = \beta_1 \epsilon^n + \beta_2 \epsilon'^n$$

where $\epsilon = \frac{1}{4}(1 + \sqrt{5})$ and $\epsilon' = \frac{1}{4}(1 - \sqrt{5})$, and this result corresponds, of course, to that given earlier.

To obtain an approximation to P_n when N is large we note that, if P_0 and P_1 are the values for the panmictic index in the zeroth and first generation,

$$P_0 = \beta_1 + \beta_2$$
$$P_1 = \frac{\beta_1 + \beta_2}{2}\left(1 - \frac{1}{N}\right) + \cdot \frac{\beta_1 - \beta_2}{2}\left(1 + \frac{1}{N^2}\right)^{1/2}$$

or

$$\beta_1 - \beta_2 = \left[2P_1 - P_0\left(1 - \frac{1}{N}\right)\right]\left(1 + \frac{1}{N^2}\right)^{-1/2}.$$
$$= 2P_1 - P_0\left(1 - \frac{1}{N}\right)$$

ignoring terms involving $1/N^2$, so that

$$\beta_1 = P_1 + \frac{1}{2N}P_0$$

Hence, since the dominant part of β_1 is P_1 if N is at all large, and since

$$\frac{1}{2}\left[\left(1 - \frac{1}{N}\right) + \left(1 + \frac{1}{N^2}\right)^{1/2}\right] = 1 - \frac{1}{2N} \quad \text{approximately}$$

we have

$$P_n = P_1\left(1 - \frac{1}{2N}\right)^n \quad \text{approximately}$$

or, since

$$(1 - \delta)^n = e^{-n\delta} \quad \text{approximately}$$

if δ is small, the form of P_n for large n is

$$P_n = P_1 \exp\left(-\frac{n}{2N}\right)$$

Malécot (1948, pp. 30, 31) has an extensive discussion of this equation and the significance of the fact that, as n tends to infinity, P_n tends to zero: that is, the population becomes homozygous. He points out that, in order for P to decrease to one tenth of its value in generation 1, the number of generations required is the solution for n of

$$\exp(-n/2N) = 0.1$$

or n equals $2N \log_e 10$ which is about $4.6N$. If for instance the two sexes are equally frequent and there are 1000 of each, N is equal to 2000, and the number of generations necessary for the panmictic index to decrease to one tenth of its initial value is of the order of 9000. In the case of man for instance this would be of the order of 270,000 years.

The second case to be considered is that where there are N monoecious individuals, and self-fertilization is equally possible with cross fertilization so that the probability of self-fertilization is $1/N$. Malécot (1948) deduces that

$$P_n = P_0 \left(1 - \frac{1}{2N}\right)^n$$

which leads to

$$P_n = (\tfrac{1}{2})^n P_0 \quad \text{for the case of selfing}$$

and P_n proportional to $\exp(-n/2N)$ as in the previous case for N large.

The case considered by Crow (1954) is that of a population of N diploid parents contributing gametes to the next generation. It is supposed that the offspring come from pairs of gametes drawn at random from the independently large pool of gametes to which each parent contributes equally. He derives the equation

$$P_n = P_0 \left(1 - \frac{1}{2N}\right)^n$$

which is the same solution as before.

A third way of looking at the problem is to suppose that the genes passed on to an offspring generation are a random sample with replacement of the parental genes. Then the sampling variance of the frequency of gene A, for example, is

$$\sigma_p^2 = \frac{p(1 - p)}{2N}$$

where p is the parental gene frequency. In each successive generation a variance similar to this arises, and the variance in the nth generation can be shown to be equal to

$$p(1 - p)\left[1 - \left(1 - \frac{1}{2N}\right)^n\right]$$

which is essentially equal to

$$p(1 - p)[1 - \exp(-n/2N)]$$

This formula was given by Wright (1942) and is derived by Crow (1954).

The case when the number of individuals varies from generation to generation is discussed by Malécot (1948), Wright (1931a), Crow (1954), and Kimura (1955). It appears that the above formulas are essentially appropriate if the harmonic mean of the numbers in the different generations is used in place of the constant N.

The reader should also refer to Fisher's book (1930) and Haldane (1939).

5.5 INBREEDING AT A POLYSOMIC LOCUS

We consider the case of a locus at which there are $2k$ chromosomes which segregate as chromosomes, and an arbitrary number of alleles at the locus. By virtue of the assumption of segregation by chromosomes, the gamete contributed to an offspring has a random sample of k chromosomes out of the total $2k$ possible. We shall now develop the probability theory of inbreeding under such conditions.

Consider an individual X with genes $a_1, a_2, \cdots, a_k, b_1, b_2, \cdots, b_k$, the genes $a_1, a_2, \cdots, a_k$ having been given to X by one parent and the genes $b_1, b_2, \cdots, b_k$ by the other parent. Let F_X be the probability that a random pair of genes of X are identical by descent. Then

$$F_X = \frac{1}{2k(2k-1)}[2k^2 P(a_i = b_j) + k(k-1)P(a_i = a_j) + k(k-1)P(b_i = b_j)]$$

$$= \frac{1}{2k-1}\left[k P(a_i = b_j) + \frac{(k-1)}{2}P(a_i = a_j) + \frac{(k-1)}{2}P(b_i = b_j)\right]$$

It is easily seen that, if X', Y' denote the parents of X and if

$r_{X'Y'}$ = probability that a random gene of X' and a random gene of Y' are identical by descent

then

$$r_{X'Y'} = P(a_i = b_j)$$

so that

$$F_X = \frac{1}{2k-1}\left[k r_{X'Y'} + \left(\frac{k-1}{2}\right)(F_{X'} + F_{Y'})\right]$$

Now consider r_{XX} which is the probability that two random genes of X with replacement are identical by descent.   We find

$$r_{XX} = \frac{1}{2k} [1 + (2k - 1)F_X]$$

since, given a random gene, the probability that another random gene is the same one is $1/2k$.

It will be recalled that with diploids ($k=1$)

$$r_{XX} = \tfrac{1}{2}(1 + F_X)$$

and

$$F_X = r_{X'Y'}.$$

Obviously if one were concerned solely with presenting the subject in the shortest possible space, one would deal with the general case only.

We now need to know the properties of the coefficient r.   As in the diploid case we have in general

$$r_{X(A\times B)} = \tfrac{1}{2}(r_{XA} + r_{XB})$$

where $A \times B$ is an offspring from the mating of A and B.   Let X_1 and Y_1 be two progeny of the mating of X and Y.   From the above we know that

$$F_{X_1} = F_{Y_1} = \frac{1}{2k - 1}\left[kr_{XY} + \frac{k - 1}{2}(F_X + F_Y) \right]$$

and also we know $r_{X_1X_1}$ and $r_{Y_1Y_1}$.   Clearly we need to know $r_{X_1Y_1}$. Let X be $a_1, a_2, \cdots, a_k,\ b_1, b_2, \cdots, b_k$, and Y be $a_1', a_2', \cdots, a_k'$, $b_1', b_2', \cdots, b_k'$.   Then X_1 will consist of a random set of k genes from X, say S_1, and a random set of k genes from Y, say D_1, and Y_1 will consist of a random set of k genes from X, say S_2, and a random set of k genes from Y, say D_2.   Then the probability that a random gene of X_1 and a random gene of Y_1 are identical by descent is equal to

$\tfrac{1}{4}$ (prob that a random gene in S_1 is identical by descent to a random gene from S_2)

$+ \tfrac{1}{4}$ (prob that a random gene in S_1 is identical by descent to a random gene from D_2)

$+ \tfrac{1}{4}$ (prob that a random gene in D_1 is identical by descent to a random gene in S_2)

$+ \tfrac{1}{4}$ (prob that a random gene in D_1 is identical by descent to a random gene in D_2)

The first probability is $(1/2k)[1 + (2k - 1)F_X]$ and   the   fourth   is

$(1/2k)[1 + (2k - 1)F_Y]$, while the second and third probabilities are equal to r_{XY}. Hence we have

$$r_{X_1Y_1} = \frac{1}{8k} [2 + (2k - 1)(F_X + F_Y) + 4kr_{XY}]$$

In this way we have proved that the coefficient of parentage of two progeny of the mating $X \times Y$ is

$$\tfrac{1}{4}(r_{XX} + 2r_{XY} + r_{YY})$$

as we would expect from previous computations. This relationship can be written down directly.

We now examine the simpler systems of inbreeding.

5.5.1 Selfing

In this case let X_1, X_2, X_3, X_4 be successive members obtained by selfing, and let F_{X_1} equal F_1, $F_{X_2} = F_2$, etc., $r_{X_1X_1} = r_1$. Then

$$r_1 = \frac{1}{2k} [1 + (2k - 1)F_1]$$

$$F_{X_2} = F_2 = \frac{1}{2k - 1} [kr_1 + (k - 1)F_1]$$

Putting everything in terms of F's, we have

$$F_1 = F_1$$

$$F_2 = \frac{1}{2k - 1} \left[\frac{1}{2} + \frac{2k - 1}{2} F_1 + (k - 1)F_1 \right]$$

$$= \frac{1}{2(2k - 1)} + \frac{4k - 3}{2(2k - 1)} F_1$$

If we let $P = 1 - F$, then we have

$$1 - P_2 = \frac{1}{2(2k - 1)} + \frac{4k - 3}{2(2k - 1)} (1 - P_1)$$

or

$$P_2 = \frac{4k - 3}{2(2k - 1)} P_1$$

With
$k = 1$, i.e. diploids $\qquad P_2 = \tfrac{1}{2} P_1$
$k = 2$, i.e. tetraploids $\qquad P_2 = \tfrac{5}{6} P_1$
$k = 3$, i.e. hexaploids $\qquad P_2 = \tfrac{9}{10} P_1$
$k = 4$, i.e. octoploids $\qquad P_2 = \tfrac{13}{14} P_1$

These results were first derived by Haldane (1930) by a matrix method and were derived by Wright (1938) by path coefficients.

5.5.2 Full-Sibbing

Let X, Y be the parents in a generation, X_1, Y_1 their offspring, X_2, Y_2 the offspring of X_1 and Y_1, and so on.   Then starting from F_X, F_Y, and r_{XY}, we have

$$F_{X_1} = F_{Y_1} = \frac{1}{2k-1}\left[kr_{XY} + \frac{k-1}{2}(F_X + F_Y)\right] = F_1 \quad \text{say}$$

$$r_{X_1Y_1} = \frac{1}{8k}[2 + (2k-1)(F_X + F_Y) + 4kr_{XY}] = r_1 \quad \text{say}$$

$$F_{X_2} = F_{Y_2} = \frac{1}{2k-1}[kr_1 + (k-1)F_1] = F_2$$

$$r_{X_2Y_2} = \frac{1}{8k}[2 + 2(2k-1)F_1 + 4kr_1] = r_2$$

$$F_{X_3} = F_{Y_3} = \frac{1}{2k-1}[kr_2 + (k-1)F_2] = F_3$$

$$r_{X_3Y_3} = \frac{1}{8k}[2 + 2(2k-1)F_2 + 4kr_2] = r_3$$

Hence

$$kr_1 = (2k-1)F_2 - (k-1)F_1$$

so

$$8kr_2 = 2 + 2(2k-1)F_1 + 4kr_1$$
$$= 2 + 2(2k-1)F_1 + (8k-4)F_2 - (4k-4)F_1$$
$$= 2 + 2F_1 + (8k-4)F_2$$

and

$$kr_2 = (2k-1)F_3 - (k-1)F_2$$

so

$$(16k-8)F_3 - (8k-8)F_2 = 2 + 2F_1 + (8k-4)F_2$$

or

$$(16k-8)F_3 = (16k-12)F_2 + 2F_1 + 2$$

or

$$(8k-4)F_3 = (8k-6)F_2 + F_1 + 1$$

Now letting $P = 1 - F$,

$$(8k-4)P_3 = (8k-6)P_2 + P_1$$

so

$$P_n = \beta_1\lambda_1^n + \beta_2\lambda_2^n$$

where λ_1 and λ_2 are the roots of

$$(8k-4)x^2 - (8k-6)x - 1 = 0$$

and β_1 and β_2 are determined by the first two generations. In this case approximately

$$P_n = \beta_1 \left[\frac{(4k - 3) + (16k^2 - 16k + 5)^{1/2}}{8k - 4} \right]^n$$

if we ignore the smaller root.

The recurrence relations in detail are:

Diploid: $\quad 4P_3 = 2P_2 + P_1 \qquad$ or $\qquad P_3 = \frac{1}{2}P_2 + \frac{1}{4}P_1$

Tetraploid: $12P_3 = 10P_2 + P_1 \qquad$ or $\qquad P_3 = \frac{5}{6}P_2 + \frac{1}{12}P_1$

Hexaploid: $20P_3 = 18P_2 + P_1 \qquad$ or $\qquad P_3 = \frac{9}{10}P_2 + \frac{1}{20}P_1$

Octoploid: $28P_3 = 26P_2 + P_1 \qquad$ or $\qquad P_3 = \frac{13}{14}P_2 + \frac{1}{28}P_1$

These results were first obtained by Wright (1938) by path coefficients. See also Wright (1951).

5.5.3 Parent–Offspring Inbreeding

Let the particular system be that given in Figure 5.6. Denote F_{X_i} by F_i and $r_{X_i X_j}$ by r_{ij}. Then, given F_1, F_2, r_{12}, we have

$$F_3 = \frac{1}{2k - 1} \left[kr_{12} + \frac{k - 1}{2} (F_1 + F_2) \right]$$

$$r_{23} = \frac{1}{2}(r_{22} + r_{12})$$

$$= \frac{1}{2} \left\{ \frac{1}{2k} [1 + (2k - 1)F_2] + r_{12} \right\}$$

$$= \frac{1}{4k} + \frac{2k - 1}{4k} F_2 + \frac{1}{2}r_{12}$$

$$F_4 = \frac{1}{2k - 1} \left[kr_{23} + \frac{k - 1}{2} (F_2 + F_3) \right]$$

so

$$(2k - 1)F_4 - \frac{k - 1}{2} (F_2 + F_3) = kr_{23} = \frac{1}{4} + \frac{2k - 1}{4} F_2 + \frac{k}{2} r_{12}$$

$$= \frac{1}{4} + \frac{2k - 1}{4} F_2 + \frac{2k - 1}{2} F_3 - \frac{k - 1}{4} (F_1 + F_2)$$

or

$$(8k - 4)F_4 - (6k - 4)F_3 - (3k - 2)F_2 + (k - 1)F_1 - 1 = 0$$

If following the standard pattern we let $P = 1 - F$, we have

$$(8k - 4)P_4 - (6k - 4)P_3 - (3k - 2)P_2 + (k - 1)P_1 = 0$$

Note that, with diploids for which k equals 1, the recurrence equation involves only three generations in all, whereas with all other polyploids

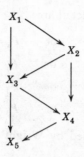

FIGURE 5.6. Parent–offspring inbreeding.

the recurrence equation involves four generations. The recurrence equations for the various cases are:

Diploid: $\quad\quad 4P_4 - 2P_3 - P_2 = 0 \quad$ or $\quad P_4 = \frac{1}{2}P_3 + \frac{1}{4}P_2$

Tetraploid: $\quad\quad 12P_4 - 8P_3 - 4P_2 + P_1 = 0$

Hexaploid: $\quad\quad 20P_4 - 14P_3 - 7P_2 + 2P_1 = 0$

Octoploid: $\quad\quad 28P_4 - 20P_3 - 10P_2 + 3P_1 = 0$

The largest roots in these cases are

Diploid: 0.809

Tetraploid: 0.929

Hexaploid: 0.957

Octoploid: 0.969

It is left as an exercise to the reader to work out other systems of inbreeding.

5.6 THE EXACT TREATMENT OF TETRAPLOIDS

In the case of the tetraploid *abcd* the actual array of gametes is

$$\frac{1}{4}\alpha(aa + bb + cc + dd)$$
$$+ \frac{1}{6}(1 - \alpha)(ab + ac + ad + bc + bd + cd)$$

The previous discussion assumed that α is zero. The value of α will depend on the position of the locus relative to the centromere: If the locus is near the centromere, α will be near to zero. If the locus is distant from the centromere, then the segregation will consist of picking out 2 chromatids at random from the 8 chromatids formed. This extreme corresponds to the value of α being $\frac{1}{7}$. Thus the range on α is from 0 to $\frac{1}{7}$.

Now consider an individual X with genes a, b, c, d. Then

$$F_X = \tfrac{1}{6}[P(a{=}b) + P(a{=}c) + P(a{=}d) + P(b{=}c) + P(b{=}d) + P(c{=}d)]$$

The gametic array from X is (ef) where

$$(ef) = \tfrac{1}{4}\alpha\,(aa + bb + cc + dd) + \left(\frac{1-\alpha}{6}\right)(ab + ac + ad + bc + bd + cd)$$

so

$$P(e{=}f) = \alpha + (1 - \alpha)F_X$$

Take now another individual Y with genes $a_1 b_1 c_1 d_1$ and with inbreeding F_Y and gametic output (gh). The offspring $X \times Y$ will have genotype $(efgh)$ and we proceed to calculate its inbreeding coefficient. We have

$$P(e{=}f) = \alpha + (1 - \alpha)F_X$$
$$P(g{=}h) = \alpha + (1 - \alpha)F_Y$$
$$P(e{=}g) = P(e{=}h) = P(f{=}g) = P(f{=}h) = r_{XY}$$

so that

$$F_{X \times Y} = \tfrac{1}{6}[4r_{XY} + 2\alpha + (1 - \alpha)(F_X + F_Y)]$$

Also as in all cases of autosomal genes

$$r_{X, X \times Y} = \tfrac{1}{2}(r_{XX} + r_{XY})$$
$$r_{X \times Y, X \times Y} = \tfrac{1}{4}(r_{XX} + 2r_{XY} + r_{YY})$$

for two different progeny from $X \times Y$.

5.6.1 Selfing

Let X_1 be the offspring of X_0 by selfing, and let $F_{X_0} = F_0$. Then

$$r_{X_0 X_0} = \tfrac{1}{4}(1 + 3F_0)$$
$$F_1 = F_{X_1} = \tfrac{1}{6}[4r_{X_0 X_0} + 2\alpha + 2(1 - \alpha)F_0]$$

so

$$6F_1 = 1 + 2\alpha + (5 - 2\alpha)F_0$$

or, if $P = 1 - F$,

$$6P_1 = (5 - 2\alpha)P_0$$
$$P_1 = \left(\frac{5 - 2\alpha}{6}\right)P_0$$

5.6.2 Full-Sibbing

Let X_0 and Y_0, X_1 and Y_1, X_2 and Y_2 be successive sib pairs with coefficients of inbreeding of F_0, F_1, F_2, respectively, and coefficients of parentage of r_0, r_1, r_2, respectively. Then

$$F_1 = \tfrac{1}{6}[4r_0 + 2\alpha + 2(1 - \alpha)F_0]$$
$$\begin{aligned}r_1 &= \tfrac{1}{4}(r_{X_0X_0} + r_{Y_0Y_0} + 2r_{X_0Y_0})\\
&= \tfrac{1}{4}[\tfrac{1}{4}(1 + 3F_0) + \tfrac{1}{4}(1 + 3F_0) + 2r_0]\\
&= \tfrac{1}{8}(1 + 3F_0 + 4r_0)\end{aligned}$$

and

$$F_2 = \tfrac{1}{6}[4r_1 + 2\alpha + 2(1 - \alpha)F_1]$$

So we have

$$6F_2 - 2\alpha - 2(1 - \alpha)F_1 = 4r_1$$
$$1 + 3F_0 = 8r_1 - 4r_0$$
$$6F_1 - 2\alpha - 2(1 - \alpha)F_0 = 4r_0$$

and

$$12F_2 - 4\alpha - 4(1 - \alpha)F_1 - (1 + 3F_0) - [6F_1 - 2\alpha - 2(1 - \alpha)F_0] = 0$$

or

$$12F_2 - (10 - 4\alpha)F_1 - (1 + 2\alpha)F_0 - (1 + 2\alpha) = 0$$

or, if $P = 1 - F$,

$$12P_2 - (10 - 4\alpha)P_1 - (1 + 2\alpha)P_0 = 0$$

Hence

$$P_n = \beta_1\lambda_1^n + \beta_2\lambda_2^n$$

where

$$\lambda_1 = \frac{5 - 2\alpha + (37 + 4\alpha + 4\alpha^2)^{1/2}}{12}$$

$$\lambda_2 = \frac{5 - 2\alpha - (37 + 4\alpha + 4\alpha^2)^{1/2}}{12}$$

5.6.3 Parent–Offspring Inbreeding

Let the system be as represented in Figure 5.7.

Let X_0, X_1 be specified by F_0, F_1 and r_{01}. Then we have

$$F_2 = F_{X_2} = \tfrac{1}{6}[4r_{01} + 2\alpha + (1 - \alpha)(F_0 + F_1)]$$
$$\begin{aligned}r_{12} = r_{X_1(X_1 \times X_0)} &= \tfrac{1}{2}(r_{X_1X_1} + r_{X_1X_0})\\
&= \tfrac{1}{2}[\tfrac{1}{4}(1 + 3F_1) + r_{01}] = \tfrac{1}{8}(1 + 3F_1 + 4r_{01})\end{aligned}$$
$$F_3 = F_{X_3} = F_{X_1 \times X_2} = \tfrac{1}{6}[4r_{12} + 2\alpha + (1 - \alpha)(F_1 + F_2)]$$

We therefore have

$$6F_3 - 2\alpha - (1 - \alpha)(F_1 + F_2) = 4r_{12}$$
$$1 + 3F_1 = 8r_{12} - 4r_{01}$$
$$6F_2 - 2\alpha - (1 - \alpha)(F_0 + F_1) = 4r_{01}$$

so

$$12F_3 - 4\alpha - 2(1 - \alpha)(F_1 + F_2) - (1 + 3F_1) - [6F_2 - 2\alpha - (1 - \alpha)(F_0 + F_1)] = 0$$

or

$$12F_3 - (8 - 2\alpha)F_2 - (4 - \alpha)F_1 + (1 - \alpha)F_0 - (1 + 2\alpha) = 0$$

or, with $P = 1 - F$,

$$12P_3 - (8 - 2\alpha)P_2 - (4 - \alpha)P_1 + (1 - \alpha)P_0 = 0$$

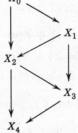

FIGURE 5.7. Parent–offspring inbreeding.

Note that, if α is placed equal to zero, the recurrence equation is

$$12\lambda^3 - 8\lambda^2 - 4\lambda + 1 = 0$$

which is a factor of the characteristic equation given by Fisher (1949). We have not managed to find expressions for the roots of

$$12\lambda^3 - (8 - 2\alpha)\lambda^2 - (4 - \alpha)\lambda + (1 - \alpha) = 0$$

Of course, given a value for α, the roots can be computed with very minor difficulty.

5.7 THE EXACT TREATMENT OF HEXAPLOIDS

In the case of hexaploids, or perhaps more strictly, loci which behave as an hexasomic locus, account can be taken of double reduction because, if the genotype of an individual X is ($abcdef$), then the gametic array of that individual is

$$\tfrac{1}{30}\beta \; [aab + aac + aad + aae + aaf$$
$$+ \; bba + bbc + bbd + bbe + bbf$$
$$+ \; cca + ccb + ccd + cce + ccf$$
$$+ \; dda + ddb + ddc + dde + ddf$$
$$+ \; eea + eeb + eec + eed + eef$$
$$+ \; ffa + ffb + ffc + ffd + ffe]$$
$$+ \; \frac{1-\beta}{20} \; [abc + abd + abe + abf + acd + ace + acf + ade$$
$$+ \; adf + aef$$
$$+ \; bcd + bce + bcf + bde + bdf + bef$$
$$+ \; cde + cdf + cef + def]$$

Again the inbreeding coefficient of X is

$$F_X = \tfrac{1}{15} \; [P(a{=}b) + P(a{=}c) + P(a{=}d) + P(a{=}e) + P(a{=}f)$$
$$+ \; P(b{=}c) + P(b{=}d) + P(b{=}e) + P(b{=}f) + P(c{=}d)$$
$$+ \; P(c{=}e) + P(c{=}f) + P(d{=}e) + P(d{=}f) + P(e{=}f)]$$

If the gametic array produced by X is denoted by (ghk), then

$$P(g{=}h) = P(g{=}k) = P(h{=}k)$$
$$= \tfrac{1}{90}\beta(30 + 60F_X) + (1 - \beta)F_X$$
$$= \tfrac{1}{3}[\beta + (3 - \beta)F_X]$$

We shall work out only the case of selfing. Let X_0 be the initial individual, $X_1 (= X_0 \times X_0)$, the individual in the next generation and so on. Then

$$F_1 = F_{X_1} = \tfrac{1}{15}\{3 \times \tfrac{1}{3}[\beta + (3 - \beta)F_{X_0}] \times 2 + 9r_{X_0 X_0}\}$$
$$= \tfrac{1}{15}[2\beta + (6 - 2\beta)F_{X_0} + 9r_{X_0 X_0}]$$

and

$$r_{X_0 X_0} = \tfrac{1}{6}(1 + 5F_{X_0}) = \tfrac{1}{6}(1 + 5F_0)$$

We have

$$15F_{X_1} - 2\beta - (6 - 2\beta)F_{X_0} = 9r_{X_0 X_0}$$
$$1 + 5F_{X_0} = 6r_{X_0 X_0}$$

so

$$30F_{X_1} - 4\beta - (12 - 4\beta)F_{X_0} - 3 - 15F_{X_0} = 0$$

or

$$30F_1 - (27 - 4\beta)F_0 - (3 + 4\beta) = 0$$

or

$$30P_1 = (27 - 4\beta)P_0$$

The reader may note that the largest root given by Fisher (1949) for this case is $(27 - 4\beta)/30$, as here.

5.8 PARTIALLY SEX-LINKED GENES*

A partially sex-linked gene is a gene which is carried on the pairing segment of the X and Y chromosomes. These are of considerable interest particularly in the case of man, and our knowledge of them is largely due to Haldane (1936). Owing to crossing over, the Y-linked genes pass sometimes to the son and sometimes to the daughter, the proportion depending on the crossing-over distance between the gene and the segment with complete sex linkage (see, for example, Darlington and Mather, 1950).

The relationships set up earlier in this chapter for the coefficient of inbreeding F, and the coefficient of parentage of two individuals A and B which we have denoted by r_{AB} were established for autosomal loci. It now behooves us to develop these concepts for the case of partially sex-linked genes. The parameter inherent in the development of r, the crossing-over percentage of the locus and the $X-Y$ chromosomes' differential segments. If r is 0, the locus is completely sex-linked in the sense that a Y gene stays on the Y chromosome. If r is equal to $\frac{1}{2}$, the formulas reduce to those for an autosomal locus in which the genes at a locus are equally likely to be passed to any offspring.

Let a male and a female be designated as in Figure 5.8. The upper pair of individuals are in a given (say the first) generation and the lower individual or individuals in the succeeding generation. The upper

		Male		Female
		X a		X c
Generation 1	A		B	
		Y b		X d
		X a'		X c'
Generation 2	$(A\male \times B\female)_\male$		$(A\male \times B\female)_\female$	
		Y b'		X d'

FIGURE 5.8. Reference diagram for partially sex-linked genes

* Parts of this section require elementary knowledge of matrices which is given in the next chapter.

chromosomes of the pairs will be those which are transmitted to the individual by its dam and the lower chromosomes by the sire.

We now make definitions as follows:

$$F_A = P(a=b), \qquad F_B = P(c=d)$$
$$r_{AB} = \tfrac{1}{4}[P(a=c) + P(a=d) + P(b=c) + P(b=d)]$$
$$F_{(A\delta \times B\female)_\delta} = P(a'=b'), \qquad F_{(A\delta \times B\female)_\female} = P(c'=d')$$

with other coefficients defined analogously. Consider now the coefficients for offspring in terms of parents. We have the following probability arrays:

$$a' = \tfrac{1}{2}c + \tfrac{1}{2}d$$
$$b' = (1 - r)b + ra$$
$$c' = \tfrac{1}{2}c + \tfrac{1}{2}d$$
$$d' = rb + (1 - r)a$$

Hence we have

$$F_{(A\delta \times B\female)_\delta} = P(a'=b')$$
$$= \tfrac{1}{2}r\, P(a=c) + \tfrac{1}{2}r\, P(a=d) + \tfrac{1}{2}(1 - r)\, P(b=c)$$
$$+ \tfrac{1}{2}(1 - r)\, P(b=d)$$
$$= \tfrac{1}{4}[P(a=c) + P(a=d) + P(b=c) + P(b=d)]$$
$$- \tfrac{1}{2}(\tfrac{1}{2} - r)[P(a=c) + P(a=d) - P(b=c) - P(b=d)]$$

The quantity $\tfrac{1}{2}[P(a=c) + P(a=d) - P(b=c) - P(b=d)]$ which occurs here does not have useful properties.

We find that

$$r_{A\delta(A\delta \times B\female)} = \tfrac{1}{2}(r_{AA} + r_{AB})$$

for any offspring of $A \times B$, but that

$$r_{B\female(A\delta \times B\female)} \neq \tfrac{1}{2}(r_{AB} + r_{BB})$$

and in fact depends on the sex of the offspring. Also the inbreeding coefficient of an offspring of $A \times B$ depends on its sex and in neither case is equal to r_{AB}.

As a general rule one should work entirely with gametes, though in special cases this may be unduly tedious.

To illustrate the examination of inbreeding under the present circumstances we consider full-sibbing. We may refer to Figure 5.8 but note that primes therein and in what follows denote the succeeding generation and not the previous generation.

Then we have the following relationships:

$$P(a'=b') = \tfrac{1}{2}r[P(a=c) + P(a=d)] + \tfrac{1}{2}(1-r)[P(b=c) + P(b=d)]$$
$$P(a'=c') = \tfrac{1}{2} + \tfrac{1}{2}P(c=d)$$
$$P(a'=d') = \tfrac{1}{2}(1-r)[P(a=c) + P(a=d)] + \tfrac{1}{2}r[P(b=c) + P(b=d)]$$
$$P(b'=c') = \tfrac{1}{2}r[P(a=c) + P(a=d)] + \tfrac{1}{2}(1-r)[P(b=c) + P(b=d)]$$
$$P(b'=d') = 2r(1-r) + [r^2 + (1-r)^2]\, P(a=b)$$
$$P(c'=d') = \tfrac{1}{2}(1-r)[P(a=c) + P(a=d)] + \tfrac{1}{2}r[P(b=c) + P(b=d)]$$

If we work in terms of the probabilities of unlikeness by descent such as $P(a\neq b)$, $P(a'\neq b')$, etc., we have the recurrence relationships in the matrix form

$$
\begin{pmatrix} P(a'\neq b') \\ P(a'\neq c') \\ P(a'\neq d') \\ P(b'\neq c') \\ P(b'\neq d') \\ P(c'\neq d') \end{pmatrix}
=
\begin{pmatrix}
0 & \tfrac{1}{2}r & \tfrac{1}{2}r & \tfrac{1}{2}(1-r) & \tfrac{1}{2}(1-r) & 0 \\
0 & 0 & 0 & 0 & 0 & \tfrac{1}{2} \\
0 & \tfrac{1}{2}(1-r) & \tfrac{1}{2}(1-r) & \tfrac{1}{2}r & \tfrac{1}{2}r & 0 \\
0 & \tfrac{1}{2}r & \tfrac{1}{2}r & \tfrac{1}{2}(1-r) & \tfrac{1}{2}(1-r) & 0 \\
1-2r+2r^2 & 0 & 0 & 0 & 0 & 0 \\
0 & \tfrac{1}{2}(1-r) & \tfrac{1}{2}(1-r) & \tfrac{1}{2}r & \tfrac{1}{2}r & 0
\end{pmatrix}
\begin{pmatrix} P(a\neq b) \\ P(a\neq c) \\ P(a\neq d) \\ P(b\neq c) \\ P(b\neq d) \\ P(c\neq d) \end{pmatrix}
$$

or in short

$$P' = AP$$

so that after n generations

$$P^{(n)} = A^n P$$

This would be the equation for an arbitrary starting point. We may simplify matters further by supposing that the brother–sister mating has gone on for at least one generation so that, in view of the above equations,

$$P(a\neq b) = P(b\neq c), \qquad P(a'\neq b') = P(b'\neq c')$$
and
$$P(a\neq d) = P(c\neq d), \qquad P(a'\neq d') = P(c'\neq d')$$

The equations then reduce to

$$
\begin{pmatrix} P(a'\neq b') \\ P(a'\neq c') \\ P(a'\neq d') \\ P(b'\neq d') \end{pmatrix}
=
\begin{pmatrix}
\tfrac{1}{2}(1-r) & \tfrac{1}{2}r & \tfrac{1}{2}r & \tfrac{1}{2}(1-r) \\
0 & 0 & \tfrac{1}{2} & 0 \\
\tfrac{1}{2}r & \tfrac{1}{2}(1-r) & \tfrac{1}{2}(1-r) & \tfrac{1}{2}r \\
1-2r+2r^2 & 0 & 0 & 0
\end{pmatrix}
\begin{pmatrix} P(a\neq b) \\ P(a\neq c) \\ P(a\neq d) \\ P(b\neq d) \end{pmatrix}
$$

The matrix here is identical with that given by Tukey (1954) if we replace $1 - r$ by θ. The procedures outlined in the following chapter may be applied to specify each P for an arbitrary generation.

REFERENCES

Crow, J. F. 1954. Breeding structure of populations: II. Effective population number. Chapter 43 of *Statistics and mathematics in biology*, edited by O. Kempthorne et al. Iowa State College Press, Ames.

Darlington, C. D., and K. Mather. 1950. *The elements of genetics*. Macmillan & Co., London.

Fisher, R. A. 1930. *The genetical theory of natural selection*. Clarendon Press, Oxford.

Fisher, R. A. 1949. *The theory of inbreeding*. Oliver and Boyd, Edinburgh.

Haldane, J. B. S. 1936. A search for incomplete sex linkage in man. *Ann. Eugen. Lond.*, **7**, 28–57.

Haldane, J. B. S. 1939. The equilibrium between mutation and random extinction. *Ann. Eugen. Lond.*, **9**, 400–405.

Haldane, J. B. S. 1942. *New paths in genetics*. Harper, London.

Kimura, M. 1955. Random genetic drift in multi-allelic locus. *Evolution*, **9**, 419–435.

Malécot, G. 1948. *Les mathématiques de l'hérédité*. Masson et Cie., Paris.

Tukey, J. W. 1954. Causation, regression and path analysis. Chapter 3 of *Statistics and mathematics in biology*, Iowa State College Press, Ames.

Wright, Sewall. 1921. Systems of mating I–V. *Genetics*, **6**, 111–178.

Wright, Sewall. 1931a, Evolution in Mendelian populations. *Genetics*, **16**, 97–159.

Wright, Sewall. 1931b. Statistical methods in biology. *J. Amer. statist. Ass.*, **26**, Suppl., 155–163.

Wright, Sewall. 1938. The distribution of gene frequencies in populations of polyploids. *Proc. nat. Acad. Aci. Wash.*, **24**, 372–377.

Wright, Sewall. 1942. Statistical genetics and evolution. *Bull. Amer. math. Soc.*, **48**, 223–246.

Wright, Sewall. 1951. The genetical structure of populations. *Ann. Eugen. Lond.*, **15**, 323–354.

FURTHER READING

Lush, J. L. 1954. Breeding structure of populations. I. General considerations. Chapter 42 of *Statistics and mathematics in biology*, edited by O. Kempthorne, et al. Iowa State College Press, Ames.

Crow, J. F., and S. C. Roberts. 1950. Inbreeding and homozygosis in bees. *Genetics*. **35**, 612–621.

Emik, L. O., and C. E. Terrill. 1949. Systematic procedures for calculating inbreeding coefficients. *J. Hered.*, **40**, 51–55.

Fish, H. D. 1914. On the progressive increase of homozygosis in brother–sister matings. *Amer. Nat.*, **48**, 759–761.

Haldane, J. B. S. 1930. Theoretical genetics of autopolyploids. *J. Genet.*, **22**, 359–372.

Haldane, J. B. S., and Pearl Moshinsky. 1939. Inbreeding in Mendelian populations with special reference to human cousin marriage. *Ann. Eugen. Lond.*, **9**, 321–340.

Haldane, J. B. S., and C. H. Waddington. 1931. Inbreeding and linkage. *Genetics*, **16**, 357–374.

Jennings, H. S. 1912. The production of pure homozygotic organisms from heterozygotes by self-fertilization. *Amer. Nat.*, **45**, 487–491.

Jennings, H. S. 1914. Formulae for the results of inbreeding. *Amer. Nat.*, **48**, 693–696.

Jennings, H. S. 1916. The numerical results of diverse systems of breeding. *Genetics*, **1**, 53–89.

Jennings, H. S. 1917. The numerical results of diverse systems of breeding with respect to two pairs of characters, linked or independent, with special relation to the effects of linkage. *Genetics*, **2**, 97–154.

Kalmus, H., and C. A. B. Smith. 1948. Production of pure lines in bees. *J. Genet.*, **49**, 153–158.

Wright, Sewall. 1922a. Coefficients of inbreeding and relationship. *Amer. Nat.*, **56**, 330–338.

Wright, Sewall. 1922b. The effects of inbreeding and crossbreeding on guinea pigs. I. Decline in vigor. *Bull. U.S. Dep. Agric.*, **1090**, 1–36. II. Differentiation among inbred families. *Ibid.*, 37–63. III. Crosses between inbred families. *Ibid.*, **1121**.

Wright, Sewall. 1923. Mendelian analysis of the pure breeds of livestock. I. The measurement of inbreeding and relationship. *J. Hered.*, **14**, 339–348.

Wright, Sewall. 1933a. Inbreeding and homozygosis. *Proc. nat. Acad. Sci. Wash.*, **19**, 411–419.

Wright, Sewall. 1933b. Inbreeding and recombination. *Proc. nat. Acad. Sci. Wash.*, **19**, 420–433.

Wright, Sewall, and H. C. McPhee. 1925. An approximate method of calculating coefficients of inbreeding and relationship from livestock pedigrees. *J. agric. Res.*, **31**, 377–383.

PROBLEMS

1. Given that individual X possesses a gene A unpossessed by any other individual mating with himself or his progeny, what is the probability that two of his grandchildren possess gene A (i) if they are full-sibs, (ii) if they are cousins?

2. Suppose we have 1000 loci segregating independently. What do the coefficients of parentage and of inbreeding mean with respect to the number of like genes?

3. Consider the pedigree shown in Figure 5.9. What is the coefficient of inbreeding of individual F, assuming that all individuals entering the pedigree are unrelated?

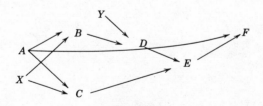

FIGURE 5.9.

4. Suppose A and X in Figure 5.9 are full-sibs resulting from the mating of two random individuals. What is the coefficient of inbreeding of individual F?

5. Obtain some animal pedigrees and work out the F values of individuals.

6. Work out the progress of the panmictic index for the case of selfing and full-sibbing in alternate generations for diploids.

7. Work out the progress of the panmictic index for the case of full-sibbing and parent–offspring in alternate generations for diploids.

8. Verify Wright's formula for quadruple second-cousin mating.

9. Verify Wright's formula for octuple third-cousin mating.

10. Work out the case of a population of N (constant) monoecious individuals in which fertilization is random except for a probability h of self-fertilization (Wright, 1951).

11. Work out the case of a population with separate sexes, N_p permanent pairs, with probability h of full-sib mating (Wright, 1951).

12. Work out the progress of the panmictic index for double first-cousin mating in tetraploids.

13. Work out the progress of F with complete sex linkage and full-sibbing.

CHAPTER 6

The Generation Matrix
Theory of Inbreeding

6.1 INTRODUCTION

In the previous chapter we considered the simplest aspect of the inbreeding process, namely the probability that the two alleles at a locus of an individual are alike by descent and hence in state. This is clearly not all that we require from a theory of inbreeding. We would like for instance to know the relative frequency of types of sib pairs according to genotype under any system of inbreeding. We would like to know this because we shall be concerned with the correlations between relatives under inbreeding. The full specification of all the properties of populations which have undergone a specified number of generations of inbreeding according to some system of consanguineous mating is a problem which does not appear to have been solved, practically speaking. However, a method has been developed by which all the properties can with sufficient labor be elucidated, and the purpose of the present chapter is to present the elementary aspects of this method. The method is known as the generation matrix method. It is closely related mathematically to the solution of a whole batch of recurrence relations of the type found in the previous chapter. It was first presented in the literature apparently by Bartlett and Haldane and has been developed to a considerable extent by R. A. Fisher in his book *The Theory of Inbreeding*. An understanding of the mechanics of this method requires a knowledge of the elementary properties of matrices. The necessary knowledge will be set down with some attempt at motivating the reader to acquire this tool of mathematics which is rapidly becoming as necessary for the quick comprehension of deductive arguments in genetics as is the entirely accepted tool of algebra. We should warn the reader that this section is rather formidable, but will be useful not only in the present context, but also in acquiring some knowledge of matrices which is difficult to get, in the sense that mathematical texts are not usually written except for the training of mathematicians and would probably prove entirely indigestible for the biologist. I know of no text on matrices which I could honestly recommend to the "average" biologist.

6.2 SELFING

Selfing is, of course, possible in general only with plants.* With regard to any one locus, there are two classes of individuals, namely homozygotes and heterozygotes. These we shall represent by HH and Hh, respectively, realizing that hh individuals are also homozygous and fall in the HH class. This situation is very simple. The HH individuals reproduce themselves and the Hh individuals produce HH and Hh individuals in equal proportions. If then we let f_1 denote the total frequency of homozygotes and f_2 the total frequency of heterozygotes and we use superscripts in brackets to denote the generation number, we will have

$$f_1^{(1)} = f_1^{(0)} + \tfrac{1}{2} f_2^{(0)}$$
$$f_2^{(1)} = \tfrac{1}{2} f_2^{(0)}$$

This, of course, assumes equal mortality and fertility over all genotypes. The situation is completely specified as regards homozygosity by f_2, since f_1 equals $(1 - f_2)$.

We have

$$f_2^{(1)} = \tfrac{1}{2} f_2^{(0)}$$
$$f_2^{(2)} = \tfrac{1}{2} f_2^{(1)} = (\tfrac{1}{2})^2 f_2^{(0)} \quad \text{etc.}$$

and generally

$$f_2^{(n)} = (\tfrac{1}{2})^n f_2^{(0)}$$

It is a simple exercise to show that, if F_i is the frequency of the ith allele in the original population, then the limiting state of the population is that in which the frequency of individuals homozygous for the ith allele is F_i. Also, if F_{i1} is the original frequency of individuals homozygous for the ith allele and F_{i2} the original frequency of individuals heterozygous for this allele, then the frequency of individuals homozygous *for this allele* in the nth generation is

$$F_{i1} + F_{i2}(\tfrac{1}{4} + \tfrac{1}{8} + \tfrac{1}{16} + \cdots \tfrac{1}{2}^{n+1}) = F_{i1} + \tfrac{1}{2}F_{i2}(1 - \tfrac{1}{2}^n)$$

6.3 FULL-SIB MATING FOR AN AUTOSOMAL GENE

Here we consider the case when inheritance is equal from each parent as regards gametes. We suppose that the alleles at the locus are represented by $a, b, c, \cdots$. We may suppose generation 0 has been produced

---

* Also bees, oysters, snails.

and that the full-sib matings have been made. There are seven distinct possible types of mating possible in this situation, namely

1. $aa \times aa$ with frequency $f_1^{(0)}$.

2. $ab \times ab$ with frequency $f_2^{(0)}$.

3. $aa \times bb$ with frequency $f_3^{(0)}$.

4. $aa \times ab$ with frequency $f_4^{(0)}$.

5. $aa \times bc$ with frequency $f_5^{(0)}$.

6. $ab \times ac$ with frequency $f_6^{(0)}$.

7. $ab \times cd$ with frequency $f_7^{(0)}$.

Note that here we are talking about *types* of mating, so that for instance $aa \times ab$ and $bb \times ab$ are of the same type, both involving a homozygote mating with a heterozygote having one gene which is common with the homozygote, and that the case of arbitrary number of alleles is thereby covered. Note also that type 1 involves only one gene in a particular line, types 2, 3, and 4 involve two genes, types 5 and 6 involve three genes, and type 7 involves four genes. We now ask what types of mating will be present and with what frequencies in generation 1, *assuming* equal fertility of all matings.

1. The mating type $aa \times aa$ will result in full-sibs which are all of type aa, and hence all full-sib matings from matings of $aa \times aa$ will be of the same type.

2. The mating type $ab \times ab$ produces $\frac{1}{4}aa$, $\frac{2}{4}ab$, and $\frac{1}{4}bb$ individuals so that the resultant full-sib matings will be

$$\frac{1}{16}aa \times aa, \text{ type 1}$$
$$\frac{4}{16}aa \times ab, \text{ type 4}$$
$$\frac{2}{16}aa \times bb, \text{ type 3}$$
$$\frac{4}{16}ab \times ab, \text{ type 2}$$
$$\frac{4}{16}ab \times bb, \text{ type 4}$$
$$\frac{1}{16}bb \times bb, \text{ type 1}$$

or

$$\begin{cases} \frac{2}{16} \text{ of type 1} \\ \frac{4}{16} \text{ of type 2} \\ \frac{2}{16} \text{ of type 3} \\ \frac{8}{16} \text{ of type 4} \end{cases}$$

3. The mating type $aa \times bb$ produces full-sibs with the genotype ab, and hence all full-sib matings will be of type 2.

4. The mating type $aa \times ab$ will result in aa and ab individuals with equal frequencies, so that $\frac{1}{4}$ of the full-sib matings will be $aa \times aa$, i.e., of type 1, $\frac{1}{2}$ will be $aa \times ab$, i.e., of type 4, and $\frac{1}{4}$ will be $ab \times ab$, i.e., of type 2.

5. The mating type $aa \times bc$ produces ab and ac individuals with equal frequencies, so that the full-sib matings will be

$$\frac{1}{4}ab \times ab, \text{ type 2}$$
$$\frac{1}{2}ab \times ac, \text{ type 6} \qquad \text{or} \qquad \begin{cases} \frac{1}{2} \text{ of type 2} \\ \frac{1}{2} \text{ of type 6} \end{cases}$$
$$\frac{1}{4}ac \times ac, \text{ type 2}$$

6. The mating type $ab \times ac$ produces $\frac{1}{4}aa, \frac{1}{4}ab, \frac{1}{4}ac, \frac{1}{4}bc$. The types of full-sib mating are

$$\frac{1}{16}aa \times aa, \text{ type 1}$$
$$\frac{2}{16}aa \times ab, \text{ type 4}$$
$$\frac{2}{16}aa \times ac, \text{ type 4}$$
$$\frac{2}{16}aa \times bc, \text{ type 5}$$
$$\frac{1}{16}ab \times ab, \text{ type 2}$$
$$\frac{2}{16}ab \times ac, \text{ type 6} \qquad \text{or} \qquad \begin{cases} \frac{1}{16} \text{ of type 1} \\ \frac{3}{16} \text{ of type 2} \\ \frac{4}{16} \text{ of type 4} \\ \frac{2}{16} \text{ of type 5} \\ \frac{6}{16} \text{ of type 6} \end{cases}$$
$$\frac{2}{16}ab \times bc, \text{ type 6}$$
$$\frac{1}{16}ac \times ac, \text{ type 2}$$
$$\frac{2}{16}ac \times bc, \text{ type 6}$$
$$\frac{1}{16}bc \times bc, \text{ type 2}$$

7. The mating type $ab \times cd$ produces $\frac{1}{4}ac, \frac{1}{4}ad, \frac{1}{4}bc, \frac{1}{4}bd$. The types of full-sib mating are

$$\frac{1}{16}ac \times ac, \text{ type 2}$$
$$\frac{2}{16}ac \times ad, \text{ type 6}$$
$$\frac{2}{16}ac \times bc, \text{ type 6}$$
$$\frac{2}{16}ac \times bd, \text{ type 7}$$
$$\frac{1}{16}ad \times ad, \text{ type 2} \qquad \text{or} \qquad \begin{cases} \frac{4}{16} \text{ type 2} \\ \frac{8}{16} \text{ type 6} \\ \frac{4}{16} \text{ type 7} \end{cases}$$
$$\frac{2}{16}ad \times bc, \text{ type 7}$$
$$\frac{2}{16}ad \times bd, \text{ type 6}$$
$$\frac{1}{16}bc \times bc, \text{ type 2}$$
$$\frac{2}{16}bc \times bd, \text{ type 6}$$
$$\frac{1}{16}bd \times bd, \text{ type 2}$$

We may now combine these results weighting with the original frequencies of the types of mating giving the following frequencies in generation 1:

Type   Frequency

1    $f_1^{(1)} = f_1^{(0)} + \frac{2}{16}f_2^{(0)} \qquad\qquad + \frac{1}{4}f_4^{(0)} \qquad\qquad\qquad + \frac{1}{16}f_6^{(0)}$

2    $f_2^{(1)} = \qquad\quad \frac{4}{16}f_2^{(0)} + f_3^{(0)} + \frac{1}{4}f_4^{(0)} + \frac{1}{2}f_5^{(0)} + \frac{3}{16}f_6^{(0)} + \frac{4}{16}f_7^{(0)}$

3    $f_3^{(1)} = \qquad\quad \frac{2}{16}f_2^{(0)}$

4    $f_4^{(1)} = \qquad\quad \frac{8}{16}f_2^{(0)} \qquad\qquad + \frac{2}{4}f_4^{(0)} + \qquad\qquad \frac{4}{16}f_6^{(0)}$

5    $f_5^{(1)} = \qquad\qquad\qquad\qquad\qquad\qquad\qquad\qquad \frac{2}{16}f_6^{(0)}$

6    $f_6^{(1)} = \qquad\qquad\qquad\qquad\qquad\qquad\qquad \frac{1}{2}f_5^{(0)} + \frac{6}{16}f_6^{(0)} + \frac{8}{16}f_7^{(0)}$

7    $f_7^{(1)} = \qquad\qquad\qquad\qquad\qquad\qquad\qquad\qquad\qquad\qquad \frac{4}{16}f_7^{(0)}$

These equations look rather formidable at first sight. However, they merely express the fact that, for instance, if the number of matings of type 2 in generation 0 is $f_2^{(0)}$, then the number of matings of type 3 in generation 1 which arises from generation 0 by full-sibbing is equal to $\frac{2}{16}f_2^{(0)}$. Note that the frequencies which occur in the equations can be absolute frequencies, and, if there were different fertilities of the different mating types, such as for instance that mating $ab \times ab$ produced twice as many offspring as mating $aa \times aa$, we would have to "fix up" the equations to take account of the differential fertilities. It is assumed that all mating types are equally fertile and there is no differential viability of gametes or individuals. The frequencies may then be equally well regarded as relative frequencies such that

$$f_1 + f_2 + f_3 + f_4 + f_5 + f_6 + f_7 = 1$$

regardless of the superscript attached to the f's.

In this way we have constructed the equations which determine the frequency of types of mating in one generation in terms of the frequencies of the types of mating in the previous generation. It is then a matter of mere computation to calculate the frequencies in generation n from given frequencies in generation 0. The word "mere" is used here perhaps ill-advisedly because a colossal amount of work would be involved in computing the frequencies of types of mating in even the 20th generation, let alone the 100th or 1000th which may be of some interest. As we find frequently in scientific work there are two aspects of the solution of a problem:

1. The specification of rules which determine the desired figures.
2. The actual obtaining of those figures.

We have completed aspect 1 of the problem and shall have to introduce some mathematical notions which will be entirely new to many geneticists in order to present aspect 2. These mathematical notions are those of matrices and characteristic roots and characteristic vectors.

6.4 MATRICES

The problem of computing the types of mating in an arbitrary generation from the starting point is simplified by the use of the notions of matrices. We shall attempt to motivate the introduction of matrices in this problem.

Suppose we write

$$\mathbf{f}^{(1)} = \begin{pmatrix} f_1^{(1)} \\ f_2^{(1)} \\ f_3^{(1)} \\ f_4^{(1)} \\ f_5^{(1)} \\ f_6^{(1)} \\ f_7^{(1)} \end{pmatrix} \qquad \mathbf{f}^{(0)} = \begin{pmatrix} f_1^{(0)} \\ f_2^{(0)} \\ f_3^{(0)} \\ f_4^{(0)} \\ f_5^{(0)} \\ f_6^{(0)} \\ f_7^{(0)} \end{pmatrix}$$

where for the moment we regard $\mathbf{f}^{(0)}$ and $\mathbf{f}^{(1)}$ as rather complex quantities, each of which has seven components. We have written down in the previous section rules by which the components of $\mathbf{f}^{(1)}$ can be calculated from the components of $\mathbf{f}^{(0)}$. Let us denote the operation by which this is done by $\mathbf{A}$; then we have

$$\mathbf{f}^{(1)} = \mathbf{A}\mathbf{f}^{(0)}$$

We would furthermore have

$$\mathbf{f}^{(2)} = \mathbf{A}\mathbf{f}^{(1)} = \mathbf{A}\mathbf{A}\mathbf{f}^{(0)} = \mathbf{A}^2\mathbf{f}^{(0)}$$
$$\mathbf{f}^{(3)} = \mathbf{A}\mathbf{f}^{(2)} = \mathbf{A}\mathbf{A}\mathbf{A}\mathbf{f}^{(0)} = \mathbf{A}^3\mathbf{f}^{(0)}$$

and so on, with $\mathbf{f}^{(n)} = \mathbf{A}^n\mathbf{f}^{(0)}$. The situation here is of essentially the same nature as the equation

$$\Delta^{(1)} = (1 - r)\Delta^{(0)}$$
$$\Delta^{(2)} = (1 - r)\Delta^{(1)} = (1 - r)^2\Delta^{(0)}, \qquad \text{and so on}$$

In this case to get $\Delta^{(1)}$ we multiply $\Delta^{(0)}$ by $(1 - r)$, which is a pure number; to get $\Delta^{(2)}$ we multiply $\Delta^{(1)}$ by $(1 - r)$ or multiply $\Delta^{(0)}$ by $(1 - r)^2$. In the more complex case we have to perform the operation $\mathbf{A}$ on $\mathbf{f}^{(0)}$ to get $\mathbf{f}^{(1)}$, where operation $\mathbf{A}$ is defined by the equations we obtained, such as for example

$$f_1^{(1)} = f_1^{(0)} + \tfrac{2}{16}f_2^{(0)} + \tfrac{1}{4}f_4^{(0)} + \tfrac{1}{16}f_6^{(0)}$$

and so on. Thus the operation $\mathbf{A}$ is specified, and our only difficulty is to calculate $\mathbf{A}^2$, $\mathbf{A}^3$, and so on.

We now write the equations connecting $\mathbf{f}^{(1)}$ and $\mathbf{f}^{(0)}$ in a particular way, namely:

$$
\begin{pmatrix} f_1^{(1)} \\ f_2^{(1)} \\ f_3^{(1)} \\ f_4^{(1)} \\ f_5^{(1)} \\ f_6^{(1)} \\ f_7^{(1)} \end{pmatrix}
=
\begin{pmatrix}
1 & \frac{2}{16} & 0 & \frac{1}{4} & 0 & \frac{1}{16} & 0 \\
0 & \frac{4}{16} & 1 & \frac{1}{4} & \frac{1}{2} & \frac{3}{16} & \frac{4}{16} \\
0 & \frac{2}{16} & 0 & 0 & 0 & 0 & 0 \\
0 & \frac{8}{16} & 0 & \frac{2}{4} & 0 & \frac{4}{16} & 0 \\
0 & 0 & 0 & 0 & 0 & \frac{2}{16} & 0 \\
0 & 0 & 0 & 0 & \frac{1}{2} & \frac{6}{16} & \frac{8}{16} \\
0 & 0 & 0 & 0 & 0 & 0 & \frac{4}{16}
\end{pmatrix}
\begin{pmatrix} f_1^{(0)} \\ f_2^{(0)} \\ f_3^{(0)} \\ f_4^{(0)} \\ f_5^{(0)} \\ f_6^{(0)} \\ f_7^{(0)} \end{pmatrix}
$$

or

$$\mathbf{f}^{(1)} = \mathbf{A}\mathbf{f}^{(0)}$$

The way we interpret the equation

$$\mathbf{f}^{(1)} = \mathbf{A}\mathbf{f}^{(0)}$$

is that it is a shorthand representation of the full set of seven equations. Having set up such a shorthand representation, we must determine the rules by which the symbols of the shorthand may be manipulated. For example, if we have n families with x offspring each, the total number of offspring is nx or xn. So with ordinary algebraic symbols we may write them down in any order. This is not, however, true for the symbols we now use. The entities represented by symbols $\mathbf{A}$ and $\mathbf{f}$ given above are known as matrices, and we shall now give some formal definitions which are necessary in our present context.

6.5 DETERMINANTS AND MATRICES

A *matrix* is a rectangular array of numbers; the individual numbers in the matrix are known as the elements of the matrix. We shall be concerned only with matrices whose elements are ordinary real numbers. A matrix with r rows and s columns is called a $r \times s$ matrix. If r equals s, the matrix is said to be square. The element in the ith row and jth column of $\mathbf{A}$ is usually denoted by $\mathbf{a}_{ij}$ or $\mathbf{A}_{ij}$. The diagonal elements of a square matrix are the elements $\mathbf{A}_{ii}$, $i = 1, 2, \cdots, n$. A *diagonal matrix* is a square one in which the elements not on the diagonal are zero. The *determinant* of a matrix is defined only if the matrix is square. We shall define determinants in an operational way:

The *2×2 matrix*

$$
\begin{pmatrix} a_{11} & a_{12} \\ a_{21} & a_{22} \end{pmatrix}
$$

has determinants $a_{11}a_{22} - a_{12}a_{21}$, which is usually written as

$$\begin{vmatrix} a_{11} & a_{12} \\ a_{21} & a_{22} \end{vmatrix}$$

The *3 × 3 matrix*

$$\begin{pmatrix} a_{11} & a_{12} & a_{13} \\ a_{21} & a_{22} & a_{23} \\ a_{31} & a_{32} & a_{33} \end{pmatrix}$$

has a determinant equal to

$$(1)a_{11} \begin{vmatrix} a_{22} & a_{23} \\ a_{32} & a_{33} \end{vmatrix} + (-1)a_{12} \begin{vmatrix} a_{21} & a_{23} \\ a_{31} & a_{33} \end{vmatrix} + (1)a_{13} \begin{vmatrix} a_{21} & a_{22} \\ a_{31} & a_{32} \end{vmatrix}$$

and is denoted by

$$\begin{vmatrix} a_{11} & a_{12} & a_{13} \\ a_{21} & a_{22} & a_{23} \\ a_{31} & a_{32} & a_{33} \end{vmatrix}$$

The *4 × 4 matrix*

$$\begin{pmatrix} a_{11} & a_{12} & a_{13} & a_{14} \\ a_{21} & a_{22} & a_{23} & a_{24} \\ a_{31} & a_{32} & a_{33} & a_{34} \\ a_{41} & a_{42} & a_{43} & a_{44} \end{pmatrix}$$

has determinant equal to

$$a_{11} \begin{vmatrix} a_{22} & a_{23} & a_{24} \\ a_{32} & a_{33} & a_{34} \\ a_{42} & a_{43} & a_{44} \end{vmatrix} - a_{12} \begin{vmatrix} a_{21} & a_{23} & a_{24} \\ a_{31} & a_{33} & a_{34} \\ a_{41} & a_{43} & a_{44} \end{vmatrix}$$

$$+ a_{13} \begin{vmatrix} a_{21} & a_{22} & a_{24} \\ a_{31} & a_{32} & a_{34} \\ a_{41} & a_{42} & a_{44} \end{vmatrix} - a_{14} \begin{vmatrix} a_{21} & a_{22} & a_{23} \\ a_{31} & a_{32} & a_{33} \\ a_{41} & a_{42} & a_{43} \end{vmatrix}$$

The rule which is followed is really quite straightforward. We define the determinant of an $n \times n$ matrix in terms of determinants of $(n-1) \times (n-1)$ matrices obtained by deleting a row and successively the first column, the second column, and so on, or vice versa, a column and then successively the rows. The coefficient of the determinant of the $(n-1) \times (n-1)$ matrix obtained by deleting the ith row and the jth column is $(-1)^{i+j}a_{ij}$. The $(n-1) \times (n-1)$ determinants are then expressed in terms of $(n-2) \times (n-2)$ determinants using the same rule, and so on, until we reach 2×2 matrices for which we have the simple rule stated above. We may note that we can expand the determinant by any row not necessarily the first or by any column, and we choose the row or column by which we expand to minimize the total computation. For example, if all the elements of a row are zero except one element, we should expand by that row, thus immediately expressing the $n \times n$ determinant as an $(n-1) \times (n-1)$ determinant.

So far we have only defined matrices and a single property of square matrices, namely determinants. We shall now very quickly review the basic operations which may be performed with matrices. Insofar as matrices are much like ordinary numbers, we would like to be able to perform some of the simpler arithmetical processes such as addition, subtraction, multiplication, and division.

Addition. Two matrices **A** and **B** can be added only if they have the same dimensions, and their sum **C** is given by

$$(\mathbf{A} + \mathbf{B})_{ij} = \mathbf{C}_{ij} = \mathbf{A}_{ij} + \mathbf{B}_{ij}$$

Thus

$$\begin{pmatrix} 1 & 2 \\ 3 & 4 \end{pmatrix} + \begin{pmatrix} 2 & -3 \\ 5 & -6 \end{pmatrix} = \begin{pmatrix} 3 & -1 \\ 8 & -2 \end{pmatrix}$$

Subtraction is possible under the same circumstances as addition: i.e., **A** and **B** must have the same dimensions and then

$$(\mathbf{A} - \mathbf{B})_{ij} = \mathbf{A}_{ij} - \mathbf{B}_{ij}$$

Multiplication. We have already found the need for this because we wrote $\mathbf{f}^{(1)} = \mathbf{A}\mathbf{f}^{(0)}$. In general we can multiply **A** by **B** on the right if **B** has the same number of rows as **A** has columns and we then have

$$(\mathbf{AB})_{ij} = \sum_k \mathbf{A}_{ik}\mathbf{B}_{kj}$$

and **AB** has the number of rows of **A** and the number of columns of **B**. Thus if **A** is $m \times n$, **B** is $n \times p$, then **AB** is $m \times p$. We should note that the product **AB** can exist with the product **BA** not existing. In the above case **BA** would exist only if $p = m$. The rule of multiplication is very simply expressed as follows: to get the (ij)th element of **AB**, take the ith row of **A** and the jth column of **B** and form the sum of products of elements, going along the row and down the column at the same rate.

Thus for example, if

$$\mathbf{A} = \begin{pmatrix} 3 & 1 \\ 2 & 4 \end{pmatrix} \quad \text{and} \quad \mathbf{B} = \begin{pmatrix} 2 \\ 5 \end{pmatrix}$$

AB has dimensions 2×1 and

$$(\mathbf{AB})_{11} \text{ is equal to } 3 \times 2 + 1 \times 5 = 11$$
$$(\mathbf{AB})_{21} \text{ is equal to } 2 \times 2 + 4 \times 5 = 24$$

So we write

$$\begin{pmatrix} 3 & 1 \\ 2 & 4 \end{pmatrix} \begin{pmatrix} 2 \\ 5 \end{pmatrix} = \begin{pmatrix} 11 \\ 24 \end{pmatrix}$$

The $n \times n$ matrix with diagonal elements equal to unity and the off-diagonal elements equal to zero is denoted by $\mathbf{I}$ (or sometimes $\mathbf{I}_n$), and it is a simple exercise to show that $\mathbf{AI} = \mathbf{A}$, $\mathbf{IB} = \mathbf{B}$, where the size of the $\mathbf{I}$ matrix is chosen so that the product $\mathbf{AI}$ exists in the first case and $\mathbf{IB}$ exists in the second case. The inverse of a matrix $\mathbf{B}$ is defined if $\mathbf{B}$ is square and has a non-zero determinant and is the solution $\mathbf{X}$ of the equation $\mathbf{BX} = \mathbf{I}$, and $\mathbf{X}$ is denoted by $\mathbf{B}^{-1}$. The inverse is the analogue of the reciprocal of an ordinary number.

We are now in a position to see the equations relating frequencies of mating types in one generation to the frequencies in the previous generation in matrix form.

For we have

$$\mathbf{f}^{(1)} = \begin{pmatrix} f_1^{(1)} \\ f_2^{(1)} \\ f_3^{(1)} \\ f_4^{(1)} \\ f_5^{(1)} \\ f_6^{(1)} \\ f_7^{(1)} \end{pmatrix} = \begin{pmatrix} 1 & \frac{2}{16} & 0 & \frac{1}{4} & 0 & \frac{1}{16} & 0 \\ 0 & \frac{4}{16} & 1 & \frac{1}{4} & \frac{1}{2} & \frac{3}{16} & \frac{4}{16} \\ 0 & \frac{2}{16} & 0 & 0 & 0 & 0 & 0 \\ 0 & \frac{8}{16} & 0 & \frac{2}{4} & 0 & \frac{4}{16} & 0 \\ 0 & 0 & 0 & 0 & 0 & \frac{2}{16} & 0 \\ 0 & 0 & 0 & 0 & \frac{1}{2} & \frac{6}{16} & \frac{8}{16} \\ 0 & 0 & 0 & 0 & 0 & 0 & \frac{4}{16} \end{pmatrix} \begin{pmatrix} f_1^{(0)} \\ f_2^{(0)} \\ f_3^{(0)} \\ f_4^{(0)} \\ f_5^{(0)} \\ f_6^{(0)} \\ f_7^{(0)} \end{pmatrix} = \mathbf{Af}^{(0)}$$

so

$$\mathbf{f}^{(2)} = \mathbf{Af}^{(1)} = \mathbf{A}^2\mathbf{f}^{(0)}$$

and it is left as an exercise to the reader to verify that $\mathbf{A}^2$ is equal to

$$\begin{pmatrix} 1 & \frac{9}{32} & \frac{1}{8} & \frac{13}{32} & \frac{3}{32} & \frac{11}{64} & \frac{1}{16} \\ 0 & \frac{5}{16} & \frac{1}{4} & \frac{3}{16} & \frac{7}{32} & \frac{31}{128} & \frac{7}{32} \\ 0 & \frac{1}{32} & \frac{1}{8} & \frac{1}{32} & \frac{1}{16} & \frac{3}{128} & \frac{1}{32} \\ 0 & \frac{3}{8} & \frac{1}{2} & \frac{3}{8} & \frac{3}{8} & \frac{5}{16} & \frac{1}{4} \\ 0 & 0 & 0 & 0 & \frac{1}{16} & \frac{3}{64} & \frac{1}{16} \\ 0 & 0 & 0 & 0 & \frac{3}{16} & \frac{13}{64} & \frac{5}{16} \\ 0 & 0 & 0 & 0 & 0 & 0 & \frac{1}{16} \end{pmatrix}$$

We may read off from this matrix that for instance the frequency of type-3 matings in generation 2 is equal to $\frac{1}{32}$ of the frequency of type-2 matings plus $\frac{1}{8}$ of the frequency of type-3 matings plus $\frac{1}{32}$ of the frequency of type-4 matings plus $\frac{1}{16}$ of the frequency of type-5 matings plus $\frac{3}{128}$ of the frequency of type-6 matings plus $\frac{1}{32}$ of the frequency of type-7 matings, all in generation 0.

The direct multiplication of matrices is very tedious, and we shall describe a short-cut method, which gives the general result for any power of $\mathbf{A}$.

6.6 DIAGONALIZATION OF MATRICES

The basic equation is

$$\mathbf{f}^{(1)} = \mathbf{A}\mathbf{f}^{(0)}$$

and we have noted that the calculation of $\mathbf{A}^2$, $\mathbf{A}^3$, etc. is very tedious. But we note that, if a matrix is *diagonal*, then its powers may be written down at sight. Consider the diagonal matrix

$$\mathbf{\Lambda} = \begin{pmatrix} \lambda_1 & & & \\ & \lambda_2 & & 0 \\ & & \cdot & \\ & & & \cdot \\ & 0 & & \cdot \\ & & & & \lambda_p \end{pmatrix}$$

in which all non-diagonal elements are zero. Then it is verified easily that

$$\mathbf{\Lambda}^n = \begin{pmatrix} \lambda_1^n & & & \\ & \lambda_2^n & & 0 \\ & & \cdot & \\ & & & \cdot \\ & 0 & & \cdot \\ & & & & \lambda_p^n \end{pmatrix}$$

Consider then the substitution, for all generations

$$\mathbf{g} = \mathbf{C}\mathbf{f}$$

where $\mathbf{g}$ is 7×1, $\mathbf{C}$ is 7×7, and $\mathbf{f}$ is 7×1, all being matrices. Since

$$\mathbf{f}^{(1)} = \mathbf{A}\mathbf{f}^{(0)}$$

$$\mathbf{g}^{(1)} = \mathbf{C}\mathbf{f}^{(1)} = \mathbf{C}\mathbf{A}\mathbf{f}^{(0)} = \mathbf{C}\mathbf{A}\mathbf{C}^{-1}\mathbf{g}^{(0)}, \text{ since } \mathbf{f} = \mathbf{C}^{-1}\mathbf{g}$$

Here so far $\mathbf{C}$ is an arbitrary 7×7 matrix which must have a non-zero determinant. If we could find $\mathbf{C}$ such that

$$\mathbf{C}\mathbf{A}\mathbf{C}^{-1} = \begin{pmatrix} \lambda_1 & & & \\ & \lambda_2 & & 0 \\ & & \cdot & \\ & & & \cdot \\ & 0 & & \cdot \\ & & & & \lambda_7 \end{pmatrix}$$

Then we would have

$$
\mathbf{g}^{(1)} = \begin{pmatrix} g_1^{(1)} \\ g_2^{(1)} \\ g_3^{(1)} \\ g_4^{(1)} \\ g_5^{(1)} \\ g_6^{(1)} \\ g_7^{(1)} \end{pmatrix} = \begin{pmatrix} \lambda_1 & & & & & & \\ & \lambda_2 & & & & & \\ & & \lambda_3 & & & 0 & \\ & & & \lambda_4 & & & \\ & & 0 & & \lambda_5 & & \\ & & & & & \lambda_6 & \\ & & & & & & \lambda_7 \end{pmatrix} \begin{pmatrix} g_1^{(0)} \\ g_2^{(0)} \\ g_3^{(0)} \\ g_4^{(0)} \\ g_5^{(0)} \\ g_6^{(0)} \\ g_7^{(0)} \end{pmatrix}
$$

or that

$$g_i^{(1)} = \lambda_i g_i^{(0)}$$

and

$$g_i^{(n)} = \lambda_i^n g_i^{(0)}$$

Once we have found the λ's and the matrix $\mathbf{C}$ and $\mathbf{C}^{-1}$, we can write down $\mathbf{g}^{(n)}$ and hence write down $\mathbf{f}^{(n)}$ since $\mathbf{f}^{(n)} = \mathbf{C}^{-1}\mathbf{g}^{(n)}$.

A theorem in algebra states that there exists a matrix $\mathbf{C}$ such that $\mathbf{C}\mathbf{A}\mathbf{C}^{-1}$ is diagonal, and that the resulting λ's are independent of the particular $\mathbf{C}$ which diagonalizes $\mathbf{A}$, except that the λ's may arise in a different order.

Let us find the matrix $\mathbf{C}$, or first write down rules by which we can get $\mathbf{C}$. We have to find $\mathbf{C}$ such that

$$\mathbf{C}\mathbf{A}\mathbf{C}^{-1} = \mathbf{\Lambda} \quad \text{where } \mathbf{\Lambda} \text{ is diagonal}$$

so that

$$\mathbf{C}\mathbf{A} = \mathbf{\Lambda}\mathbf{C}$$

If we write out these equations in full, we find that the elements of a *row* of $\mathbf{C}$, say $c_1, c_2, c_3, \cdots, c_7$ must satisfy the equations

$$(c_1, c_2, \cdots, c_7)A = \lambda(c_1, c_2, \cdots, c_7)$$

where λ is one of the diagonal elements of $\mathbf{\Lambda}$. If we write this equation in full and bring the c's which are the unknowns to the left-hand side, we note that the equations for the c's may be written in the form

$$
(\mathbf{A} - \lambda\mathbf{I})' \begin{pmatrix} c_1 \\ c_2 \\ c_3 \\ c_4 \\ c_5 \\ c_6 \\ c_7 \end{pmatrix} = \begin{pmatrix} 0 \\ 0 \\ 0 \\ 0 \\ 0 \\ 0 \\ 0 \end{pmatrix}
$$

where $(A - \lambda I)'$ is the *transpose* of $(A - \lambda I)$, i.e., $(A - \lambda I)$ with rows and columns interchanged. In fact,

$$A = \begin{pmatrix} a_{11} & a_{12} & a_{13} & \cdots & a_{17} \\ a_{21} & a_{22} & a_{23} & \cdots & a_{27} \\ a_{31} & a_{32} & a_{33} & \cdots & a_{37} \\ \cdot & \cdot & \cdot & \cdots & \cdot \\ \cdot & \cdot & \cdot & \cdots & \cdot \\ \cdot & \cdot & \cdot & \cdots & \cdot \\ a_{71} & a_{72} & a_{73} & \cdots & a_{77} \end{pmatrix}, \quad \lambda I = \begin{pmatrix} \lambda & 0 & 0 & 0 & 0 & 0 & 0 \\ 0 & \lambda & 0 & 0 & 0 & 0 & 0 \\ 0 & 0 & \lambda & 0 & 0 & 0 & 0 \\ 0 & 0 & 0 & \lambda & 0 & 0 & 0 \\ 0 & 0 & 0 & 0 & \lambda & 0 & 0 \\ 0 & 0 & 0 & 0 & 0 & \lambda & 0 \\ 0 & 0 & 0 & 0 & 0 & 0 & \lambda \end{pmatrix}$$

and

$$(A - \lambda I) = \begin{pmatrix} a_{11} - \lambda & a_{12} & a_{13} & \cdots & a_{17} \\ a_{21} & a_{22} - \lambda & a_{23} & \cdots & a_{27} \\ a_{31} & a_{32} & a_{33} - \lambda & \cdots & a_{37} \\ \cdot & \cdot & \cdot & \cdots & \cdot \\ \cdot & \cdot & \cdot & \cdots & \cdot \\ \cdot & \cdot & \cdot & \cdots & \cdot \\ a_{71} & a_{72} & a_{73} & \cdots & a_{77} - \lambda \end{pmatrix}$$

and

$$(A - \lambda I)' = \begin{pmatrix} a_{11} - \lambda & a_{21} & a_{31} & \cdots & a_{71} \\ a_{12} & a_{22} - \lambda & a_{32} & \cdots & a_{72} \\ \cdot & \cdot & \cdot & \cdots & \cdot \\ \cdot & \cdot & \cdot & \cdots & \cdot \\ \cdot & \cdot & \cdot & \cdots & \cdot \\ a_{17} & a_{27} & a_{37} & \cdots & a_{77} - \lambda \end{pmatrix}$$

This is a set of linear homogeneous equations in the c's, and a theorem in algebra states that non-zero solutions exist for these equations only if $\det (A - \lambda I)' = 0$. Now $\det (A - \lambda I)' = \det (A - \lambda I)$, as is obvious from our operational definition of a determinant. So we have to find the values of λ for which

$$\det (A - \lambda I) = 0$$

This equation is called the characteristic equation of the matrix A, and the values of λ for which it is satisfied are called the latent roots or the characteristic roots or sometimes the eigenvalues of A.

Our first job is to find these latent roots, and then we shall have to find the set of c's for each root. We will then be able to construct the matrix C.

There is one fact about the evaluation of determinants which is useful and which we will be advised to use. It is that a determinant of a matrix of the form

$$\begin{pmatrix} A & B & C & D \\ 0 & E & F & G \\ 0 & 0 & H & J \\ 0 & 0 & 0 & K \end{pmatrix}$$

where A, E, H, K are square blocks and all the blocks below the diagonal blocks are occupied by zero elements, is equal to

$$\det A \det E \det H \det K$$

It is also known that the latent roots of a matrix and the other properties we shall be interested in are not changed by permutation of rows with the same permutation of the columns.

In the present case this property holds without permutation of rows and columns.

Our description has been in terms of 7×7 matrices but is quite general with 7 replaced by an arbitrary number p wherever it occurs. We now exemplify the whole procedure.

6.7 TREATMENT OF SELFING BY THE USE OF MATRICES

We shall illustrate the matrix method first by a discussion of selfing with one locus under consideration. We have already seen that

$$f_1^{(1)} = f_1^{(0)} + \tfrac{1}{2} f_2^{(0)}$$
$$f_2^{(1)} = \tfrac{1}{2} f_2^{(0)}$$

when f_1 is the frequency of selfing of homozygotes and f_2 is the frequency of selfing heterozygotes. Hence

$$\mathbf{f}^{(1)} = A\mathbf{f}^{(0)} \quad \text{where} \quad A = \begin{pmatrix} 1 & \tfrac{1}{2} \\ 0 & \tfrac{1}{2} \end{pmatrix}$$

First we find the latent roots of A, i.e., the values of λ for which

$$\det \begin{pmatrix} 1-\lambda & \tfrac{1}{2} \\ 0 & \tfrac{1}{2}-\lambda \end{pmatrix} = 0$$

i.e. for which $(1 - \lambda)(\tfrac{1}{2} - \lambda) = 0$. Clearly the roots are $\lambda_1 = 1$, $\lambda_2 = \tfrac{1}{2}$. Now we find c_1, c_2, both of which cannot be zero, such that

$$\begin{pmatrix} 1-\lambda_1 & 0 \\ \tfrac{1}{2} & \tfrac{1}{2}-\lambda_1 \end{pmatrix} \begin{pmatrix} c_1 \\ c_2 \end{pmatrix} = \begin{pmatrix} 0 \\ 0 \end{pmatrix}$$

i.e.

$$\begin{pmatrix} 0 & 0 \\ \tfrac{1}{2} & -\tfrac{1}{2} \end{pmatrix} \begin{pmatrix} c_1 \\ c_2 \end{pmatrix} = \begin{pmatrix} 0 \\ 0 \end{pmatrix}$$

If (c_1, c_2) satisfies these equations, so does (kc_1, kc_2) where k is any number, so that we will take the simplest solution in all cases. Here we take $c_1 = 1$, $c_2 = 1$. For the second root, $\lambda_2 = \frac{1}{2}$ we have the equations

$$\begin{pmatrix} \frac{1}{2} & 0 \\ \frac{1}{2} & 0 \end{pmatrix} \begin{pmatrix} c_1 \\ c_2 \end{pmatrix} = \begin{pmatrix} 0 \\ 0 \end{pmatrix}$$

of which the simplest solution is $c_1 = 0$, $c_2 = 1$. Hence we take the matrix $\mathbf{C}$ to be

$$\mathbf{C} = \begin{pmatrix} 1 & 1 \\ 0 & 1 \end{pmatrix}$$

and we have

$$\mathbf{g} = \mathbf{Cf}$$

i.e.
$$g_1 = f_1 + f_2$$
$$g_2 = f_2$$

Since g_1 corresponds to the root $\lambda_1 = 1$ and g_2 to the root $\lambda_2 = \frac{1}{2}$, we know that

$$g_1^{(n)} = g_1^{(0)}$$
$$g_2^{(n)} = (\tfrac{1}{2})^n g_2^{(0)}$$

Finally
$$f_1 = g_1 - g_2$$
$$f_2 = g_2$$

so that

$$f_1^{(n)} = g_1^{(n)} - g_2^{(n)} = g_1^{(0)} - (\tfrac{1}{2})^n g_2^{(0)} = f_1^{(0)} + f_2^{(0)} - (\tfrac{1}{2})^n f_2^{(0)}$$
$$f_2^{(n)} = g_2^{(n)} \qquad = (\tfrac{1}{2})^n g_2^{(0)} \qquad = (\tfrac{1}{2})^n f_2^{(0)}$$

The results are of course, quite trivial and obvious, but it is hoped that this example has served a useful purpose in exhibiting the method which is used for the general situation.

6.8 FULL-SIB MATING

We have already established the generation equation, namely

$$\begin{pmatrix} f_1^{(1)} \\ f_2^{(1)} \\ f_3^{(1)} \\ f_4^{(1)} \\ f_5^{(1)} \\ f_6^{(1)} \\ f_7^{(1)} \end{pmatrix} = \begin{pmatrix} 1 & \frac{1}{8} & 0 & \frac{1}{4} & 0 & \frac{1}{16} & 0 \\ 0 & \frac{1}{4} & 1 & \frac{1}{4} & \frac{1}{2} & \frac{3}{16} & \frac{1}{4} \\ 0 & \frac{1}{8} & 0 & 0 & 0 & 0 & 0 \\ 0 & \frac{1}{2} & 0 & \frac{1}{4} & 0 & \frac{1}{4} & 0 \\ 0 & 0 & 0 & 0 & 0 & \frac{1}{8} & 0 \\ 0 & 0 & 0 & 0 & \frac{1}{2} & \frac{3}{8} & \frac{1}{2} \\ 0 & 0 & 0 & 0 & 0 & 0 & \frac{1}{4} \end{pmatrix} \begin{pmatrix} f_1^{(0)} \\ f_2^{(0)} \\ f_3^{(0)} \\ f_4^{(0)} \\ f_5^{(0)} \\ f_6^{(0)} \\ f_7^{(0)} \end{pmatrix}$$

We now find the latent roots of **A**, which are the values of λ for which

$$\det \begin{vmatrix} 1-\lambda & \frac{1}{8} & 0 & \frac{1}{4} & 0 & \frac{1}{16} & 0 \\ 0 & \frac{1}{4}-\lambda & 1 & \frac{1}{4} & \frac{1}{2} & \frac{3}{16} & \frac{1}{4} \\ 0 & \frac{1}{8} & -\lambda & 0 & 0 & 0 & 0 \\ 0 & \frac{1}{2} & 0 & \frac{1}{2}-\lambda & 0 & \frac{1}{4} & 0 \\ 0 & 0 & 0 & 0 & -\lambda & \frac{1}{8} & 0 \\ 0 & 0 & 0 & 0 & \frac{1}{2} & \frac{3}{8}-\lambda & \frac{1}{2} \\ 0 & 0 & 0 & 0 & 0 & 0 & \frac{1}{4}-\lambda \end{vmatrix} = 0$$

The determinant reduces to

$$(1-\lambda)\det\begin{pmatrix} \frac{1}{4}-\lambda & 1 & \frac{1}{4} \\ \frac{1}{8} & -\lambda & 0 \\ \frac{1}{2} & 0 & \frac{1}{2}-\lambda \end{pmatrix} \det\begin{pmatrix} -\lambda & \frac{1}{8} \\ \frac{1}{2} & \frac{3}{8}-\lambda \end{pmatrix} (\frac{1}{4}-\lambda)$$

which is equal to

$$(1-\lambda)(-\lambda^3 + \tfrac{3}{4}\lambda^2 + \tfrac{1}{8}\lambda - \tfrac{1}{16})(\lambda^2 - \tfrac{3}{8}\lambda - \tfrac{1}{16})(\tfrac{1}{4}-\lambda)$$

Obvious roots are $\lambda = 1$, $\lambda = \frac{1}{4}$. Also

$$(\lambda^2 - \tfrac{3}{8}\lambda - \tfrac{1}{16}) = (\lambda - \tfrac{1}{2})(\lambda + \tfrac{1}{8})$$

and

$$(-\lambda^3 + \tfrac{3}{4}\lambda^2 + \tfrac{1}{8}\lambda - \tfrac{1}{16}) = -(\lambda - \tfrac{1}{4})(\lambda^2 - \tfrac{1}{2}\lambda - \tfrac{1}{4})$$
$$= -(\lambda - \tfrac{1}{4})[\lambda - \tfrac{1}{4}(1 + \sqrt{5})][\lambda - \tfrac{1}{4}(1 - \sqrt{5})]$$

Hence the roots are

$$1, \tfrac{1}{4}, \tfrac{1}{4}(1+\sqrt{5}), \tfrac{1}{4}(1-\sqrt{5}), \tfrac{1}{2}, -\tfrac{1}{8}, \text{ and } \tfrac{1}{4}$$

Note that the root $\frac{1}{4}$ occurs twice. We shall have to extend our procedure slightly for this root. To shorten expressions somewhat we shall follow Fisher and denote $\frac{1}{4}(1+\sqrt{5})$ by ϵ, and $\frac{1}{4}(1-\sqrt{5})$ by ϵ'. We may note the following relations:

$$\epsilon' = \tfrac{1}{2} - \epsilon, \qquad \epsilon = \tfrac{1}{2} - \epsilon'$$

both ϵ and ϵ' satisfy the equation in λ, $\lambda^2 - \frac{1}{2}\lambda - \frac{1}{4} = 0$, so that

$$\epsilon^2 = \tfrac{1}{4} + \epsilon/2, \qquad \epsilon'^2 = \tfrac{1}{4} + \epsilon'/2$$
$$\epsilon + \epsilon' = \tfrac{1}{2}, \qquad \epsilon\epsilon' = -\tfrac{1}{4}$$

Now we shall find the row matrix of c's corresponding to each latent root. The equations to be satisfied are

$$\begin{pmatrix} 1-\lambda & 0 & 0 & 0 & 0 & 0 & 0 \\ \frac{1}{8} & \frac{1}{4}-\lambda & \frac{1}{8} & \frac{1}{2} & 0 & 0 & 0 \\ 0 & 1 & -\lambda & 0 & 0 & 0 & 0 \\ \frac{1}{4} & \frac{1}{4} & 0 & \frac{1}{2}-\lambda & 0 & 0 & 0 \\ 0 & \frac{1}{2} & 0 & 0 & -\lambda & \frac{1}{2} & 0 \\ \frac{1}{16} & \frac{3}{16} & 0 & \frac{1}{4} & \frac{1}{8} & \frac{3}{8}-\lambda & 0 \\ 0 & \frac{1}{4} & 0 & 0 & 0 & \frac{1}{2} & \frac{1}{4}-\lambda \end{pmatrix} \begin{pmatrix} c_1 \\ c_2 \\ c_3 \\ c_4 \\ c_5 \\ c_6 \\ c_7 \end{pmatrix} = \begin{pmatrix} 0 \\ 0 \\ 0 \\ 0 \\ 0 \\ 0 \\ 0 \end{pmatrix}$$

where the roots are entered in turn.

1. The root $\lambda = 1$. An obvious solution is

$$(c_1, c_2, c_3, c_4, c_5, c_6, c_7) = (1, 1, 1, 1, 1, 1, 1)$$

2. The root $\lambda = \epsilon$. Clearly $c_1 = 0$, and we have

$$c_2 = \epsilon c_3, \qquad \tfrac{1}{4}c_2 = -(\tfrac{1}{2} - \epsilon)c_4 = -\epsilon' c_4$$

Hence

$$c_2 = -4\epsilon' c_4 = (4\epsilon - 2)c_4$$

Now we take the equations (where we have multiplied by an appropriate integer to avoid fractions):

Row 5: $c_2 - 2\epsilon c_5 + c_6 = 0$

Row 6: $3c_2 + 4c_4 + 2c_5 + (6 - 16\epsilon)c_6 = 0$

and, expressing c_2 in terms of c_4, we get

$$2\epsilon c_5 - c_6 = -4\epsilon' c_4$$
$$2c_5 + (6 - 16\epsilon)c_6 = (12\epsilon' - 4)c_4$$

or

$$2\epsilon c_5 - (4 + 2\epsilon)c_6 = -(3 + 4\epsilon)c_4$$

so

$$(3 + 2\epsilon)c_6 = (3 + 4\epsilon - 4\epsilon')c_4$$
$$= (1 + 8\epsilon)c_4$$

so

$$(3 + 2\epsilon')(3 + 2\epsilon)c_6 = (3 + 2\epsilon')(1 + 8\epsilon)c_4$$

or

$$[9 + 6(\epsilon + \epsilon') + 4\epsilon\epsilon']c_6 = (3 + 2\epsilon' + 24\epsilon + 16\epsilon\epsilon')c_4$$

or

$$11c_6 = 22\epsilon c_4$$

or

$$c_6 = 2\epsilon c_4$$

Also

$$2\epsilon c_5 = c_2 + c_6 = (2\epsilon - 4\epsilon')c_4 = (6\epsilon - 2)c_4$$

or

$$4\epsilon\epsilon' c_5 = (12\epsilon\epsilon' - 4\epsilon')c_4$$

or

$$-c_5 = (-3 - 2 + 4\epsilon)c_4$$

or

$$c_5 = (5 - 4\epsilon)c_4$$

Finally

$$c_2 + 2c_6 + (1 - 4\epsilon)c_7 = 0$$

or

$$(4\epsilon - 1)c_7 = c_2 + 2c_6$$
$$= (-4\epsilon' + 4\epsilon)c_4$$

or

$$(4\epsilon' - 1)(4\epsilon - 1)c_7 = (4\epsilon' - 1)(4\epsilon - 4\epsilon')c_4 = (4\epsilon' - 1)(8\epsilon - 2)c_4$$

or

$$-5c_7 = -10c_4$$

or

$$c_7 = 2c_4$$

We take c_4 to be unity and get

$$(c_1, c_2, c_3, c_4, c_5, c_6, c_7) = (0, 4\epsilon - 2, 8 - 8\epsilon, 1, 5 - 4\epsilon, 2\epsilon, 2)$$

3. *The root* $\lambda = \epsilon'$. Here we substitute ϵ' for ϵ and get

$$(c_1, c_2, c_3, c_4, c_5, c_6, c_7) = (0, 4\epsilon' - 2, 8 - 8\epsilon', 1, 5 - 4\epsilon', 2\epsilon', 2)$$

4. *The root* $\lambda = \frac{1}{2}$. Clearly $c_1 = 0$ (1st equation), and also $c_2 = 0$ (4th equation), and hence $c_3 = 0$ (3rd equation), and hence $c_4 = 0$ (2nd equation). So

$$\tfrac{1}{2}c_6 - \tfrac{1}{4}c_7 = 0, \quad \text{or} \quad c_7 = 2c_6$$

and

$$c_5 = c_6$$

So, taking $c_6 = 1$, we have

$$(c_1, c_2, c_3, c_4, c_5, c_6, c_7) = (0, 0, 0, 0, 1, 1, 2)$$

5. *The root* $\lambda = -\frac{1}{8}$. Clearly $c_1 = 0$ (1st equation). We have:

(3rd equation) $c_2 + \tfrac{1}{8}c_3 = 0$ or $c_3 = -8c_2$

(4th equation) $\tfrac{1}{4}c_2 + \tfrac{5}{8}c_4 = 0$ or $c_4 = -\tfrac{2}{5}c_2$

and

(2nd equation) $c_2 = 0$

Hence

$$\tfrac{1}{8}c_5 + \tfrac{1}{2}c_6 = 0 \quad \text{or} \quad c_5 = -4c_6$$

$$\tfrac{1}{2}c_6 + \tfrac{3}{8}c_7 = 0 \quad \text{or} \quad c_7 = -\tfrac{4}{3}c_6$$

So, taking $c_6 = -3$, we have

$$(c_1, c_2, c_3, c_4, c_5, c_6, c_7) = (0, 0, 0, 0, 12, -3, 4)$$

6. *The double root* $\lambda = \tfrac{1}{4}$. Clearly $c_1 = 0$, and we could take $c_2 = c_3 = c_4 = c_5 = c_6 = 0, c_7 = 1$. Another solution again with $c_1 = 0$ in which we take $c_7 = 0$ to ensure linear independence is as follows. We have from the 3rd row, $c_2 - \tfrac{1}{4}c_3 = 0$; so $c_3 = 4c_2$. Also from the 4th row, $\tfrac{1}{4}c_2 + \tfrac{1}{4}c_4 = 0$; so $c_4 = -c_2$. Using the 5th and 6th equations, we have

$$\left.\begin{array}{r}\tfrac{1}{2}c_2 - \tfrac{1}{4}c_5 + \tfrac{1}{2}c_6 = 0 \\ \tfrac{3}{16}c_2 + \tfrac{1}{4}c_4 + \tfrac{1}{8}c_5 + \tfrac{1}{8}c_6 = 0\end{array}\right\} \text{ or } \left\{\begin{array}{r}2c_2 = c_5 - 2c_6 \\ -3c_2 - 4c_4 = 2c_5 + 2c_6\end{array}\right.$$

So

$$c_5 - 2c_6 = 2c_2$$
$$2c_5 + 2c_6 = c_2$$

giving

$$c_5 = c_2$$
$$c_6 = -\tfrac{1}{2}c_2$$

Taking $c_2 = 2$, we have

$$(c_1, c_2, c_3, c_4, c_5, c_6, c_7) = (0, 2, 8, -2, 2, -1, 0)$$

We should note here that the two solutions are linearly independent in that one solution is not a multiple of the other. In fact there is a whole double infinity of solutions denoted by

$$k_1 S_1 + k_2 S_2$$
$$l_1 S_1 + l_2 S_2$$

where $k_1/k_2 \neq l_1/l_2$ and S_1 and S_2 are the two solutions we have obtained. We can now write down explicitly the matrix we have denoted by $\mathbf{C}$ as

$$\mathbf{C} = \begin{pmatrix} 1 & 1 & 1 & 1 & 1 & 1 & 1 \\ 0 & 4\epsilon-2 & 8-8\epsilon & 1 & 5-4\epsilon & 2\epsilon & 2 \\ 0 & 4\epsilon'-2 & 8-8\epsilon' & 1 & 5-4\epsilon' & 2\epsilon' & 2 \\ 0 & 0 & 0 & 0 & 1 & 1 & 2 \\ 0 & 0 & 0 & 0 & 12 & -3 & 4 \\ 0 & 2 & 8 & -2 & 2 & -1 & 0 \\ 0 & 0 & 0 & 0 & 0 & 0 & 1 \end{pmatrix}$$

and the quantities given by

$$\mathbf{g} = \mathbf{Cf}$$

are such that

$$g_1^{(1)} = g_1^{(0)} \qquad\qquad g_1^{(n)} = g_1^{(0)}$$
$$g_2^{(1)} = \epsilon g_2^{(0)} \qquad\qquad g_2^{(n)} = \epsilon^n g_2^{(0)}$$
$$g_3^{(1)} = \epsilon' g_3^{(0)} \qquad\qquad g_3^{(n)} = \epsilon'^n g_3^{(0)}$$
$$g_4^{(1)} = \tfrac{1}{2} g_4^{(0)} \qquad\qquad g_4^{(n)} = (\tfrac{1}{2})^n g_4^{(0)}$$
$$g_5^{(1)} = (-\tfrac{1}{8}) g_5^{(0)} \qquad\qquad g_5^{(n)} = (-\tfrac{1}{8})^n g_5^{(0)}$$
$$g_6^{(1)} = \tfrac{1}{4} g_6^{(0)} \qquad\qquad g_6^{(n)} = (\tfrac{1}{4})^n g_6^{(0)}$$
$$g_7^{(1)} = \tfrac{1}{4} g_7^{(0)} \qquad\qquad g_7^{(n)} = (\tfrac{1}{4})^n g_7^{(0)}$$

Now we are not really interested in the g's per se at the moment, but in using them to determine the f's for any generation. All that we have to do is to invert the matrix $\mathbf{C}$, and use

$$\mathbf{f} = \mathbf{C}^{-1}\mathbf{g}$$

In fact we have to solve for the f's in terms of the g's. We have

$$g_7 = f_7$$
$$g_4 = f_5 + f_6 + 2f_7$$
$$g_5 = 12f_5 - 3f_6 + 4f_7$$

so

$$f_5 + f_6 = g_4 - 2g_7$$
$$12f_5 - 3f_6 = g_5 - 4g_7$$
$$3f_5 + 3f_6 = 3g_4 - 6g_7$$
$$15f_5 = 3g_4 + g_5 - 10g_7$$
$$f_5 = \tfrac{1}{5}g_4 + \tfrac{1}{15}g_5 - \tfrac{2}{3}g_7$$

and

$$f_6 = g_4 - 2g_7 - f_5$$
$$= g_4 - 2g_7 - \tfrac{1}{5}g_4 - \tfrac{1}{15}g_5 + \tfrac{2}{3}g_7$$
$$= \tfrac{4}{5}g_4 - \tfrac{1}{15}g_5 - \tfrac{4}{3}g_7$$

If we write down the position now reached in terms of matrices, it is clear that we have to solve for f_2, f_3, and f_4, given three equations in these unknowns. This can be done by inverting the matrix given in Table 6.1. A computational routine which is useful in other contexts is given in this table. What we have to do is to solve equations say $\mathbf{Bx} = \mathbf{y}$, where $\mathbf{B}$,

$\mathbf{x}$, and $\mathbf{y}$ are matrices, and to do this we first get $\mathbf{B}^{-1}$ as the solution of the equation $\mathbf{BX} = \mathbf{I}$.

TABLE 6.1

COMPUTATION OF INVERSE

$$\begin{pmatrix} 4\epsilon-2 & 8-8\epsilon & 1 \\ 4\epsilon'-2 & 8-8\epsilon' & 1 \\ 2 & 8 & -2 \end{pmatrix}$$

Instructions				Check			
(1)	$4\epsilon-2$	$8-8\epsilon$	1	$8-4\epsilon$	1	0	0
(2)	$4\epsilon'-2$	$8-8\epsilon'$	1	$8-4\epsilon'$	0	1	0
(3)	2	8	-2	9	0	0	1
(4) = (1)	$4\epsilon-2$	$8-8\epsilon$	1	$8-4\epsilon$	1	0	0
(5) = (2)×(2ε−2)	$4\epsilon-2$	-4	$2\epsilon-2$	$-10+8\epsilon$	0	$2\epsilon-2$	0
(6) = (3)×(2ε−1)	$4\epsilon-2$	$16\epsilon-8$	$2-4\epsilon$	$18\epsilon-9$	0	0	$2\epsilon-1$
(7) = (4)−(5)		$12-8\epsilon$	$3-2\epsilon$	$18-12\epsilon$	1	$2-2\epsilon$	0
(8) = (4)−(6)		$16-24\epsilon$	$-1+4\epsilon$	$17-22\epsilon$	1	0	$1-2\epsilon$
(9) = (7)		$12-8\epsilon$	$3-2\epsilon$	$18-12\epsilon$	1	$2-2\epsilon$	0
(10) = (8)×(−2ε)		$12-8\epsilon$	$-2\epsilon-2$	$11-12\epsilon$	-2ϵ	0	1
(11) = (9)−(10)			5	7	$1+2\epsilon$	$2-2\epsilon$	-1

Inverse equals

$$\begin{pmatrix} 2\epsilon/5 & (1-2\epsilon)/5 & \frac{1}{10} \\ \frac{1}{20} & \frac{1}{20} & \frac{1}{20} \\ (1+2\epsilon)/5 & (2-2\epsilon)/5 & -\frac{1}{5} \end{pmatrix}$$

Hence we have

$$\begin{pmatrix} f_2 \\ f_3 \\ f_4 \end{pmatrix} = \begin{pmatrix} 2\epsilon/5 & (1-2\epsilon)/5 & \frac{1}{10} \\ \frac{1}{20} & \frac{1}{20} & \frac{1}{20} \\ (1+2\epsilon)/5 & (2-2\epsilon)/5 & -\frac{1}{5} \end{pmatrix} \begin{pmatrix} g_2 - (5-4\epsilon)f_5 - 2\epsilon f_6 - 2g_7 \\ g_3 - (5-4\epsilon')f_5 - 2\epsilon'f_6 - 2g_7 \\ g_6 - 2f_5 + f_6 \end{pmatrix}$$

$$= \begin{pmatrix} 2\epsilon/5 & (1-2\epsilon)/5 & \frac{1}{10} \\ \frac{1}{20} & \frac{1}{20} & \frac{1}{20} \\ (1+2\epsilon)/5 & (2-2\epsilon)/5 & -\frac{1}{5} \end{pmatrix} \begin{pmatrix} g_2 \\ g_3 \\ g_6 \end{pmatrix} -f_5 \begin{pmatrix} 0 \\ \frac{1}{2} \\ 1 \end{pmatrix} -f_6 \begin{pmatrix} \frac{1}{2} \\ 0 \\ 1 \end{pmatrix} -g_7 \begin{pmatrix} \frac{2}{5} \\ \frac{1}{5} \\ \frac{6}{5} \end{pmatrix}$$

Inserting the values of f_5 and f_6 in terms of the g's, we get for the whole system

$$\begin{pmatrix} f_1 \\ f_2 \\ f_3 \\ f_4 \\ f_5 \\ f_6 \\ f_7 \end{pmatrix} = \begin{pmatrix} 1 & -(5+16\epsilon)/20 & -(13-16\epsilon)/20 & +\frac{1}{2} & 0 & \frac{1}{20} & -\frac{1}{5} \\ 0 & 2\epsilon/5 & (1-2\epsilon)/5 & -\frac{2}{5} & \frac{1}{30} & \frac{1}{10} & -\frac{4}{15} \\ 0 & \frac{1}{20} & \frac{1}{20} & -\frac{1}{10} & -\frac{1}{30} & \frac{1}{20} & +\frac{2}{15} \\ 0 & (1+2\epsilon)/5 & (2-2\epsilon)/5 & -1 & 0 & -\frac{1}{5} & \frac{4}{5} \\ 0 & 0 & 0 & \frac{1}{5} & \frac{1}{15} & 0 & -\frac{2}{3} \\ 0 & 0 & 0 & \frac{4}{5} & -\frac{1}{15} & 0 & -\frac{4}{3} \\ 0 & 0 & 0 & 0 & 0 & 0 & 1 \end{pmatrix} \begin{pmatrix} g_1 \\ g_2 \\ g_3 \\ g_4 \\ g_5 \\ g_6 \\ g_7 \end{pmatrix}$$

From this matrix we can write down the value of any f_j in any generation, because the relations between the f's and the g's hold for all generations and we already know how the g's change.

6.9 FISHER'S MEASURE OF THE RATE OF INBREEDING

We see that the proportion of matings which are not of type $aa \times aa$ is given by $(f_2 + f_3 + f_4 + f_5 + f_6 + f_7)$ so that it is equal in the nth generation to

$$\epsilon^n[(5 + 16\epsilon)/20]g_2^{(0)} + \epsilon'^n[(13 - 16\epsilon)/20]g_3^{(0)} - (\tfrac{1}{2})^n(\tfrac{1}{2})g_4^{(0)}$$
$$+ (\tfrac{1}{4})^n[-\tfrac{1}{20}g_6^{(0)} + \tfrac{1}{5}g_7^{(0)}]$$

Now the root ϵ is much larger than any other root:

In fact
$$\epsilon = 0.8090$$
and
$$\epsilon' = -0.3090$$

Hence the proportion of matings which are heterogeneous (not $aa \times aa$) is determined very largely by the contribution from the largest or dominant root. In determining the rate of inbreeding of a mating system for comparison with other mating systems, Fisher proposed that the quantity $\log_e 1/\lambda$, where λ is the dominant root, be used. This is reasonable in that

1. In selfing the proportion of heterogeneous matings is reduced by a factor of 2 in each generation.

2. The number of generations required in order that full-sibbing produce the same reduction in heterogeneous matings as n generations of selfing is

$$n(\log 2/(- \log \lambda)$$

Alternatively n generations of full-sibbing are equivalent essentially to $n \log (1/\lambda)/\log 2$ generations of selfing.

In the case of full-sibbing the dominant root is ϵ, so that Fisher's quantity for evaluating the speed of an inbreeding system is $\log_e 1/\epsilon$.

6.10 THE COMPLEXITY OF A MATING TYPE

We have seen that ϵ is the largest latent root and that the proportion of heterogeneous matings in the nth generation is mainly determined by the contribution arising from $g_2^{(0)}$ if n is at all large. We may therefore as an approximation say that the proportion of heterogeneous matings in the nth generation is ϵ^n times

$$[(5 + 16\epsilon)/20]g_2^{(0)}$$

which equals

$$[(5 + 16\epsilon)/20](4\epsilon - 2)f_2^{(0)} + (8 - 8\epsilon)f_3^{(0)} + f_4^{(0)} + (5 - 4\epsilon)f_5^{(0)}$$
$$+ 2\epsilon f_6^{(0)} + 2f_7^{(0)}]$$

$$= \tfrac{1}{20}[(6 + 20\epsilon)f_2^{(0)} + (8 + 24\epsilon)f_3^{(0)} + (5 + 16\epsilon)f_4^{(0)}$$
$$+ (9 + 28\epsilon)f_5^{(0)} + (8 + 26\epsilon)f_6^{(0)} + (10 + 32\epsilon)f_7^{(0)}]$$

The coefficients of the initial frequencies of types of mating determine essentially the relative contributions of the mating types to non-homogeneous matings in any succeeding generation. Fisher has used the term "complexity" to characterize each coefficient, and we therefore have Table 6.2. The interpretation to be placed on these complexities is as

TABLE 6.2

COMPLEXITIES OF MATING TYPES

Type	Actual	Complexity	
2	$ab \times ab$	$(6 + 20\epsilon)/20$	1.1090
3	$aa \times bb$	$(8 + 24\epsilon)/20$	1.3708
4	$aa \times ab$	$(5 + 16\epsilon)/20$	0.8972
5	$aa \times bc$	$(9 + 28\epsilon)/20$	1.5826
6	$ab \times ac$	$(8 + 26\epsilon)/20$	1.4517
7	$ab \times cd$	$(10 + 32\epsilon)/20$	1.7944

follows. Suppose the initial population of matings consisted entirely of type i with complexity c_i say. Then after n_1 generations the proportion of heterogeneous matings is essentially

$$\epsilon^{n_1} c_i$$

If on the other hand the initial population consisted of mating types with total complexity of unity, the proportion of heterogeneous matings after n_2 generations would be

$$\epsilon^{n_2}$$

In order that these proportions be the same we must have

$$n_1 \log \epsilon + \log c_i = n_2 \log \epsilon$$

or

$$n_1 - n_2 = \frac{\log c_i}{-\log \epsilon} = \frac{\log c_i}{\log (1/\lambda)}$$

where λ is the dominant root. Thus we see that matings of type i will be behind matings of unit complexity by a number of generations equal to $n_1 - n_2$ which

$$= \frac{\log c_i}{-\log \epsilon}$$

Fisher points out that for example no locus can be in worse condition than would result from the mating type $ab \times cd$. Hence no locus can be more than 0.5847 unit behind the standard condition, i.e. the condition in which average complexity is unity. He also points out that this is equivalent to 2.759 generations since $(- \log \epsilon)$ is equal to 0.21194.

We shall now merely sketch some of Fisher's (1949b) results.

Fisher shows that full-sib mating and parent–offspring mating systems are equally effective in the long run in the reduction of heterogeneous matings. He shows that the effect of a parent–offspring mating intercalated in a full-sib mating system is equal to the effect of a full-sib mating intercalated in a parent–offspring system. He discusses the frequency distribution of length of tracts of heterogeneous origin. He considers other inbreeding problems, and has a very extensive discussion of polysomic segregation. Some of the problems have been pursued further by Bennett (1953a, b, 1954a, b, c) and Bennett and Binet (1956).

6.11 COMPARISON OF THE PROBABILITY METHOD AND THE GENERATION MATRIX METHOD*

In the previous chapter we have discussed at length the examination of inbreeding systems by the use of probabilities of genes being identical by descent. This we term, for brevity, the probability method. In the present chapter we have given the generation matrix method approach to the study of brother–sister inbreeding. This method is also based on probability, of course, and the theory is an elementary topic in stochastic process theory, the matrix being essentially a matrix of transition probabilities. It is of interest and importance to give a comparative evaluation of these two methods. In passing, we note that the probability of identical descent approach is very closely related to the method of path coefficients approach which was the method used by Wright to obtain many of the results given in the previous chapter. The exact nature of the correspondence of these two closely related methods will be deferred until the method of path coefficients is discussed (Chapter 14). Here, we shall merely make the statement that the properties of the probability method are essentially those of the path coefficient method for all problems in which the method of path coefficients can be used. The probability approach

* This section may be read independently of the previous parts of this chapter.

has, however, greater generality than the method of path coefficients in its basic form.

The characteristics of the probability approach are as follows:

1. It is based on the most primitive concept possible, namely that the gene transmitted by an individual is a copy of a gene the individual possesses, except for the possible occurrence of mutation.

2. The probability approach yields the probability that a random pair of genes at a locus possessed by an individual are identical by descent. In the case of diploids this is directly related to the probability of homozygosity since we can write:

$$\text{Probability of homozygosity} = F + (1 - F)U$$

where F is the probability that the two genes are identical by descent and U is the probability that two *different* genes in the original pool are identical in state. In the case of tetraploids, for example, the correspondence of probability of alikeness by descent and probability of homozygosity is not perfect as can be seen in the following table:

Genotype	P	H
AAAA	0	0
AAAa	$\frac{1}{2}$	1
AAaa	$\frac{2}{3}$	1
Aaaa	$\frac{1}{2}$	1
aaaa	0	0

where P is the probability that two random genes are unlike in state and H is the score for heterozygosity.

We may also note that the probability method gives coefficients of parentage of individuals, that is, the probability that a random gene of individual A and a random gene of individual B are identical by descent.

3. The panmictic index P which is the probability of unlikeness by descent will be found in the case of all regular systems of inbreeding to follow a recurrence relation of the type

$$P^{(n)} = a_1 P^{(n-1)} + a_2 P^{(n-2)} + a_3 P^{(n-3)} + \cdots a_r P^{(n-r)}$$

where the superscript indicates the generation. This recurrence relation is very easily obtained for the simple regular inbreeding systems. Consequently, if the roots of the characteristic equation

$$x^r - a_1 x^{r-1} - a_2 x^{r-2} - \cdots - a_r = 0$$

are $v_1, v_2, \cdots, v_r$, the panmictic index in generation n is given by

$$P^{(n)} = \beta_1 v_1^n + \beta_2 v_2^n + \cdots + \beta_r v_r^n$$

where $\beta_1, \beta_2, \ldots, \beta_r$ are determined by the values of the panmictic index in the first r generations.

4. If we are concerned with the approximate value of the panmictic index for an arbitrary generation n in which n is large, we can use the formula

$$P^{(n)} = \beta_1 \nu_1^n$$

where ν_1 is the *largest* root of the characteristic equation of the probability recurrence equation, or of the probability recurrence relation for shortness. Just what we mean by "large" here will depend on the relative magnitudes of the roots.   In the case of full-sibbing, for instance, the largest root ν_1 equals $\frac{1}{4}(1 + \sqrt{5})$ or about 0.809, and the other root ν_2 equals $\frac{1}{4}(1 - \sqrt{5})$ or about -0.309.   Clearly, if n is 10 say, the error in replacing

$$\beta_1 (0.809)^{10} + \beta_2 (-0.309)^{10}$$

by

$$\beta_1 (0.809)^{10}$$

will be small.

5. The probability method does *not* give the genotypic array for an arbitrary generation arising from an arbitrary initial population with a particular system of inbreeding.   This can be seen from the fact that, when we deduce the genotypic array by the generation matrix method, we get frequencies which involve powers of quantities which are not roots of the probability recurrence relation.

6. We cannot regard the probability method and the generation matrix method as being entirely distinct methods, and to substantiate this statement we need merely recall the examination of partially sex-linked genes given in the previous chapter which necessitated the use of a generation matrix methodology on probabilities of unlikeness by descent.

We now turn to the enumeration of the characteristics of the generation matrix method.

1. The generation matrix method is also based on the primitive concepts of the genotype and the results of Mendelian segregation, and also ignores mutation, unless this is specifically introduced with resultant complications.

2. The generation matrix method gives the mating types (or whatever else is considered) in an arbitrary generation arising from an arbitrary population by a regular system of inbreeding.   We find in fact that, if the frequencies of mating types are arranged as a column matrix $\mathbf{f}$ say, and generations are denoted by superscripts in parentheses, then

$$\mathbf{f}^{(n)} = A f^{(n-1)}$$

where **A** is the generation matrix. A typical equation in the totality represented by the one-matrix equation is

$$f_j^{(n)} = a_{j1}f_1^{(n-1)} + a_{j2}f_2^{(n-1)} + \cdots + a_{jm}f_m^{(n-1)}$$

where $f_r^{(n-1)}$ is the frequency of the rth mating type in generation $(n-1)$. It follows that

$$\mathbf{f}^{(n)} = \mathbf{A}^n\mathbf{f}^{(0)}$$

and the mathematical processes for getting specific formulas lead to formulas such as

$$f_j^{(n)} = \sum_k C^{jk} \lambda_k^n g_k^{(0)}$$

where the λ_k's are the latent roots (or eigenvalues) of the characteristic equation of **A**, the $g_k^{(0)}$'s are "principal components" (Fisher, 1949b) which can be determined, given **A**, and the roots of **A**, and the coefficients C^{jk} are likewise obtainable from **A** and its roots. The equation can be further expanded so that f's are given in terms of original f's because the g's are given by

$$g_k^{(0)} = \sum_l C_{kl}f_l^{(0)}$$

where the numbers C_{kl} are determinable. Hence we have

$$f_j^{(n)} = \sum_k C^{jk} \lambda_k^n \sum_l C_{kl}f_l^{(0)}$$
$$= \sum_l \left(\sum_k C^{jk} \lambda_k^n C_{kl}\right) f_l^{(0)}$$

We may note in passing that the equations giving $f_j^{(n)}$ in terms of $g_k^{(0)}$ are such that with some manipulation we could derive an equation

$$f_j^{(n)} = \beta_1 f_j^{(n-1)} + \beta_2 f_j^{(n-2)} + \beta_3 f_j^{(n-3)} + \cdots$$

which is a probability recurrence relation on the frequencies of mating types. It is entirely mathematical convenience that we work in terms of the generation matrix rather than in terms of a probability recurrence relation. It can be taken as a purely mathematical fact that, if we can use a generation matrix method with fixed elements in the matrix, then we can use a probability recurrence equation or vice versa.

3. In view of the fact that we have the mating types with their frequencies in an arbitrary generation, we can deduce therefrom any property of the frequencies of types of individual such as homozygote, heterozygote, nulliplex, simplex, etc., in any generation. For example, if the mating

system were uncle–niece, we would merely add over the uncle types for given niece type to get the frequency of the niece type.   In the niece generation, we can therefore deduce from the results of the generation matrix method the total probability of heterozygosity for diploids or for tetraploids and so on.   We may note that it is not possible to deduce the probability of heterozygosity in polyploids merely by considering the panmictic index.   Whether we need, on the other hand, to go to the full generation matrix methodology to deduce the probability of hetero-zygosity is a matter of mathematical ingenuity.   The probability of heterozygosity in tetraploids was first deduced by Haldane by probability considerations without the necessity of introducing the generation matrix. It is apparent, however, that, in the age of electronic computers which can evaluate latent roots and perform matrix operations with ease, the generation matrix method is one which requires no input of ingenuity and is in fact entirely mechanical.   If we were concerned with a new situation and had a good electronic computer available, we would use the generation matrix method unless the size of the generation matrix were such that the computer could not handle it.   This actually happens rather easily because the number of mating types can approach astronomical figures rather easily.

4. The generation matrix method can of course be used to obtain frequencies of mating kinds under a system of inbreeding, where by a mating kind we mean mating as specified by the genotypes.   The genera-tion matrix for mating kinds may not be necessary, and we shall in most circumstances of interest be able to deduce the frequencies of mating kinds from the frequencies of mating types.

5. The generation matrix may be modified very easily to take account of selection whereas the examination of the effects of inbreeding in the presence of selection by means of the panmictic index seems to be impossible.   The matrix manipulations may, of course, become rather complex.   The reader may refer to Hayman and Mather (1953) and to Reeve (1955) for an examination of full-sibbing with selection.

6. We may be concerned with the properties of a system of inbreeding after an indefinitely large number of generations, which will be determined by the roots equal to unity of the generation matrix.   In this case there is clearly no need for the generation matrix methodology.

7. We may be concerned with the properties of a system of inbreeding after a large number of generations, for instance the relative frequencies of different genotypes.   It is not obvious that the generation matrix method is not needed to determine such properties.   It is clear from the equations relating to the generation matrix given above that the properties will be determined by the roots equal to unity and the largest *non-unit*

root of the generation matrix. It may be stated as a mathematical fact that the largest non-unit root of the generation matrix is equal to the largest root of the probability recurrence equation. Mathematical proof will not be given here. The result is intuitively obvious from a heuristic argument. Since the panmictic index is a linear function of the frequencies of mating types, and since both methods are mathematically correct with regard to what they are aimed to obtain, we must obviously get the same answer asymptotically (as the number of generations gets large) by both methods. The asymptotic answer given by the probability method will depend only on the largest root of the probability recurrence equation. The asymptotic answer given by the generation matrix method will depend only on the largest non-unit root of the generation matrix (the unit roots being always present). It is clear therefore that, if we are concerned with obtaining the complexities of mating types, we need not get involved in the generation matrix method computations. This particular aspect will be described in a separate section below.

8. If the system of inbreeding should be irregular, the full generation matrix method becomes very tedious. In fact, each irregularity will involve its own generation matrix in addition to the generation matrix of the regular system. Fisher's (1949b) procedure for such circumstances is to use the largest non-unit latent root of the generation matrix of the regular system with the generation matrix of the irregularity. The case for the generation matrix method is not overwhelming because, if we are going to ignore all the roots of the regular generation matrix except the largest non-unit one, there does not appear to be a strong case for taking account of *all* the roots of the generation matrix of the irregularity.

6.12 THE DETERMINATION OF THE LIMITING DISTRIBUTION

The limiting distribution of mating types is that distribution which holds if all roots of the generation matrix are ignored except the unit roots and the largest non-unit root. This limiting distribution gives the relative frequencies of non-homogeneous mating types after a large number of generations. The reasoning to be applied to mating types could equally well be applied to kinds of mating or to frequencies of genotypes and so on. We shall exemplify the process by the case of mating types with full-sibbing.

We have given above the general equation for the frequencies of mating types as

$$f_j^{(n)} = \sum_k C^{jk} \lambda_k^n g_k^{(0)}$$

If now we ignore all roots except the ones equal to unity and the largest non-unit one which we denote by λ, we can write

$$f_j^{(n)} = a_j + b_j g_\lambda^{(0)} \lambda^n$$

where $g_\lambda^{(0)}$ is the principal component of frequencies corresponding to the largest non-unit root. This largest root will be determined easily by the probability method. All we have to do, clearly, is to determine a_j and $b_j g_\lambda^{(0)}$. We shall take the case of full-sibbing with two alleles. The basic considerations are given in Table 6.3 and Table 6.4.

TABLE 6.3

FREQUENCIES OF MATING TYPES IN GENERATIONS n AND $n+1$

Mating Type	Frequency in Generation	
	n	$n+1$
$aa \times aa$	$f_1^{(n)} = a_1 + b_1 g_\lambda^{(0)} \lambda^n$	$f_1^{(n+1)} = a_1 + b_1 g_\lambda^{(0)} \lambda^{n+1}$
$aa \times ab$	$f_2^{(n)} = a_2 + b_2 g_\lambda^{(0)} \lambda^n$	$f_2^{(n+1)} = a_2 + b_2 g_\lambda^{(0)} \lambda^{n+1}$
$ab \times ab$	$f_3^{(n)} = a_3 + b_3 g_\lambda^{(0)} \lambda^n$	$f_3^{(n+1)} = a_3 + b_3 g_\lambda^{(0)} \lambda^{n+1}$
$aa \times bb$	$f_4^{(n)} = a_4 + b_4 g_\lambda^{(0)} \lambda^n$	$f_4^{(n+1)} = a_4 + b_4 g_\lambda^{(0)} \lambda^{n+1}$

TABLE 6.4

GENERATION MATRIX EQUATIONS FOR CASE CONSIDERED

$$
\begin{aligned}
f_1^{(n+1)} &= f_1^{(n)} + \tfrac{1}{4} f_2^{(n)} + \tfrac{1}{8} f_3^{(n)} \\
f_2^{(n+1)} &= \tfrac{1}{2} f_2^{(n)} + \tfrac{1}{2} f_3^{(n)} \\
f_3^{(n+1)} &= \tfrac{1}{4} f_2^{(n)} + \tfrac{1}{4} f_3^{(n)} + f_4^{(n)} \\
f_4^{(n+1)} &= \tfrac{1}{8} f_3^{(n)}
\end{aligned}
$$

Hence, since the relationships in Tables 6.3 and 6.4 must hold identically in n, we have

$$
\begin{array}{lll}
a_1 = a_1 + \tfrac{1}{4} a_2 + \tfrac{1}{8} a_3 & & a_1 = a_1 \\
a_2 = \tfrac{1}{2} a_2 + \tfrac{1}{2} a_3 & & a_2 = 0 \\
a_3 = \tfrac{1}{4} a_2 + \tfrac{1}{4} a_3 + a_4 & \text{or} & a_3 = 0 \\
a_4 = \tfrac{1}{8} a_3 & & a_4 = 0
\end{array}
$$

and

$$
\begin{aligned}
b_1 \lambda &= b_1 + \tfrac{1}{4} b_2 + \tfrac{1}{8} b_3 \\
b_2 \lambda &= \tfrac{1}{2} b_2 + \tfrac{1}{2} b_3 \\
b_3 \lambda &= \tfrac{1}{4} b_2 + \tfrac{1}{4} b_3 + b_4 \\
b_4 \lambda &= \tfrac{1}{8} b_3
\end{aligned}
$$

The solution to the b equations, using the fact that $\lambda = \epsilon = \frac{1}{4}(1 + \sqrt{5})$ is as follows:

$$b_1 = -(\tfrac{3}{4} + \tfrac{5}{2}\epsilon)b_3, \qquad b_2 = 2\epsilon b_3, \qquad b_3 = b_3, \qquad b_4 = (\epsilon/2 - \tfrac{1}{4})b_3$$

The relative proportions of the three heterogeneous types are therefore as follows:

$$aa \times ab: \quad 2\epsilon/(\tfrac{3}{4} + \tfrac{5}{2}\epsilon) = 20 - 24\epsilon \qquad = 0.58$$
$$ab \times ab: \quad 1/(\tfrac{3}{4} + \tfrac{5}{2}\epsilon) = 40\epsilon - 32 \qquad = 0.36$$
$$aa \times bb: \quad (\epsilon/2 - \tfrac{1}{4})/(\tfrac{3}{4} + \tfrac{5}{2}\epsilon) = 13 - 16\epsilon = 0.06$$

This result is given by Fisher (1949b, p. 40) and by Wright (1931) in terms of mating kinds.

If we wish to go further by imposing initial conditions, the quantity b_3 may be obtained from the fact that the proportion of heterozygous individuals in generation n, with n large, is $(\tfrac{1}{2}b_2 + b_3)g_\lambda^{(0)}\lambda^n$, and this proportion is, as we have seen, easily obtained by the probability argument.

6.13 THE DETERMINATION OF COMPLEXITIES

These can be obtained by an elementary argument, which will be illustrated by the general case of complexities of mating types with full-sibbing. We have seen that the frequency of homogeneous matings in generation n is with large n equal to

$$f_1^{(n)} = \sum_l d_{1l}f_l^{(0)} + \lambda^n \sum_l d_{2l}f_l^{(0)}$$

Now the term independent of n must equal unity in the case of full-sibbing because, with n infinite, $f_1^{(n)}$ is unity, all matings being homogeneous. Hence, the frequency of heterogeneous matings in generation n is

$$-\lambda^n[d_{21}f_1^{(0)} + d_{22}f_2^{(0)} + \cdots + d_{27}f_7^{(0)}]$$

since there are seven mating types. The largest non-unit root is again ϵ, so that we put λ equal to ϵ. The mating types in the order used by Fisher and earlier in this chapter are as follows:

Number	Mating Type
1	$aa \times aa$
2	$aa \times ab$
3	$ab \times ab$
4	$aa \times bb$
5	$ab \times ac$
6	$aa \times bc$
7	$ab \times cd$

Now we consider the hypothetical case in which all initial matings are of type 1. Clearly these give no contributions to heterogeneous matings at any later generation, so that d_{21} is zero. The contributions of mating type 2 to heterogeneous matings n generations later is equal to the contributions of ($\frac{1}{4}$ type $1 + \frac{1}{2}$ type $2 + \frac{1}{4}$ type 3) to heterogeneous matings $(n-1)$ generations later. Hence

$$\epsilon d_{22} = \tfrac{1}{4}d_{21} + \tfrac{1}{2}d_{22} + \tfrac{1}{4}d_{23}$$

or

$$(\epsilon - \tfrac{1}{2})d_{22} = \tfrac{1}{4}d_{23}$$
$$d_{22} = \epsilon d_{23}$$

The contributions of mating type 3 to heterogeneous matings n generations later is equal to the contributions of ($\frac{1}{8}$ type $1 + \frac{1}{2}$ type $2 + \frac{1}{4}$ type 3 $+ \frac{1}{8}$ type 4) to heterogeneous matings $(n-1)$ generations later so that

$$\epsilon d_{23} = \tfrac{1}{8}d_{21} + \tfrac{1}{2}d_{22} + \tfrac{1}{4}d_{23} + \tfrac{1}{8}d_{24}$$

Similarly we find

$$\epsilon d_{24} = d_{23}$$
$$\epsilon d_{25} = \tfrac{1}{16}d_{21} + \tfrac{1}{4}d_{22} + \tfrac{3}{16}d_{23} + \tfrac{3}{8}d_{25} + \tfrac{1}{8}d_{26}$$
$$\epsilon d_{26} = \tfrac{1}{2}d_{23} + \tfrac{1}{2}d_{25}$$
$$\epsilon d_{27} = \tfrac{1}{4}d_{23} + \tfrac{1}{2}d_{25} + \tfrac{1}{4}d_{27}$$

It is easy to solve these equations, and, if we make the requirement that the average complexity of the limiting distribution be unity, i.e.

$$(20 - 24\epsilon)d_{22} + (40\epsilon - 32)d_{23} + (13 - 16\epsilon)d_{24} = 1$$

the values for d_{22}, d_{23}, d_{24}, d_{25}, d_{26}, d_{27} are those given earlier in this chapter and denoted by Fisher as U, V, W, X, Y, Z (1949b, p. 41).

Final Note

In connection with the above discussion the reader will get a picture of some of the points discussed by reading the paper by Bennett (1954b) and the paper by Crow (1954) which tackle the same problem, the former in generation matrix terms and the latter in terms of elementary probability. Crow was able to deduce the essential results of Bennett very rapidly and easily.

REFERENCES

Bartlett, M. S., and J. B. S. Haldane. 1934. The theory of inbreeding in autotetraploids. *J. Genet.* **29**, 175–180.

Bartlett, M. S., and J. B. S. Haldane. 1935. The theory of inbreeding with forced
heterozygosis. *J. Genet.*, **31**, 327–340.

Bennett, J. H. 1953a. Junctions in inbreeding. *Genetica*, **26**, 392–406.

Bennett, J. H. 1953b. Linkage in hexasomic inheritance. *Heredity*, **7**, 265–284.

Bennett, J. H.   1954a.   Panmixia with tetrasomic and hexasomic inheritance. *Genetics*, **39**, 150–158.

Bennett, J. H.   1954b.   On the theory of random mating. *Ann. Eugen. Lond.*, **18**, 311–317.

Bennett, J. H.   1954c.   The distribution of heterogeneity upon inbreeding. *J. Roy. Stat. Soc. B*, **16**, 88–99.

Bennett, J. H., and F. E. Binet.   1956.   Association between Mendelian factors with mixed selfing and random mating. *Heredity*, **10**, 51–56.

Crow, J. E.   1954.   Random mating with linkage in polysomics. *Amer. Nat.*, **88**, 431–434.

Fisher, R. A.   1947.   The theory of linkage in polysomic inheritance. *Phil. Trans. B*, **233**, 55–87.

Fisher, R. A.   1949a.   The linkage problem in a tetrasomic wild plant *Lythrum salicaria*. *Proc. 8th int. Congr. Genet., Hereditas*, Suppl. Vol., 225–233.

Fisher, R. A.   1949b.   *The theory of inbreeding.* Oliver and Boyd, Edinburgh.

Fisher, R. A.   1954.   A fuller theory of "junctions" in inbreeding. *Heredity*, **8**, 187–199.

Hayman, B. I.   1953.   Mixed selfing and random mating when homozygotes are at a disadvantage. *Heredity*, **7**, 185–192.

Hayman, B. I., and K. Mather.   1953.   The progress of inbreeding when homozygotes are at a disadvantage. *Heredity*, **7**, 165–184.

Reeve, E. C. R.   1955.   Inbreeding with the homozygotes at a disadvantage. *Ann. hum. Genet.*, **19**, 332–346.

Wright, Sewall.   1931.   Evolution in Mendelian populations. *Genetics*, **16**, 97–159.

FURTHER READING

Garber, M. J.   1951.   Approach to genotypic equilibrium with varying percentages of self-fertilization and cross fertilization. *J. Hered.*, **42**, 299–300.

Gowen, J. W., J. Stadler, and L. E. Johnson.   1946.   On the mechanism of heterosis —the chromosomal or cytoplasmic basis of heterosis in *Drosophila melanogaster*. *J. Genet.* **34**, 265–274.

Haldane, J. B. S.   1936.   The amount of heterozygosis to be expected in an approximately pure line. *J. Genet.*, **32**, 375–391.

Haldane, J. B. S.   1949.   The association of characters as a result of inbreeding and linkage. *Ann. Eugen. Lond.*, **15**, 15–23.

Haldane, J. B. S.   1955.   The complete matrices for brother–sister and alternate parent–offspring mating involving one locus. *J. Genet.*, **53**, 315–324.

Haldane, J. B. S.   1956.   The conflict between inbreeding and selection. I. Self-fertilization. *J. Genet.*, **54**, 56–63.

Hogben, Lancelot.   1932.   Filial and fraternal correlations in sex-linked inheritance. *Proc. roy. Soc. Edinb.*, **52**, 331–336.

Hogben, Lancelot.   1933.   A matrix notation for Mendelian populations. *Proc. roy. Soc. Edinb.*, **53**, 7–25.

Li, C. C., and L. Sacks.   1954.   The derivation of joint distribution and correlation between relatives by the use of stochastic matrices. *Biometrics*, **10**, 347–360.

PROBLEMS

1. Enumerate the mating types in the case of a sex-linked factor with an arbitrary number of alleles.

2. Consider full-sibbing starting from random mating in the population $p^2AA + 2pqAa + q^2aa$. Evaluate the g functions.

3. Following question 2 show by direct elementary methods that the g's decrease in the appropriate fashion from the zeroth generation to the first generation.

4. Add the following matrices

$$\begin{pmatrix} 4 & 2 \\ 5 & 3 \end{pmatrix} \qquad \begin{pmatrix} -1 & -2 \\ 3 & 4 \end{pmatrix} \qquad \begin{pmatrix} 5 & -2 \\ -3 & 4 \end{pmatrix}$$

5. Evaluate

$$\begin{pmatrix} 1 & 3 & 2 \\ 4 & 1 & 6 \\ 7 & 2 & 5 \end{pmatrix} \times \begin{pmatrix} 2 & 1 & 6 \\ 8 & 3 & 7 \\ 4 & 5 & 1 \end{pmatrix}$$

6. Evaluate $\mathbf{AB}$ where

$$\mathbf{A} = \begin{pmatrix} 1 & 3 \\ 2 & 5 \\ 6 & 7 \end{pmatrix}, \qquad \mathbf{B} = \begin{pmatrix} 1 & 4 & 7 \\ 2 & 1 & 5 \end{pmatrix}$$

Does $\mathbf{BA}$ exist?

7. What are the latent or characteristic roots of the following matrix?

$$\begin{pmatrix} 2 & 1 \\ 5 & 6 \end{pmatrix}$$

8. What are the latent or characteristic roots of the following matrix?

$$\begin{pmatrix} 3 & 2 & 5 \\ 4 & 1 & 3 \\ 2 & 2 & 1 \end{pmatrix}$$

9. Find the matrix $\mathbf{C}$ such that

$$\mathbf{C} \begin{pmatrix} 2 & 1 \\ 5 & 6 \end{pmatrix} \mathbf{C}^{-1}$$

is diagonal.

10. Find the matrix $\mathbf{C}$ such that

$$\mathbf{C} \begin{pmatrix} 3 & 2 & 5 \\ 4 & 1 & 3 \\ 2 & 2 & 1 \end{pmatrix} \mathbf{C}^{-1}$$

is diagonal.

11. Deduce, from the results of the generation matrix method applied to full-sibbing, how the proportion of heterozygous individuals in the population changes in successive generations.

12. Use the generation matrix method and the results derived by it in this chapter to deduce the genotypic array of the population which results from the population,

$$p^2AA + 2pqAa + q^2aa$$

by n generations of full-sibbing.

13. It is entirely reasonable that the mating type $aa \times bb$ should be one generation behind the mating type $ab \times ab$. Show that the complexities of type $aa \times bb$ and of type $ab \times ab$ are such that the statement is correct.

14. Apply the same reasoning as in question 13 to the mating type $aa \times ab$ and the resulting mating types.

15. Deduce the complexities of the mating types for parent–offspring mating without going through all the manipulations of the generation matrix method.

16. Show how it would be possible to define complexities by reference to the proportion of heterozygous individuals rather than by reference to the proportion of heterogeneous matings.

17. Show that for selfing of autotetraploids without double reduction, with two alleles, the roots are $1, \frac{1}{2}, \frac{5}{6}, \frac{1}{6}, 1$, and that a suitable $\mathbf{C}$ matrix is

$$\mathbf{C} = \begin{pmatrix} 1 & 1 & 1 & 1 & 1 \\ 0 & 1 & 0 & -1 & 0 \\ 0 & 3 & 4 & 3 & 0 \\ 0 & -3 & 4 & -3 & 0 \\ 3 & 2 & 1 & 0 & -1 \end{pmatrix}$$

with

$$\mathbf{C}^{-1} = \begin{pmatrix} \frac{1}{4} & -\frac{1}{4} & -\frac{7}{48} & \frac{1}{48} & \frac{1}{4} \\ 0 & \frac{1}{2} & \frac{1}{12} & -\frac{1}{12} & 0 \\ 0 & 0 & \frac{1}{8} & \frac{1}{8} & 0 \\ 0 & -\frac{1}{2} & \frac{1}{12} & -\frac{1}{12} & 0 \\ \frac{3}{4} & \frac{1}{4} & -\frac{7}{48} & \frac{1}{48} & -\frac{1}{4} \end{pmatrix}$$

Complete the picture. (*R. L. Plaisted*)

CHAPTER 7

Tests of Genetic Hypotheses

7.1 INTRODUCTION

We have dealt fairly extensively with the problems of calculation of genetic expectations in previous chapters and now turn to the problems of statistical inference about the expectations or about parameters in the expectations. The simplest such problem is the testing of a simple Mendelian ratio. For example, genetic theory and observation may lead us to expect an observed ratio of 3 to 1 or a proportion of $\frac{3}{4}$. A count of 100 progeny gives a proportion of $\frac{4}{5}$. Are we to conclude that the genetic hypothesis is supported by the data, or are we to decide that the observed ratio is unlikely to have come from the hypothesized proportion and that the genetic expectations do not hold in the situation we are examining? Such a problem involves a test of a genetic hypothesis. We should note that all statistical techniques can tell us is that the data do not support the hypothesis. The question of why not requires further experimentation to determine if for example there are hidden selective forces at work, which cause a deviation from the simple expectation.

7.2 THE TESTING OF HYPOTHESES

Our first job is to define precisely what we mean by a test of a hypothesis. In the example mentioned above we can write down the probabilities of each of the possible number of successes as functions of n the number of progeny, and P the probability of a success. In fact, the probability of r successes is

$$\frac{n!}{r!(n-r)!} P^r Q^{n-r}, \qquad Q = 1 - P$$

We can observe any number of successes between 0 and n, and we need a set of rules which tells us what inferences we may draw for each of the possible numbers of successes.

For the sake of clarity we shall consider the simple situation of testing a sire. We wish to determine if an individual is AA or Aa. We mate this individual to individuals known to be *aa*, and obtain say six progeny. The possible results and their probabilities are shown in Table 7.1. It is

TABLE 7.1

Number of *aa*'s	Probability if Sire Is	
	AA	*Aa*
0	1	$(\frac{1}{2})^6$
1	0	$6(\frac{1}{2})^6$
2	0	$15(\frac{1}{2})^6$
3	0	$20(\frac{1}{2})^6$
4	0	$15(\frac{1}{2})^6$
5	0	$6(\frac{1}{2})^6$
6	0	$(\frac{1}{2})^6$

fairly obvious what we should do in the present instance, but we shall follow the argument through in some detail. One possible rule of inference would be: If in six progeny we obtain at least one *aa*, then reject the hypothesis that the sire is *AA* and accept the hypothesis that the sire is *Aa*. Is this a good rule of inference? In this situation we can state the following probabilities:

Probability of an *AA* individual being classified as $AA = 1$

Probability of an *AA* individual being classified as $Aa = 0$

Probability of an *Aa* individual being classified as $AA = (\frac{1}{2})^6$

Probability of an *Aa* individual being classified as $Aa = 1 - (\frac{1}{2})^6$

We wish to make the possibility of drawing an incorrect inference as small as possible. Actually there are two possible errors: (1) of concluding that the sire is *Aa* when in fact he is *AA*, and (2) of concluding that the sire is *AA* when in fact he is *Aa*. We have certainly minimized the probability of the first kind of error, and it is obvious that we cannot make the probability of the second type of error at all smaller. Given six progeny then, we cannot do better than to use the stated rule. The probability of the second type of error can be made as small as we wish by increasing the number of progeny, and it is the geneticist's job to specify how small he wishes this probability to be, and then we can tell him how many progeny he should collect. Alternatively, if he can take only a definite number of progeny, say *n*, we can tell him that there is no possibility of·reducing the probability of this type of error below $(\frac{1}{2})^n$.

The position here can be stated in the general form, that we wish to test the hypothesis that a binomial proportion *P* is one half agaiɪ alternative that it is zero. A more general situation is the testing of a hypothesis that a binomial proportion is P_1 against the alternative that it is P_2, and a still more general situation is that of testing that a binomial proportion is P_0 against a class of alternative possibilities that P is greater than P_0, or less than P_0, or unequal to P_0 with no choice of direction. In each of the cases to be considered we can consider probabilities on the hypothesis to be tested and on alternative hypotheses that are to be considered.

7.3 THE TEST OF SIGNIFICANCE

In many cases we can calculate the probability of the observed result and of all results which deviate as far as or further from expectation than the observed result. The number which is obtained is called the significance level of the observed result, and the procedure of evaluating a level of significance is called a test of significance.

The calculation of significance levels is a guide to the interpretation of the observed results. The experimenter must make a decision on the level of significance which he will regard as sufficient for the rejection of the hypothesis under test, or, as it is frequently named, the null hypothesis. Frequently the experimenter will say that, if the significance level is less than some chosen number, then the null hypothesis is to be rejected. There are two common practices in this respect, namely to specify the levels which must be passed (in a downward direction) as being 5 per cent or 1 per cent. In these cases the experimenter is said to be using a 5 per cent significance test or a 1 per cent significance test, respectively. The exact meaning of these terms follows from the description we have given above. If the experimenter is using a 5 per cent level of significance, then his chances of rejecting the null hypothesis when it is true are 5 per cent, or 1 in 20. With a 1 per cent test the chances are 1 in 100.

The choice of level of significance to be used depends on many considerations, and we shall give only a brief discussion of these matters. From the way we have described the use of the level of significance, it is clear that the choice of level depends on the risks which the experimenter is prepared to face. Inductive inference is an uncertain procedure, and the job of statistics is to bring the uncertainties in the procedure in clear view, and to indicate how an experimenter can incorporate his desires, providing they are reasonable and consistent, into the inferential process. In general it is entirely impossible to eliminate errors in drawing inferences. For example, if we are testing an individual for whether he is AA or Aa by mating him to an aa individual, and in fact have an Aa individual, it is possible that a chosen number of progeny will contain no recessives, so that, no matter how many progeny we obtain, there is a probability of concluding that the individual is AA. The size of experiment, in this case the number of progeny, can be chosen to make this probability take on any arbitrary chosen value, but no finite number of progeny will make the probability zero.

The experimenter must then decide what levels of risk he wishes to operate with. He may decide that the rejection of the null hypothesis 1 in 20 times when it is in fact true is quite reasonable and satisfactory. The choice of level of significance must be related to another risk, namely the risk of failing to reject the null hypothesis when it is in fact false. If a test of very high significance, i.e. small probability, is used, the experiment which is within the resources of the experimenter may be so insensitive as to be barely worth performing, except that, of course, a properly designed experiment will provide an estimate with an estimate of error.

Detailed consideration of these matters is not possible here, and we shall merely mention that levels of 1 in 20 or 1 in 100 are generally used, and that the size of experiment is frequently such that a 1 in 10 level should be used.

There is considerable confusion in the statistical literature on the roles of tests of hypotheses and tests of significance. In many cases the two concepts lead to the same end result. However, the test of hypothesis concept requires the strict use of probabilities of error of prechosen magnitude, while in the significance test procedure it is feasible to inquire what the level of significance of the observed results is and to use the resulting number as a rough guide to one's future thoughts and actions. If the level of significance is say 6 per cent, the experimenter may regard the hypothesis being examined as being somewhat doubtful and reserve judgment. To a "test of hypothesis man" the verdict is restricted to "accept" or "reject" the hypothesis under test, and this strikes many people as being far too rigid a rule.

7.4 ACTUAL TEST PROCEDURES ON SIMPLE PROPORTIONS

The test procedure which has been devised for these cases is as follows, where r is the number of successes observed:

1. Test of the hypothesis that a binomial proportion is P with reference to alternatives that the proportion is greater than P: Evaluate the probability of there arising r or more successes, which will be the sum of the probabilities of all possibilities with r or more successes. If the number obtained is α, then the level of significance of the observed result is α.

2. Test of the hypothesis that a binomial proportion is P with reference

to alternatives that the proportion is less than P: Evaluate the probability of there arising r or less successes, which will be the sum of the probabilities of all possibilities with r or less successes. This will give the significance of the observed result.

3. Test of the hypothesis that a binomial proportion is P with reference to all alternatives: If the number of successes is r, obtain the absolute value of $(r - nP)$, which is denoted by $|r - nP|$, and obtain the probability of the number of successes being less than or equal to $nP - |r - nP|$ or greater than or equal to $nP + |r - nP|$. This will give the significance level of the observed result.

As we saw in Chapter 1, the probabilities required above may be obtained approximately and quickly by finding the appropriate area of a section of the normal distribution with mean zero and variance unity. A quantity which follows this distribution is called a normal deviate. Using the formula given therein, we see that the following approximations hold for the above cases:

(1) $P\left[ND \geq \dfrac{r - nP}{\sqrt{nPQ}}\right]$ which we read as the probability that a normal deviate exceeds $(r - nP)/\sqrt{nPQ}$

(2) $P\left[ND \leq \dfrac{r - nP}{\sqrt{nPQ}}\right]$

(3) $P\left[ND \geq \dfrac{r - nP}{\sqrt{nPQ}} \quad \text{or} \quad ND \leq -\dfrac{r - nP}{\sqrt{nPQ}}\right]$

These approximations can be improved by the use of the "continuity" correction (p. 19).

Size of Experiment

How large should an experiment be is always a perplexing question because most experiments are devised to give information on more than one aspect of a problem. In some simple cases it is easy to lay down quite clear firm rules. We shall consider two situations.

First consider the simple question of testing a sire as to whether he is AA or Aa. We have seen that a rule will be: Take n offspring, and, if at least one offspring is aa, conclude that the sire is Aa; otherwise conclude that the sire is AA. We have seen that there is 0 probability of concluding that an AA sire is Aa, but the probability of concluding that an Aa sire is AA is $(\frac{1}{2})^n$. We can make this arbitrarily small by increasing n. If we wish it to be δ say, then n is equal to $\log(1/\delta)/\log 2$; with δ equal to 0.05, it turns out that n is just over 4, so that we should use 5, and, with δ equal to 0.01, n is between 6 and 7, so we should use 7. A more realistic approach to the matter of testing would involve the consideration of cost of testing and cost of errors. The cost of concluding that an Aa sire is AA could be denoted by C_1, the cost of each offspring by C_2. The total risk with n offspring is therefore $(\frac{1}{2})^n C_1 + nC_2$. The experimenter might well choose n to make this risk a minimum, which would be when

$$n = (\log C_1/C_2 + \log \log 2)/\log 2$$

There is also the possibility in some cases of answering the question of the previous paragraph by sequential testing. This would be the case if we could take offspring in order and did not have to specify the total number of offspring that would be taken. If we had one offspring and it was aa, we would conclude immediately that the sire is Aa and would not consider any further offspring. Likewise, if the first offspring were AA and the second offspring were aa, we would conclude that the sire is Aa without further observations which would be quite useless with regard to the question at issue. A sequential rule could be to take successive observations up to say 7. The probability of concluding that an Aa sire is AA would then be $(\frac{1}{2})^7$ or $\frac{1}{128}$, but the average number of observations required to reach the decision would be $(\frac{1}{2})1 + (\frac{1}{4})2 + (\frac{1}{8})3 + (\frac{1}{16})4 + (\frac{1}{32})5 + (\frac{1}{64})6 + (\frac{2}{128})7$ which equals $\frac{254}{128}$ or a little less than 2. Note that this is the average or expected number of observations. The actual number will be between 1 and 7 with the probabilities $\frac{1}{2}$, $\frac{1}{4}$, $\frac{1}{8}$, etc. For a pure decision question of this sort there is no doubt of the superiority of the sequential method.

A similar problem which arises occasionally is the following. Under one genetic hypothesis the proportion of successes (which may be a particular genotype, sex, or something else) is p_1, while under an alternative which is the most likely the proportion is p_2 which is greater than p_1. Now suppose we wish to specify a number n of observations, and a rule which states: "If we get r or less we will conclude that the true proportion is p_1 and if we get more than r we will conclude that the true proportion is p_2." We would like the following conditions:

1. The probability of concluding that the proportion is p_2 when in fact it is p_1 to be 0.05 approximately.
2. The probability of concluding that the proportion is p_1 when in fact it is p_2 to be 0.05 approximately.

The "approximately" is included because with a discrete number of possible results of the test it is not possible (except by the use of an artificial device) to make the probabilities exactly 0.05. We use the normal approximation to the binomial to give us a good working answer. (This can be refined by the use of the continuity correction or by making up partial binomial sums, but either would be "gilding the lily.") We must have

$$\frac{r - np_1}{[np_1(1 - p_1)]^{1/2}} = 1.645$$

$$\frac{np_2 - r}{[np_2(1 - p_2)]^{1/2}} = 1.645$$

The number 1.645 is the value of a normal deviate which is exceeded with probability 0.05. This gives us two equations in r and n which can be solved. It is left as an example to the reader to verify that, if p_1 is 0.70 and p_2 is 0.824, then n equals 124 and r equals 95 approximately.

7.5 GOODNESS OF FIT TESTS

We are now in a position to make the transition to the simplest goodness of fit test, which also applies to situation 3 above. Let x be a normal deviate; then x^2 follows the χ^2 distribution with one degree of freedom. The probability in the case 3 above may be written

$$P\left[x^2 > \frac{(r - nP)^2}{nPQ}\right]$$

Hence all we have to do is to calculate the quantity

$$\frac{(r - nP)^2}{nPQ}$$

and ascertain from a table of the χ^2 distribution with one degree of freedom the probability that a value equal to or greater than this would be obtained. We may improve the accuracy of the calculation by finding the probability for

$$\frac{[|r - nP| - \frac{1}{2}]^2}{nPQ}$$

Either of the quantities here specified, i.e. without or with the "$\frac{1}{2}$" are usually denoted by χ^2, the former being unadjusted and the latter adjusted. The χ^2 goodness of fit test is a widely usable test of conformity of data to a hypothesis, which is sensitive to a broad class of deviations from the hypothesis.

EXAMPLE. Suppose we make a backcross $Aa \times aa$ and find in 256 progeny, 144 *Aa*'s and 112 *aa*'s. Do these results contradict the hypothesis that the true proportions are one-half?

$$\chi^2 \text{ unadjusted} = \frac{(144 - 128)^2}{256 \cdot \frac{1}{2} \cdot \frac{1}{2}} = \frac{16^2}{64} = 4$$

$$\chi^2 \text{ adjusted} \quad = \frac{(15.5)^2}{64} = \frac{240.25}{64} = 3.75$$

The χ^2 adjusted has a significance level between 0.10 and 0.05, so that, if we were using a 5 per cent test, we would accept the hypothesis that the data conform to expectation. It may be noted that frequently the adjustment to χ^2 will have little effect on the significance level of the results, but, if we desire to use a strict 5 per cent test and the χ^2 unadjusted gives a value near 5 per cent, we should make the adjustment. It should be noted that the unadjusted χ^2 attributes too much significance to the deviations from expectation.

The unadjusted value to be calculated as χ^2 can be interpreted as the ratio of the square of a deviate to its variance. It has also another property which brings to light the general test of goodness of fit. Consider the quantity

$$\sum \frac{(O - E)^2}{E}$$

where E is the expected number in a class, O is the observed number, and the summation is over all the mutually exclusive classes in which the totality of observations has been divided. In the case of testing a simple segregation ratio, this reduces to

$$\frac{(r - nP)^2}{nP} + \frac{[(n - r) - nQ]^2}{nQ}$$

and, since $n - r - nQ = n - r - n + nP$, this equals

$$(r - nP)^2 \left(\frac{1}{nP} + \frac{1}{nQ} \right)$$

$$= (r - nP)^2 \left(\frac{Q + P}{nPQ} \right) = \frac{(r - nP)^2}{nPQ}$$

Thus the normal deviate test given first is also given by the more general formula which is called the χ^2 goodness of fit criterion. The adjusted χ^2 goodness of fit in the case of two classes is obtained by reducing the absolute magnitude of $(O - E)$ by $\frac{1}{2}$.

It should be noted that we developed the χ^2 goodness of fit test from the test of a binomial proportion. In some cases we can make either a χ^2 test or a binomial test, and there is little basis for choosing between them. Either one correctly applied will be generally acceptable.

In the general case of testing a segregation which should be in the ratio m to unity, i.e., m in class 1 to one in class 2 if a_1 and a_2 are observed, we find

$$\chi^2 = \frac{\left(a_1 - \dfrac{m}{m+1}\,n\right)^2}{\dfrac{m}{m+1}\,n} + \frac{\left(a_2 - \dfrac{n}{m+1}\right)^2}{\dfrac{n}{m+1}}$$

$$= \frac{\left(a_1 - \dfrac{mn}{m+1}\right)^2}{\dfrac{mn}{(m+1)^2}} = \frac{[(m+1)a_1 - m(a_1 + a_2)]^2}{mn}, \quad \text{since} \quad a_1 + a_2 = n$$

$$= \frac{(a_1 - ma_2)^2}{mn}$$

So, if we are testing a 3:1 ratio, we calculate

$$\chi^2 = \frac{(a_1 - 3a_2)^2}{3n}$$

EXAMPLE. *Testing a 1:1 Ratio.* The following numbers of maroon (ma) and wild type (+) were obtained in a backcross trial by Bridges and Morgan (1923):

+	ma	Total
389	364	753

Here χ^2 for testing a 1:1 ratio is

$$\frac{(389 - 364)^2}{753} = \frac{625}{753} = 0.83$$

This has one degree of freedom, and the probability of getting a value as large or larger is between 0.5 and 0.3; so the fit is satisfactory.

Testing a 3:1 Ratio. The following numbers of vestigial (vg) and wild type (+) were obtained in an F_2 by Bridges and Morgan (1923):

vg	+	Total
118	347	465

Here χ^2 for testing a $3:1$ ratio is

$$\frac{(347 - 354)^2}{3 \times 465} = \frac{49}{3 \times 465} = 0.04$$

This has one degree of freedom, and the probability of getting a value as large or larger is between 0.8 and 0.9; so the fit is satisfactory.

We have now dealt with the case of testing a single two-class segregation situation and shall now turn to the comparison of several two-class segregations.

7.6 THE AGREEMENT OF INDEPENDENT SEGREGATION RATIOS

Frequently independent estimates of segregation ratios will be obtained from different experiments to provide confirmatory evidence, either of the agreement of a genetic situation with genetic expectation or to establish that the lack of agreement with expectation is consistent over repetitions of the experiment. Thus for example, a theoretical genetic expectation may be disturbed by differences in viability between the segregating classes. In fact, when segregation ratios do not agree with genetic expectation, there are several possible explanations:

1. The genetic model is wrong: for example instead of a $3:1$ expectation from a one-locus model, the expectation is $13:3$ from a two-locus model in which epistacy is occurring, or there is a mutation effect.

2. The viability is not constant over the segregating classes.

3. The experimenter does not have a random sample of the whole population which is to be partitioned into the classes. For example, one genotype may be easier than others for the experimenter to discover and include in his enumeration.

4. There is incorrect classification of the numbers of the population. An example of this is as follows. Rust resistance in oats is not a character which is visible to the naked eye, and has to be tested by inoculation with rust spores. Incomplete viability of the spores will result in some susceptible plants or seeds being classified as resistant. In this case classification of resistants as susceptible is not possible. In general, errors of classification will disturb segregating ratios in a way which is impossible to disentangle without prior information. If, for example, it is known from prior evidence that individuals of class A have a probability of p_{AA} of being classed as A individuals and a probability of p_{AB} ($= 1 - p_{AA}$) of being classed as B individuals, and that individuals of class B have a probability p_{BA} of being classed as A individuals and of p_{BB} of being

classed as B individuals, then the observed frequencies corresponding to true frequencies of A and B of p and q $(= 1 - p)$, respectively, will be

$$p^{\star} = pP_{AA} + qP_{BA} \text{ of } A \text{ individuals}$$

and

$$q^{\star} = pP_{AB} + qP_{BB} \text{ of } B \text{ individuals}$$

It is then easy to estimate p and q if the P_{AA}, etc. are known. The above list of explanations is probably complete in that any other source of disturbance can be classified under one of the four headings.

In any case, when a segregation ratio different from genetic expectation is found, this ratio should be checked by repeating the experiment. Here we shall consider the comparison of independent estimates of segregation ratios. (It should be noted that the case when a second estimate is obtained because the first estimate is odd does not constitute a case of *independent* estimates.)

We may suppose that we have r experiments giving the results shown in Table 7.2. The criterion we may use for testing homogeneity of the

TABLE 7.2

Numbers

Experiment	Class 1	Class 2	Total	Proportion $\left(\dfrac{n_{i1}}{N_{i.}} \right)$
1	n_{11}	n_{12}	$N_1.$	p_1
2	n_{21}	n_{22}	$N_2.$	p_2
.	.	.	.	.
.	.	.	.	.
.	.	.	.	.
r	n_{r1}	n_{r2}	$N_r.$	p_r
Total	$N_{.1}$	$N_{.2}$	$N_{..}$	

proportions is the standard one for testing association in a contingency table. In the general contingency table with r rows, s columns, and n_{ij} in the ith row and jth column, lack of association means that the probability of an individual being in row i and in column j is equal to the product of the probabilities of the individual being in row i and the probability of its being in column j. In symbols this means

$$P_{ij} = P_{(r)i}P_{(c)j}$$

and, if this is the case,

$$\frac{P_{ij}}{P_{ij'}} = \frac{P_{(c)j}}{P_{(c)j'}}$$

which is the same for all i, that is, for all rows.   Hence, if there is lack of association in the table, the proportions in the rows are equal.

The general procedure is to calculate the quantity

$$\sum_{\text{all cells}} \frac{(O - E)^2}{E}$$

where O = observed number and E = number expected on the basis of independence; that is,

$$\frac{N_i . N_{.j}}{N_{..}}$$

This quantity is distributed essentially as χ^2 with $(r-1)(s-1)$ degrees of freedom.   In the case of the $n \times 2$ table we may use Brandt and Snedecor's formula: namely,

$$\chi^2 = \frac{\sum_i p_i n_{i1} - \bar{p} N_{.1}}{\bar{p}\bar{q}}$$

where $N_{.1}$ is the total of the first column, p_i is the proportion in the ith row, and $\bar{p}$ is the proportion calculated for the total.

Fisher and Mather [described extensively in Mather (1938)] have developed the use of the "heterogeneity" χ^2, which is an approximation to the association χ^2.   Suppose that in the above situation, that is, r experiments on a segregation ratio, for which genetic expectation gives a ratio of m to 1, we calculate a χ^2 for each experiment and then a χ^2 for the total over the r experiments.   The sum of the individual χ^2 will be distributed again as χ^2 with r degrees of freedom, since there are r individual χ^2 with one degree of freedom each.   The χ^2 with one degree of freedom for the total may be subtracted from the total of the r χ^2's, each with one degree of freedom, and the result will be a quantity which is distributed approximately as χ^2 with $(r-1)$ degrees of freedom.   It is this quantity which Fisher and Mather call the heterogeneity χ^2.

The use of the heterogeneity χ^2 will not in general result in false conclusions.   However, if the total segregation ratio differs markedly from the expected ratio, which was used in calculating each of the above χ^2's, the association χ^2 should be computed and used in place of the heterogeneity χ^2.

EXAMPLE.   Table 7.3 shows backcross results (actually as part of a linkage study) obtained by various workers as given by Emerson, Beadle, and Fraser (1935) for the segregation of brachytic in maize.

TABLE 7.3

Br	br	Total	$p = $ Br/total
203	174	377	0.5385
361	321	682	0.5293
377	327	704	0.5355
669	658	1327	0.5041
892	726	1618	0.5513
1818	1794	3612	0.5033
565	599	1164	0.4854
269	253	522	0.5153
5154	4852	10,006	$\bar{p} = 0.51509$

$$\sum p_i n_{i1} = 0.5385 \times 203 + 0.5293 \times 361 + \text{etc.}$$
$$= 2659.1449$$

$$\bar{p}N_{.1} = 2654.7739$$

$$\bar{p}\bar{q} = 0.24977$$

$$\chi^2 = 17.50 \text{ with 7 degrees of freedom}$$

The probability of getting a value as large or larger is between 0.02 and 0.01. One would tend to conclude that the various ratios are not homogeneous.

7.7 THE GOODNESS OF FIT OF AN OBSERVED SEGREGATION INTO MORE THAN TWO CLASSES

Suppose that more than two classes can be identified and we have a genetic theory for the situation. Can we test for goodness of fit of observations to expectations? For example, an F_2, $Aa \times Aa$, should give

$$\tfrac{1}{4}AA + \tfrac{1}{2}Aa + \tfrac{1}{4}aa$$

The procedure for testing is again to use χ^2,

$$\sum_{\text{classes}} \frac{(O - E)^2}{E}$$

If for instance we observe

AA	Aa	aa
25	45	30

we may compute expected values as 25, 50, 25, respectively, so that

$$\chi^2 = 0 + 5^2/50 + 5^2/25 = \tfrac{1}{2} + 1.0 = 1.50$$

and we should look up the χ^2 distribution with two degrees of freedom. The number of degrees of freedom is in all cases the number of freely adjustable numbers. In the present case the total is fixed so that two frequencies can be varied. Alternatively we have three proportions which must sum to unity, so that two of them are free to vary. In the example quoted there is clearly no evidence for rejecting the hypothesis of consistency with expectation since the observed value of χ^2 would be exceeded in a proportion between 0.3 and 0.5 of trials in sampling from a population given by the expectations.

EXAMPLE. Bridges and Morgan (1923) give the following results for the F_2 of the cross vestigial (vg) $\times$ ebony (e)

	+	vg	e	vge	Total
	268	94	79	24	465

Do these results conform to the expected $9:3:3:1$ ratios? We have the following:

	+	vg	e	vge
Expected values	261.56	87.19	87.19	29.06
Observed − expected	6.44	6.81	−8.19	−5.06
$\dfrac{(O-E)^2}{E}$	0.16	0.53	0.77	0.88

$$\sum \frac{(O-E)^2}{E} = 2.34$$

The probability that χ^2 with three degrees of freedom is equal to or exceeds 2.34 is between 0.5 and 0.3; so the fit is satisfactory.

The extension of the use of χ^2 to test the equality of several segregations into more than two classes is illustrated in the following example.

EXAMPLE. Bridges and Morgan (1923) give the following results for the backcross of progeny of arc maroon (a ma) $\times$ wild type (+) with the arc maroon males:

	a ma	+	a	ma
Trial 1	98	131	94	108
Trial 2	85	81	83	73
Total	183	212	177	181

Do the trials agree on the segregation ratios? Note that we do not specify here what these should be.

The computations are shown in Table 7.4, O denoting the observed values and E the expected values.

TABLE 7.4

O	98	131	94	108	431
E	104.7	121.3	101.3	103.6	
$O-E$	−6.7	9.7	−7.3	4.4	
$(O-E)^2/E$	0.43	0.78	0.53	0.19	
O	85	81	83	73	322
E	78.3	90.7	75.7	77.4	
$O-E$	6.7	−9.7	7.3	−4.4	
$(O-E)^2/E$	0.57	1.04	0.70	0.25	
Total	183	212	177	181	753

$\chi^2 = 4.49$ with three degrees of freedom. The probability of a larger value is between 0.3 and 0.2; so the agreement of the two sets of data is satisfactory.

7.8 TESTS INVOLVING VERY SMALL GENETIC RATIOS

Frequently, particularly in radiation work, one is concerned with testing and comparing very small rates or proportions. For example, prior information may suggest a mutation rate of 1 in 1000, and we observe say 20 mutants in a stock of 10,000. Can we state that the observations are consistent with the prior information?

Tests in situations such as this are facilitated by the use of a table constructed by W. L. Stevens (1942) and given in an extended form by Fisher and Yates (1948). The structure of this table is as follows. Suppose an event is observed to occur a times out of N. Then a lower limit π_1 is calculated such that, if the true probability were π_1, the probability of a number of successes out of N equal to or greater than a is P. Similarly an upper limit π_2 is calculated such that, if the probability of a success were π_2, the probability of observing a or less successes in N trials is P. The numbers actually given in Fisher and Yates's table are $\pi_1 N$ and $\pi_2 N$, for values of P equal to 0.1, 0.025, and 0.005. If the expected number is large or the probability of a success is approximately halfway between 0 and 1, we can use the formulas

$$a - t_\infty \sqrt{Npq} \quad \text{and} \quad a + t_\infty \sqrt{Npq}$$

where t_∞ is the normal deviate corresponding to the appropriate P in the lower tail or in the upper tail, and p equals a/N. The table gives adjustments to these limits with instructions for interpolation. Thus in the example of 20 out of 10,000, we find that, if the true frequency is about 11.4 in 10,000, the probability of observing 20 or more in a sample of 10,000 is about 2.5 per cent.   Hence we would have to conclude that the observed rate is not in conformity with our prior information.

The reader should consult Stevens's paper for the case of comparison of mutation rates, or other observed small frequencies.

7.9 THE DETECTION OF LINKAGE

We now turn to the situation where more than one attribute of an individual is observed.   For example, we may have the four classes given in the following 2×2 table:

	B	b
A	n_{11}	n_{12}
a	n_{21}	n_{22}

where the n_{ij} denote the observed frequencies in the cells.   We ask if the occurrence of A is associated with the occurrence of B.   This is the situation with linkage.   If we cross the individual AB/ab with an individual which is ab/ab, the progeny AB/ab and ab/ab contain parental gametes, while progeny Ab/ab and aB/ab are formed from recombinations among the gametes of the double heterozygote.   If the loci are segregating independently, the proportion in each cell will be $\frac{1}{4}$ and if the proportion of recombinants is r, the proportions are

$$\begin{array}{cccc} AB & Ab & aB & ab \\ \frac{1}{2}(1-r) & \frac{1}{2}r & \frac{1}{2}r & \frac{1}{2}(1-r) \end{array}$$

Regardless of the value of r, the proportion of individuals carrying A is $\frac{1}{2}$ and the proportion carrying B is $\frac{1}{2}$.   These values can be disturbed only by causes such as those mentioned earlier for single segregation ratios.   Independence of assortment corresponds to $r = \frac{1}{2}$, and complete linkage to $r = 0$.

If we obtain n_1, n_2, n_3, and n_4, respectively, of the four possibilities, we may make a general test of goodness of fit to the genetic hypothesis of independent assortment by calculating

$$\sum \frac{(n_i - n/4)^2}{n/4} = \sum \frac{(4n_i - n)^2}{4n}$$

where $n = n_1 + n_2 + n_3 + n_4$.   This quantity will, if the hypotheses are correct, be distributed approximately as χ^2 with three degrees of freedom. It is, however, reasonable to expect that there will be tests for the goodness of fit for the segregation at the A locus, at the B locus, and for independence.

Such tests can be obtained by utilizing the properties of the multinomial distribution. Let us suppose for generality that there are s classes with probabilities under the genetic hypothesis being tested of P_i for the ith class. Suppose also that n_i have been observed in the ith class, with $\sum n_i$ equal to n the total size of sample.

Consider two linear functions of the observed frequencies

$$F = \sum \lambda_i n_i$$
$$G = \sum \nu_i n_i$$

Since the n_i have the multinomial distribution, we have, from Chapter 1,

$$E(n_i) = nP_i, \qquad V(n_i) = n(P_i - P_i^2)$$
$$\text{Cov}(n_i, n_j) = -nP_iP_j$$

Hence

$$E(F) = n\sum \lambda_i P_i, \qquad E(G) = n\sum \nu_i P_i$$

The variance of F is easily calculated from the formula

$$V\left(\sum_{i=1}^{n} x_i\right) = \sum_{i=1}^{n} V(x_i) + \sum_{\substack{\text{all } i,\, i' \\ i \neq i'}} \text{Cov}(x_i, x_{i'})$$

Hence

$$V(F) = n\left[\sum \lambda_i^2(P_i - P_i^2) - \sum_{i \neq i'} \lambda_i \lambda_{i'} P_i P_{i'}\right]$$
$$= n[\sum \lambda_i^2 P_i - (\sum \lambda_i P_i)^2]$$

Similarly

$$V(G) = n[\sum \nu_i^2 P_i - (\sum \nu_i P_i)^2]$$

Also, since

$$\text{Cov}\left(\sum \lambda_i n_i, \sum \nu_i n_i\right) = \sum_i \lambda_i \nu_i V(n_i) + \sum_{i \neq i'} \lambda_i \nu_{i'} \text{Cov}(n_i n_{i'})$$

we have

$$\text{Cov}(F, G) = n\left[\sum_i \lambda_i \nu_i P_i - (\sum \lambda_i P_i)(\sum \nu_i P_i)\right]$$

Now suppose that the λ_i's and ν_i's are chosen so that

(1) $$\sum \lambda_i P_i = 0$$
(2) $$\sum \nu_i P_i = 0$$
(3) $$\sum \lambda_i \nu_i P_i = 0$$

Then we have

$$E(F) = 0, \qquad V(F) = E(F^2) = n\sum \lambda_i^2 P_i$$
$$E(G) = 0, \qquad V(G) = E(G^2) = n\sum \nu_i^2 P_i$$

and $\text{Cov}(F, G) = 0$.

It is intuitively reasonable and can be proved that, as n gets large, F and G each tend to be normally distributed around means of zero with the stated variances and are uncorrelated. Hence $F^2/V(F)$ and $G^2/V(G)$ tend to be distributed independently each as χ^2 with one degree of freedom.

Now we consider the particular case of testing for linkage with the progeny of a double heterozygote mated to the double recessive. In this case i runs from 1 to 4, and each P_i is equal to $\frac{1}{4}$. We can now find the coefficients like the λ's and ν's above. In fact, the equations to be satisfied are

$$\sum \lambda_i = 0$$
$$\sum \nu_i = 0$$
$$\sum \lambda_i \nu_i = 0$$

The quantities F, G are said to be orthogonal functions of the frequencies, and it is a mathematical fact that there are $(s-1)$ such functions with s classes, which can be chosen partly at will. It is natural to set them up as follows, where ρ is used for the third set

	AB	Ab	aB	ab
λ or F	1	1	−1	−1
ν or G	1	−1	1	−1
ρ or H	1	−1	−1	1

Clearly F measures the extent to which A and a occur equally frequently, G the extent to which B and b are segregating equally frequently, while H, which is determined uniquely apart from a constant multiplier once F and G are specified, measures the extent to which there is linkage. Hence we have the partition of χ^2:

		d.f.
$A\nu a$	$\dfrac{(n_1+n_2-n_3-n_4)^2}{n}$	1
$B\nu b$	$\dfrac{(n_1-n_2+n_3-n_4)^2}{n}$	1
Linkage	$\dfrac{(n_1-n_2-n_3+n_4)^2}{n}$	1
Total		3

EXAMPLE. Consider the results given earlier for the arc maroon genes. They are of the form

ab	AB	aB	Ab
183	212	177	181

What is the partition of χ^2 to test for $1:1$ ratios and linkage? Here the partition of χ^2 is as follows:

		χ^2	
Ava	$\dfrac{(393-360)^2}{753}$	1.45	
Bvb	$\dfrac{(389-364)^2}{753}$	0.83	Each with 1 d.f.
Linkage	$\dfrac{(395-358)^2}{753}$	1.81	
Total		4.09	

The 10 per cent and 5 per cent of the χ^2 distribution with one degree of freedom are 2.706 and 3.841; so the hypothesis of equal independent segregation gives a satisfactory fit to all three aspects of the observed segregation.

The partitioning of χ^2 is not unique, but is made with a view to testing different aspects of the complete genetic hypothesis. In the above case the subdivision is entirely reasonable. In other situations, we might see the desirability of more than one breakdown. It should be realized that the different χ^2's given with one breakdown are essentially independent, while χ^2 with one degree of freedom (or more) obtained from different partitions of the same total χ^2 may not be uncorrelated and will therefore be certainly dependent. In such a case, the tests of significance are correlated, so that the evidence provided by them cannot be regarded as independent in the colloquial sense of the word.

A simple example of partition of χ^2 is the following. Suppose we observe F_2 progeny expecting

AA	Aa	aa
$\dfrac{n}{4}$	$\dfrac{n}{2}$	$\dfrac{n}{4}$

and finding n_1, n_2, and n_3, respectively.

The χ^2 for goodness of fit has two degrees of freedom which we might partition as follows:

			d.f.
A:	Equality of homozygotes	$2\dfrac{(n_1-n_3)^2}{n}$	1
B:	Equality of homozygotes with heterozygotes	$\dfrac{(n_1+n_3-n_2)^2}{n}$	1
	Total		2

Whether such a subdivision is of interest depends on the particular situation and the geneticist's ideas about possible deviations from expectation.

A slightly more complex case of the partition of χ^2 occurs with the mating involving three loci, say $\dfrac{ABC}{abc} \times \dfrac{abc}{abc}$. The linear functions of the frequencies which may be used are shown in Table 7.5. The particular

TABLE 7.5

	ABC	ABc	AbC	Abc	aBC	aBc	abC	abc
(1)	1	1	1	1	−1	−1	−1	−1
(2)	1	1	−1	−1	1	1	−1	−1
(3)	1	1	−1	−1	−1	−1	1	1
(4)	1	−1	1	−1	1	−1	1	−1
(5)	1	−1	1	−1	−1	1	−1	1
(6)	1	−1	−1	1	1	−1	−1	1
(7)	1	−1	−1	1	−1	1	1	−1

deviations from expectation which these linear functions test is quite obvious. In each case χ^2 with 1 d.f. is the square of the linear function of the frequencies divided by n. It is left to the reader to examine just what facet of the situation each χ^2 with one degree of freedom examines.

REFERENCES

Bridges, C. G., and T. H. Morgan. 1923. *The third-chromosome group of mutant characters of Drosophila melanogaster*. Carnegie Institution of Washington.

Emerson, R. A., G. W. Beadle and A. C. Fraser. 1935. A summary of linkage studies in maize. *Mem. Cornell Univ. agric. Exp. Sta.*, **180**.

Fisher, R. A., and F. Yates. 1948. *Statistical tables for biological, agricultural and medical research*. Oliver and Boyd, Edinburgh. 3rd edition.

Mather, K. 1938. *The measurement of linkage in heredity*. Methuen, London. John Wiley & Sons, New York.

Stevens, W. L. 1942. The accuracy of mutation rates. *J. Genet.*, **43**, 301–307.

FURTHER READING

Bailey, N. J. T. 1950. The influence of partial manifestation on the detection of linkage. *Heredity*, **4**, 327–336.

Cotterman, C. W. 1937. Indication of unit factor inheritance in data comprising but a single generation. *Ohio J. Sci.*, **37**, 127–140.

Fisher, R. A. 1951. A combinatorial formulation of multiple linkage tests. *Nature*, **167**, 520.

Fisher, R. A., and K. Mather. 1936. A linkage test with mice. *Ann. Eugen. Lond.*, **7**, 265–280.

Smith, H. Fairfield. 1938. The test of significance for Mendelian ratios when classification is uncertain. *Ann. Eugen. Lond.*, **8**, 94–95.

PROBLEMS

1. We obtain 60 *Aa* and 40 *aa* progeny from a mating *Aa* × *aa*. What is the strength of the evidence that the recessive is less viable than the heterozygote?

2. Suppose we are testing the hypothesis that a proportion is $\frac{1}{2}$ against the alternatives that it is $\frac{3}{4}$. Tabulate the probabilities of concluding that the proportion is $\frac{3}{4}$ on the basis of a 5 per cent test on 20, 30, 50, 100 trials. Do the same for a 10 per cent test. What is the moral of the results?

3. Suppose we are dealing with a completely dominant gene *A* and its allelomorph *a* and can identify the recessive. Our problem is to determine if an individual is *AA* or *Aa*, and we self and examine the progeny for recessives. How many progeny should we have to encounter a probability of 1 in 1000 of classifying an *Aa* individual as *AA*?

4. Suppose we wish to distinguish between *AA* and *Aa* sires and the genotype *aa* is lethal. We have *Aa* dams for test purposes. How many progeny should we obtain from each sire, and what would be the rule of classification to ensure approximate probabilities of 10 per cent of making either of the two possible errors?

5. Examine the segregation 87 *A*'s and 70 not-*A*'s for agreement with a 9:7 ratio.

6. The following results are given in the summary of Emerson et al. (1935) for the genes BrP in 3 backcross tests:

BrP	Brp	brP	brp	
57	77	112	64	(due to Beadle)
51	81	74	46	(due to Burnham)
70	71	76	44	(due to Emerson)

Do these three tests agree with each other?

7. From question 6 we have

Br	br
134	176
132	120
141	120

Apply Brandt and Snedecor's procedure to test for homogeneity of these segregations.

8. Bridges and Morgan (1923) give the following segregations:

	ama	+	a	ma
	80	121	92	145
	61	103	85	95
	96	89	66	77
Total	237	313	243	317

Are the three tests consistent with each other?

9. With the data of question 8, obtain a heterogeneity χ^2 by evaluating χ^2 for each line and the χ^2 for the total and taking the difference, under the hypothesis

that the four classes are equally frequent. Obtain the level of significance of the heterogeneity χ^2. Is this procedure questionable?

10. Emerson et al (1935) give the following data for examining the linkage of Br and P by the backcross method:

BrP	Brp	brP	brp
508	432	397	518

Make a partition of χ^2 into 3 one-degree-of-freedom parts.

CHAPTER 8

The Estimation of Genetic Parameters*

8.1 INTRODUCTION

We have considered the calculation of genetic expectations in terms of the probabilities of certain elementary events and the agreement of observations with expectations when the basic probabilities are postulated from genetic theory. We now turn to the problems of estimation of parameters, for instance, of segregation ratios, of gene frequencies, of recombination values, and so on. We shall then turn to the examination of goodness of fit with the estimated parameters and to the comparison of sets of data.

It is first necessary to state more precisely what we mean by the word "estimate." What do we mean by "estimate a parameter"? We are given for example, certain observations, say the frequencies n_i, $i = 1, 2, \cdots, s$, in s classes. The observed frequencies have come from a certain distribution which is specified by one or more unknown fixed quantities or parameters. We want to determine appropriate numerical values for these parameters. Again, suppose we observe n_1 successes in n binomial trials. The probability of this result before it happened is

$$\frac{n!}{n_1!\,(n - n_1)!}\, P^{n_1}(1 - P)^{n - n_1}$$

Our job now is to state from the observation of n_1 successes, what we think P is. We can ignore the observations completely and say that P is what our a priori knowledge told us, or, better, we may take some number which depends on the observations, i.e., which depends on n_1. The problem of estimation is then: What function of the observations shall we take to be the value of the parameter P? A fairly obvious procedure in the present instance is to estimate the parameter P by the observed proportion, n_1/n. We would write this as $\hat{P} = n_1/n$, which is read as P "hat" equals n_1/n.

Another instance which perhaps illustrates the problem of estimation

* This chapter requires elementary knowledge of calculus.

more completely is the following connected with the O, A, B blood group system. We have already seen that the probabilities, or relative proportions are as given in Table 8.1, where r, p, q are the gene frequencies for O, A, and B and random mating is assumed.

TABLE 8.1

Type	Probability	Observed Number	Observed Proportion
O	r^2	n_1	n_1/n
A	p^2+2pr	n_2	n_2/n
B	q^2+2qr	n_3	n_3/n
AB	$2pq$	n_4	n_4/n
Total	1	n	1

Here a fairly obvious procedure is to estimate r by taking

$$\hat{r} = \left(\frac{n_1}{n}\right)^{1/2}$$

Then we could take for $\hat{p}$ a solution to the quadratic in p

$$p^2 + 2p\hat{r} - \frac{n_2}{n} = 0$$

doing likewise for q. Alternatively we can follow Bernstein's procedure and note that

$$E\left(\frac{n_1 + n_2}{n}\right) = (p + r)^2$$

so that $q = 1 - (p + r)$ can be estimated by

$$\hat{q} = 1 - \left(\frac{n_1 + n_2}{n}\right)^{1/2}$$

Similarly

$$\hat{p} = 1 - \left(\frac{n_1 + n_3}{n}\right)^{1/2}$$

In this instance we may note that in fact

$$p + q + r = 1$$

but it will not happen in general that

$$\hat{p} + \hat{q} + \hat{r} = 1$$

which is a result not altogether desirable.

In fact for most situations, the number of possible estimating functions, or estimators as they are usually called, is unlimited, and the ingenious mind can devise a considerable number. The situation would be unfortunate if we had no rationale for choosing between various methods of estimation. One of the really great contributions of R. A. Fisher to the general problem of statistical inference was his consideration of this particular problem. The criteria by which Fisher felt that estimators should be valued are:

1. Consistency, which is the property that with increasing size of sample the estimator tends to give the true value.*

2. Unbiasedness, the property that the average value of the estimate over all samples to which the estimator would be applied, is equal to the true value.

3. Sufficiency, the property that the estimator utilizes all the information that the sample contains with respect to the parameter (in other words, the sample may be replaced by the sufficient estimator with no loss of knowledge on the value of the parameter).

4. Efficiency, the magnitude of the variance of the estimates given by the estimator in repeated samples, relative to some standard.

It is perhaps of value here to expand a little on these properties. The property of consistency amounts essentially to a requirement that the spread of the estimates for different samples of the same size around the true value tends to zero as the size of sample increases. The idea is that, if an estimator will not give the true answer when faced with an indefinitely large sample, it is unlikely to be reliable when applied to a sample of ordinary size.

The property of unbiasedness is of importance from the point of view of the growth of a body of knowledge, for, if the average of a large number of estimates for a particular situation does not tend to be near the true value, the whole of a branch of study may be led along an incorrect path.

The third property, sufficiency, is extremely reasonable. Our aim is always to concentrate data into as few numbers or statistics as possible, not only for ease of representation and reporting, but also for comparison with other work. If the criterion of sufficiency has been satisfied, we may replace the whole of the data by the sufficient statistic without any loss as far as the parameter is concerned. It may be noted, since otherwise confusion may result, that the characteristic which occurs is that of a sufficient statistic, that is, of a function of the observations which has the

* See, however, Fisher's *Statistical methods and scientific inference* for discussion of this concept.

property of sufficiency. The principle of sufficiency does not state what function of the sufficient statistic should be used as the estimator.

Finally the criterion of efficiency may be justified to a large extent by the following considerations. Suppose we have two estimators T_1 and T_2 for a parameter; for example, if we wish to estimate the mean of a normal population we may take the sample mean T_1 or the sample median T_2. With repeated samples both T_1 and T_2 will follow their appropriate distribution and we might have a picture like Figure 8.1. In

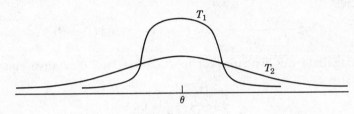

FIGURE 8.1

both cases we see that the distribution is clustered equally around θ but the distribution of T_1 is clustered more closely around θ than is the distribution of T_2. The simplest measure of the clustering of a distribution around its central point is the variance, although it should be pointed out that this is not always true (for example, a distribution may have infinite variance). The measure of efficiency of T_1 relative to T_2 is then

$$\frac{V(T_2)}{V(T_1)}$$

If $V(T_2) > V(T_1)$, this ratio will be greater than unity so that T_1 will be more efficient than T_2.

We shall now describe very briefly the more common methods of estimation.

8.2 THE METHOD OF MAXIMUM LIKELIHOOD

First let us suppose that we have discrete distributions such as the binomial or multinomial. We have a sample from a distribution and can write down the probability of any sample which we can represent as

$$P(\text{sample}, \theta_1, \theta_2, \cdots)$$

where θ_1, θ_2, $\cdots$ are the parameters. The likelihood is obtained by inserting into the probability of the sample the particular sample values obtained and regarding it as a function of θ_1, θ_2, $\cdots$. The values for

θ_1, θ_2, $\cdots$ which maximize the likelihood are taken to be the estimates and are known as the maximum-likelihood estimates.

EXAMPLE. With r successes in n binomial trials the probability is

$$\frac{n!}{r!\,(n-r)!}\,P^r(1-P)^{n-r}$$

When the particular observed r is inserted, this expression is the likelihood. To maximize it, we may first take logarithms since, if we maximize the logarithm of a quantity, we maximize the quantity itself. So we have to maximize

$$\log\frac{n!}{r!\,(n-r)!} + r\log P + (n-r)\log(1-P)$$

We differentiate this with respect to P and set the derivative equal to zero: This gives

$$\frac{r}{\hat{P}} - \frac{n-r}{1-\hat{P}} = 0$$

or

$$\frac{r}{\hat{P}} = \frac{n-r}{1-\hat{P}} = \frac{n}{1}$$

since, if $a/b = c/d$, then $a/b = (a+c)/(b+d)$; so

$$\hat{P} = \frac{r}{n}$$

The case of continuous distributions is essentially the same as the case of discrete distributions, except that the likelihood is the probability density of the sample interpreted as a function of the parameters.

8.3 THE METHOD OF MOMENTS

We may calculate the moments of the distribution from which the sample is assumed to come, in terms of the parameters. We can also compute the moments of the sample, and can then equate observed moments to true moments. The solution of the resulting equations gives the method of moments estimates. We shall need to compute and calculate as many moments as there are parameters to be estimated. In the case of the binomial distribution the observed number of successes is r, the expected number is nP, and so

$$\hat{P} = \frac{r}{n}$$

is the method of moments estimate of P.

8.4 MINIMUM χ^2

We have in previous chapters covered the calculation of χ^2 for agreement of observations with expectation. The χ^2 will be a function of the parameters, and the method of minimum χ^2 estimates are obtained by minimizing χ^2 with respect to the parameters. In the binomial case

$$\chi^2 = \frac{(r - nP)^2}{nPQ}$$

which is clearly minimized if $P = r/n$, so that we get $\hat{P} = r/n$ as the minimum χ^2 estimate also.

An example which does not lead to the same estimate as with maximum likelihood is the following. Suppose we have a population

$$
\begin{array}{ccc}
AA & Aa & aa \\
p^2 & 2p(1-p) & (1-p)^2
\end{array}
$$

and observe n_1, n_2, n_3, respectively, out of n. The χ^2 goodness of fit criterion is

$$\frac{(n_1 - np^2)^2}{np^2} + \frac{[n_2 - 2np(1 - p)]^2}{2np(1 - p)} + \frac{[n_3 - n(1 - p)^2]^2}{n(1 - p)^2}$$

It is left as an exercise to the reader to find the value for p which minimizes this expression. It will be the minimum χ^2 estimate of p. A modification of this method uses observed numbers in the denominators.

8.5 THE METHOD OF LEAST SQUARES

This method has perhaps more primitive appeal than any other method and was in fact the first general method of estimation that was proposed. Suppose we have observations $x_1, x_2, \cdots, x_n$; and suppose that we know the expectation of each observation, so that

$$x_i = E(x_i) + e_i$$

where $E(x_i)$ is the expectation and e_i is the deviation of the observed value from its expectation. The expectation of x_i will depend on the parameters, and to get the least-squares estimates we minimize the sum of squares of the deviations: that is, we minimize

$$\sum_{\text{all observations}} [x_i - E(x_i)]^2$$

with respect to the parameters. The simplest situation is when

$$x_i = \mu + e_i$$

so that each observation is an estimate of the same unknown quantity μ.

We minimize

$$\sum(x_i - \mu)^2$$

which is equal to

$$\sum(x_i - \bar{x})^2 + n(\bar{x} - \mu)^2$$

where

$$\bar{x} = \frac{\sum x_i}{n}$$

It is clear that the minimum occurs when $\mu = \bar{x}$ so that $\hat{\mu}$ by least squares equals $\bar{x}$, the average of the observations. Somewhat more is known about least-squares estimates than the estimates provided by other methods. If for instance $E(x_i)$ is a known linear function of some parameters $\theta_1, \theta_2, \cdots$, then the least-squares estimates are unbiased. If the deviations are uncorrelated and have the same variance, the estimates given by least squares are best in a certain valuable sense. For it will then happen that the estimates are linear functions of the observations, and it can be shown that the least squares estimates have minimum variance with respect to all such linear unbiased functions. Least squares may be modified if the relative variances are known: If for example, the variance of x_i is proportional to k_i, where k_i is known, then the estimates should be obtained by minimizing

$$\sum \left\{ \frac{1}{\sqrt{k_i}} [x_i - E(x_i)] \right\}^2 = \sum \frac{1}{k_i} [x_i - E(x_i)]^2$$

Also it may be modified if the variances and covariances are known except for a multiplicative constant.

8.6 GENERAL NOTES ON METHODS

We have now described the common methods of estimation and it behooves us to consider which of these methods should be used. The following points may be made:

1. In general all the methods give consistent estimates although there are freakish situations for which this does not happen.

2. As we have noted, least squares gives unbiased estimates in a certain class of situations. Likewise for each of the methods there are situations for which the estimates are unbiased. In general, however, the degree of bias given by any of the methods is very difficult to establish. The root of the trouble is the fact that an explicit expression for the estimate may not exist, and, even if such an expression exists, the derivation of its distribution may not have been accomplished.

3. Least squares and minimum χ^2 can be applied whenever the expectation of the observations in terms of the parameters is known, and it is rare that the problem of parameter estimation arises unless this is the case.

4. Maximum likelihood requires a complete specification of the distribution of the observations.

5. Under some circumstances least squares and maximum likelihood give the same estimates.

6. If in fact the form of the distribution of the observations is known, it is intuitively reasonable that a method of estimation which does not utilize this information will not do as well as one which does, other things being equal. This point favors maximum likelihood.

7. The method of moments gives equations for estimation which are unbiased, although the resulting estimates are not necessarily unbiased. (Whether this is desirable and advantageous is an open question.)

8. The method of maximum likelihood appears to have the edge in general because (*a*) it does lead to sufficient estimators if they exist, (*b*) in a class of situations it gives estimates with the minimum possible variance, (*c*) in virtually all cases the method of maximum likelihood leads to estimates which are asymptotically efficient. This property has been improperly described in many places, and, though it is essentially a mathematical property, we shall attempt a non-mathematical description. Consider the use of maximum-likelihood estimates with samples of varying sizes, and suppose for each sample size we obtain the variance of the maximum-likelihood estimate. We may consider the relation of this variance to sample size, and we shall find in many situations that the variance is approximately representable by K/n, when n is indefinitely large. The term asymptotically efficient means that no other method of estimation can lead to a relationship variance $= L/n$, for which L is less than K. The extent to which it is correct to assume from these considerations that maximum likelihood is the best method of estimation in general is unknown at the present time. However, for the general situation no method of estimation has been found to have properties which make it generally preferable to maximum likelihood.

9. It is for these reasons that the method of maximum likelihood is preferred to all other methods in genetic situations where it can be applied, unless it is unfeasible practically as may happen in some cases with human data, or unless some other method can be shown to be better.

8.7 OTHER ASPECTS OF MAXIMUM LIKELIHOOD

An important aspect of any method of estimation is that it should lead not only to an estimate but also a measure of the reliability of the estimate.

The method of maximum likelihood to a better degree than any other method has this property so to speak "built in" as a feature.

It was demonstrated by Fisher that the asymptotic variance of the maximum-likelihood estimate of a parameter θ is given by

$$- \frac{1}{E\left(\dfrac{\partial^2}{\partial \theta^2} \log L\right)}$$

Here L is the likelihood, $(\partial^2/\partial \theta^2)(\log L)$ denotes the second partial derivative of the logarithm of the likelihood with respect to θ, and E denotes the operation of taking the expected value.

In the case of a simple proportion

$$\log L = \text{constant} + r \log P + (n - r) \log (1 - P)$$

$$\frac{\partial \log L}{\partial P} = \frac{r}{P} - \frac{n - r}{1 - P}$$

$$\frac{\partial^2 \log L}{\partial P^2} = - \frac{r}{P^2} - \frac{(n - r)}{(1 - P)^2}$$

$$E\left(\frac{\partial^2 \log L}{\partial P^2}\right) = - \frac{nP}{P^2} - \frac{n(1 - P)}{(1 - P)^2} = - \left(\frac{n}{P} + \frac{n}{1 - P}\right) = - \frac{n}{P(1 - P)}$$

so variance $(\hat{P}) = $ variance $(r/n) = P(1 - P)/n$.

In general with parameters θ_1, θ_2, $\cdots$, we shall have a matrix

$$- E\left(\frac{\partial^2}{\partial \theta_i\, \partial \theta_j} \log L\right)$$

which must then be inverted. The variance of $\hat{\theta}_i$ is the (ii)th element of the inverse and the covariance of $\hat{\theta}_i$ and $\hat{\theta}_j$ is the (ij)th element of the inverse. The usual procedure is then to regard the interval $\hat{\theta}_i - t\sqrt{V(\hat{\theta}_i)}$ to $\hat{\theta}_i + t\sqrt{V(\hat{\theta}_i)}$, where t is a normal deviate such that there is probability $(1 - \alpha)$ between $-t$ and t, as a $(1 - \alpha)$ 100 per cent interval for the true value.

8.8 AN EXAMPLE OF THE USE OF MAXIMUM LIKELIHOOD

We shall now apply the method of maximum likelihood to a situation which will illustrate the full properties of the method and the procedure which has to be followed generally.

Consider a random mating population with respect to the O, A, B locus, and suppose the gene frequencies are r, p, and q, respectively.

Then the expected and observed frequencies are recorded in the accompanying table. The numbers in the various groups in the sample

Group	Expected Proportion	Observed Number
O	r^2	n_1
A	$p^2 + 2pr$	n_2
B	$q^2 + 2qr$	n_3
AB	$2pq$	n_4
Total	1	n

are determined by the multinomial distribution, so that the probability of observing n_1 O's, n_2 A's, n_3 B's, and n_4 AB's is

$$\frac{n!}{n_1!\, n_2!\, n_3!\, n_4!}\, (r^2)^{n_1}(p^2 + 2pr)^{n_2}(q^2 + 2qr)^{n_3}(2pq)^{n_4}$$

Inserting the particular observed values for n_1 to n_4, we have the likelihood which is to be maximized for variations in p, q, and r subject to $p + q + r = 1$. It is a general rule that the values of p, q, r which will maximize the likelihood will also maximize the logarithm of the likelihood, and so we shall work with the logarithm of the likelihood. We have then

$$\log L = \text{constant} + n_1 \log r^2 + n_2 \log (p^2 + 2pr) \\ + n_3 \log (q^2 + 2qr) + n_4 \log (2pq)$$

where the constant is equal to the logarithm of

$$\frac{n!}{n_1!\, n_2!\, n_3!.n_4!}$$

which is independent of p, q, and r. This may be written as

$$\log L = \text{constant} + 2n_1 \log r + (n_2 + n_4) \log p + (n_3 + n_4) \log q \\ + n_2 \log (p + 2r) + n_3 \log (q + 2r)$$

which is the quantity to be maximized. We may get rid of one of the parameters by using the relation $p + q + r = 1$; so, substituting for r, we have

$$\log L = \text{constant} + 2n_1 \log (1 - p - q) + (n_2 + n_4) \log p \\ + (n_3 + n_4) \log q + n_2 \log (2 - p - 2q) + n_3 \log (2 - 2p - q)$$

A fairly standard way to find the maximum (or minimum) of a function with respect to a parameter is to differentiate it with respect to the parameters and to set the derivatives equal to zero. This is reasonable in that the slope will be zero for most situations at the point where the function is maximized, and the slope is in fact equal to the derivative. So we have to solve the equations

$$\frac{\partial \log L}{\partial p} = 0 \quad \text{or} \quad -\frac{2n_1}{1-p-q} + \frac{n_2+n_4}{p} - \frac{n_2}{2-p-2q} - \frac{2n_3}{2-2p-q} = 0$$

$$\frac{\partial \log L}{\partial q} = 0 \quad \text{or} \quad -\frac{2n_1}{1-p-q} + \frac{n_3+n_4}{q} - \frac{2n_2}{2-p-2q} - \frac{n_3}{2-2p-q} = 0$$

It may not appear to the reader that we have simplified the situation at all, because these two equations involve rather awkward expressions. However, we shall see that the situation may be alleviated somewhat. No explicit expressions for the solutions of these equations is known, and this is more often than not the situation with maximum-likelihood equations.

We now utilize the following facts. A function say $f(x, y)$ can be approximated in the following way:

$$f(x, y) = f(x_0, y_0) + \frac{\partial f}{\partial x}\bigg|_{x_0, y_0} (x - x_0) + \frac{\partial f}{\partial y}\bigg|_{x_0, y_0} (y - y_0)$$

Here $\dfrac{\partial f}{\partial x}\bigg|_{x_0, y_0}$ is the derivative of f with respect to x evaluated at the point x_0, y_0, and $\dfrac{\partial f}{\partial y}\bigg|_{x_0, y_0}$ is the derivative of f with respect to y, evaluated at the point x_0, y_0. In this case we have two functions $\dfrac{\partial \log L}{\partial p}$ and $\dfrac{\partial \log L}{\partial q}$. Using the above relation in turn for each, we have

$$\frac{\partial \log L}{\partial p}\bigg|_{p_1, q_1} = \frac{\partial \log L}{\partial p}\bigg|_{p_0, q_0} + (p_1 - p_0) \frac{\partial^2 \log L}{\partial p^2}\bigg|_{p_0, q_0}$$
$$+ (q_1 - q_0) \frac{\partial^2 \log L}{\partial p\, \partial q}\bigg|_{p_0, q_0}$$

$$\frac{\partial \log L}{\partial q}\bigg|_{p_1, q_1} = \frac{\partial \log L}{\partial q}\bigg|_{p_0, q_0} + (p_1 - p_0) \frac{\partial^2 \log L}{\partial p\, \partial q}\bigg|_{p_0, q_0}$$
$$+ (q_1 - q_0) \frac{\partial^2 \log L}{\partial q^2}\bigg|_{p_0, q_0}$$

Now suppose that p_0, q_0 are approximations to the maximum-likelihood estimates p_1, q_1. We can evaluate the derivatives on the right-hand side of the equations, and we know that the left-hand sides of the equations are to be zero. So, starting from p_0, q_0, we may obtain new approximations to the maximum likelihood solution by solving the following equations in $(p_1 - p_0)$ and $(q_1 - q_0)$:

$$0 = \frac{\partial \log L}{\partial p}\bigg|_{p_0, q_0} + (p_1 - p_0)\frac{\partial^2 \log L}{\partial p^2}\bigg|_{p_0, q_0} + (q_1 - q_0)\frac{\partial^2 \log L}{\partial p\, \partial q}\bigg|_{p_0, q_0}$$

$$0 = \frac{\partial \log L}{\partial q}\bigg|_{p_0, q_0} + (p_1 - p_0)\frac{\partial^2 \log L}{\partial p\, \partial q}\bigg|_{p_0, q_0} + (q_1 - q_0)\frac{\partial^2 \log L}{\partial q^2}\bigg|_{p_0, q_0}$$

Or, as a perhaps more usually recognized form,

$$\frac{\partial^2 \log L}{\partial p^2}\bigg|_{p_0, q_0}(p_1 - p_0) + \frac{\partial^2 \log L}{\partial p\, \partial q}\bigg|_{p_0, q_0}(q_1 - q_0) = -\frac{\partial \log L}{\partial p}\bigg|_{p_0, q_0}$$

and

$$\frac{\partial^2 \log L}{\partial p\, \partial q}\bigg|_{p_0, q_0}(p_1 - p_0) + \frac{\partial^2 \log L}{\partial q^2}\bigg|_{p_0, q_0}(q_1 - q_0) = -\frac{\partial \log L}{\partial q}\bigg|_{p_0, q_0}$$

These equations are of the form

$$s_{11}x + s_{12}y = \delta_1$$
$$s_{12}x + s_{22}y = \delta_2$$

where $s_{11}, s_{12}, s_{22}, \delta_1,$ and δ_2 are known numbers. The solution of these equations is

$$x = \frac{s_{22}}{s_{11}s_{22} - s_{12}{}^2}\delta_1 - \frac{s_{12}}{s_{11}s_{22} - s_{12}{}^2}\delta_2$$

$$y = \frac{-s_{12}}{s_{11}s_{22} - s_{12}{}^2}\delta_1 + \frac{s_{11}}{s_{11}s_{22} - s_{12}{}^2}\delta_2$$

It is a simple matter then to compute x and y, and we have

$$p_1 - p_0 = x$$
$$q_1 - q_0 = y$$

or

$$p_1 = p_0 + x$$
$$q_1 = q_0 + y$$

The values for p_1 and q_1 may be regarded as new approximations to the maximum-likelihood solutions, and we may now repeat the process, using them as p_0, q_0, respectively, and getting new values for p_1 and q_1. Such a process is called an iterative (step by step) process, and each step leads to a new approximation to the solution of the maximum-likelihood equations.

In the present case we have

$$\frac{\partial^2 \log L}{\partial p^2} = -\frac{2n_1}{(1 - p - q)^2} - \frac{n_2 + n_4}{p^2} - \frac{n_2}{(2 - p - 2q)^2} - \frac{4n_3}{(2 - 2p - q)^2}$$

$$\frac{\partial^2 \log L}{\partial p \, \partial q} = -\frac{2n_1}{(1 - p - q)^2} - \frac{2n_2}{(2 - p - 2q)^2} - \frac{2n_3}{(2 - 2p - q)^2}$$

$$\frac{\partial^2 \log L}{\partial q^2} = -\frac{2n_1}{(1 - p - q)^2} - \frac{n_3 + n_4}{q^2} - \frac{4n_2}{(2 - p - 2q)^2} - \frac{n_3}{(2 - 2p - q)^2}$$

Taking the case of data from Taylor and Prior (1938) which consisted of

$$\begin{array}{lll} \text{O} & n_1 = & 202 \\ \text{A} & n_2 = & 179 \\ \text{B} & n_3 = & 35 \\ \text{AB} & n_4 = & 6 \end{array}$$

We may guess

$$p = 1 - \sqrt{\frac{202 + 35}{422}} = 0.25060$$

$$q = 1 - \sqrt{\frac{202 + 179}{422}} = 0.04985$$

so that $r = 0.69955$.

We find

$$\frac{\partial \log L}{\partial p} = 3.89871$$

$$\frac{\partial \log L}{\partial q} = 3.78870$$

$$\frac{\partial^2 \log L}{\partial p^2} = -3903.85009$$

$$\frac{\partial^2 \log L}{\partial p \, \partial q} = -990.43746$$

$$\frac{\partial^2 \log L}{\partial q^2} = -17587.48465$$

so our equations for the adjustments are

$$-3903.85009(p_1 - p_0) - 990.43746(q_1 - q_0) = -3.89871$$
$$-990.43746(p_1 - p_0) - 17587.48465(q_1 - q_0) = -3.78870$$

giving adjustments

$$p_1 - p_0 = 0.00096$$
$$q_1 - q_0 = 0.00016$$

The estimates of p, q, and r are therefore

$$\hat{p} = 0.25156$$
$$\hat{q} = 0.05001$$
$$\hat{r} = 0.69843$$

Actually maximum-likelihood estimates are defined so that $p_1 - p_0$ and $q_1 - q_0$ should be zero. Strictly the iterative process should be continued until this happens, but it is clearly not worth while. In the present case another cycle gave no change with five decimals. Also the variances and covariances of the estimates of p and q are given essentially by the elements of the inverse of the matrix of the expected values of second partial derivatives. In this case the inverse is

$$\begin{pmatrix} \dfrac{s_{22}}{\Delta} & \dfrac{-s_{12}}{\Delta} \\ \dfrac{-s_{12}}{\Delta} & \dfrac{s_{11}}{\Delta} \end{pmatrix}$$

where $\Delta = s_{11}s_{22} - s_{12}^2$.

After a second iteration, it is found that this inverse matrix is

$$\begin{pmatrix} 0.00026024 & -0.00001484 \\ -0.00001484 & 0.00005776 \end{pmatrix}$$

Also $\hat{r} = 1 - \hat{p} - \hat{q}$; so

$$V(\hat{r}) = V(\hat{p}) + V(\hat{q}) + 2\,\text{Cov}\,(\hat{p}\hat{q})$$

In summary then, we have

$$\hat{p} = 0.25156 \pm 0.01613$$
$$\hat{q} = 0.05001 \pm 0.00760$$
$$\hat{r} = 0.69843 \pm 0.01698$$

Notes on Above Procedure

Actually there are various minor modifications of the above procedure which may be used. For instance the expansion is frequently made using $E\left(\dfrac{\partial^2 \log L}{\partial \theta^2}\right)$ instead of $\dfrac{\partial^2 \log L}{\partial \theta^2}$ as given exactly by the guess. (See for example Stevens, 1938.)   These modifications have no effect on the final answer.   There is perhaps some need for agreement by mutual consent on just what exactly the definitive maximum-likelihood solution is, particularly in view of the fact that, since the process of fitting is iterative, the stopping point needs definition.   This is, however, not a major criticism of the procedure.

The procedure of expansion described herein is of broad utility whether the method of fitting be maximum likelihood, least squares, or minimum χ^2, and that is the reason for describing it in the particular chosen way.

8.9 TESTING GOODNESS OF FIT WITH CLASSIFICATION DATA AND ESTIMATED PARAMETERS

The problem of testing of goodness of fit when the parameters have been estimated is relatively simple, and is solved by the use of a χ^2 test. It is a straightforward matter to calculate the expectations from the estimated parameters and hence to calculate χ^2 as

$$\sum_{\text{classes}} \frac{(\text{observed–expected})^2}{\text{expected}}$$

The only question is the number of degrees of freedom to be attached to the computed χ^2.   This question is also easily solved.   In fact

Number of degrees of freedom = number of classes minus unity minus

number of independent parameters fitted

Thus in the case of the O, A, B example, we start off with four classes, subtract unity because the observed total n is used in calculating the expectations, and then subtract two because p and q were estimated while r was given by $1 - \hat{p} - \hat{q}$.   Hence in this case there is just one degree of freedom for the computed χ^2.

8.10 COMBINED ESTIMATION

The utilization of maximum likelihood in cases when we have two or more sets of data, say by different methods, proceeds in the usual way. For example, we may have a recombination value which can be estimated from backcross data we have and from F_2 data in our possession.   The procedure is to write out the likelihood for each set of data, obtain the logarithms, add the logarithms, and we then have the likelihood for the combined data.   We then carry on as if we had only one set of data. An example is given by Mather (1938).

If the question arises as to whether the two sets of data agree on the recombination value, we may

1. Obtain separate estimates and compare them by their standard errors: In fact,

$$V(\hat{p}_1 - \hat{p}_2) = V(\hat{p}_1) + V(\hat{p}_2)$$

and, if $(\hat{p}_1 - \hat{p}_2)$ is greater than $2[V(\hat{p}_1 - \hat{p}_2)]^{1/2}$, we can conclude that the values are different in the two sets of data. This is a rather approximate device, 2 being near 1.96; or

2. We may follow a procedure described by Mather in his book, *The Measurement of Linkage in Heredity* (1938), in which more sensitive or more powerful tests are used.

8.11 SOME GENERAL NOTES ON ESTIMATION OF GENE FREQUENCY

The reader is referred to the excellent paper by Cotterman (1954) for a discussion of statistical methodology for estimating gene frequencies in unselected and selected data.   The example of estimating the frequencies of the O, A, and B genes in the OAB system is presented above to illustrate the general procedure for maximum likelihood estimation.   In this particular case it was shown by Stevens (1938) that the method of Bernstein (1930) is efficient asymptotically.   Bernstein's method is to take the primitive estimates

$$p' = 1 - \left(\frac{n_1 + n_3}{n}\right)^{1/2}$$

$$q' = 1 - \left(\frac{n_1 + n_2}{n}\right)^{1/2}$$

$$r' = \left(\frac{n_1}{n}\right)^{1/2}$$

and, if

$$D = 1 - p' - q' - r'$$

use as estimates

$$\hat{p} = p'\left(1 + \frac{D}{2}\right)$$

$$\hat{q} = q'\left(1 + \frac{D}{2}\right)$$

$$\hat{r} = \left(r' + \frac{D}{2}\right)\left(1 + \frac{D}{2}\right)$$

Note that the sum of these is

$$(p' + q' + r' + \tfrac{1}{2}D)(1 + \tfrac{1}{2}D) = 1 - \tfrac{1}{4}D^2$$

This procedure also has the advantage that the measure of goodness of fit is given by

$$\chi^2 = 2n \left(1 + \frac{\hat{r}}{\hat{p}\hat{q}}\right) D^2$$

with one degree of freedom.

8.12 ESTIMATION WITH RELATED DATA

We now turn to the case of unselected data on a sample of individuals, some of whom are related, and take the case when there is one parameter to be estimated. This is discussed extensively by Fisher (1940) for the case of a recessive gene. The general procedure would be to write out the joint likelihood (L) of the whole sample and then find the solution to the equation

$$\frac{d(\log L)}{d\theta} = 0$$

where θ is the parameter to be estimated. One would inevitably encounter a non-linear equation or equations, and the procedure suggested by Fisher is to assign scores to individuals based on the way they occur in the sample. This is essentially equivalent to solving the likelihood equation, and differs from it only in that the scores of unrelated individuals are forced to be zero or unity, as they would be in a simple enumeration of unrelated individuals. The derivation of scores proceeds in the following way. We have to solve the equation

$$\frac{d(\log L)}{d\theta} = 0$$

and, if the individuals in the population are denoted by $i = 1, 2, \cdots, n$ with true probabilities p_i, the maximum likelihood equation is

$$\sum \frac{d}{d\theta} (\log p_i) = 0$$

where summation extends over all the individuals. Now suppose that we have a guess of θ, say θ_0, perhaps from those individuals in the sample; we have

$$\sum \frac{d}{d\theta} (\log p_i) = \sum \frac{d}{d\theta} (\log p_i)\Big|_{\theta_0} + (\theta - \theta_0) \sum \frac{d^2}{d\theta^2} (\log p_i)\Big|_{\theta_0} + R$$

We want the left-hand side to be zero, and, if we ignore R, we have

$$\hat{\theta} = \theta_0 + \frac{\sum \dfrac{d}{d\theta} (\log p_i)\Big|_{\theta_0}}{-\sum \dfrac{d^2}{d\theta^2} (\log p_i)\Big|_{\theta_0}}$$

with a variance equal essentially to

$$1 \Big/ - \sum \frac{d^2}{d\theta^2} (\log p_i) \Big|_{\theta_0}$$

If now we write w_i' as $-(d^2/d\theta^2)(\log p_i)\big|_{\theta_0}$, the estimate is

$$\hat{\theta} = \frac{\sum \left[w_i' \, \theta_0 + \frac{d}{d\theta} (\log p_i) \Big|_{\theta_0} \right]}{\sum w_i'}$$

The individual term in the numerator is called the score of the ith individual, and the individual term in the denominator the weight contributed by the individual.

The scores given above may be modified by using scores of 0 and 1, and weight $[\theta(1 - \theta)]^{-1}$ for individuals whose probabilities are $(1 - \theta)$ and θ, respectively, which corresponds to an exact likelihood fitting for the section of data involving such individuals. Also we may eliminate the possibility of negative weights by using expected weights w_i in place of w_i' where

$$w_i = \frac{1}{p_i^2} \left(\frac{dp_i}{d\theta} \right)^2$$

The details are given by Fisher (1940). Other procedures which are not necessarily asymptotically efficient are given by Cotterman (1947) and Finney (1948a). It may be mentioned in passing (cf. above) that it is by no means clear why one should choose an estimator on the basis of asymptotic efficiency. Some would, however, take the point of view that one should maximize the likelihood under all circumstances, and this has intuitive appeal to me.

REFERENCES

Bernstein, F. 1930. Fortgesetzte Untersuchungen aus der Theorie der Blutgruppen. *Z. indukt. Abstamm.-u. VererbLehre*, **56**, 233–273.

Bridges, C. G., and T. H. Morgan. 1932. *The third chromosome group of mutant characters of* Drosophila melanogaster. Carnegie Institution of Washington.

Cotterman, C. W. 1947. A weighting system for the estimation of gene frequencies from family records. *Contr. Lab. Vertebr. Biol.* Univ. Mich., **33**, 1–21.

Cotterman, C. W. 1954. Estimation of gene frequency in non-experimental populations. Chapter 35 of *Statistics and mathematics in biology*, edited by O. Kempthorne et al. Iowa State College Press, Ames.

Emerson, R. A., G. W. Beadle and A. C. Frazer. 1935. A summary of linkage studies in maize. *Mem. Cornell Univ. agric. Exp. Sta.*, **180**.

Finney, D. J. 1948. The estimation of the frequency of recombinations. I. Matings of known phase. *J. Genet.*, **49**, 159–176.

Finney, D. J.   1950.   Scores for the estimation of genetic parameters.   *Biometrics*, **6**, 221–227.

Fisher, R. A.   1925.   *Statistical methods for research workers* and succeeding editions. Oliver and Boyd, Edinburgh.

Fisher, R. A.   1934.   The use of simultaneous estimation in the evaluation of linkage. *Ann. Eugen. Lond.*, **6**, 71–76.

Fisher, R. A.   1937.   *The design of experiments* and succeeding editions.   Oliver and Boyd, Edinburgh.

Fisher, R. A.   1939.   The precision of the product formula for the estimation of linkage.   *Ann. Eugen. Lond.*, **9**, 50–54.

Fisher, R. A.   1940.   The estimation of the proportion of recessives from tests carried out on a sample not wholly unrelated.   *Ann. Eugen. Lond.*, **10**, 160–170.

Fisher, R. A.   1953.   The linkage of *polydactyl* with *leaden* in the house mouse. *Heredity*, **7**, 91–96.

Fisher, R. A., and N. T. J. Bailey.   1949.   The estimation of linkage with different viability.   *Heredity*, **3**, 215–225.

Fisher, R. A., and B. Balmukand.   1928.   The estimation of linkage from the offspring of selfed heterozygotes.   *J. Genet.*, **20**, 79–92.

Fisher, R. A., and K. Mather.   1936.   A linkage test with mice.   *Ann. Eugen. Lond.*, **7**, 265–280.

Fisher, R. A., and F. Yates.   1948.   *Statistical tables for biological, agricultural and medical research*.   Oliver and Boyd, Edinburgh.   3rd edition.

Mather, K.   1938.   *The measurement of linkage in heredity*.   Methuen, London. John Wiley & Sons, New York.

Stevens, W. L.   1938.   Estimation of blood-group gene frequencies.   *Ann. Eugen. Lond.*, **8**, 362–375.

Stevens, W. L.   1942.   The accuracy of mutation rates.   *J. Genet.*, **43**, 301–307.

Taylor, G. L., and Aileen M. Prior.   1938.   Blood groups in England.   *Ann. Eugen, Lond.*, **8**, 343–355.

FURTHER READING

Ceppilini, R., M. Siniscalco, and C. A. B. Smith.   1955.   The estimation of gene frequencies in a random mating population.   *Ann. Eugen. Lond.*, **20**, 97–115.

Falconer, D. S.   1948.   The estimation of mutation rates from incompletely tested gametes, and the detection of mutations in mammals.   *J. Genet.*, **49**, 226–234.

Fisher, R. A.   1922.   On the mathematical foundations of theoretical statistics. *Phil. Trans. A*, **222**, 309–368.

Fisher, R. A.   1925.   Theory of statistical estimation.   *Proc. Camb. phil. Soc.*, **22**, 700–725.

Fisher, R. A.   1946.   The fitting of gene frequencies to data on rhesus reactions. *Ann. Eugen. Lond.*, **13**, 150–155.

Haldane, J. B. S.   1953a.   A class of efficient estimates of a parameter.   *Proc. int. statist. Conf. India*, 1951.

Haldane, J. B. S.   1953b.   The estimation of two parameters from a sample.   *Sankhya*, **12**, 313–320.

Haldane, J. B. S.   1956.   The estimation of viabilities.   *J. Genet.*, **54**, 294–296.

Kosambi, D. D.   1943.   The estimation of map distances from recombination values. *Ann. Eugen. Lond.*, **12**, 172–175.

Murty, V. N.   1954.   Estimation of linkage by the method of minimum discrepancy. *Genetics*, **39**, 581–586.

Owen, A. R. G. 1953. The analysis of multiple linkage data. *Heredity*, **7**, 247–264.
Rao, C. R. 1950. Methods of scoring linkage data giving the simultaneous segregation of three factors. *Heredity*, **4**, 37–59.
Sanchez-Monge, E 1952. The estimation of linkage with incomplete penetrance. *Heredity*, **6**, 111–120.
Woolf, Barnet. 1954. Estimation of mutation rates. I. Visible recessive characters detected in inbred lines maintained by single sib-matings. *J. Genet.*, **52**, 332–353.

PROBLEMS

1. Suppose we have taken n observations from a Poisson distribution,

$$\text{Prob } (x) = e^{-m} \frac{m^x}{x!}$$

obtaining $x_1, x_2, \cdots, x_n$. Find the maximum-likelihood estimate of m and its variance.

2. Suppose we have a pair of alleles A, a with A completely dominant to a and a sample of N dominant individuals. We obtain n progeny by selfing from each individual of a sample and find that D have no recessive progeny and H have one or more recessive progeny. The problem is to estimate the proportion of homozygous dominants in the population. Set up the maximum-likelihood equations, and derive the estimate and its variance.

3. The situation is the same as in question 2, but we intercross at random and get n progeny. Do as in question 2.

4. The situation is the same as in question 2, and we obtain n testcross progeny. Do as in question 2.

5. Suppose we have two dominant factors A, a and B, b and obtain an F_2 from a coupling double heterozygote. Assume the recombination percentage in male gametogenesis is p_1 and in female gametogenesis is p_2. Obtain the expectations for the four phenotypic classes, and show that one can estimate $(1 - p_1)(1 - p_2)$ but not p_1 and p_2 separately. Obtain the maximum-likelihood estimate of $(1 - p_1)(1 - p_2)$ and its variance.

CHAPTER 9

The Planning of Experiments

9.1 GENERAL IDEAS

We have seen that the variance of the maximum likelihood estimate may be estimated by

$$- \frac{1}{E\left[\dfrac{\partial^2}{\partial \theta^2} (\log L)\right]}$$

Fisher then proposed the reciprocal of this, namely,

$$I_\theta = -E\left[\frac{\partial^2}{\partial \theta^2} (\log L)\right]$$

as the amount of information contained by a sample of n observations on the parameter θ. We see that maximum likelihood tends to extract all this information, though in fact this is generally true only asymptotically.

It is reasonable to define the information of a single observation i_θ as I_θ/n, and in fact

$$n i_\theta = -E\left(\frac{\partial^2 \log L}{\partial \theta^2}\right)$$

where L is the likelihood of sample of n observations.

Now let us consider the situation when the observation consists of the classification of an individual into one of s classes denoted by i which takes the values $1, 2, \cdots, s$. Suppose the probability that the individual occurs in class j is P_j which will be a function of the parameter θ (or of the parameters, if there are more than one). In that case

$$\log L = \text{constant} + \sum n_j \log P_j$$

$$\frac{\partial \log L}{\partial \theta} = \sum \frac{n_j}{P_j} \frac{\partial P_j}{\partial \theta}$$

$$\frac{\partial^2 \log L}{\partial \theta^2} = -\sum \frac{n_j}{P_j^2}\left(\frac{\partial P_j}{\partial \theta}\right)^2 + \sum \frac{n_j}{P_j} \frac{\partial^2 P_j}{\partial \theta^2}$$

The expectation is obtained by replacing n_j by nP_j so that

$$E\left(\frac{\partial^2 \log L}{\partial \theta^2}\right) = -n\sum \frac{1}{P_j}\left(\frac{\partial P_j}{\partial \theta}\right)^2 + n\sum \frac{\partial^2 P_j}{\partial \theta^2}$$

$$= -n\sum \frac{1}{P_j}\left(\frac{\partial P_j}{\partial \theta}\right)^2$$

since

$$\sum \frac{\partial^2 P_j}{\partial \theta^2} = \frac{\partial^2}{\partial \theta^2}(\sum P_j) = \frac{\partial^2(1)}{\partial \theta^2} = 0$$

Hence

$$I_\theta = n\sum \frac{1}{P_j}\left(\frac{\partial P_j}{\partial \theta}\right)^2$$

and

$$i_\theta = \sum \frac{1}{P_j}\left(\frac{\partial P_j}{\partial \theta}\right)^2$$

This formula is very useful in that it enables us to make a comparison of different experiments which are concerned with the estimation of the same parameter.

Perhaps the simplest example which can be given is the following. Suppose we are concerned with the estimation of the frequency of a gene in a random mating population. The probabilities of the genotypes are then

AA	Aa	aa
$(1-p)^2$	$2p(1-p)$	p^2

We now consider two alternative possibilities:

1. That there is almost complete dominance so that AA and Aa are nearly indistinguishable except by a rather time-consuming technique; so we merely observe the classification

AA or Aa	aa
$1-p^2$	p^2

2. That we use the afore-mentioned technique. We ask the question, which method of taking observations is better? The answer is intuitively obvious, namely, that possibility 2 gives more information. However, the work involved in possibility 2 may be such as to outweigh the intuitive advantage. We therefore evaluate the information given by each method or possibility.

Possibility One

For clarity we construct Table 9.1. The information on p given per single observation is then

$$i_{p1} = 4 + \frac{4p^2}{1 - p^2} = \frac{4}{1 - p^2}$$

TABLE 9.1

Class	Class Number (i)	P_i	$\dfrac{\partial P_i}{\partial p}$	$\dfrac{1}{P_i}\left(\dfrac{\partial P_i}{\partial p}\right)^2$
AA or Aa	1	$1-p^2$	$-2p$	$\dfrac{4p^2}{1-p^2}$
aa	2	p^2	$2p$	$\dfrac{4p^2}{p^2} = 4$

Possibility Two

We construct Table 9.2. The information on p given per single observation is then

TABLE 9.2

Class	Number (i)	P_i	$\dfrac{\partial P_i}{\partial p}$	$\dfrac{1}{P_i}\left(\dfrac{\partial P_i}{\partial p}\right)^2$
AA	1	$(1-p)^2$	$-2(1-p)$	4
Aa	2	$2p(1-p)$	$2(1-2p)$	$\dfrac{2(1-2p)^2}{p(1-p)}$
aa	3	p^2	$2p$	4

$$i_{p2} = 8 + \frac{2(1 - 2p)^2}{p(1 - p)} = \frac{2}{p(1 - p)}$$

The information on p depends on p itself, and we may construct a simple table showing the general story (Table 9.3). Thus, if p is about 0.5, we can say that 100 observations taken according to method 2 are equivalent to 150 observations taken with method 1. As p gets close to unity, there is little to choose between the methods, but, as p approaches small values,

TABLE 9.3

p	i_{p1}	i_{p2}	i_{p2}/i_{p1}
1	∞	∞	1
0.9	21.05	22.22	1.06
0.8	11.11	12.50	1.12
0.7	7.84	9.52	1.21
0.6	6.25	8.33	1.33
0.5	5.33	8.00	1.50
0.4	4.76	8.33	1.75
0.3	4.40	9.52	2.17
0.2	4.17	12.50	3.00
0.1	4.04	22.22	5.50
0	4.00	∞	∞

method 2 gets progressively better than method 1. If in fact p is 0.0001, we have

$$\frac{i_{p2}}{i_{p1}} = 5000.50$$

so that 100 observations by method 2 are equivalent to 500,050 observations by method 1. The result is intuitively very reasonable in that, when p is near zero, the aa class will have very low frequency and the occurrence of the a gene is shown mainly in the heterozygote. Under method 1 these are not separated from the AA homozygote whereas in method 2 they are separated.

9.2 LINKAGE ESTIMATION WITH TWO ALLELES PER LOCUS

The information per unit observation using the backcross method is easily seen to be $1/p(1-p)$, as we can verify by the binomial variance formula. It is of some interest to compare other methods with this one, and in fact we can envisage the following situations:

1. All genotypes identified, including the identification of the $AaBb$ as being in the coupling or repulsion phase. (This presumably requires in general a progeny test and is therefore not particularly useful.)
2. Incomplete dominance occurring at each locus, so that the nine possible gene combinations are identified.
3. Incomplete dominance at one locus and complete dominance at the other, so that six phenotypes are identified.
4. Complete dominance at both loci.

In the case of F_2 data, the recombination fraction is assumed to be the same in both male and female gametogenesis. We shall illustrate the calculation of amount of information for one of these cases,

1. F_2 *completely classified.* Coupling heterozygotes mated; see Table 9.4. Thus i_p for the mating of two coupling heterozygotes is $2/p(1 - p)$

TABLE 9.4

Class	P_i	$\dfrac{dP_i}{dp}$	$\dfrac{1}{P_i}\left(\dfrac{dP_i}{dp}\right)^2$
AB/AB	$(\tfrac{1}{4})(1-p)^2$	$-(\tfrac{1}{2})(1-p)$	1
AB/Ab	$(\tfrac{1}{2})p(1-p)$	$(\tfrac{1}{2})(1-2p)$	$\dfrac{(\tfrac{1}{2})(1-2p)^2}{p(1-p)}$
AB/aB	$(\tfrac{1}{2})p(1-p)$	$(\tfrac{1}{2})(1-2p)$	$\dfrac{(\tfrac{1}{2})(1-2p)^2}{p(1-p)}$
AB/ab	$(\tfrac{1}{2})(1-p)^2$	$-(1-p)$	2
Ab/Ab	$(\tfrac{1}{4})p^2$	$(\tfrac{1}{2})p$	1
Ab/aB	$(\tfrac{1}{2})p^2$	p	2
Ab/ab	$(\tfrac{1}{2})p(1-p)$	$(\tfrac{1}{2})(1-2p)$	$\dfrac{(\tfrac{1}{2})(1-2p)^2}{p(1-p)}$
aB/aB	$(\tfrac{1}{4})p^2$	$(\tfrac{1}{2})p$	1
aB/ab	$(\tfrac{1}{2})p(1-p)$	$(\tfrac{1}{2})(1-2p)$	$\dfrac{(\tfrac{1}{2})(1-2p)^2}{p(1-p)}$
ab/ab	$(\tfrac{1}{4})(1-p)^2$	$-(\tfrac{1}{2})(1-p)$	1
Sum	1	0	$\dfrac{2}{p(1-p)}$

which may be verified to be the value also for repulsion heterozygotes. This value is twice that for the backcross, corresponding to a complete count of gamete formation in the two parents, as opposed to a complete count of gamete formation for one parent in the case of the backcross.

2. *Incomplete dominance.* Here it may be verified that i_p is given by

$$\frac{2(1 - 3p + 3p^2)}{p(1 - p)(1 - 2p + 2p^2)} = \frac{3(1 - p)^2 + 3p^2 - 1}{p(1 - p)[p^2 + (1 - p)^2]}$$

the latter form showing that the information is symmetrical with respect to p and $(1 - p)$.

3. *Incomplete dominance at one locus.* With coupling heterozygotes mated the information is

$$2 + \frac{p^2}{1 - p^2} + \frac{2(p - \frac{1}{2})^2}{1 - p + p^2} + \frac{(1 - p)^2}{p(2 - p)} + \frac{2(p - \frac{1}{2})^2}{p(1 - p)}$$

With repulsion heterozygotes mated the information is obtainable from this expression by replacing p by $(1 - p)$.

4. *Complete dominance at both loci.* Mather (1936) states the results as follows:

$$\text{Coupling:} \quad i_p = \frac{2(1 - p)(3 - 4p + 2p^2)}{(2 - p)(3 - 2p + p^2)}$$

$$\text{Repulsion:} \quad i_p = \frac{2p(1 + 2p^2)}{(2 + p^2)(1 + p)}$$

Finally we may compare these methods by taking the information given by them relative to the information given by the backcross.

Each method requires a definite amount of work under particular circumstances, and the experimenter should choose the method which results in the minimum amount of work for a preassigned accuracy, or should plan to obtain the maximum accuracy with the amount of work he wishes to devote to the problem. See the references Immer (1934) and Mather (1936) for detailed discussion.

REFERENCES

Fisher, R. A. 1925. *Statistical methods for research workers.* Oliver and Boyd, Edinburgh. Editions since 1925.

Immer, F. R. 1934. Calculating linkage intensities from F_3 data. *Genetics,* **19,** 119–136.

Mather, K. 1936. Types of linkage data and their value. *Ann. Eugen. Lond.,* **7,** 251–264.

FURTHER READING

Bailey, N. T. J. 1951. The estimation of linkage in bacteria. *Heredity,* **5,** 111–124.

PROBLEMS

1. Verify the formula for the information on recombination fraction given by the mating of two coupling heterozygotes when there is complete dominance at one locus and incomplete dominance at the other.

2. Suppose we have two linked loci with genes M, m and U, u, which behave according to the classical duplicate factor model. We self MU/mu and the offspring are tested by selfing. Genotypes with the double dose of M or of U are resistant and produce resistant progeny only. Genotypes with a single dose

of M or of U are resistant and produce some resistant individuals and some susceptible individuals, while genotypes with no M or U are susceptible. The testing is presumed to be without error and leads to a classification of the individuals of the F_2 as resistant, segregating, or susceptible. Set up the maximum-likelihood equations for estimating the recombination fraction and evaluate the information on it.

3. Discuss the estimation of linkage in the presence of complementary factors.

CHAPTER 10

Statistical Problems in Human Genetics

10.1 INTRODUCTION

The paper which will be the basis of the present chapter is Fisher's (1934d) paper on the effects of methods of ascertainment. It is not thereby intended to imply that this paper is the only one worth studying, but merely that in my opinion this paper is remarkable for the precision of the attack on a class of statistical problems and is basic.

There is the class of problems in human genetics which can be treated by the standard methods which we have already described, for example, simple tests of hypotheses about segregation ratios, the estimation of gene frequencies, and so on. The basic assumption in these situations is that the researcher has a random sample of some prior specified population. In the example of the O, A, B gene frequencies it was assumed that the probability of an individual being included in the sample is the same, regardless of gene structure. Strictly speaking, a sample is a random one only if it is drawn by a procedure which is known to be random. For example, the obtaining of a random sample of humans can be done by forming a list of all humans in the population, either in fact or by an objective set of rules which attach a definite order number to every individual. Then to get a 1-in-1000 sample we may draw a random number between 1 and 1000 for each member of the population. If the random number drawn is 1, the individual is to be included in the sample; otherwise not. In fact this is rarely done, and the randomness of a sample is assumed, because the researcher can think of no way in which the sample should deviate systematically from the average of the population. This is by no means as valid an assumption to make as may appear on the surface. (See for example Yates, 1934.)

Now consider a simple problem in human genetics such as checking that albinism is carried by a simple recessive gene; i.e. AA and Aa are normal, while aa is albinotic. One procedure would be to obtain a random sample of all families, and we would then obtain a random sample of the following types of couple:

$$AA \times AA$$
$$AA \times Aa$$
$$AA \times aa$$
$$Aa \times Aa$$
$$Aa \times aa$$
$$aa \times aa$$

The trait that we are considering is rather rare, and, if in fact the gene frequency for a were p and there were random mating, the probabilities of the particular mating types occurring would be shown in the accompanying table. Now p will be rather small so that the frequency of

Type	Probability
$AA \times AA$	$(1-p)^4$
$AA \times Aa$	$4p(1-p)^3$
$AA \times aa$	$2p^2(1-p)^2$
$Aa \times Aa$	$4p^2(1-p)^2$
$Aa \times aa$	$4p^3(1-p)$
$aa \times aa$	p^4

$Aa \times aa$ and $aa \times aa$ types will be very small. The types of high frequency $AA \times AA$, $AA \times Aa$, and $AA \times aa$ tell us nothing about the problem because these matings produce no albinos. We are, therefore, left with the matings $Aa \times Aa$ which should give a proportion of $\frac{1}{4}$ of albino offspring. If, in fact, p were 1 per cent, these matings would constitute about 4/10,000 of the population, so that a random sample of say 20,000 couples would result in only 8 couples on the average, and such a sample would be a tremendous one by almost any yardstick. In fact, there is frequently not random mating for such human traits, but the moral is evident, namely that the human geneticist can use random samples only as a last resort or when the question can be answered only from a completely random sample. The general procedure is to obtain in some way a sample of matings which produce at least one recessive, and the great bulk of such matings will be of the type $Aa \times Aa$, i.e. normal $\times$ normal. The problem reduces then to the estimation of a segregation ratio for matings of this type, taking account in a reasonable way of the procedure by which the sample is obtained. Now we strike another difficulty: namely, how do we know that a mating is actually of type $Aa \times Aa$? This is a mating of two normal individuals, and we can determine if the mating is $Aa \times Aa$ only if the mating results in at least one aa offspring.

Consider the general case when the probability of the mating producing an individual of the specified type, say recessive, is p, and suppose we have families of k offspring. The probabilities of such families producing none, 1, 2, $\cdots$, k individuals are

$$(1 - p)^k, \quad kp(1 - p)^{k-1}, \quad \frac{k(k - 1)}{2!} p^2(1 - p)^{k-2}, \quad \cdots, \quad p^k$$

Families which do not produce any recessives will not be recognized as being of the proper mating type, so that we have to work with conditional probabilities and distributions, namely the probability of a family containing say s recessives, given that it contains at least one recessive. By the standard rule for obtaining conditional probabilities this is

Probability that family produces s recessives (s greater than zero)
───
Probability that family contains at least one recessive

which is

$$\frac{k!}{s!(k - s)!} \frac{p^s(1 - p)^{k-s}}{1 - (1 - p)^k}$$

being the probability for a truncated binomial distribution.

10.2 THE DIRECT METHOD

This method was introduced by Weinberg (1912a). Fisher (1934c) refers to the method as the proband method, but it seems preferable to follow the terminology of Weinberg, as indicated by Bailey (1951b). Suppose that we have taken a random sample of all couples and have then abstracted the records of the offspring of all couples with k offspring who have produced at least one recessive. Let us suppose that we have in our sample n couples with at least one recessive and in fact have the distribution of observations given in Table 10.1.

The procedure for estimating p is to note the following fact. The expected number of recessives is equal to

$$\frac{1}{1 - (1 - p)^k} \left[kp(1 - p)^{k-1} + 2 \frac{k(k - 1)}{2!} p^2(1 - p)^{k-2} \right.$$
$$\left. + 3 \frac{k(k - 1)(k - 2)}{3!} p^3(1 - p)^{k-3} + \cdots + kp^k \right]$$

which is equal to

$$\frac{kp}{1 - (1 - p)^k}$$

TABLE 10.1

No. of Recessives	Number of Families	Probability
1	n_1	$kp(1-p)^{k-1}/[1-(1-p)^k]$
2	n_2	$k\dfrac{(k-1)}{2!}p^2(1-p)^{k-2}/[1-(1-p)^k]$
3	n_3	$\dfrac{k(k-1)(k-2)}{3!}p^3(1-p)^{k-3}/[1-(1-p)^k]$
.	.	.
.	.	.
.	.	.
k	n_k	$p^k/[1-(1-p)^k]$
Total	n	1

since the quantity in square brackets is equal to the mean of the corresponding complete binomial distribution. To estimate p it is then reasonable to equate the observed mean number of recessives $\bar{r}$ to the expected mean, and solve for p. That is, we find the value of p for which

$$\bar{r} = \frac{kp}{1 - (1 - p)^k} \tag{1}$$

It may be noted that this is, in fact, fitting by the method of moments. It is left as an exercise to the reader to show that the maximum likelihood estimate is given by the same equation. This is known from general considerations, since the observed mean of the complete binomial distribution is a sufficient statistic and is the maximum likelihood estimate of the unknown proportion. (See Tukey, 1949.) The variance of the estimate can be obtained in the following way. The variance of $\bar{r}$ is equal to

$$(1/n)[\sum P_r r^2 - (\sum P_r r)^2]$$

by the general formula given earlier. Hence

$$nV(\bar{r}) = \frac{kp(1 - p)}{1 - (1 - p)^k} - \frac{k^2 p^2 (1 - p)^k}{[1 - (1 - p)^k]^2}$$

To get from $V(\bar{r})$ to $V(\hat{p})$ where $\hat{p}$ is the solution to the equation (1) above we use the approximate formula for the variance of $\hat{p}$ given as a function of $\bar{r}$,

$$V(\hat{p}) = \left(\frac{dp}{d\bar{r}}\right)^2 V(\bar{r}) = V(\bar{r})\bigg/\left(\frac{d\bar{r}}{dp}\right)^2$$

In this case we find

$$n\,V(\hat{p}) = \frac{p(1 - p)[1 - (1 - p)^k]^2}{k[1 - (1 - p)^k - kp(1 - p)^{k-1}]}$$

For example, if $p = \frac{1}{4}$ and $k = 5$,

$$n\,V(\hat{p}) = 0.0594$$

so that, with 100 families, $V(\hat{p}) = 0.000594$ and the standard error of $\hat{p}$ is equal to 0.0244. This method is discussed at length by Haldane (1932, 1938).

10.3 THE EFFECT OF METHOD OF ASCERTAINMENT

The strict assumptions necessary for the validity of the direct method were stated above, and these assumptions will rarely be satisfied in human genetic problems. In fact, the researcher usually obtains his data by combing hospital records for individuals who have been listed as having the trait under consideration. He then tries to locate the families from which such individuals came and determines how many of the individual's sibs carry the trait. It is not entirely clear under these circumstances what is the probability that a family of k offspring with s recessives will be included in the data to be analyzed.

Let us suppose that the probability of a recessive individual coming to our knowledge other than by investigation of sibs of a recessive individual located already, is p', a constant, regardless of the composition of the family to which he belongs. This assumption is basic in Fisher's paper, but whether it is valid in a particular situation is a moot point in my opinion. Also there is the question of whether the binomial distribution holds. It is possible that the size of family depends on the composition of the family. If, for example, a couple have one child with an hereditary defect, they may decide to have no further children. The possibility of taking account of such a sequential process by which the total family is obtained does not appear to have been considered. Undoubtedly this would be very difficult and would require other information which is probably unobtainable.

In a population of N matings of the specified type the frequencies of families with each possible number of recessives will be as given in Table 10.2, where $q = 1 - p$. We have also inserted the probability of the

TABLE 10.2

Number of Recessives	Frequency of Family in Population	Probability of Number of Times Family is Located					
		0	1	2	3	4 $\cdots$	k
1	$N\dfrac{k!}{1!(k-1)!}pq^{k-1}$	$1-p'$	p'	0	0	0 $\cdots$	0
2	$N\dfrac{k!}{2!(k-2)!}p^2q^{k-2}$	$(1-p')^2$	$2p'(1-p')$	p'^2	0	0 $\cdots$	0
3	$N\dfrac{k!}{3!(k-3)!}p^3q^{k-3}$	$(1-p'^3)$	$3p'(1-p')^2$	$3p'^2(1-p')$	p'^3	0 $\cdots$	0
4	$N\dfrac{k!}{4!(k-4)!}p^4q^{k-4}$	$(1-p')^4$	$4p'(1-p')^3$	$6p'^2(1-p')^2$	$4p'^3(1-p')$	$p'^4 \cdots$	0
.	.	.	.	.	.	. . . .	.
.	.	.	.	.	.	. . . .	.
.	.	.	.	.	.	. . . .	.
k	Np^k	.	.	.	.	. . . .	.

family being found 0, 1, 2, $\cdots$, k times independently.   Now let us find the mean number of recessive sibs possessed by a recessive sib, weighting each case by the number of times the family was located independently.

With a family containing s recessives the mean number of times it will be ascertained or located is sp', and in each case the number of recessive sibs is $(s-1)$. So we have as the expectation of the total number of recessive sibs

$$\sum_{s=1}^{k} N \frac{k!}{s!(k-s)!} p^s q^{k-s} sp'(s-1)$$

which can be shown to be equal to

$$Nk(k-1)p^2p'$$

The total number of sibs possessed by the ascertained sibs is an expectation of

$$(k-1)\sum_{s=1}^{k} N \frac{k!}{s!(k-s)!} p^s q^{k-s} sp'$$

which can be shown to be equal to

$$Nk(k-1)pp'$$

Hence we have

$$\frac{\text{Expectation of total number of recessive sibs}}{\text{Expectation of total number of sibs}} = p$$

which is the desired proportion. As we have stated above, each expectation is calculated using each family the number of times it has been ascertained independently. This is the procedure to be followed with the *proband method* (called the sib method by Fisher (1934c)).

The example given by Fisher is as follows. Suppose there are 340 families of 5, derived from 432 ascertainments with structure given in Table. 10.3. The number of ascertainments for the different numbers of recessives are given in Table 10.4.

TABLE 10.3

ASCERTAINMENTS

Number of Recessives	Number of Recessives Ascertained Independently					
	1	2	3	4	5	Total
1	140	—	—	—	—	140
2	80	52	—	—	—	132
3	35	12	7	—	—	54
4	4	7	0	2	—	13
5	0	1	0	0	0	1
Total	259	72	7	2	0	340

TABLE 10.4

	Number of Recessives					
	1	2	3	4	5	Total
Number of ascertainments	140	184	80	26	2	432

As Fisher points out, no matter how incomplete the ascertainment or unequal the probabilities of inclusion, the numbers in this table must be proportional to the terms of the binomial expansion $(q + p)^4$. The total number of recessive sibs of recessive individuals is then

$$0 \times 140 + 1 \times 184 + 2 \times 80 + 3 \times 26 + 4 \times 2 = 430$$

and the total number of sibs of recessive individuals is

$$4 \times 432$$

so that the estimate of p is $430/(4 \times 432) = 0.2488$.

The general formula for the proband method may be stated as follows. The families are all of size s. A family of s contains r recessives, of which t have been ascertained or located independently. The number of families of this particular type is n_{rt}. Then

(1)   the total number of independent ascertainments

$$= \sum(tn_{rt})$$

(2)   the total number of sibs

$$= (s - 1)\sum(tn_{rt})$$

(3)   the total number of recessives

$$= \sum t(r - 1)n_{rt}$$

in each case summation being over the different families.

The estimate of p is

$$\hat{p} = \frac{\sum[t(r - 1)n_{rt}]}{(s - 1)\sum(tn_{rt})}$$

An intuitive way of looking at this expression is to note that the expectation of $(r-1)$ is $p(s-1)$ so that, if we could take the expectation first with respect to r and then with respect to t, we would find the expectation of $\hat{p}$ to be p. This reasoning is not, however, correct.

Fisher furthermore derives an estimate of variance for the estimate $\hat{p}$, the estimate of variance being dependent on the assumption of constant probability of ascertainment. He found that, if we write

$$T = \sum t(t - 1)n_{rt}$$
$$R = \sum t(r - 1)n_{rt}$$
$$S = \sum t(s - 1)n_{rt}$$

then as we have stated

$$\hat{p} = \frac{R}{S}$$

and

$$\hat{p}' = \frac{T}{R}$$

and the estimated variance of $\hat{p}$ is given by

$$V(\hat{p}_s) = \frac{(S - R)}{S^4} [RS + ST + RT(s - 3)]$$

where the subscript s denotes $\hat{p}$ for families of size s.

In the case of families of different sizes, estimates would be obtained for each size say $s_1, s_2, \cdots, s_n$, and the combined estimate would be

$$\sum_i \frac{\hat{p}_{s_i}}{V(\hat{p}_{s_i})} \bigg/ \sum_i \frac{1}{V(\hat{p}_{s_i})}$$

with a variance of

$$\frac{1}{\sum_i \left[\dfrac{1}{V(\hat{p}_{s_i})} \right]}$$

In this paper Fisher shows how the proband method may be extended to utilize the information on the number of pairs, trios, quartets, etc. which were ascertained.

10.4 EXTENSION OF FISHER'S WORK

The work of Fisher (1934d) has been extended by Bailey (1951a, b). In his latter paper Bailey points out that the method which Fisher refers to as the sib method should be called the proband method in line with the original terminology of Weinberg (1912a, 1912b, 1927). This method is a generalization of the simple sib method in which each family is counted as many times as the number of abnormals it contains. The proband method, referred to by Fisher as the sib method, consists of counting each family only as many times as it has been ascertained. The main part of Fisher's examination of this method is presented above. He also showed that the method was not efficient in the maximum likelihood sense and indicated how it could be supplemented.

Bailey's work (1951a) consists of setting up the general likelihood function based on the segregation ratio and the probability of ascertainment. Suppose that there are N families in the population with normal parents capable of producing a proportion p of children with the characteristic under consideration, say albinism. Suppose first that the families are all of size s, and let the ascertainment be by affected individuals only with the probability of any such affected individual entering the records be p'. Let q equal $1 - p$, and q' equal $1 - p'$. Then the situation is as indicated in Table 10.5.

TABLE 10.5

Enumeration of Possible Occurrences

Number of Recessives	Number of Times Family Is Ascertained				
	0	1	2	$\cdots$	s
0	P_{00}	—	—	—	—
1	P_{10}	P_{11}	—	—	—
2	P_{20}	P_{21}	P_{22}	—	—
.					
.					
.					
s	P_{s0}	P_{s1}	P_{s2}		P_{ss}

Table 10.5 indicates that a family of size s can fall into any cell on or below the diagonal. The probability of falling in the rt cell is

$$P_{rt} = \frac{s!}{r!(s-r)!}\, p^r q^{s-r}\, \frac{r!}{t!(r-t)!}\, (p')^t (q')^{r-t}$$

The observable cells in the enumeration are those with r and t greater than or equal to unity. The whole class of families with t equal to zero is not observed, and the probability of a family falling in this class is

$$\sum_{r=0}^{s} P_{r0} = \sum_{r=0}^{s} \frac{s!}{r!(s-r)!}\, p^r q^{s-r} q'^r$$
$$= (pq' + q)^s$$
$$= (1 - pp')^s$$

Hence the situation is that we have an unknown number of families N in the population, of which an unknown number $(N-n)$ have the probability $(1-pp')^s$ of not being in the sample, and of which the probability of a family with r albinos and t ascertainments $(t > 0)$ being in the sample is P_{rt}. Hence the likelihood is

$$\frac{N!}{(N-n)!}\, \frac{[(1-pp')^s]^{(N-n)}}{\Pi(n_{rt}!)}\, \Pi(P_{rt})^{n_{rt}}$$

where the products Π extend over the whole of Table 10.5 on or below the diagonal and excluding the first column. The logarithm of the likelihood is therefore

$$L = \text{constant} + \log N! - \log(N-n)! + (N-n)s \log(1-pp')$$
$$+ \sum_{\substack{rt \\ 0 < t \leqslant r}} n_{rt}[r \log p + (s-r) \log q + t \log p' + (r-t) \log q']$$

or, if we let

$$A = \sum r n_{rt}, \qquad B = ns = \sum s n_{rt}, \qquad C = \sum t n_{rt}$$

the summations extending over the range $0 < t \leqslant r$, the logarithm of the likelihood is

$$L = \text{constant} + \log N! - \log (N - n)! + (N - n)s \log (1 - pp')$$
$$+ A \log p + (B - A) \log q + C \log p' + (A - C) \log q'$$

It is of interest that A, B, and C are jointly sufficient for the parameters p, p', and N, since n equals B/s, and s is the constant size of family. Bailey gives the full maximum likelihood solution obtained by iteration in the usual way (though complicated by the trouble of taking derivatives of the logarithms of factorials) and also a method which consists of equating A, B, C to their expectations and solving the resulting equations. Since the n_{rt} have the multinomial distribution specified above, we can write immediately

$$E(n_{rt}) = NP_{rt}, \qquad V(n_{rt}) = NP_{rt}(1 - P_{rt})$$

and

$$\text{Cov}\,(n_{rt}, n_{r't'}) = -NP_{rt}P_{r't'}$$

and the expectations of A, B, and C can be written down. Thus we have

$$E(A) = N \left(sp - \sum_{r=1}^{s} r P_{r0} \right)$$
$$= N \left[sp - \sum_{r=1}^{s} r \frac{s!}{r!(s-r)!} (pq')^r q^{s-r} \right]$$
$$= Nsp - Nspq'(1 - pp')^{s-1}$$
$$= Nsp[1 - q'(1 - pp')^{s-1}]$$
$$E(B) = Ns[1 - (1 - pp')^s]$$

and

$$E(C) = E_{(r)} \cdot E \left[\sum_t t n_{rt} \Big| r \right]$$
$$= E_{(r)} \left(\sum_r r p' \right)$$
$$= Nspp'$$

where $E_{(r)} \cdot E(v/r)$ means the taking of expectation of v first conditionally with r fixed, and then with respect to r.

Bailey notes that, if we solve the equations

$$A = E(A)$$
$$B = E(B)$$
$$C = E(C)$$

the derivatives of the logarithm of the likelihood with regard to p and p' are satisfied exactly, and that the derivative with regard to N is nearly satisfied, and therefore denotes this method of estimation as a quasi-likelihood method (Bailey, 1951b).   The solution of the equations is

$$p = C/Nsp'$$

$$p' = \frac{1 - \theta}{A/C - \theta}$$

where $\theta = (1 - C/Ns)^{s-1}$.   A solution for N can be obtained from the equation

$$B = Ns[1 - (1 - C/Ns)^s]$$

by iteration.   Bailey (1951a) also gives the variances of the estimates.

Finally the procedure with various sizes of family is to obtain separate estimates for each size of family and combine these estimates weighting inversely as their variances as in Fisher's treatment described above.

The procedure developed by Bailey for the full maximum likelihood solution, the procedure described above (designated as "moments"), and Fisher's procedure given earlier in the chapter lead to estimates given in Table 10.6 for the data of Table 10.3.

TABLE 10.6

ESTIMATES OF PARAMETERS

	Fisher's Method (Proband)	Bailey's Method (Moments)	Bailey's Method (Maximum Likelihood)
p	0.2488 ± 0.0137	0.2526 ± 0.0129	0.2529 ± 0.0129
p'	0.4884	0.4753 ± 0.0311	0.4761 ± 0.0312
N	——	720 ± 58	718 ± 57

Concluding Notes

We conclude with some notes on terminology and general conclusion in the light of Bailey's work.

The term "propositus" is used generally in the literature in English to denote the individual through whom the ascertainment is made while the word "proband" is used in the German literature.

Bailey (1951b) uses the term "selection" with modifying adjectives in place of "ascertainment" as follows:

(a) Single selection = single ascertainment when the chance of a family having more than one propositus is small (p' very small).

(b) Complete selection = complete ascertainment, when all abnormal individuals will be propositi ($p' = 1$).

(c) Incomplete multiple selection = incomplete ascertainment

$$(0 < p' < 1).$$

The case of complete selection or ascertainment is equivalent from the statistical point of view to random selection of families for which the direct method is appropriate (if the binomial distribution may be assumed to hold). For single selection or ascertainment the proband method is consistent but not efficient (in the asymptotic sense). When there is incomplete selection or ascertainment and the number of independent ascertainments is known, Bailey's moment method presented above is to be preferred, whereas, if the chance of ascertainment is known but not the number of ascertainments, the maximum likelihood method of Haldane (1938) is appropriate.

The methods which appear to be best are those which follow by application of the general method of maximum likelihood, and other situations would be worked out likewise.

We shall not review here the extensive work of Fisher (1934a, b, c, 1946) and Finney (1940, 1941a, b, c, d, 1943, 1948a) on linkage tests with selected data.

REFERENCES

Bailey, N. T. J. 1951a. The estimation of the frequencies of recessives with incomplete multiple selection. *Ann. Eugen. Lond.*, **16**, 215–222.

Bailey, N. T. J. 1951b. A classification of methods of ascertainment and analysis in estimating the frequencies of recessives in man. *Ann. Eugen. Lond.*, **16**, 223–225.

Bailey, N. T. J. 1951c. On simplifying the use of Fisher's u-statistics in the detection of linkage in man. *Ann. Eugen. Lond.*, **16**, 26–32.

Bailey, N. T. J. 1951d. The detection of linkage for partially manifesting rare "dominant" and recessive abnormalities. *Ann. Eugen. Lond.*, **16**, 33–44.

Cotterman, C. W. 1947. A weighting system for the estimation of gene frequencies from family records. *Contr. Lab. Vertebr. Biol. Univ. Mich.*, **33**, 1–21.

Cotterman, C. W. 1954. Estimation of gene frequencies in non-experimental populations. Chapter 35 of *Statistics and mathematics in biology*, edited by O. Kempthorne et al. Iowa State College Press. Ames.

Finney, D. J. 1940. The detection of linkage. *Ann. Eugen. Lond.*, **10**, 171–214.

Finney, D. J. 1941a. The detection of linkage. II. Further mating types; scoring of Boyd's data. *Ann. Eugen. Lond.*, **11**, 10–30.

Finney, D. J. 1941b. The detection of linkage. III. Incomplete parental testing. *Ann. Eugen. Lond.*, **11**, 115–135.

Finney, D. J. 1941c. The detection of linkage. V. Supplementary tables. *Ann Eugen. Lond.*, **11**, 224–232.

Finney, D. J. 1941d. The detection of linkage. VI. The loss of information from incompleteness of parental records. *Ann. Eugen. Lond.*, **11**, 233–244.

Finney, D. J. 1943. The detection of linkage. VII. Combination of data from matings of known and unknown phase. *Ann. Eugen. Lond.*, **12**, 31–43.

Finney, D. J. 1948a. The estimation of the frequency of recombinations. I. Matings of known phase. *J. Genet.*, **49**, 159–176.

Finney, D. J. 1948b. The estimation of gene frequencies from family records. I. Factors without dominance. *Heredity*, **2**, 199–213.

Finney, D. J. 1948c. The estimation of gene frequencies from family records. II. Factors with dominance. *Heredity*, **2**, 369–389.

Finney, D. J. 1950. Scores for the estimation of genetic parameters. *Biometrics*, **6**, 221–227.

Fisher, R. A. 1934a. The amount of information supplied by records of families as a function of the linkage in the population samples. *Ann. Eugen. Lond.*, **6**, 66–70.

Fisher, R. A. 1934b. The detection of linkage with "dominant" abnormalities. *Ann. Eugen. Lond.*, **6**, 187–201.

Fisher, R. A. 1934c. The detection of linkage with "recessive" abnormalities. *Ann. Eugen. Lond.*, **6**, 339–351.

Fisher, R. A. 1934d. The effect of methods of ascertainment upon the estimation of frequencies. *Ann. Eugen. Lond.*, **6**, 13–25.

Haldane, J. B. S. 1932. A method for investigating recessive characteristics in man. *J. Genet.* **25**, 251–255.

Haldane, J. B. S. 1938. The estimation of the frequencies of recessive conditions in man. *Ann. Eugen. Lond.*, **8**, 255–262.

Tukey, J. W. 1949. Sufficiency, truncation and selection. *Ann. math. Statist.*, **20**, 310–311.

Weinberg, W. 1912a. Methode und Fehlerquellen der Untersuchung auf Mendelsche Zahlen beim Menschen. *Arch. Rass.-u. GesBiol.*, **6**, 165–174.

Weinberg, W. 1912b. Zur Vererbung der Anlage der Bluterkrankheit mit methodol. Ergäzungen meiner Geschwistermethode. *Arch. Rass.-u. GesBiol.*, **6**, 694–709.

Weinberg, W. 1927. Mathematische Grundlagen der Probandenmethode. *Z. indukt. Abstamm.-u. VererbLehre*, **48**, 179–228.

Yates, F. 1934. Some examples of biased sampling. *Ann. Eugen. Lond.*, **6**, 202–213.

FURTHER READING

Boyd, William C. 1954a. Maximum likelihood method for estimation of gene frequency from MNS data. *Amer. J. hum. Genet.*, **6**, 1–10.

Boyd, William C. 1954b. Shortened maximum likelihood estimation of Rh gene frequencies. *Amer. J. hum. Genet.*, **6**, 303–318.

Boyd, William C. 1956. Variances of gene frequency estimates. *Amer. J. hum. Genet.*, **8**, 24–38.

Cotterman, C. W. 1937. The detection of sex-linkage in families collected at random. *Ohio J. Sci.*, **37**, 75–81.

Cotterman, C. W. 1953. Regular two-allele and three-allele phenotype systems. I. *Amer. J. hum. Genet.*, **5**, 193–235.

Cotterman, C. W., and L. H. Snyder. 1937. Studies in human inheritance. XVII. Gene frequency analysis of double recessive inheritance involving one autosomal and one sex-linked gene substitution. *Genetica*, **19**, 537–552.

Fisher, R. A. 1936. Tests of significance applied to Haldane's data on partial sex-linkage. *Ann. Eugen. Lond.*, **7**, 87–104.

Fisher, R. A. 1951. Standard calculations for evaluating a blood-group system. *Heredity*, **5**, 95–102.

Haldane, J. B. S. 1938. A hitherto unexpected complication in the genetics of human recessives. *Ann. Eugen. Lond.*, **8**, 263–265.

Haldane, J. B. S., and C. A. B. Smith. 1947*a*. A new estimate of the linkage between the genes for color-blindness and hemophilia in man. *Ann. Eugen. Lond.*, **14**, 10–31.

Haldane, J. B. S., and C. A. B. Smith. 1947*b*. A simple exact test for birth-order effect. *Ann. Eugen. Lond.*, **14**, 117–124.

Hogben, L. 1934. The detection of linkage in human families. *Proc. roy. Soc. Lond. B*, **114**, 340–363.

Morton, Newton E. 1955. Sequential tests for the detection of linkage. *Amer. J. hum. Genet.*, **7**, 277–318.

Neel, James V. 1954. Problems in the estimation of the frequency of uncommon inherited traits. *Amer. J. hum. Genet.*, **6**, 51–59.

Penrose, L. S. 1934. The detection of autosomal linkage in data which consists of pairs of brothers and sisters of unspecified parentage. *Ann. Eugen. Lond.*, **6**, 133–138.

Penrose, L. S. 1938. Genetic linkage in graded human characters. *Ann. Eugen. Lond.*, **8**, 233–237.

Penrose, L. S. 1946. A further note on the sib-pair linkage method. *Ann. Eugen. Lond.*, **13**, 25–29.

Schull, William J. 1954. Ascertainment and the study of discontinuous characteristics in man. *Amer. J. hum. Genet.*, **6**, 124–129.

Smith, C. A. B. 1953. The detection of linkage in human genetics. *J. R. statist. Soc. B*, **15**, 153–192.

Smith, C. A. B. 1954. The separation of the sexes of parents in the detection of linkage in man. *Ann. Eugen. Lond.*, **18**, 278–301.

CHAPTER 11

Introduction to Chapters 12 to 23

11.1 THE STUDY OF QUANTITATIVE INHERITANCE

Up to the present we have been concerned with what may be called formal genetics, in which we have been dealing with problems of segregation at individual loci. Thus we have gone into the calculation of expectations of the frequencies of genotypes and phenotypes under various systems of mating and selection. These calculations led to the binomial and multinomial distributions. We were then confronted with the problem of determining whether observational data are in conformity with expectations based on possible genetic hypotheses. We have also dealt with the estimation of population parameters with respect to single loci or two loci, such as gene frequencies or recombination fractions.

We now turn to problems which are considerably more difficult and at least as important socially and economically. We shall be concerned with the study of phenotypic characteristics which do not fall into a small number of distinct homogeneous classes, such as color of endosperm or the Rh system of antigens and antibodies, but have the essential feature of being continuous and graded. The milk production of cows for example can range anywhere between 0 pounds and say 18,000 pounds (perhaps more) for each lactation. This characteristic is certainly under genetic control to some extent, because there are very definite breed differences, and breed crosses exhibit further differences. A more striking example is hybrid corn which has permeated the Corn Belt and yields of which appear to have risen tremendously compared to the yields of open-pollinated corn. These yields are controlled to a considerable extent genetically, because programs of genetic selection have produced them.

Characters such as those mentioned in the previous paragraph are controlled to some extent genetically and to some extent environmentally, for example, by good husbandry practices, and also they may arise by the interaction of genetic and environmental forces. This particular concept of interaction will be discussed later and is introduced here only for the sake of completeness. Our reason for mentioning these ideas is to give a little background for the notion that under some circumstances we can imagine the total observed value for a character (y) to be made up additively of two parts:

(1) G say, which is determined genetically.
(2) E say, which is determined environmentally.

Thus we have

$$y = G + E$$

It is then natural to ask how much of the variation in y in a population can be attributed to genetic forces and how much to environmental forces. Note that we have not even mentioned how we shall measure variation, but it is reasonable to suppose that, if the environment were held constant, there would be less variation in y than if the environment varied.

The remaining chapters of this book will discuss some of the elementary aspects of the study of quantitative inheritance.   Notions such as G and E above will be clarified and made definite as will notions of variation and of covariation, that is, the togetherness of variation of two or more characters.

CHAPTER 12

The Analysis of Variation*

12.1 INTRODUCTION

In the first chapter we encountered the fact that observations are not perfectly reproducible or repeatable. In the simple case of the crossing of Aa by aa we found that with n progeny the number of aa offspring is not exactly one half of n, but that the number of such offspring can be anywhere between zero and n, each possible number having a probability given by the binomial expansion. Such randomness of the result of the mating is inherent in our picture of genetics at the present time.

Randomness of the result of an observational process occurs even without the randomness introduced by Mendelian segregation. If for example we make a number of different measurements of the height of a plant with a finely graduated measuring stick, we shall not achieve the same result everytime. With a measuring stick graduated in millimeters we might have 40 measurements achieve a set of measurements such as the following:

Length, mm	No. of Times Observed
361	2
362	8
363	10
364	11
365	6
366	3
	—
	40

What meaning are we to ascribe to this variation? There are several possibilities, for example:

1. That the height we are measuring itself varies from measurement to measurement.

* In this chapter there is a small amount of repetition of material from earlier chapters. This will probably not harm the beginning student of quantitative inheritance.

2. That our measuring stick is undergoing slight expansions and contractions.

3. That in fact both the height and the measuring stick are constant, but that the operator makes an error of greater or less magnitude each time he measures the height.

In all cases it is reasonable to assume that the actual observed height is composed of two parts, a true value and an error which could arise in any or all of the above three ways and other ways also. It is possible that there is association between the errors of successive measurements, for example, a tendency for positive errors to be followed by positive errors, but we shall assume that this disturbance is not present. With the above considerations it is then reasonable to assume that the ith observation y_i is given by

$$y_i = \mu + e_i$$

where μ is the true value, and e_i the error of the ith observation. We have already made one assumption, namely that the e_i's are not associated, or, in other words, are independent.

12.2 STATISTICAL DISTRIBUTION

We now suppose that the e_i's are a random sample from a certain statistical distribution. The notions here perhaps need clarification. A statistical distribution is a mathematical representation of an infinite population. Thus the binomial distribution for n trials is a representation of the results of an infinite population of experiments, each consisting of n trials. In this population a proportion p^n have n successes as the result, $np^{n-1}q$ have $(n-1)$ successes as the result, and so on. Given a population, it is relatively easy to obtain a random sample by the use of a device which has been shown to produce sets of numbers having the mathematical properties of random samples. Such a device is, in a rough sense, a table of random numbers.

Before we continue, it is necessary to introduce another mathematical simplification for the cases when the observation is not necessarily a whole number. In using a measuring stick, we arrive at definite markers such as $361mm$. If we were using a finer stick we might be able to say that the measurement gives 361.1 say. It will always be the case that the possible numbers that we obtain are elements of a finite set, that is, a set of numbers which can be enumerated. Thus we may be able to get a measurement between 340.0 and 360.0 by intervals of 0.1. On the other hand, we may always imagine in making measurements that we could have a more finely graduated stick, and we can in fact envisage a series of sticks, each more finely graduated than the previous one in the sequence.

It is therefore reasonable to suppose that we can in fact get any number such as 360.0135426, etc. apart from a rounding error.† We think then of the basic population of errors or statistical distribution of errors as being represented by a mathematical picture such as Figure 12.1, in which

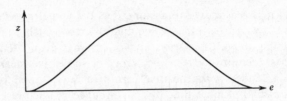

FIGURE 12.1. A statistical distribution.

the height of the curve z is given as a mathematical function of e, such as the well-known normal curve

$$z = \frac{1}{(2\pi\sigma^2)^{1/2}} \exp\left(-e^2/2\sigma^2\right)$$

where σ is a definite number to be assigned to the situation. The meaning to be attributed to such a mathematical distribution is that the probability of a random member of the population being between say e_1 and e_2 is the proportion of the total area under the curve which lies between ordinates erected at e_1 and e_2. Alternatively we can put e equal to $y - \mu$ and get the form

$$z = \frac{1}{(2\pi\sigma^2)^{1/2}} \exp\left(-(y - \mu)^2/2\sigma^2\right)$$

It is usually reasonable to assume that the observations we have are a random sample from the population of possible observations. Strictly speaking, we can say that a sample is random only if it has been obtained by a process known to give random samples, so that we can make the assumption that the sample is a random one strictly only when previous samples obtained by the same method have been found to have the properties of random samples. These properties can all be condensed into one statement, that each observation is as good in a colloquial sense as any other and there is no tendency for errors in successive observations to be related.

† This argument is not at all rigorous, but is intended merely to indicate the reasonableness of an approximation to a discrete distribution by a continuous distribution.

When we have made the assumption that the sample is a random one, we are in a position to ask certain obviously relevant questions. These questions are all based on the notion of *expectation*. Suppose we take an indefinitely large number of observations, so that we have a good facsimile of the population; we would then compute certain characteristics of the large sample and regard the results as being characteristics of the population. For instance, the population will have a certain mean value. This mean value of the population of e's say is called the expectation of e and is denoted by $E(e)$. Likewise we can consider the population of squares of e, and the mean value of this population is called the expectation of e^2 and is denoted by $E(e^2)$. There are of course an indefinitely large number of such expectations, and usually we are interested in only a few of them.

12.3 THE VARIANCE OF A DISTRIBUTION

We have already defined the mean of the distribution. It is then a simple matter conceptually to consider the deviation of each member of the population from the mean of the population, that is, the quantities $e - E(e)$, for example, and then to consider the mean of the squares of these quantities, or as we may write it

$$E[e - E(e)]^2$$

This quantity is known as the *variance* of the distribution. Why is this quantity of interest? It is clear that, being the average of the squares of $[e - E(e)]$, it is a measure of the spread of the e's around the mean. In a few cases the average value turns out to be infinity (that is, a number larger than any number one specifies), and it loses its utility as a measure of spread. Such cases will be quite rare in the material we shall consider, because the observation we can obtain can be said from a priori knowledge to lie within a definite range. (For example, the yield of corn in bushels per acre is definitely between 0 and 1000 for any situation we shall strike.) In all such cases the variance will be a definite number. We can construct other measures of the spread of a distribution around its mean value, and show that, according to another measure, two populations with the same variance have different degrees of spreads around the mean. It suffices to state here that, for a variety of reasons, the notion of variance has overwhelming advantages in genetical statistics.

These two properties of a real, as opposed to a theoretical, distribution, the mean and the variance, must remain unknown to us because their exact determination requires samples of infinite size. However, we should clarify what we mean by "unknown." It is clearly possible to obtain some idea of what the mean and variance of a distribution are, for, if we draw a sample from the distribution, we can surely make some statements about the true values. The making of such statements from samples is the substance of modern statistics. We shall not be concerned here with a complete statement of the situation, insofar as it is known, but only with portions of knowledge which are directly useful to us.

12.4 ESTIMATION OF MEAN AND VARIANCE

The question of the choice of an estimator has been given considerable attention since the subject was defined formally by Fisher in 1922 and is discussed in Chapter 8. It suffices here to state that the best estimate of a population mean in a very broad class of situations is the sample mean. It can be shown for example, that the sample mean is an *unbiased* estimator of the population mean, where "unbiased" means that the expectation of the estimate (which will itself be distributed in a definite way) is equal to the true value. Also it can be shown that the sample mean has the smallest possible variance of all unbiased estimators.

From most points of view the best estimator of the variance of a population of x's, given a sample of x's, denoted by $x_1, x_2, \cdots, x_n$ is

$$s^2 = \frac{1}{n-1} \sum (x - \bar{x})^2 = \frac{1}{n-1} [(x_1 - \bar{x})^2 + (x_2 - \bar{x})^2 + \cdots + (x_n - \bar{x})^2]$$

where $\bar{x} = \frac{1}{n} \sum x = \frac{1}{n}(x_1 + x_2 + \cdots x_n)$, or the sample mean.

12.5 VARIANCE OF SAMPLE STATISTICS

A sample *statistic* is a number calculated from the sample. Generally it is also an *estimator*, although frequently we calculate numbers from samples with no intention of using the resulting numbers as estimates of population parameters. This is the reason for having two different names for concepts which are very similar.

Any statistic is then a variable number, depending on the sample that is drawn. We can imagine drawing an indefinitely large number of samples, and calculating for each sample the statistic. In this way we would generate the distribution of the statistic. Naturally we are interested in the parameters of the distribution of the statistic, or the derived distribution as it is frequently called. Here we could get involved in a large portion of theoretical statistics, but shall confine ourselves to certain simple statistics.

We have already indicated the paramount importance of the sample mean, and we have already stated that the sample mean is unbiased.

Thus, if X_1, X_2, $\cdot$ $\cdot$ $\cdot$, X_n constitute a random sample from a population with mean θ (called theta), then

$$E(\bar{X}) = \theta$$

So the mean of the statistic $\bar{X}$ is the mean of the original population.

It is now reasonable to inquire about the variance of $\bar{X}$. The result is very simple, for, if we denote the variance of the original population by σ^2 (sigma squared) then the variance of the mean of a sample of size is σ^2/n. We may write this as $V(\bar{x})$ equals σ^2/n.

This formula is best derived by the use of a more general formula stating the variance of a sum. We have as a general relation

$$V(x_1 + x_2) = V(x_1) + V(x_2)$$

This holds only if the observations x_1 and x_2 are uncorrelated. This is a weaker condition than independence. More generally

$$V(x_1 + x_2 + \cdots + x_n) = V(x_1) + V(x_2) + \cdots + V(x_n)$$

for a random sample x_1, x_2, $\cdot$ $\cdot$ $\cdot$, x_n.

We also need two other simple general formulas. Suppose x is a random variable and k is a constant; then

$$E(kx) = k\,E(x)$$

and

$$V(kx) = k^2\,V(x)$$

These formulas are easily seen to follow from the definitions already given. Now

$$x_1 + x_2 + \cdots + x_n = n\bar{x}$$

and

$$V(x_1) = V(x_2) = \cdots = V(x_n) = \sigma^2$$

so that

$$V(n\bar{x}) = n\sigma^2$$

or

$$V(\bar{x}) = \frac{\sigma^2}{n}$$

Frequently we shall be concerned with linear functions of random sample values, or *random variables*.

Consider for example

$$k_1x_1 + k_2x_2 + \cdots + k_nx_n$$

where x_1, x_2, $\cdot$ $\cdot$ $\cdot$, x_n are independent (or merely uncorrelated) random sample values, and $k_1, k_2, \cdots, k_n$ are fixed numbers. To save space we write this as $\displaystyle\sum_{i=1}^{n} k_i x_i$ or just $\sum k_i x_i$. Then

$$V(\textstyle\sum k_i x_i) = k_1^2\, V(x_1) + k_2^2\, V(x_2) + \cdots + k_n^2\, V(x_n)$$
$$= \sum_{i=1}^{n} k_i^2\, V(x_i)$$

In the above we have been talking about functions of the values obtained in a random sample from a population. We now consider simple functions of $x_1, x_2, \cdots, x_n$, where x_1 is a random member of a population π_1 (say pi-one), x_2 a random member of a population π_2, and so on. The formula given above generalizes easily, so that we have

$$E(\textstyle\sum k_i x_i) = \sum k_i\, E(x_i)$$
$$V(\textstyle\sum k_i x_i) = \sum k_i^2\, V(x_i)$$

12.6 COVARIATION

In a large number of practical instances we cannot assume that our observations are entirely independent of each other. It is likely that, for example, height h and weight w will tend to go together in a population of humans. If we enumerated a large population and represented each individual by a dot on a graph in which the horizontal coordinate is height and the vertical coordinate is weight we would get a picture something like Figure 12.2.

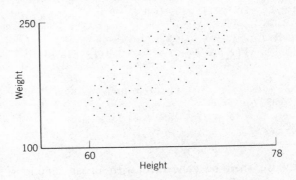

FIGURE 12.2. Example of covariation.

We draw a random member of this population and will get an individual of height h_1. We then look at his weight w_1. Clearly, if h_1 is greater than 72, it is extremely unlikely that w_1 is less than 120. If h_1 is around 60, it is very unlikely that w_1 is greater than say 180. We say that h and w are *dependent* random variables. A strict definition would be the following: The random variables h and w are dependent if for any two arbitrary number h_1 and h_2, the probability that h lies between h_1 and h_2, given that w equals w_0, depends on w_0: or, alternatively, given arbitrary numbers w_1 and w_2, the probability that w lies between w_1 and w_2, given that h equals h_0, depends on h_0. On the basis of this definition we can invent a number of tests for dependency. For instance, we may determine number w_1 and w_2 such that as close as possible to $\frac{1}{3}$ of the sample have w greater than w_1 and as close as possible to $\frac{1}{3}$ of the sample have w less than w_2: We can determine two numbers h_1 and h_2 with similar properties with respect to the sample values for h. We can then set up a frequency table of the form shown in Table 12.1. Here n_{11}, n_{12}, etc. denote the

TABLE 12.1

Weight	Height			
	Less than h_2	Between h_2 and h_1	Greater than h_1	Totals
Less than w_2	n_{11}	n_{12}	n_{13}	N_1 .
Between w_1 and w_2	n_{21}	n_{22}	n_{23}	N_2 .
Greater than w_2	n_{31}	n_{32}	n_{33}	N_3 .
Totals	$N_{.1}$	$N_{.2}$	$N_{.3}$	$N_{..}$

number of observations which fall into each cell. We can examine this table for association by

$$\chi^2 = \sum_{ij} \frac{(n_{ij} - N_i \, . \, N_{.\,j} / N_{..})^2}{(N_i \, . \, N_{.\,j} / N_{..})}$$

with four degrees of freedom.

There is no simple general measure of dependency of two random variables. Measures which have some utility and extreme simplicity are the covariance and the product moment correlation. The covariance of two random variables x_1 and x_2 with means μ_1 and μ_2, respectively, is equal to the expected value of the product $(x_1 - \mu_1)(x_2 - \mu_2)$ and is denoted by Cov (x_1, x_2). This is a natural enough measure, for, if x_1 is less than μ_1, and x_1 and x_2 are associated, then there should be a tendency for x_2 to be less than μ_2 or greater than μ_2. In the former case the covariance will be positive, and in the second case negative If deviations from mean as regards x_2 are not associated with deviations from mean as regards x_1, the expected value of the product will be zero. On the other hand, one can visualize situations in which this expected value is zero, but there is a non-linear average relation between x_1 and x_2. This fact makes the covariance an incompletely adequate measure of dependency, except when x_1 and x_2 have what is known as the bivariate normal distribution. The product moment correlation of x_1 and x_2 is equal to

$$\frac{\text{Cov}(x_1, x_2)}{[V(x_1)\ V(x_2)]^{1/2}}$$

and has the convenience of having a possible range of minus unity to plus unity. Uncorrelated variables are variables for which this quantity is zero. A frequent difficulty in interpreting a correlation is doubt of linearity of the relationship.

12.7 VARIANCE OF LINEAR FUNCTIONS OF CORRELATED VARIABLES

We are now in the position of being able to talk about the variance of linear functions of correlated variables. Consider first the simple sum of two variables, x_1 and x_2, and the variance of $x_1 + x_2$. Now $x_1 + x_2$ has expectation equal to $\mu_1 + \mu_2$, and

$$
\begin{aligned}
(x_1 + x_2 - \mu_1 - \mu_2)^2 &= [(x_1 - \mu_1) + (x_2 - \mu_2)]^2 \\
&= (x_1 - \mu_1)^2 + (x_2 - \mu_2)^2 + 2(x_1 - \mu_1)(x_2 - \mu_2)
\end{aligned}
$$

Taking expectations of both sides, we get

$$V(x_1 + x_2) = V(x_1) + V(x_2) + 2\,\text{Cov}(x_1, x_2)$$

It is a simple matter from this to develop the general formula

$$V\left(\sum_{i=1}^{n} \lambda_i x_i\right) = \sum_{i=1}^{n} \lambda_i^2\, V(x_i) + \sum_{i \neq j} \lambda_i \lambda_j\, \text{Cov}(x_i, x_j)$$

where $\displaystyle\sum_{i \neq j} \lambda_i \lambda_j\, \text{Cov}(x_i, x_j)$ means that we consider all the possible $n(n-1)$ number pairs i and j, with i not equal to j, and write down $\lambda_i \lambda_j\, \text{Cov}(x_i x_j)$ for each pair and sum.

This formula is the completely general one for the variance of a linear function of random variables, from which all previous formulas on variances of linear functions for special cases can be obtained.

12.8 THE NORMAL DISTRIBUTION

We have already encountered the formula for the normal distribution: namely

$$f(y) = \frac{1}{(2\pi\sigma^2)^{1/2}} \exp\left(-(y-\mu)^2/2\sigma^2\right)$$

from which, given particular values for μ and σ, we can plot $f(y)$ as a function of y to give the well-known bell shaped curve (Figure 12.3). We

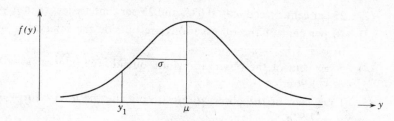

FIGURE 12.3. The normal distribution.

can state that the probability, or relative frequency in an indefinitely large population, of observation less than y_1, say, is the area under the curve and to the left of the ordinate erected at y_1.

Why should this particular distribution especially enter into our description of statistical genetics or of statistics? There are several reasons more or less connected mathematically and coming from the fact that it can be shown mathematically that, if an observation is made up of a large number of small parts, which parts are given to the total observation as the result of random draws from reasonable populations, then the sum will tend to have a normal distribution. Very early in these notes we utilized this property in approximating the probability that the number of successes in a large number n binomial trials is less than any chosen number. The total number of successes is made up by adding zero's and one's, which will be small relative to n. Similarly our picture of the height say of an individual is that it is determined by a large number of loci, at each of which two or more genes are possible, and it is reasonable to suppose that the genes and hence the gene effects have been combined randomly in the population. Hence it is not surprising that heights of a human population are essentially normally distributed, providing we separate by sex and hence eliminate one genetic effect which we know does not conform to the requirement of being small, and perhaps also giants and dwarfs.

It can be shown mathematically that the mean of the population, or alternatively the expectation of the random variable y, is equal to μ and the variance is σ^2. The normal curve is symmetrical about μ, and 50 per cent of observations lie on each side of μ, so that μ is the median. It is an interesting geometrical note that the curve has points of inflection at $\mu - \sigma$ and $\mu + \sigma$. It is useful to carry in one's mind certain other features of the normal curve. These are:

(1) 50 per cent of the population lies between $\mu - 0.67\sigma$ and $\mu + 0.67\sigma$, or

(2) 25 per cent exceed $\mu + 0.67\sigma$, and 25 per cent are less than $\mu - 0.67\sigma$.

(3) 10 per cent of the observations are outside the interval $\mu - 1.645\sigma$ to $\mu + 1.645\sigma$.

(4) 5 per cent of the observations are outside the interval $\mu - 1.96\sigma$ to $\mu + 1.96\sigma$.

(5) 1 per cent of the observations are outside the interval $\mu - 2.57\sigma$ to $\mu + 2.57\sigma$.

It can be shown that the estimates

$$\hat{\mu} = \bar{y}$$

and

$$s^2 = \frac{1}{n-1} \sum(y - \bar{y})^2 = \hat{\sigma}^2$$

are the best for most practical purposes. It can be shown that they are both unbiased; i.e.

$$E(\hat{\mu}) = \mu$$
$$E(s^2) = \sigma^2$$

12.9 TESTS ON NORMAL DISTRIBUTIONS

In all cases to be considered in this text, any statistical test consists of the calculation of a number from the sample which will be examined as a possible random member from some distribution which the number would follow under the null hypothesis, i.e. the hypothesis being tested. As we have seen, with frequency data this consisted usually of calculating a quantity which we designated as χ^2, because under the null hypothesis this quantity would be distributed according to the χ^2 distribution with certain degrees of freedom. To complete the process of testing it is necessary to pick out a distinctive part of the null hypothesis distribution and to reject the null hypothesis, or conclude that the null hypothesis is untenable, if the number obtained from the sample falls in this part. The question of what part to use has been the subject of considerable mathematical investigation over the years, but we can take the position here, that, with the problems we consider or are likely to meet, the choice is intuitively obvious. Suppose the number calculated from the sample is C, and under the null hypothesis it would be C_0. Clearly the distinctive part of the distribution is the part where C differs widely from C_0. In certain instances we may feel that any deviations from the null hypothesis we may be encountering may be such that $C - C_0$ could be a large positive or negative number. At other times, as indeed with the case of χ^2 goodness of fit tests, we may feel that deviations from the null hypothesis will tend to make $C - C_0$ a positive number. Now suppose we wish to use a 5 per cent significance level. In the first case the distinctive part or region will consist of either

1. The part for which $C - C_0$ is greater in absolute magnitude than some number d, where the probability of this part on the null hypothesis is 5 per cent, or

2. Two separate subparts (a) the upper $2\frac{1}{2}$ per cent of the distribution and (b) the lower $2\frac{1}{2}$ per cent of the distribution.

Frequently these two procedures will lead to the same total region, but the choice is not at all obvious in many instances. In the second case, if deviations tend to produce a positive (negative) number, we choose the region as the upper (lower) 5 per cent part of the distribution. In the first case we use a two-tail test or region, and in the second case a one-tail test or region. The three distributions which arise most in tests on normal populations are the t distribution, the χ^2 distribution, and the F distribution.

With these preliminaries we may list the common tests on means and variances:

I. Given $x_1, x_2, \cdots, x_n$ assumed to be a random sample from the normal distribution with unknown mean μ and known variance σ^2 to test $\mu = \mu_0$. Calculate

$$y = \frac{\bar{x} - \mu_0}{\sigma/\sqrt{n}}$$

and compare this with the normal distribution with mean zero and unit variance.

II. Given $x_1, x_2, \cdots, x_n$ assumed to be a random sample from the normal distribution with unknown mean μ and unknown variance σ^2, to test $\mu = \mu_0$. Calculate

$$t = \frac{\bar{x} - \mu_0}{\left[\dfrac{\sum(x - \bar{x})^2}{(n - 1)n}\right]^{1/2}}$$

and compare this observed value with the t distribution with $(n-1)$ degrees of freedom.

III. Given two random samples $x_1, x_2, \cdots, x_{n_1}$, and $y_1, y_2, \cdots, y_{n_2}$ from normal distributions with variance σ^2 and unknown means μ_1 and μ_2, respectively, to test $\mu_1 = \mu_2$. Calculate

$$z = \frac{\bar{x} - \bar{y}}{\sigma \left(\dfrac{1}{n_1} + \dfrac{1}{n_2}\right)^{1/2}}$$

and compare this with the normal distribution with mean zero and variance unity.

IV. Given two random samples $x_1, x_2, \cdots, x_{n_1}$, and $y_1, y_2, \cdots, y_{n_2}$ from normal distributions with unknown variance σ^2 and means μ_1 and μ_2, respectively, to test $\mu_1 = \mu_2$. Calculate

$$t = \frac{\bar{x} - \bar{y}}{\left[\dfrac{\sum(x - \bar{x})^2 + \sum(y - \bar{y})^2}{n_1 + n_2 - 2}\right]^{1/2} \left(\dfrac{1}{n_1} + \dfrac{1}{n_2}\right)^{1/2}}$$

and compare this with the t distribution with $n_1 + n_2 - 2$ degrees of freedom.

V. Given a random sample $x_1, x_2, \cdots, x_n$ from a normal distribution with known mean μ and unknown variance σ^2 to test $\sigma^2 = \sigma_0^2$. Calculate

$$\chi^2 = \frac{\sum(x - \mu)^2}{\sigma_0^2}$$

and compare this with the χ^2 distribution with n degrees of freedom.

VI. Given two random samples, $x_1, x_2, \cdots, x_{n_1}$, and $y_1, y_2, \cdots, y_{n_2}$, from normal distributions with known means μ_1 and μ_2 and unknown variances σ_1^2 and σ_2^2, to test $\sigma_1^2 = \sigma_2^2$. Calculate

$$\frac{\sum(x - \mu_1)^2}{n_1} \quad \text{and} \quad \frac{\sum(y - \mu_2)^2}{n_2}$$

divide the larger by the smaller, and call the resulting number F. Compare F with the usual tabulated F distribution, doubling the percentages indicated by the table. The degrees of freedom are the sample size for both numerator and denominator.

VII. Given two random samples, $x_1, x_2, \cdots, x_{n_1}$, and $y_1, y_2, \cdots, y_{n_2}$, from normal distribution with unknown means and variances σ_1^2 and

σ_2^2, respectively, to test $\sigma_1^2 = \sigma_2^2$. Calculate $\sum(x - \bar{x})^2/(n_1 - 1)$ and $\sum(y - \bar{y})^2/(n_2 - 1)$; divide the larger by the smaller and compare the resultant number with usual table of the F distribution, doubling the percentages indicated by the table, the degrees of freedom being sample size less unity for numerator and denominator.

12.10 INTERCLASS CORRELATION

We have already described a basic property of joint distributions of two random variables, x_1 and x_2 say, in defining the product moment correlation as

$$\frac{\text{Cov}(x_1, x_2)}{[V(x_1)\, V(x_2)]^{1/2}}$$

This is also known as the interclass correlation of x_1 and x_2. The word "interclass" is used because the population consists of a large number of classes, each with a single member which has two attributes x_1 and x_2. Corresponding to this population property, we have the same quantity defined for a sample of n paired observations (x_{11}, x_{21}), (x_{12}, x_{22}), $\cdots$, (x_{1n}, x_{2n}) where, in x_{ij}, i denotes the attribute and j the member. The formula is

$$\frac{\sum(x_{1j} - \bar{x}_1)(x_{2j} - \bar{x}_2)}{[\sum(x_{1j} - \bar{x}_1)^2 \sum(x_{2j} - \bar{x}_2)^2]^{1/2}}$$

This is usually denoted by r, and is an estimate of the corresponding population property which is usually denoted by ρ (rho). If it can be assumed that the observations are a random sample from the joint bivariate normal distribution, we can test if ρ could be zero by calculating

$$t = \frac{r(n - 2)^{1/2}}{(1 - r^2)^{1/2}}$$

and comparing this value with the t distribution with $(n-2)$ degrees of freedom.

For other purposes such as testing if a correlation could be specified non-zero value or if two correlations could be the same, or to average correlation coefficients, the quantity

$$z = \tfrac{1}{2} \log \frac{1 + r}{1 - r}$$

should be used. This quantity has a distribution which is essentially normal even for small n with mean $\tfrac{1}{2} \log(1 + \rho)/(1 - \rho)$ and a variance of $1/(n-3)$.   It is to be noted that the variance depends only on the sample size and not on ρ, so that the tests described above for comparisons of means and so on can be used.   In averaging estimates of ρ the values of z are obtained and a mean is obtained weighting inversely as the variance.

It is sometimes of utility to consider partial correlations, such as that between x_1 and x_2 when the *linear* effect of x_3 has been eliminated.   There is a simple formula for doing this process in general:

$$r_{12.3} = \frac{r_{12} - r_{13}r_{23}}{[(1 - r_{13}^2)(1 - r_{23}^2)]^{1/2}}$$

The variables eliminated are indicated by suffices after the dot.   This formula may be extended by replacing all correlations in it by partial correlations, to give $r_{12.34}$ say which is obtained from $r_{12.4}$, $r_{13.4}$, and $r_{23.4}$. The student should beware of statements like "the correlation of x_1 and x_2 keeping x_3 constant" which occur rather frequently in statistical texts. Linearity of regressions throughout the possible range is necessary for validity of interpreting partial correlations in this way.

Tests on partial correlation coefficients are made in exactly the same way as for ordinary total correlations, except that the quantity n in the formula for t is reduced by unity for each factor whose effect is eliminated. Readers interested in further information on correlation coefficients should study Chapter VI of R. A. Fisher's *Statistical Methods for Research Workers*, Snedecor's *Statistical Methods*, or Goulden's *Methods of Statistical Analysis*.   Tables of t, z, etc. are given in Fisher and Yates's *Statistical Tables* and other sets of tables and texts.

PROBLEMS

1.   Prove $E(kx) = k\,E(x)$ if k is a constant.

2.   Prove $V(kx) = k^2\,V(x)$ if k is a constant.

3.   Prove $V(x_1 + x_2 + \cdots + x_n) = V(x_1) + V(x_2) + \cdots + V(x_n)$ if the x_i are uncorrelated.

4.   Prove $V\left(\sum_i k_i x_i\right) = \sum_i k_i^2 V(x_i)$ if the x_i's are uncorrelated.

5.   Prove the general formula

$$V\left(\sum_{i=1}^{n} k_i x_i\right) = \sum_{i=1}^{n} k_i^2 V(x_i) + \sum_{i \neq j} k_i k_j\, \mathrm{Cov}\,(x_i, x_j)$$

6.   Prove that

$$\mathrm{Cov}\left(\sum_{i=1}^{n} \lambda_i x_i, \sum_{i=1}^{n} \nu_i x_i\right) = \sum_{i=1}^{n} \lambda_i \nu_i\, V(x_i) + \sum_{i \neq j} \lambda_i \nu_j\, \mathrm{Cov}\,(x_i, x_j)$$

7. Evaluate the correlations of x_1 and x_2, of x_1 and x_3, and of x_2 and x_3 with the five observations

x_1	x_2	x_3
4	1	3
6	3	2
8	2	4
9	4	5
1	− 3	1

Evaluate the significance of these correlations.

8. Obtain the three possible partial correlations for the data of problem 7, and evaluate their significance.

CHAPTER 13

The Partition of Variance

13.1 INTRODUCTION

In Chapter 11 it was mentioned that in some instances it may be reasonable to suppose that an observation y is determined additively by genotypic effects and environmental effects; i.e.

$$y = G + E$$

It is preferable here to make a redefinition writing this equation as

$$y = \mu + G + E$$

in which μ is a constant, and G and E are now redefined as deviations, which sum to zero over the whole population of genotypes and environments. We shall use this example to illustrate the ideas of the partition of variance.

The first question which strikes us is how much of the variability of y is due to variation in G and how much to variation in E. We know that

$$V(y) = V(G) + V(E) + 2 \operatorname{Cov}(G, E)$$

It is clearly of importance to the geneticist and breeder to know what the contributions of G and E to the variance of y are. Suppose $\operatorname{Cov}(G, E)$ is zero, i.e. that the genotypes and environments are associated at random, and that $V(y)$ equals $V(E)$. Then $V(G)$ equals zero, or, in other words, there is no contribution to the variability of y which is associated with the genotypes. Under these circumstances it would be useless for the geneticist to attempt genetic selection, i.e. selection of better genotypes. If it is desired to change y, all that can be done is to vary the environment E and choose the best one.

The magnitude of $V(G)$ is useful to the breeder so that he can have some idea of the utility of practicing a selection scheme. The magnitude of $V(E)$ specifies the variability of environmental effects and must be considered in relation to $V(G)$. We now consider a simple idealized situation in which $V(G)$ and $V(E)$ may be estimated.

Suppose we have a population of varieties of corn and wish to determine the genetic variability in the population. We shall select from this population at random say n varieties and grow them in the field. Because of variability in the field and errors of measurement and technique, we know that we should have several measurements on each variety, r say. In all then we shall need nr plots, and we suppose this number of plots is available. We shall then assign the varieties at random to the plots, each variety occurring on r plots. The randomness of the assignment of varieties to plots will ensure no correlation between genotypes and environments in the field. We denote the observations by y_{ij} in which i denotes the variety and j designates the yield on the jth plot which has variety i. It is then reasonable to write the equation, or model

$$y_{ij} = \mu + g_i + e_{ij}$$

in which i goes from 1 to n, and j from 1 to r. We want to estimate $V(g_i)$ which we shall denote for convenience by σ_g^2 and $V(e_{ij})$ which we denote by σ_e^2.

It is not our purpose here to develop *ab initio* the theory of estimation of σ_g^2 and σ_e^2. (See for example Kempthorne, 1952, Chapter 6.) Instead we shall present the procedure and attempt to demonstrate its reasonableness.

Consider $\dfrac{1}{r}\sum_j y_{ij}$, i.e. the mean of the observations on variety i which we denote by y_i. By the model this is equal to

$$\mu + g_i + \frac{1}{r}\sum_j e_{ij}$$

Hence $y_{i\cdot}$ is distributed around μ with variance $\sigma_g^2 + \dfrac{1}{r}\sigma_e^2$ since

$$V(y_{i\cdot}) = V\left(g_i + \frac{1}{r}\sum_j e_{ij}\right)$$

$$= V(g_i) + V\left(\frac{1}{r}\sum_j e_{ij}\right) \quad \text{because } g_i \text{ and } e_{ij} \text{ are uncorrelated}$$

and

$$V(g_i) = \sigma_g^2$$

$$V\left(\frac{1}{r}\sum_j e_{ij}\right)^2 = \frac{1}{r^2}[r\sigma_e^2] = \frac{\sigma_e^2}{r}$$

Hence we may estimate $\left(\sigma_g^2 + \dfrac{\sigma_e^2}{r}\right)$ by $\dfrac{1}{n-1}\sum_i (y_i. - \bar{y}_i.)^2$ or, letting $\dfrac{1}{nr}\sum_{ij} y_{ij}$ equal $y..$, by $\dfrac{1}{n-1}\sum_i (y_i. - y..)^2$. Now consider

$$\sum_{ij} (y_{ij} - y_i.)^2$$

We have from the model

$$y_{ij} - y_i. = e_{ij} - \frac{1}{r}\sum_j e_{ij}$$

and

$$E(y_{ij} - y_i.)^2 = \sigma_e^2 \left(\frac{r-1}{r}\right)$$

Hence $\sum_{ij} (y_{ij} - y_i.)^2$ estimates $nr\sigma_e^2 \left(\dfrac{r-1}{r}\right)$ equals $n(r-1)\sigma_e^2$. Therefore we may write the following:

$$\hat{\sigma}_e^2 = \frac{1}{n(r-1)}\sum_{ij} (y_{ij} - y_i.)^2$$

$$\sigma_e^2 \hat{+} r\sigma_g^2 = \frac{r}{n-1}\sum_i (y_i. - y..)^2$$

These results are conveniently given in the analysis of variance in Table 13.1.

TABLE 13.1
ANALYSIS OF VARIANCE

Source	d.f.	S.S.	M.S.	E.M.S.
Among varieties	$n-1$	$r\sum_i(y_i. -y..)^2$	V	$\sigma_e^2 + r\sigma_g^2$
Within varieties	$n(r-1)$	$\sum_{ij}(y_{ij}-y_i.)^2$	E	σ_e^2
Total	$nr-1$	$\sum_{ij}(y_{ij}-y..)^2$	T	$\sigma_e^2 + \dfrac{(n-1)r}{(nr-1)}\sigma_g^2$

This table gives in shortened form the computations we have gone through. The sum of squares (S.S.) $r\sum_i (y_i. - y..)^2$ is r times the sum of squares between the variety means and hence is described as coming from the source, among variety means. The sum of squares $\sum_{ij} (y_{ij} - y_i.)^2$

is the sum of squares of the observations around the variety means and hence is described as coming from the source, within varieties. The symbols 'd.f.' stand for degrees of freedom. In the variety sum of squares we have n variety means, and the degrees of freedom is $n - 1$, one less than the number. In the within-variety sum of squares, each quantity $\sum_j (y_{ij} - y_i .)^2$ is the sum of squares of r quantities about their mean and hence has $(r-1)$ degrees of freedom. There are n sets in all, giving the total of $n(r-1)$ degrees of freedom. The mean squares (M.S.) are obtained by dividing the sums of squares by their respective degrees of freedom. The last column gives the expectation of the mean square (E.M.S.) in each case. Finally as a check on the computations the degrees of freedom add up to one less than the total number of observations, and the sums of squares add up to the sum of squares of the observations about the over-all mean. Usually it is convenient to use the addition of the sums of squares to the total as a device for calculating the within sum of squares by subtraction. Also it can be shown that

$$r \sum_i (y_i . - y. .)^2 = \frac{1}{r} \sum_i Y_i^2 . - \frac{Y^2 .}{nr}$$

$$\sum_{ij} (y_{ij} - y. .)^2 = \sum_{ij} y_{ij}^2 - \frac{Y^2 .}{nr}$$

where

$$Y_i . = \sum_j y_{ij} , \qquad Y. . = \sum_{i,j} y_{ij}$$

and the quantity $Y^2 . /nr$ is known as the correction factor. The whole matter of estimation of σ_g^2 and σ_e^2 is reduced then to a computational routine, and we have

$$\hat{\sigma}_e^2 = E$$

$$\hat{\sigma}_g^2 = \frac{1}{r}(V - E)$$

These estimates are unbiased. To obtain their sampling variances it is necessary to make some assumptions about the distribution of g_i and e_{ij}. If they are normally distributed,

$$V(\hat{\sigma}_e^2) = \frac{2\sigma_e^4}{n(r - 1)}$$

$$V(\widehat{\sigma_e^2 + r\sigma_g^2}) = \frac{2(\sigma_e^2 + r\sigma_g^2)^2}{n - 1}$$

Since $\hat{\sigma}_e^2$ and $\overparen{\sigma_e^2 + r\sigma_g^2}$ are independent

$$V(\hat{\sigma}_g^2) = \frac{2}{r^2}\left[\frac{(\sigma_e^2 + r\sigma_g^2)^2}{n-1} + \frac{\sigma_e^4}{n(r-1)}\right]$$

These variances may be estimated unbiasedly by

$$V(\hat{\sigma}_e^2) = \frac{2(\hat{\sigma}_e^2)^2}{n(r-1)+2}$$

$$V(\hat{\sigma}_g^2) = \frac{2}{r^2}\left[\frac{\overparen{(\sigma_e^2 + r\sigma_g^2)^2}}{n+1} + \frac{(\hat{\sigma}_e^2)^2}{n(r-1)+2}\right]$$

13.2 INTRACLASS CORRELATIONS

We are now in a position to give the essential features of another correlation coefficient. In the previous section we had the model

$$y_{ij} = \mu + g_i + e_{ij}$$

and we defined μ so that

$$E(g_i) = E(e_{ij}) = 0$$

Hence we have

$$E(y_{ij}) = \mu$$

Now consider the variances and covariances of the y_{ij}'s. We have

$$\begin{aligned}V(y_{ij}) &= V(g_i) + V(e_{ij})\\ &= \sigma_g^2 + \sigma_e^2 \quad \text{for all } i \text{ and } j\end{aligned}$$

When we consider covariances, something unusual happens for we have, for j' unequal to j,

$$\begin{aligned}\text{Cov}\,(y_{ij}, y_{ij'}) &= E(g_i + e_{ij})(g_i + e_{ij'})\\ &= E(g_i^2) + E(g_i e_{ij'}) + E(g_i e_{ij}) + E(e_{ij}e_{ij'})\end{aligned}$$

and the g's are uncorrelated with the e's, and the e's are uncorrelated with each other. Hence

$$\text{Cov}\,(y_{ij}, y_{ij'}) = \sigma_g^2$$

so that we have

$$\rho(y_{ij}, y_{ij'}) = \frac{\sigma_g^2}{[(\sigma_g^2 + \sigma_e^2)(\sigma_g^2 + \sigma_e^2)]^{1/2}} = \frac{\sigma_g^2}{\sigma_g^2 + \sigma_e^2}$$

On the other hand, for two observations from different varieties i, i' say, we have

$$\text{Cov}(y_{ij}, y_{i'j'}) = E(g_i + e_{ij})(g_{i'} + e_{i'j'})$$
$$= 0$$

so that

$$\rho(y_{ij}, y_{i'j'}) = 0, \qquad i' \neq i$$

Thus we see that there is a correlation between observations on the same variety, and no correlation between observations on different varieties. To justify the name "intraclass correlation," the varieties may be regarded as classes, and we see that there is a correlation *within classes* and not between classes. In the interclass case every member has two attributes; in the simple intraclass case every member has only one attribute.

That the intraclass correlation is in fact intrinsically a correlation can be seen from the way it was obtained, as a ratio of the covariance of two variables to the geometric mean of their variances. It will be remembered that the interclass correlation was defined in exactly this way. Another way of seeing this correspondence is indicated by Fisher in *Statistical Methods for Research Workers* (1925 and succeeding editions). Briefly it is as follows: Let x_{ij} denote any observation on variety one, $x_{ij'}$ any other observation on this variety. Make up the complete array in which the variate z is x_{ij} and the corresponding variate u is any $x_{ij'}$; i.e., z is any observation, and u is another observation on the same variety. Each observation will then occur $(r-1)$ times as z and $(r-1)$ times as u. Now with the resultant $nr(r-1)$ pairs of numbers calculate the ordinary product–moment or interclass correlation. We shall have

$$\sum z = nr(r-1)y_{..} = \sum u$$

$$\sum z^2 = (r-1)\sum y_{ij}^2 = \sum u^2$$

$$\sum (z - \bar{z})^2 = \sum (u - \bar{u})^2 = (r-1)\sum_{ij} y_{ij}^2 - nr(r-1)y_{..}^2$$

$$= (r-1)\left(\sum_{ij} y_{ij}^2 - nry_{..}^2\right)$$

$$= (r-1)\sum_{ij}(y_{ij} - y_{..})^2$$

$$\sum zu = \sum_i \sum_j \sum_{j' \neq j} y_{ij}y_{ij'}$$

$$= \sum_i \left[\left(\sum_j y_{ij}\right)^2 - \sum_j y_{ij}^2\right]$$

$$= \sum_i Y_{i.}^2 - \sum_{ij} y_{ij}^2 \qquad \text{where} \quad Y_{i.} = \sum_j y_{ij}$$

$$\sum_i (z - \bar{z})(u - \bar{u}) = \sum_i Y_i^2 . - \sum_{ij} y_{ij}^2 - nr(r - 1)y_{..}^2 .$$

$$= r \left(\frac{1}{r} \sum_i Y_i^2 . - nry_{..}^2 \right) - \left(\sum_{ij} y_{ij}^2 - nry_{..}^2 \right)$$

$$= r(n - 1)V - (nr - 1)T$$

where V and T are taken from Table 13.1. Hence

$$\rho_{zu} = \frac{r(n - 1)V - (nr - 1)T}{(nr - 1)(r - 1)T} = \frac{V - \dfrac{n}{n - 1}E}{V + (r - 1)\dfrac{n}{(n - 1)}E}$$

If now we let n get very large, then

$$V \text{ tends to the value } \sigma_e^2 + r\sigma_g^2$$

$$T \text{ tends to } \sigma_e^2 + \frac{(n - 1)r}{(nr - 1)} \sigma_g^2$$

so that ρ_{zu} tends to

$$\frac{r(n - 1)(\sigma_e^2 + r\sigma_g^2) - [(nr - 1)\sigma_e^2 + (n - 1)r\sigma_g^2]}{(r - 1)[(nr - 1)\sigma_e^2 + (n - 1)r\sigma_g^2]}$$

Since n is large, we may replace $n - 1$ by n and $nr - 1$ by nr, and we get as the limit for ρ_{zu}

$$\rho_{zu} = \frac{nr\sigma_e^2 + nr^2\sigma_g^2 - nr\sigma_e^2 - nr\sigma_g^2}{(r - 1)\,nr(\sigma_e^2 + \sigma_g^2)}$$

$$= \frac{nr(r - 1)\sigma_g^2}{(r - 1)\,nr(\sigma_e^2 + \sigma_g^2)}$$

$$= \frac{\sigma_g^2}{\sigma_e^2 + \sigma_g^2}$$

From the previous argument we may state that the intraclass correlation is the interclass correlation we would observe if the number of classes were indefinitely large and we found the average correlation between a member of a class and another member of the same class.

13.3 THE NOTION OF REPEATABILITY

The previous section leads easily into the notion of repeatability which is used considerably in animal breeding work. The notion dates back to early psychological statistical work. Suppose that instead of varieties in the previous situation we had several scores on animals. Then it is reasonable to think of the observed score for animal i as being given by

$$y_{ij} = \mu + g_i + e_{ij}$$

where the term e_{ij} is an observational error and the true score of the ith animal is $\mu + g_i$. Suppose too that μ is the mean of the true scores for the population of animals, so that the average of the g_i contribution over all animals is zero. Then the correlation among scores of the same animal is $\sigma_g^2/(\sigma_g^2 + \sigma_e^2)$. This is called the repeatability of the score.

Now consider the following problem. Suppose we have r_i measurements on the ith individual and wish to rank the individuals. We could rank the animals in the order of their observed mean scores, but it is clear that an animal may give a high mean score because his true mean score is high, or because positive errors of observation were made consistently on him. Let us suppose that the true value of μ is known. We wish to obtain scores which we will take to be $K_i(y_i. - \mu)$, which are to give the best indication of the true values of the animals. We wish then to obtain K_i so that

$$E[K_i(y_i. - \mu) - g_i]^2$$

is a minimum. Now this has the expectation

$$K_i^2 E(y_i. - \mu)^2 - 2K_i E[(y_i. - \mu)(g_i)] + E(g_i^2)$$

$$= K_i^2 \left(\sigma_g^2 + \frac{\sigma_e^2}{r_i}\right) - 2K_i \sigma_g^2 + \sigma_g^2$$

The minimum value of

$$ax^2 + 2bx + c$$

with respect to x is achieved when $x = -b/a$. So the minimum deviation squared is achieved when

$$K_i = \frac{\sigma_g^2}{\sigma_g^2 + \sigma_e^2/r_i} = \frac{\sigma_g^2/\sigma_e^2}{\sigma_g^2/\sigma_e^2 + 1/r_i}$$

Now denote the intraclass correlation by ρ so that

$$\rho = \frac{\sigma_g^2}{\sigma_g^2 + \sigma_e^2} = \frac{\sigma_g^2/\sigma_e^2}{\sigma_g^2/\sigma_e^2 + 1}$$

then

$$\sigma_g^2/\sigma_e^2 = \rho/(1 - \rho)$$

then

$$K_i = \frac{\rho/(1 - \rho)}{\rho/(1 - \rho) + 1/r_i} = \frac{r_i \rho}{\rho r_i + 1 - \rho} = \frac{r_i \rho}{1 + (r_i - 1)\rho}$$

Hence the best predictor of g_i is

$$\frac{r_i \rho}{1 + (r_i - 1)\rho} (y_i . - \mu)$$

In words, the best predictor of an animal's true score is equal to

(Population true mean score) $+ \dfrac{r_i \rho}{1 + (r_i - 1)\rho}$

$\times$ (animal's mean score $-$ population true mean score)

The utility of this formula is discussed extensively by Lush (*Animal Breeding Plans*, 1937 and succeeding editions, Chapter 13). In this work on animals, the population true mean score is taken to be the herd average.

13.4 A DIRECT APPLICATION OF INTRACLASS CORRELATIONS

It is probably useful to the reader to give a more direct application of the intraclass correlation to a genetic situation. Consider then a large animal population in which mating is at random, and from this population consider sires and their offspring. As we shall see later, we may regard a sire as having the value

$$y_i = \mu + g_i + e_i$$

and an offspring as having the value

$$x_i = \mu + \tfrac{1}{2}g_i + f_i$$

in which μ is the population average, $\tfrac{1}{2}g_i$ is the contribution which the sire hands on by Mendelian inheritance to his offspring, and e_i and f_i are random errors. The argument for this representation is not based on blending inheritance.

Consider first the interclass correlation of offspring and sire. We have

$$\text{Cov}(y_i, x_i) = E(g_i + e_i)(\tfrac{1}{2}g_i + f_i) = \tfrac{1}{2}E(g_i^2) = \tfrac{1}{2}\sigma_g^2, \quad \text{say}$$

$$V(y_i) = E(g_i + e_i)^2 = \sigma_g^2 + \sigma_e^2$$

and we shall here assume that the offspring are subject to this same variance. Then

$$\rho_{xy} = \frac{1}{2}\frac{\sigma_g^2}{\sigma_g^2 + \sigma_e^2}$$

Now this looks very much like one half of an intraclass correlation.

To exhibit the whole matter clearly, suppose we have n sires and r offspring from each sire, each offspring having been produced by a mating of the sire to a random dam. Then we may write as the model for our observations, where x_{ij} is the value for the jth offspring of sire i,

$$x_{ij} = \mu + \tfrac{1}{2}g_i + f_{ij}$$

and we have a model which looks exactly like the one we used for the varieties. Before proceeding let us note that, if this is written as

$$x_{ij} = \mu + v_i + f_{ij}$$

then

$$E(v_i^2) = \tfrac{1}{4}\sigma_g^2$$

$$E(x_{ij} - \mu)^2 = \sigma_g^2 + \sigma_e^2$$

$$= \tfrac{1}{4}\sigma_g^2 + E(f_{ij}^2)$$

so

$$E(f_{ij}^2) = \tfrac{3}{4}\sigma_g^2 + \sigma_e^2$$

Now suppose we make the analysis of variance as in Table 13.2.

TABLE 13.2

Source	d.f.	M.S.	E.M.S.
Among sire groups	$n-1$	S	$(\tfrac{3}{4}\sigma_g^2 + \sigma_e^2) + r(\tfrac{1}{4}\sigma_g^2)$
Within sire groups	$n(r-1)$	W	$\tfrac{3}{4}\sigma_g^2 + \sigma_e^2$
Total	$nr-1$		

Clearly we may estimate as follows:

$$\widehat{\tfrac{3}{4}\sigma_g^2 + \sigma_e^2} = W$$

$$\tfrac{1}{4}(\sigma_g^2) = (1/r)(S - W)$$

so

$$\widehat{\sigma_g^2 + \sigma_e^2} = W + (1/r)(S - W) = (1/r)[S + (r - 1)W]$$

and

$$\frac{\widehat{\sigma_g^2}}{\sigma_g^2 + \sigma_e^2} = \frac{(4/r)(S - W)}{\dfrac{S + (r - 1)W}{r}} = \frac{4(S - W)}{S + (r - 1)W}$$

The assumptions behind the use of the model in this instance and the limitations and utility of the procedure for estimating the intraclass correlation will be discussed in a later chapter. Our sole purpose here was to illustrate how in a genetic situation an intraclass correlation, which is a ratio of linear functions of variances, may be estimated either by interclass correlation methods (in this case, regression of offspring on parent) or by intraclass correlation methods. The latter method is more aptly described as the analysis of variance method in which the total variance is partitioned into separate variances.

13.5 ARITHMETIC OF THE ANALYSIS OF VARIANCE

The analysis of variance is perhaps the most widely used computational procedure in biometrics and the analysis of quantitative inheritance. It is a computational procedure which is based on simple arithmetical processes but has widely different functions. The more important of those functions are as follows:

1. The study of the variation of a population, that is, the decomposition of the total variance in a population into distinct parts, such as for example the division of variance into genotypic and environmental components. In this respect the analysis of variance is essentially a procedure for estimation of statistical parameters. It is frequently a source of confusion that the analysis of variance may be used for the analysis of real finite populations, conceptual finite populations, and conceptually defined infinite populations.

2. The testing of hypotheses, or if one prefers, the making of tests of significance, for any of the populations mentioned above.

3. The testing of formulas which give the dependence of one variate on other variates, e.g. in regression analysis.

The understanding of the matter is made more difficult also by the fact that identical analyses of variance can be obtained for two cases for which the structure of the observations is the same but the model which specifies the origin of the observations is different. It would be foolish to attempt to cover all the possibilities in this text. We shall therefore attempt to describe the more simple basic situations and the statistical procedures pertaining to these.

Our first step will be to describe in some detail the arithmetical processes, because these are essentially very simple, as they relate to the first function mentioned above.

Populations which we may be interested in studying belong frequently to one of two pure types. The first type is the hierarchal population in which the members are in groups or families, subfamilies, subsub-families and so on. The second is the population which can be classified according to the levels of independent factors and is called the cross classification. A third type of classification occurs when the levels of one factor are linked at random with the levels of another factor. This occurs, for example, with the random assignment of treatments (the levels of one factor) to plots (the levels of another factor). This may be termed random fractional confounding (Wilk and Kempthorne, 1956).

13.5.1 The Hierarchal Classification

Individuals in the population are related to each other in different ways in an obvious sense. For example, we could consider the population of young sheep and classify them into a hierarchal classification by breed, farm, and sire, in which we suppose that all the sheep on any one farm belong to one of the breeds only. In that case an individual sheep is in a breed which we denote by i, it occurs on a particular farm out of the farms which have breed i, say on farm ij, and it was sired by one of the rams on this farm, say ram k of farm ij. There will be a number of individuals which have all these attributes, and a particular one is identified by saying it is the lth one which occurs. In all then an individual is designated by four numbers, i, j, k, l, and we shall have a number such as for example body weight at six months for each individual, which we denote by y_{ijkl}. It is to be noted that the subscripts on y have no general significance, but merely state that the observation belongs to the individual which is in the breed which we numbered with i, on the particular farm which we denote by j, sired by the particular sire on this farm which received the number k, and was given the number l to differentiate it from other individuals from breed i, farm j within this breed, and sire k within the farm. The subscripts are stated to have no general significance because they serve merely to give the structure of the observations. The farm denoted by the jth within the breed numbered as one has no relation to the farm denoted as the jth within the breed numbered as two. In general the number of observations within the classes arising at each level of the classification will be different, unless the observations are taken according to a definite plan which enforces equal numbers. Thus we may have four breeds, which we number for identification as breed number 1, number 2, number 3, number 4. Breed number 1 may occur on 500 farms, breed number 2 on 100 farms, breed number 3 on 79 farms, and so on. The 469th farm which has breed 1 may have five sires, and the 300th just one sire, and so on.

To describe matters in full generality, we suppose that the number of individuals from sire k on farm j of breed i is n_{ijk}. The number of individuals on farm j of breed i is then the sum of n_{ijk} over all the values for k which occur on farm j of breed i, which we may write as

$$\sum_k n_{ijk}$$

or more shortly as

$$N_{ij.}$$

Likewise the number of individuals in breed i will be denoted by $N_{i..}$ $\left(= \sum_{j,k} n_{ijk} \right)$. Also we shall need to use quantities such as $\sum_k y_{ijk}$, which for brevity we write as $Y_{ij.}$ and $\sum_{j,k} y_{ijk}$ which we write as $Y_{i..}$, so that for instance $Y_{i..}$ is the sum of the measurements for all individuals of breed i. The grand total of all observations is denoted by $Y_{...}$. Note that in this situation $Y_{.j.}$ is a meaningless quantity. We are now in a position to describe the way in which the total sum of squares is divided into portions of obvious relevance.

In the first place, suppose that we had numbered the sires from 1 to the total number we have. We could then make the analysis of variance corresponding to the previous variety example. We would obtain the total sum of squares about the over-all mean. We could find for each sire the sum of squares of observations about their mean for individuals coming from that sire. The sum of these over all the sires is called the within-sire sum of squares. Next we could find the sum of squares within farms in an analogous manner, and finally the sum of squares within breeds. Actually the computational routine that should be followed is not exactly what we have just described. Formulas best for computation will be given later. Using the rule that the degrees of freedom for a sum of squares between n observations is $(n-1)$, we can write Table 13.3.

TABLE 13.3

SOURCES OF VARIATION

Nature of Sum of Squares	Value	d.f.
Total	T	$N_{...}-1$
Within sires	S_1	$\sum_{ijk}(n_{ijk}-1)$
Within farms	S_2	$\sum_{ij}(N_{ij.}-1)$
Within breeds	S_3	$\sum_i(N_{i..}-1)$

We are now in a position to present in Table 13.4 the analysis of variance table in its usual form.

TABLE 13.4

ANALYSIS OF VARIANCE FOR HIERARCHAL CLASSIFICATION

Source	d.f.	S.S.
Among breeds	$(N_{\ldots}-1)-\sum_i(N_{i\,.\,.}-1)$	$T-S_3=B$
Among farms within breeds	$\sum_i(N_{i\,.\,.}-1)-\sum_{ij}(N_{ij\,.}-1)$	$S_3-S_2=F$
Among sires within farms	$\sum_{ij}(N_{ij\,.}-1)-\sum_{ijk}(n_{ijk}-1)$	$S_2-S_1=S$
Among individuals within sires	$\sum_{ijk}(n_{ijk}-1)$	$S_1=I$
Total	$N_{\ldots}-1$	T

The best way of obtaining the sums of squares is as follows:

$$S_1 = \sum_{ijkl} y_{ijkl}^2 - \sum_{ijk}\frac{1}{n_{ijk}}\,Y_{ijk}^2\,.$$

$$S_2 = \sum_{ijkl} y_{ijkl}^2 - \sum_{ij}\frac{1}{N_{ij\,.}}\,Y_{ij}^2\,.\,.$$

$$S_3 = \sum_{ijkl} y_{ijkl}^2 - \sum_{i}\frac{1}{N_{i\,.\,.}}\,Y_{i}^2\,.\,.$$

$$T = \sum_{ijkl} y_{ijkl}^2 - \frac{1}{N_{\ldots}}\,Y_{\ldots}^2$$

so that

$$S = S_2 - S_1 = \sum_{ijk}\frac{1}{n_{ijk}}\,Y_{ijk}^2\,. - \sum_{ij}\frac{1}{N_{ij\,.}}\,Y_{ij}^2\,.\,.$$

$$F = S_3 - S_2 = \sum_{ij}\frac{1}{N_{ij\,.}}\,Y_{ij}^2\,.\,. - \sum_{i}\frac{1}{N_{i\,.\,.}}\,Y_{i}^2\,.\,.\,.$$

$$B = T - S_3 = \sum_{i}\frac{1}{N_{i\,.\,.}}\,Y_{i}^2\,.\,.\,. - \frac{1}{N_{\ldots}}\,Y_{\ldots}^2$$

We now raise the question of the use which can be made of Table 13.4. As it stands at the present point in our discussion, it is merely a breakdown of T into parts which appear to have some value intuitively. However, if there were no differences between the sires, we would expect the mean square deviation about farm means to be the same as the mean square deviation about sire means. In other words we would expect

$$\frac{S_2}{\sum_{ij}(N_{ij.} - 1)} = \frac{S_1}{\sum_{ijk}(n_{ijk} - 1)}$$

and consequently each of these would be equal to

$$\frac{S_2 - S_1}{\sum_{ij}(N_{ij.} - 1) - \sum_{ijk}(n_{ijk} - 1)}$$

What does this mean in terms of Table 13.4? It means that we would expect the mean square for sires within farms to be equal to the mean square for individuals within sires.

13.5.2 Expectations of Sums of Squares

To utilize further the analysis of variance we must make some assumptions. It should be noted that so far we have made none. We may suppose that an observation y_{ijkl} is made up of distinct portions which are added together: thus

$$y_{ijkl} = \mu + b_i + f_{ij} + s_{ijk} + e_{ijkl}$$

Here μ is a constant which all observations contain, b_i is a portion of the observation which is the same for all individuals of breed i, f_{ij} a portion which is the same for all individuals from farm ij, s_{ijk} a portion common to all individuals with the sire ijk, that is, the kth sire on farm j of breed i, leaving e_{ijkl} as a portion which is individual or peculiar to every individual. We shall also assume that the breeds we have in our sample of observations are a random sample (with equal probability) of all breeds; that the farms within each breed are a random sample of the number of farms with that breed, this number being very large; that the sires in the sample may be regarded as a random sample from a large conceptual population of sires which could have occurred; and finally that the individuals we observe are a random sample from a large population (conceptual at least) of individuals which could have arisen from the sires. Also let us assume that the variability at each level of the classification is constant over all the possible classes at that level: i.e. that the variance of b_i is σ_b^2, the variance of f_{ij}, given i, is constant and equal to σ_f^2; the variance of s_{ijk} given i and j, is constant and equal to σ_s^2; and finally the variance of e_{ijkl}, given i, j, and k, is constant and equal to σ_e^2. The assumptions we have written out above include, tacitly, one assumption which may vitiate interpretation of the arithmetic results of the analysis of variance; this assumption is that the terms such as b_i, or f_{ij}, or s_{ijk}, or e_{ijkl} are randomly chosen from large populations. As a result there can be no competition, in the sense that competition may exist between the individuals of a litter. The existence of such competition makes interpretation of the analysis of variance very difficult.

Given the above assumption and definitions, it is then reasonable to attempt to estimate the quantities σ_b^2, σ_f^2, σ_s^2, and σ_e^2. The analysis of variance given in Table 13.4 leads almost automatically to estimates.

It is a simple matter to obtain the mean squares by dividing each sum of squares by its respective degrees of freedom. Also it is possible to obtain the expectation of each mean square.

Let us exemplify the process of taking expectation of mean squares. Suppose $x_1, x_2, \cdots, x_n$ are a random sample from a population with mean μ and variance σ^2. Consider $\sum (x - \bar{x})^2$. This is equal to

$$\sum x^2 - \frac{(\sum x)^2}{n}$$

Each x_i is of the form

$$x_i = \mu + e_i$$

and the e_i's are independently distributed with an expectation of zero and variance σ^2. Then

$$E(x_i^2) = \mu^2 + \sigma^2$$

so

$$E(\sum x_i^2) = n(\mu^2 + \sigma^2)$$

also

$$\sum x = n\mu + \sum_{i=1}^{n} e_i$$

so

$$E(\sum x)^2 = E(n^2\mu^2) + E\left(\sum_{i=1}^{n} e_i\right)^2 + 2E\left(n\mu \sum_{i=1}^{n} e_i\right)$$

$$= n^2\mu^2 + E\left(\sum_{i=1}^{n} e_i\right)^2 + 0$$

and

$$E\left(\sum_{i=1}^{n} e_i\right)^2 = E\left(\sum_{i=1}^{n} e_i^2 + \sum_{i' \neq i} e_i e_{i'}\right)$$

$$= n\sigma^2 + 0$$

Hence

$$E\left[\frac{(\sum x)^2}{n}\right] = \frac{1}{n}(n^2\mu^2 + n\sigma^2) = n\mu^2 + \sigma^2$$

so that

$$E\left[\sum x^2 - \frac{(\sum x)^2}{n}\right] = n\mu^2 + n\sigma^2 - (n\mu^2 + \sigma^2)$$

$$= (n-1)\sigma^2$$

Hence

$$E\frac{\sum(x - \bar{x})^2}{n-1} = \sigma^2$$

This proves the fact mentioned earlier that s^2 is an unbiased estimate of σ^2.

In our present case, we can proceed along the same lines, although the algebra will be more tedious. The quantities which enter into the sums of squares are derived from the five quantities,

$$\frac{Y^2_{\ldots}}{N_{\ldots}}, \quad \sum_{ijk}\frac{1}{n_{ijk}} Y^2_{ijk\,\cdot}, \quad \sum_{ij}\frac{1}{N_{ij\,\cdot}} Y^2_{ij\,\cdot\,\cdot}, \quad \text{and} \quad \sum_{i}\frac{1}{N_{i\,\cdot\,\cdot}} Y^2_{i\,\cdot\,\cdot\,\cdot}$$

and

$$\sum_{ijkl} y^2_{ijkl}$$

so let us find the expectation of each of these. In the following for example, $\sum_{ij}(1)$ means that we add unity over all the possibilities for i and j.

(1) $\dfrac{Y^2_{\ldots}}{N_{\ldots}}$

We have

$$Y_{\ldots} = N_{\ldots}\mu + \sum_{i}N_{i\,\cdot\,\cdot}\,b_i + \sum_{ij}N_{ij\,\cdot}\,f_{ij} + \sum_{ijk}n_{ijk}s_{ijk} + \sum_{ijkl}e_{ijkl}$$

We square this and take expectations. In doing so, we note that

$$(a_1 + a_2 + \cdots + a_n)^2 = (\sum a_i^2) + \sum_{i \neq i'}a_i a_{i'}$$

In the present case

$$a_1 = N_{\ldots}\mu, \quad a_2 = N_{1\,\cdot\,\cdot}\,b_1, \quad a_3 = N_{2\,\cdot\,\cdot}\,b_2, \quad \text{etc.}$$

We also utilize the facts that $E(b_i) = 0$, $E(f_{ij}) = 0$, $E(s_{ijk}) = 0$, and

$E(e_{ijkl}) = 0$ for any subscripts and that b_i, f_{ij}, s_{ijk}, and e_{ijkl} are independent, so that the expectation of any product is zero. So we have

$$E(Y^2_{\ldots}) = N^2_{\ldots}\mu^2 + \left(\sum_i N^2_{i..}\right)\sigma^2_b + \left(\sum_{ij} N^2_{ij.}\right)\sigma^2_f$$
$$+ \left(\sum_{ijk} n^2_{ijk}\right)\sigma^2_s + N_{\ldots}\sigma^2_e$$

and

$$E\left(\frac{Y^2_{\ldots}}{N_{\ldots}}\right) = N_{\ldots}\mu^2 + \left(\frac{1}{N_{\ldots}}\sum_i N^2_{i..}\right)\sigma^2_b + \left(\frac{1}{N_{\ldots}}\sum_{ij} N^2_{ij.}\right)\sigma^2_f$$
$$+ \left(\frac{1}{N_{\ldots}}\sum_{ijk} n^2_{ijk}\right)\sigma^2_s + \sigma^2_e$$

(2) $\displaystyle\sum_{ijk}\frac{Y^2_{ijk.}}{n_{ijk}}$

$$Y_{ijk.} = n_{ijk}\mu + n_{ijk}b_i + n_{ijk}f_{ij} + n_{ijk}s_{ijk} + \sum_l e_{ijkl}$$

so

$$E\left(\frac{Y^2_{ijk.}}{n_{ijk}}\right) = n_{ijk}\mu^2 + n_{ijk}\sigma^2_b + n_{ijk}\sigma^2_f + n_{ijk}\sigma^2_s + \sigma^2_e$$

and

$$E\sum_{ijk}\left(\frac{Y^2_{ijk.}}{n_{ijk}}\right) = N_{\ldots}\mu^2 + N_{\ldots}\sigma^2_b + N_{\ldots}\sigma^2_f + N_{\ldots}\sigma^2_s + \sum_{ijk}(1)\,\sigma^2_e$$

(3) $\displaystyle\sum_{ij}\frac{Y^2_{ij..}}{N_{ij.}}$

$$Y_{ij..} = N_{ij.}\mu + N_{ij.}b_i + N_{ij.}f_{ij} + \sum_k n_{ijk}s_{ijk} + \sum_{kl} e_{ijkl}$$

so

$$E\left(\sum_{ij}\frac{Y^2_{ij..}}{N_{ij.}}\right) = N_{\ldots}\mu^2 + N_{\ldots}\sigma^2_b + N_{\ldots}\sigma^2_f$$
$$+ \left(\sum_{ij}\sum_k\frac{n^2_{ijk}}{N_{ij.}}\right)\sigma^2_s + \left(\sum_{ij}(1)\right)\sigma^2_e$$

(4) $\displaystyle\sum_i\frac{Y^2_{i\ldots}}{N_{i..}}$

$$Y_{i\ldots} = N_{i..}\mu + N_{i..}b_i + \sum_j N_{ij.}f_{ij} + \sum_{jk} n_{ijk}s_{ijk} + \sum_{jkl} e_{ijkl}$$

so

$$E\left(\sum_i \frac{Y_{i\ldots}^2}{N_{i\ldots}}\right) = N_{\ldots}\mu^2 + N_{\ldots}\sigma_b^2 + \left(\sum_{ij}\frac{N_{ij\cdot}^2}{N_{i\ldots}}\right)\sigma_f^2$$

$$+ \left(\sum_{ijk}\frac{n_{ijk}^2}{N_{i\ldots}}\right)\sigma_s^2 + \left(\sum_i (1)\right)\sigma_e^2$$

(5) $\displaystyle\sum_{ijkl} y_{ijkl}^2$

$$E\left(\sum_{ijkl} y_{ijkl}^2\right) = N_{\ldots}(\mu^2 + \sigma_b^2 + \sigma_f^2 + \sigma_s^2 + \sigma_e^2)$$

It is now a simple matter to get the expectations of the sums of squares in Table 13.4. We have

$$E(B) = E\left(\sum_i \frac{1}{N_{i\ldots}} Y_{i\ldots}^2 - \frac{Y_{\ldots}^2}{N_{\ldots}}\right)$$

$$= \left[\sum_i (1) - 1\right]\sigma_e^2 + \left(\sum_{ijk}\frac{n_{ijk}^2}{N_{i\ldots}} - \frac{1}{N_{\ldots}}\sum_{ijk} n_{ijk}^2\right)\sigma_s^2$$

$$+ \left(\sum_{ij}\frac{N_{ij\cdot}^2}{N_{i\ldots}} - \frac{1}{N_{\ldots}}\sum_{ij} N_{ij\cdot}^2\right)\sigma_f^2 + \left(N_{\ldots} - \frac{1}{N_{\ldots}}\sum_i N_{i\ldots}^2\right)\sigma_b^2$$

$$E(F) = \left[\sum_{ij} (1) - \sum_i (1)\right]\sigma_e^2 + \left(\sum_{ijk}\frac{n_{ijk}^2}{N_{ij\cdot}} - \sum_{ijk}\frac{n_{ijk}^2}{N_{i\ldots}}\right)\sigma_s^2$$

$$+ \left(N_{\ldots} - \sum_{ij}\frac{N_{ij\cdot}^2}{N_{i\ldots}}\right)\sigma_f^2$$

$$E(S) = \left[\sum_{ijk} (1) - \sum_{ij} (1)\right]\sigma_e^2 + \left(N_{\ldots} - \sum_{ijk}\frac{n_{ijk}^2}{N_{ij\cdot}}\right)\sigma_s^2$$

and

$$E(I) = \left[N_{\ldots} - \sum_{ijk} (1)\right]\sigma_e^2$$

It should be noted that the coefficient of σ_e^2 in each expectation is equal to the degrees of freedom for the sum of squares, since for example

$$\sum_{ij} (N_{ij\cdot} - 1) - \sum_{ijk} (n_{ijk} - 1) = \sum_{ijk} (1) - \sum_{ij} (1)$$

It is customary to complete the analysis of variance by dividing each sum of squares by the degrees of freedom to give mean squares, and the expectations of the mean squares can be obtained by dividing the above expectations of sums of squares by the appropriate degrees of freedom. In the general case it is best to work out the expectations of mean squares in this way. As a result, we have the following simple relations, where M.S. B for example denotes the mean square for B.

$$E(\text{M.S. } B) = \sigma_e^2 + k_1 \sigma_s^2 + k_2 \sigma_f^2 + k_3 \sigma_b^2$$

$$E(\text{M.S. } F) = \sigma_e^2 + k_4 \sigma_s^2 + k_5 \sigma_f^2$$

$$E(\text{M.S. } S) = \sigma_e^2 + k_6 \sigma_s^2$$

$$E(\text{M.S. } I) = \sigma_e^2$$

where $k_1, k_2, \cdots, k_6$ are numbers calculated from the frequencies as described above.

We may now obtain estimates of σ_e^2, σ_s^2, σ_f^2, and σ_b^2 by equating the observed mean squares to the expectations and solving, so that, for example,

$$\hat\sigma_e^2 = \text{M.S. } I$$

$$\hat\sigma_s^2 = (\text{M.S. } S - \text{M.S. } I)/k_6$$

and so on.

13.5.3 Derived Intraclass Correlations

In this situation our prime concern will be the estimation of these components of variance. Given the estimates, we may say that the proportions of the total variance of a randomly selected individual which are due to breed, farm, sire, and are particular to the individual are:

$$\frac{\hat\sigma_b^2}{\hat\sigma_b^2 + \hat\sigma_f^2 + \hat\sigma_s^2 + \hat\sigma_e^2}, \quad \frac{\hat\sigma_f^2}{\hat\sigma_b^2 + \hat\sigma_f^2 + \hat\sigma_s^2 + \hat\sigma_e^2}, \quad \frac{\hat\sigma_s^2}{\hat\sigma_b^2 + \hat\sigma_f^2 + \hat\sigma_s^2 + \hat\sigma_e^2}$$

and $\dfrac{\hat\sigma_e^2}{\hat\sigma_b^2 + \hat\sigma_f^2 + \hat\sigma_s^2 + \hat\sigma_e^2}$, respectively

We can also estimate various intraclass correlations for example:

1. The intraclass correlation of two random individuals from the whole population from the same sire is estimated as

$$\frac{\hat\sigma_b^2 + \hat\sigma_f^2 + \hat\sigma_s^2}{\hat\sigma_b^2 + \hat\sigma_f^2 + \hat\sigma_s^2 + \hat\sigma_e^2}$$

2. The intraclass correlation of two random individuals from the whole population on the same farm is estimated as

$$\frac{\hat\sigma_b^2 + \hat\sigma_f^2}{\hat\sigma_b^2 + \hat\sigma_f^2 + \hat\sigma_s^2 + \hat\sigma_e^2}$$

3. The intraclass correlation of two random individuals from the whole population of the same breed is estimated as

$$\frac{\hat{\sigma}_b^2}{\hat{\sigma}_b^2 + \hat{\sigma}_f^2 + \hat{\sigma}_s^2 + \hat{\sigma}_e^2}$$

4. The intraclass correlation of two random individuals in the subpopulation consisting of one breed, which have the same sire and hence farm is estimated as

$$\frac{\hat{\sigma}_f^2 + \hat{\sigma}_s^2}{\hat{\sigma}_f^2 + \hat{\sigma}_s^2 + \hat{\sigma}_e^2}$$

5. The intraclass correlation of two random individuals from the same farm in the subpopulation consisting of one breed is estimated as

$$\frac{\hat{\sigma}_f^2}{\hat{\sigma}_f^2 + \hat{\sigma}_s^2 + \hat{\sigma}_e^2}$$

6. The intraclass correlation of two random individuals from the same sire in the subpopulation consisting of one farm is

$$\frac{\hat{\sigma}_s^2}{\hat{\sigma}_s^2 + \hat{\sigma}_e^2}$$

It is seen from the above that the components of variance are the crucial features of the whole situation and that knowledge of these allows us to construct any intraclass correlation we may desire.

Tests of significance on components of variance have little use, and this is fortunate because statisticians have not developed such tests for the general situation. Whether an estimated component of variance is significant or not is of little interest, because we can be sure that each component of variance is not zero. The important question is the magnitude of each component relative to the others, and the importance of this magnitude in the type of work one is doing. It is desirable that simple approximations to the standard errors of estimated components of variance be available, but this is not yet the case in general.

It is of interest in the present connection to consider a particular case when frequencies are equal. We suppose then that i runs from 1 to b, that j runs from 1 to f for each i, that k runs from 1 to s for each combination of i and j, and that l runs from 1 to r for each combination of i, j, and k. So we have

$$n_{ijk} = r, \quad N_{ij\,.} = rs, \quad N_{i\,.\,.} = rsf, \quad N_{.\,.\,.} = rsfb$$

$$\sum_i (1) = b, \quad \sum_{ij} (1) = bf, \quad \sum_{ijk} (1) = bfs$$

Hence

$$\sum_{ijk} \frac{n_{ijk}^2}{N_{i\,.\,.}} - \frac{1}{N_{.\,.\,.}} \sum_{ijk} n_{ijk}^2 = r^2 \left(\frac{1}{rsf} - \frac{1}{rsfb} \right) \sum_{ijk} (1) = r(b-1)$$

$$\sum_{ij} \frac{N_{ij\,.}^2}{N_{i\,.\,.}} - \frac{1}{N_{.\,.\,.}} \sum_{ij} N_{ij\,.}^2 = r^2 s^2 \left(\frac{1}{rsf} - \frac{1}{rsfb} \right) bf = rs(b-1)$$

and so on. The result is the analysis of variance given in Table 13.5.

TABLE 13.5

ANALYSIS OF VARIANCE FOR BALANCED HIERARCHAL CLASSIFICATION

Source	d.f.	S.S.	M.S.	E.M.S.
Breeds	$b-1$	B	M.S. B	$\sigma_e^2 + r\sigma_s^2 + rs\sigma_f^2 + rsf\sigma_b^2$
Farms within breeds	$b(f-1)$	F	M.S. F	$\sigma_e^2 + r\sigma_s^2 + rs\sigma_f^2$
Sires within farms	$bf(s-1)$	S	M.S. S	$\sigma_e^2 + r\sigma_s^2$
Individuals within sires	$bfs(r-1)$	I	M.S. I	σ_e^2
Total	$bfsr-1$			

The estimation of the components of variance is now very simple:

$$\hat{\sigma}_b^2 = (\text{M.S. } B - \text{M.S. } F)/rsf$$
$$\hat{\sigma}_f^2 = (\text{M.S. } F - \text{M.S. } S)/rs$$
$$\hat{\sigma}_s^2 = (\text{M.S. } S - \text{M.S. } I)/r$$
$$\hat{\sigma}_e^2 = \text{M.S. } I$$

In the balanced situation, if we can make further assumptions that each of the terms in the model, b_i, f_{ij}, s_{ijk}, and e_{ijkl} are normally independently distributed, tests of significance of each component can be made, and unbiased estimation of variances of estimates can be made. To test the significance of the observed $\hat{\sigma}_b^2$, we take

$$F = \text{M.S. } B/\text{M.S. } F$$

and obtain the significance level by finding the probability with which the observed number would be exceeded in the F distribution with $b-1$ and $b(f-1)$ degrees of freedom. The other components are tested likewise. Estimated variances may be obtained by noting that each estimate is a linear function of mean squares, and the mean squares are independent.

The usual formulas for the variance of a linear function hold. The estimated variance of a mean square say X based on k degrees of freedom is equal to $2X^2/(k+2)$, the true variance being $2E(X)^2/k$. For example, the estimated variance of $\hat{\sigma}_f^2$ is equal to

$$\frac{2}{r^2 s^2}\left[\frac{(\text{M.S. } F)^2}{b(f-1)+2} + \frac{(\text{M.S. } S)^2}{bf(s-1)+2}\right]$$

13.5.4 The Variance of Estimated Intraclass Correlations

It is reasonable to inquire if some measure of accuracy of estimates of intraclass correlations can be obtained. In general, this matter is rather complex, and we shall not consider it in full generality. We shall give the results for a balanced situation, i.e. a situation in which frequencies at each level of classification are constant. The basis for the estimation of errors is the following. An estimate of intraclass correlation is of the form

$$\theta = \frac{u_1 A + u_2 B + u_3 C + \cdots}{v_1 A + v_2 B + v_3 C + \cdots} = \frac{X}{Y}$$

where u_1, u_2, u_3, etc., v_1, v_2, v_3, etc. are definite numbers and A, B, and C are mean squares in an analysis of variance.

Thus from Table 13.5 we see that

$$\sigma_f^2/(\sigma_e^2 + \sigma_s^2 + \sigma_f^2)$$

is estimated by

$$\frac{\dfrac{1}{rs}(\text{M.S. } F - \text{M.S. } S)}{\text{M.S. } I + (\text{M.S. } S - \text{M.S. } I)/r + (\text{M.S. } F - \text{M.S. } S)/rs}$$

$$= \frac{\dfrac{1}{rs}\text{M.S. } F - \dfrac{1}{rs}\text{M.S. } S}{(1 - 1/r)\text{M.S. } I + (1/r - 1/rs)\text{M.S. } S + 1/rs\,\text{M.S. } F}$$

Now it can be shown that the following relation holds approximately:

$$V(\theta) = \frac{V(X)}{Y^2} - 2\frac{X \operatorname{Cov}(X, Y)}{Y^3} + \frac{X^2}{Y^4} V(Y)$$

Also we have

$$V(X) = u_1^2\, V(A) + u_2^2\, V(B) + u_3^2\, V(C) + \cdots$$
$$V(Y) = v_1^2\, V(A) + v_2^2\, V(B) + v_3^2\, V(C) + \cdots$$

and

$$\text{Cov}(X, Y) = u_1 v_1 V(A) + u_2 v_2 V(B) + u_3 v_3 V(C) + \cdots$$

in the case when

(1) the frequencies are equal, and
(2) the errors of the model are all normally and independently distributed.

Now we have already given the variance of a mean square, and it was stated that, if X is a mean square based on k degrees of freedom, the variance of X is estimated unbiasedly by

$$2 \frac{X^2}{k + 2}$$

The true variance has the true value of X in the numerator and k in the denominator. We are therefore in a position to calculate a variance for $\hat{\theta}$.

It should be noted that by this general formulation we have covered all the cases discussed herein under the above assumptions. The particular details are purely a matter of computation.

In the case of unequal frequencies, difficulties arise and we shall not consider them here.

13.5.5 The Cross Classification

In the previous section we have dealt with the analysis of a sample from a population which has a definite structure which we called hierarchal (This is sometimes referred to as "nested.") A usual way of looking at a population to see if it has this structure is to compare it with a human population traced say through the male line: Some individuals have the same father, groups of individuals have the same grandfather, groups of groups of individuals have the same great grandfather, and so on. The characteristic of this population is that the numbering within a group is used merely to identify individuals, and there is no relation for instance between the ith subgroup of group 1 and the ith subgroup of group 2.

Now we turn to the other pure type of classification, namely the cross classification. Suppose we have a very large number V of varieties and a very large number P of places, and we imagine that we can grow each variety at each place. Then we shall have a population of numbers say τ_{ij}, the yield of variety i at place j, there being VP such numbers in all. Define the following

$$\tau_{..} = \frac{1}{VP} \sum_{ij} \tau_{ij}, \quad \tau_{i.} = \frac{1}{P} \sum_{j} \tau_{ij}, \quad \tau_{.j} = \frac{1}{V} \sum_{i} \tau_{ij}$$

which are the over-all mean, the variety mean, and the place mean, respectively. Then we have as an identity

$$(\tau_{ij} - \tau_{..}) = (\tau_{i.} - \tau_{..}) + (\tau_{.j} - \tau_{..}) + (\tau_{ij} - \tau_{i.} - \tau_{.j} + \tau_{..})$$

Note that this equation holds exactly. Now consider $\sum_{ij}(\tau_{ij} - \tau_{..})^2$, which is the total sum of squares of the number τ_{ij} about their mean. Since

$$(a + b + c)^2 = a^2 + b^2 + c^2 + 2ab + 2ac + 2bc$$

we have

$$\sum_{ij}(\tau_{ij} - \tau_{..})^2 = \sum_{ij}[(\tau_{i.} - \tau_{..})^2 + (\tau_{.j} - \tau_{..})^2$$
$$+ (\tau_{ij} + \tau_{i.} - \tau_{.j} + \tau_{..})^2 + 2(\tau_{i.} - \tau_{..})(\tau_{.j} - \tau_{..})$$
$$+ 2(\tau_{i.} - \tau_{..})(\tau_{ij} - \tau_{i.} - \tau_{.j} + \tau_{..})$$
$$+ 2(\tau_{.j} - \tau_{..})(\tau_{ij} - \tau_{i.} - \tau_{.j} + \tau_{..})]$$

Also

$$\sum_{ij}(\tau_{i.} - \tau_{..})(\tau_{.j} - \tau_{..}) = \sum_i(\tau_{i.} - \tau_{..})\left[\sum_j(\tau_{.j} - \tau_{..})\right] = 0$$

$$\sum_{ij}(\tau_{i.} - \tau_{..})(\tau_{ij} - \tau_{i.} - \tau_{.j} + \tau_{..})$$
$$= \sum_i(\tau_{i.} - \tau_{..})\left[\sum_j(\tau_{ij} - \tau_{i.} - \tau_{.j} + \tau_{..})\right] = 0$$

$$\sum_{ij}(\tau_{.j} - \tau_{..})(\tau_{ij} - \tau_{i.} - \tau_{.j} + \tau_{..}) = 0$$

and

$$\sum_{ij}(\tau_{i.} - \tau_{..})^2 = P\sum_i(\tau_{i.} - \tau_{..})^2$$

$$\sum_{ij}(\tau_{.j} - \tau_{..})^2 = V\sum_j(\tau_{.j} - \tau_{..})^2$$

So we have

$$\sum_{ij}(\tau_{ij} - \tau_{..})^2 = P\sum_i(\tau_{i.} - \tau_{..})^2 + V\sum_j(\tau_{.j} - \tau_{..})^2$$
$$+ \sum_{ij}(\tau_{ij} - \tau_{i.} - \tau_{.j} + \tau_{..})^2$$

Note that we have partitioned the total variance about the mean in our population, $\sum_{ij} (\tau_{ij} - \tau_{..})^2$ into the sum of three parts, each of which is zero or positive. Also we may note that

(1) $\sum_{ij} (\tau_{ij} - \tau_{..})^2$ is the sum of squares of VP quantities which add to zero,

(2) $\sum_{i} (\tau_{i.} - \tau_{..})^2$ is the sum of squares of V quantities which add to zero,

(3) $\sum_{j} (\tau_{.j} - \tau_{..})^2$ is the sum of squares of P quantities which add to zero,

(4) $\sum_{ij} (\tau_{ij} - \tau_{i.} - \tau_{.j} + \tau_{..})^2$ is the sum of squares of VP quantities, say $(vp)_{ij}$, where $(vp)_{ij} = (\tau_{ij} - \tau_{i.} - \tau_{.j} + \tau_{..})$,

which are such that

$$\sum_{i} (vp)_{ij} = 0, \quad \text{for each} \quad j = 1, 2, \cdots, P$$

$$\sum_{j} (vp)_{ij} = 0, \quad \text{for each} \quad i = 1, 2, \cdots, V$$

The total number of independent relations satisfied by the $(vp)_{ij}$ is $V + P - 1$, since $\sum_{j} \left[\sum_{i} (vp)_{ij} \right]$ is equal to $\sum_{i} \left[\sum_{j} (vp)_{ij} \right]$, so that, if we use the P conditions $\sum_{i} (vp)_{ij} = 0$ for each j, then we have only $(V-1)$ independent conditions $\sum_{j} (vp)_{ij} = 0$, the remaining one being satisfied automatically because of the P conditions, $\sum_{i} (vp)_{ij} = 0$, for each j.

As we have seen in the estimation of a simple variance it is reasonable to take as the estimate of the variance of a population σ^2 from which we have a random sample $x_1, x_2, \cdots, x_n$, the quantity $\hat{\sigma}^2$ given by the equation

$$\sum (x - \bar{x})^2 = (n - 1)\hat{\sigma}^2$$

and to say that the degrees of freedom are $(n - 1)$ corresponding to the fact that $\sum (x - \bar{x})^2$ is the sum of squares of n quantities, connected by one linear relation, $\sum (x - \bar{x}) = 0$.

Now we shall adopt the convention of using the same relation for the variances of finite populations. This renders our formulas very simple, and need cause no confusion. Accordingly we now write

$$\sum_i (\tau_{i\,.} - \tau_{.\,.})^2 = (V - 1)\sigma_v^2$$

$$\sum_j (\tau_{.\,j} - \tau_{.\,.})^2 = (P - 1)\sigma_p^2$$

$$\sum_{ij} (\tau_{ij} - \tau_{i\,.} - \tau_{.\,j} + \tau_{.\,.})^2 = (VP - V - P + 1)\sigma_{vp}^2 = (V - 1)(P - 1)\sigma_{vp}^2$$

These results are simply presentable and can be easily memorized by the analysis of variance in Table 13.6. It should be emphasized that this analysis of variance is the analysis of variance for the *whole* population.

TABLE 13.6
Population Analysis of Variance for Two-Way Classification

Source	d.f.	S.S.	M.S.
Varieties	$(V-1)$	$P(V-1)\sigma_v^2$	$P\sigma_v^2$
Places	$(P-1)$	$V(P-1)\sigma_p^2$	$V\sigma_p^2$
Variety by places	$(V-1)(P-1)$	$(V-1)(P-1)\sigma_{vp}^2$	σ_{vp}^2
Total	$(VP-1)$		

Now let us consider the case where we have a sample from the population obtained by drawing v out of the V lines at random and p out of the P places at random, so that we have vp observations from the total of VP. We shall be interested in the estimation of the population characteristics particularly with respect to variation. Hence we wish to estimate σ_v^2, σ_p^2, and σ_{vp}^2 from the specified sample. It is reasonable to consider the analysis of variance of the sample, which is exactly similar to the analysis of variance of the population, and to find the expectations of the mean squares. The process by which the operation of taking expectations is handled is a little esoteric in our present context. We shall, however, give the derivation as an illustration of a general technique for handling all problems of taking expectations. Many of our readers will not be interested in this matter and can skip the algebra.

13.5.6 Expectations of Mean Squares

Let us denote the yields of the variety place combinations in our sample by y_{ij}, i running from 1 to v and j from 1 to p. We interpret the subscripts as follows: The varieties and places in the sample are numbered arbitrarily from 1 to v and 1 to p, respectively. Then y_{ij} is equal to some τ_{lm}, namely the one for which variety l received number i and place m received the number j. We take two random variables δ_i^l and ρ_j^m. The first, δ_i^l, is equal to unity if variety l receives the number i and is zero otherwise. The second, ρ_j^m, is unity if place m receives the number j and is zero otherwise. Under random sampling these are binomial variates with the properties

$$P(\delta_i^l=1) = \frac{1}{V}, \qquad P(\delta_i^l=0) = \frac{V-1}{V}$$

$$P(\rho_j^m=1) = \frac{1}{P}, \qquad P(\rho_j^m=0) = \frac{P-1}{P}$$

Also we may write

$$y_{ij} = \sum_{lm} \delta_i^l \rho_j^m \tau_{lm}$$

corresponding to the fact that y_{ij} is the τ_{lm} for which variety l received the number i and place m received the number j. Now we juggle the numbers to achieve our results. We have

$$y_{ij} = \sum_{lm} \delta_i^l \rho_j^m [\tau_{..} + (\tau_{l.} - \tau_{..}) + (\tau_{.m} - \tau_{..}) \\ + (\tau_{lm} - \tau_{l.} - \tau_{.m} + \tau_{..})] \quad (2)$$

Also $\sum_l \delta_i^l = 1$, corresponding to the fact that one variety and only one receives the number i; $\sum_m \rho_j^m = 1$, corresponding to the fact that one place and only one place receives the number j. Consequently

$$\sum_{l,m} \delta_i^l \rho_j^m = \left(\sum_l \delta_i^l\right)\left(\sum_m \rho_j^m\right) = 1$$

Hence we may write (2) as

$$y_{ij} = \tau_{..} + \sum_l \delta_i^l(\tau_{l.} - \tau_{..}) + \sum_m \rho_j^m(\tau_{.m} - \tau_{..}) \\ + \sum_{l,m} \delta_i^l \rho_j^m(\tau_{lm} - \tau_{l.} - \tau_{.m} + \tau_{..})$$

which may appear more familiar to some readers when we write it as

$$y_{ij} = \mu + v_i + p_j + (vp)_{ij} \quad (3)$$

In fact we may give a definition of the terms μ, v_i, p_j, and $(vp)_{ij}$ by equating the separate terms in the two equations, so that

$$\mu = \tau_{..}$$

$$v_i = \sum_l \delta_i^l(\tau_{l.} - \tau_{..})$$

$$p_j = \sum_m \rho_j^m(\tau_{.m} - \tau_{..})$$

$$(vp)_{ij} = \sum_{lm} \delta_i^l \rho_j^m(\tau_{lm} - \tau_{l.} - \tau_{.m} + \tau_{..})$$

Now consider the terms in the analysis of variance. As in the population case we have

Sum of squares for varieties $= p \sum_i (y_{i.} - y_{..})^2 = \dfrac{1}{p} \sum_i Y_{i.}^2 - \dfrac{Y_{..}^2}{vp}$

Sum of squares for places $\quad = v \sum_j (y_{.j} - y_{..})^2 = \dfrac{1}{v} \sum_j Y_{.j}^2 - \dfrac{Y_{..}^2}{vp}$

Total sum of squares $\qquad = \sum_{ij} (y_{ij} - y_{..})^2 = \sum_{ij} y_{ij}^2 - \dfrac{Y_{..}^2}{vp}$

The variety × place sum of squares is obtained by subtraction, and as usual

$$Y_{i.} = \sum_j y_{ij}, \qquad Y_{.j} = \sum_i y_{ij}, \qquad Y_{..} = \sum_{ij} y_{ij}$$

It may be verified that the v_i, p_j, $(vp)_{ij}$ have the following properties:

$$\mu \text{ is a constant}$$

$$E(v_i) = 0, \quad E(v_i^2) = \frac{V-1}{V}\sigma_v^2, \quad E(v_i v_{i'}) = -\frac{1}{V}\sigma_v^2$$

$$E(p_j) = 0, \quad E(p_j^2) = \frac{P-1}{P}\sigma_p^2, \quad E(p_j p_{j'}) = -\frac{1}{P}\sigma_p^2$$

$$E(vp)_{ij} = 0, \quad E[(vp)_{ij}]^2 = \frac{(V-1)(P-1)}{VP}\sigma_{vp}^2$$

$$E[(vp)_{ij}(vp)_{ij'}] = -\frac{V-1}{VP}\sigma_{vp}^2, \quad E[(vp)_{ij}(vp)_{i'j}] = -\frac{P-1}{VP}\sigma_{vp}^2$$

$$E[(vp)_{ij}(vp)_{i'j'}] = \frac{1}{VP}\sigma_{vp}^2$$

all other covariances being identically zero. It is of interest to note here that the elementary properties of the terms v_i, p_j, $(vp)_{ij}$ usually given are properties which hold if both V and P are indefinitely large. Given the above expectations, we may now obtain the expectations of the sums of squares, as follows:

(1) $\sum_{ij} y_{ij}^2$

$$y_{ij}^2 = \mu^2 + v_i^2 + p_j^2 + (vp)_{ij}^2 + \text{cross products}$$

$$E(y_{ij}^2) = \mu^2 + \frac{V-1}{V}\sigma_v^2 + \frac{P-1}{P}\sigma_p^2 + \frac{(V-1)(P-1)}{VP}\sigma_{vp}^2$$

$$E\left(\sum_{ij} y_{ij}^2\right) = vp\mu^2 + vp\left(\frac{V-1}{V}\right)\sigma_v^2 + vp\left(\frac{P-1}{P}\right)\sigma_p^2$$

$$+ vp\,\frac{(V-1)(P-1)}{VP}\sigma_{vp}^2$$

(2) $Y_{..}^2 / vp$

$$Y_{..} = vp\mu + p\sum_i v_i + v\sum_j p_j + \sum_{ij}(vp)_{ij}$$

$$Y_{..}^2 = v^2p^2\mu^2 + p^2\left(\sum_i v_i\right)^2 + v^2\left(\sum_j p_j\right)^2 + \left[\sum_{ij}(vp)_{ij}\right]^2$$

$$+ \text{cross products}$$

$$E(Y_{..}^2) = v^2p^2\mu^2 + p^2E\left(\sum_i v_i\right)^2 + v^2E\left(\sum_j p_j\right)^2 + E\left[\sum_{ij}(vp)_{ij}\right]^2$$

Now

$$\left(\sum_i v_i\right)^2 = \sum_i v_i^2 + \sum_{\substack{i,i' \\ i \neq i'}} v_i v_{i'}$$

so

$$E\left(\sum_i v_i^2\right) = v\left(\frac{V-1}{V}\right)\sigma_v^2 - v\left(\frac{v-1}{V}\right)\sigma_v^2 = v\left(\frac{V-v}{V}\right)\sigma_v^2$$

Also

$$E\left(\sum_j p_j\right)^2 = p\left(\frac{P-p}{P}\right)\sigma_p^2$$

Also

$$E\left[\sum_{ij}(vp)_{ij}\right]^2 = E\left[\sum_{ij}(vp)_{ij}^2 + \sum_{\substack{i,i'\\i\neq i'}}\sum_{j}(vp)_{ij}(vp)_{i'j} + \sum_{i}\sum_{\substack{j,j'\\j\neq j'}}(vp)_{ij}(vp)_{ij'}\right.$$

$$\left.+ \sum_{i'\neq i}\sum_{j'\neq j}(vp)_{ij}(vp)_{i'j'}\right]$$

$$= vp\,\frac{(V-1)(P-1)}{VP}\,\sigma_{vp}^2 - v(v-1)\frac{p(P-1)}{VP}\,\sigma_{vp}^2$$

$$\qquad - \frac{p(p-1)\,v(V-1)}{VP}\,\sigma_{vp}^2 + \frac{v(v-1)\,p(p-1)}{VP}\,\sigma_{vp}^2$$

$$= \frac{vp}{VP}\left[(V-1)(P-1) - (v-1)(P-1)\right.$$

$$\left. - (p-1)(V-1) + (v-1)(p-1)\right]\sigma_{vp}^2$$

$$= vp\left(\frac{V-v}{V}\right)\left(\frac{P-p}{P}\right)\sigma_{vp}^2$$

Hence

$$E\left(\frac{Y_{..}^2}{vp}\right) = vp\mu^2 + p\left(\frac{V-v}{V}\right)\sigma_v^2 + v\left(\frac{P-p}{P}\right)\sigma_p^2 + \frac{(V-v)(P-p)}{VP}\,\sigma_{vp}^2$$

(3) $\dfrac{1}{p}\displaystyle\sum_{i}Y_{i.}^2$

$$Y_{i.} = p\mu + pv_i + \sum_{j}p_j + \sum_{j}(vp)_{ij}$$

so

$$E(Y_{i.}^2) = p^2\mu^2 + p^2\left(\frac{V-1}{V}\right)\sigma_v^2 + p\left(\frac{P-p}{P}\right)\sigma_p^2$$

$$\qquad + p\left(\frac{V-1}{V}\right)\left(\frac{P-p}{P}\right)\sigma_{vp}^2$$

$$E\left(\frac{1}{p}\sum_{i}Y_{i.}^2\right) = vp\mu^2 + vp\left(\frac{V-1}{V}\right)\sigma_v^2 + v\left(\frac{P-p}{P}\right)\sigma_p^2$$

$$\qquad + v\,\frac{(V-1)(P-p)}{VP}\,\sigma_{vp}^2$$

(4) $\dfrac{1}{v}\displaystyle\sum Y_{.j}^2$

Similarly

$$E\frac{1}{v}\left(\sum Y_{.j}^2\right) = vp\mu^2 + p\left(\frac{V-v}{V}\right)\sigma_v^2 + vp\left(\frac{P-1}{P}\right)\sigma_p^2$$

$$+ p\frac{(V-v)(P-1)}{VP}\sigma_{vp}^2$$

Combining the above results, we can make up Table 13.7.

TABLE 13.7

EXPECTATIONS OF MEAN SQUARES FOR SAMPLE FROM A FINITE
TWO-WAY CLASSIFIED POPULATION

Source	d.f.	S.S.	E.S.S.	E.M.S.
Varieties	$v-1$	$\dfrac{1}{p}\sum_i Y_{i.}^2 - \dfrac{Y_{..}^2}{vp}$	$(v-1)\left(\dfrac{P-p}{P}\right)\sigma_{vp}^2$ $+p(v-1)\sigma_v^2$	$\left(\dfrac{P-p}{P}\right)\sigma_{vp}^2+p\sigma_v^2$
Places	$p-1$	$\dfrac{1}{v}\sum_j Y_{.j}^2 - \dfrac{Y_{..}^2}{vp}$	$(p-1)\left(\dfrac{V-v}{V}\right)\sigma_{vp}^2$ $+v(p-1)\sigma_p^2$	$\left(\dfrac{V-v}{V}\right)\sigma_{vp}^2+v\sigma_p^2$
Variety X Places	$(v-1)(p-1)$	By subtraction	$(v-1)(p-1)\sigma_{vp}^2$	σ_{vp}^2
Total	$vp-1$	$\sum_{ij} y_{ij}^2 - \dfrac{Y_{..}^2}{vp}$		

It is of interest here to consider three limiting cases which are frequently of relevance (Table 13.8).

TABLE 13.8

LIMITING CASES FOR TWO-WAY CLASSIFICATION

Case	V	P	v	p	Interaction	Places	Varieties
I	∞	∞	Small	Small	σ_{vp}^2	$\sigma_{vp}^2+v\sigma_p^2$	$\sigma_{vp}^2+p\sigma_v^2$
II	Small	∞	$=V$	Small	σ_{vp}^2	$v\sigma_p^2$	$\sigma_{vp}^2+p\sigma_v^2$
III	∞	Small	Small	$=P$	σ_{vp}^2	$\sigma_{vp}^2+v\sigma_p^2$	$p\sigma_v^2$

In what way are these relevant? Case I occurs when both populations are very large and small samples are taken from each; both factors are random and the interaction component of variance occurs in the mean squares for both main effects. In case II the number of varieties V is small and our sample contains every one of them; varieties are fixed and places random and the interaction component of variance does not occur in the expectation of the mean square for the main effect of places. Case III is the reverse of case II. This whole matter is here derived in extenso, because there has been disagreement on the matter. It may be noted that the rule given above was stated by Kempthorne (1952, p. 574). A full treatment is given by Wilk and Kempthorne (1955, 1956). In general, the research worker in genetics deals with situations which are equivalent to one of the limiting cases described above.

The reasoning given above may be extended easily to the general n-way classification. Here we shall not give the general formulas, but shall give the results for the two distinct types of limiting situation described above.

The first case to be described is a classification by n factors, in which the factors are a, b, c, $\cdots$, and are all random. The number of levels of the factors may also be denoted by a, b, c, $\cdots$, etc., as it will always be clear whether we are talking about the factors or the number of levels. The distinct lines of the analysis of variance table may be denoted by A, B, AB, C, AC, BC, ABC, and so on. The degrees of freedom for a line labeled say XYZ, etc., where X is one, Y is another, and Z is another, etc., of A, B, C, $\cdots$, etc., is equal to $(x-1)(y-1)(z-1) \cdots$, in which product $(a-1)$, for example, appears only if A is one of the letters X, Y, Z, $\cdots$. The sums of squares for A, B, C, etc., the "main" effects, are each obtained directly by the rule of taking the sums of squares of totals at each level, dividing by the number of individuals represented in each total, and then subtracting the correction factor which is the grand total squared divided by the total number of observations. The sum of squares for say A, B, and AB is obtained by regarding the two factors a and b as consisting of just one factor with ab levels, and using the same rule. Then the sum of squares for AB is obtained by subtracting the sum of squares for A and the sum of squares for B. Analogously the sum of squares for ABC, for example, is obtained by taking

$$[\text{S.S. for } A, B, C \text{ jointly}] - [\text{S.S. for } A + \text{S.S. for } B + \text{S.S. for } AB$$
$$+ \text{S.S. for } C + \text{S.S. for } AC + \text{S.S. for } BC]$$

The analysis of variance described in the previous paragraph may be computed always, but the interpretation of the analysis depends on the circumstances. For the first limiting case to be described, the number of levels for each factor is very large; i.e., a, b, c, etc. are very large, and a small random sample of the possible levels of each factor is taken. Suppose that the sizes of these samples are denoted by a', b', c', etc. Then the general results may be illustrated by the full details for the case of four factors a, b, c, and d, given in Table 13.9.

The rules for the expectations of mean squares are very simple. Take for example AD: The mean square involves σ^2_{ad}, σ^2_{abd}, σ^2_{acd}, and σ^2_{abcd}; i.e., involves all possible combinations of a and d with other letters; the coefficients on σ^2_{abcd} are unity; on σ^2_{acd}, i.e. with b dropped from the subscripts, is b'; on σ^2_{abd}, i.e. with c dropped from the subscripts, is c'; and on σ^2_{ad}, i.e. with b and c dropped from the subscripts, is $b'c'$. By equating observed mean squares to their expectations, we have a set of equations which may be solved for the estimates of the variance components.

Now we shall describe what happens if some of the numbers a', b', c', etc. are equal to their respective population values, a, b, c, etc. In all cases E.M.S.(X) contains σ^2_x where X is any quantity like A, BC, ABC, etc., and the only question which arises is how many other terms there are. The answer is simple: Along with σ^2_x are all terms of the form σ^2_{xy}, in which all the letters added, which are denoted collectively by y, belong to factors for which the levels used are a small random sample of the population of possible levels. Thus, if a' equals a, and c' equals c, then

$$\text{E.M.S. } (AB) = c'd' \, \sigma^2_{ab} + c' \, \sigma^2_{abd}$$
$$\text{E.M.S. } (C) = a'b'd' \, \sigma^2_c + a'b' \, \sigma^2_{cd} + a'd' \, \sigma^2_{bc} + a' \, \sigma^2_{bcd}$$

The above has dealt with estimation of components of variance for the case when there are proportional frequencies. Estimation of the errors of the estimates requires further assumptions, as in the case of the hierarchal classification. If we can assume that the terms in the original model (3) behave essentially as would normal variables (this cannot happen exactly, of course), then the same rules may be applied to mean squares as in the hierarchal case. Otherwise the situation is obscure, and must await further developments in the theory of statistics. Exact treatment of the same situation, but with non-proportional frequencies, is also a problem in statistics awaiting solution, particularly in non-limiting situations. See Wilk and Kempthorne (1956).

In the limiting situation when all random samples of levels are small relative to their respective populations, we can fall back on the model analogous to

$$y_{ij} = \mu + v_i + p_j + (vp)_{ij}$$

in which the random terms are all uncorrelated with each other, and have expectations of zero and their respective variances. This is the problem

TABLE 13.9

Expectations of Mean Squares for a Four-Way Classification

Source	Population d.f.	M.S.	Sample E.M.S.
A	$a-1$	$bcd\,\sigma_a^2$	$\sigma_{abcd}^2 + d'\sigma_{abc}^2 + c'\sigma_{abd}^2 + b'\sigma_{acd}^2 + c'd'\sigma_{ab}^2 + b'd'\sigma_{ac}^2 + b'c'\sigma_{ad}^2 + b'c'd'\sigma_a^2$
B	$(b-1)$	$acd\,\sigma_b^2$	$\sigma_{abcd}^2 + d'\sigma_{abc}^2 + c'\sigma_{abd}^2 + a'\sigma_{bcd}^2 + c'd'\sigma_{ab}^2 + a'd'\sigma_{bc}^2 + a'c'\sigma_{bd}^2 + a'c'd'\sigma_b^2$
AB	$(a-1)(b-1)$	$cd\,\sigma_{ab}^2$	$\sigma_{abcd}^2 + d'\sigma_{abc}^2 + c'\sigma_{abd}^2 + c'd'\sigma_{ab}^2$
C	$(c-1)$	$abd\,\sigma_c^2$	$\sigma_{abcd}^2 + d'\sigma_{abc}^2 + b'\sigma_{acd}^2 + a'\sigma_{bcd}^2 + b'd'\sigma_{ac}^2 + a'd'\sigma_{bc}^2 + a'b'\sigma_{cd}^2 + a'b'd'\sigma_c^2$
AC	$(a-1)(c-1)$	$bd\,\sigma_{ac}^2$	$\sigma_{abcd}^2 + d'\sigma_{abc}^2 + b'\sigma_{acd}^2 + b'd'\sigma_{ac}^2$
BC	$(b-1)(c-1)$	$ad\,\sigma_{bc}^2$	$\sigma_{abcd}^2 + d'\sigma_{abc}^2 + a'\sigma_{bcd}^2 + a'd'\sigma_{bc}^2$
ABC	$(a-1)(b-1)(c-1)$	$d\,\sigma_{abc}^2$	$\sigma_{abcd}^2 + d'\sigma_{abc}^2$
D	$(d-1)$	$abc\,\sigma_d^2$	$\sigma_{abcd}^2 + c'\sigma_{abd}^2 + b'\sigma_{acd}^2 + a'\sigma_{bcd}^2 + b'c'\sigma_{ad}^2 + a'c'\sigma_{bd}^2 + a'b'\sigma_{cd}^2 + a'b'c'\sigma_d^2$
AD	$(a-1)(d-1)$	$bc\,\sigma_{ad}^2$	$\sigma_{abcd}^2 + c'\sigma_{abd}^2 + b'\sigma_{acd}^2 + b'c'\sigma_{ad}^2$
BD	$(b-1)(d-1)$	$ac\,\sigma_{bd}^2$	$\sigma_{abcd}^2 + c'\sigma_{abd}^2 + a'\sigma_{bcd}^2 + a'c'\sigma_{bd}^2$
ABD	$(a-1)(b-1)(d-1)$	$c\,\sigma_{abd}^2$	$\sigma_{abcd}^2 + c'\sigma_{abd}^2$
CD	$(c-1)(d-1)$	$ab\,\sigma_{ca}^2$	$\sigma_{abcd}^2 + a'\sigma_{bcd}^2 + b'\sigma_{acd}^2 + a'b'\sigma_{cd}^2$
ACD	$(a-1)(c-1)(d-1)$	$b\,\sigma_{acd}^2$	$\sigma_{abcd}^2 + b'\sigma_{acd}^2$
BCD	$(b-1)(c-1)(d-1)$	$a\,\sigma_{bcd}^2$	$\sigma_{abcd}^2 + a'\sigma_{bcd}^2$
$ABCD$	$(a-1)(b-1)(c-1)(d-1)$	σ_{abcd}^2	σ_{abcd}^2

Sample d.f. may be obtained by inserting primes in population d.f.

usually treated in the literature on the estimation of components of variance. About the simplest procedure is to obtain as many sums of squares as there are components of variance, in the easiest way possible. Thus in the above case, in which all combinations of the values of i and j do not occur, we can proceed as follows:

1. Obtain the total sum of squares about the mean and its expectation.
2. Obtain the sum of squares for varieties about their mean as

$$\sum_i \frac{V_i^2}{v_i} - \frac{G^2}{V}$$

where V_i = total over places for variety i

v_i = number of places at which variety i occurs

$$V = \sum_i v_i$$

$$G = \sum_i V_i$$

and obtain its expectation.

3. Obtain the sum of squares for places about their mean as

$$\sum_j \frac{P_j^2}{p_j} - \frac{G^2}{V}$$

where P_j = total over varieties for place j

p_j = number of varieties at place j

and obtain its expectation.

We can then construct three equations, of which the left-hand sides are the expectations in terms of σ_v^2, σ_p^2, σ_{vp}^2 and the right-hand sides are numbers. These equations may be solved for σ_v^2, σ_p^2, σ_{vp}^2, the values obtained being taken as estimates.

The sampling errors of estimates obtained in this way are not known (but can be worked out by a large amount of tedious algebra), and it is not known how good the above method is relative to other methods which may be suggested.

13.5.7 Mixtures of The Two Types of Classification

The pure hierarchal classification is of fairly frequent occurrence, but the cross classification occurs usually only with a hierarchal classification, so to speak, tacked on. For instance, we might in our variety–place example, have a number of observations on each variety–place combination. In such a case we would have the model

$$y_{ijk} = \mu + v_i + p_j + (vp)_{ij} + e_{ijk}$$

in which the subscript k denotes the kth observation on the combination of variety i and place j. The additional term e_{ijk} in the model incorporates the obvious fact that observations on this combination will not agree exactly. It is usual to make the assumption that the e_{ijk} are random variables independent of all others in the model, are uncorrelated, and have the same variance σ_e^2.

The procedure to be followed in these instances is conceptually quite straightforward. Initially one may regard the combination of variety i and place j as one level of a pseudofactor, or of the second factor of classification of a hierarchal classification. This will lead to the analysis of variance with the structure

Source
Among variety–place combinations
Among observations within combinations

Total

We can then consider the variety–place means, i.e. averaging over observations, and we have a cross classification in which

$$y_{ij.} = \mu + v_i + p_j + h_{ij}$$

where $h_{ij} = (vp)_{ij} + e_{ij}$.

This cross classification can then be analyzed as described above into the breakdown

Source
Varieties
Places
Residual

Total

The degrees of freedom can in all these cases be written down by the usual rules. Expectations of all sums of squares or mean squares can be obtained and all the components of variance estimated.

In certain situations, particularly when the number of observations is constant, the two analyses of variance can be combined by an arithmetical dodge into one analysis of variance with the structure

Source

Varieties
Places
Variety × places
Between observations

Total

The arithmetical dodge consists of multiplying the sums of squares obtained in the analysis of the means by the number of observations which contribute to each mean. This number must be constant for this device to work.

13.5.8 Summary of Rules for Finding Expectations of Sums of Squares

The situations which the geneticist will meet will be almost always of a special type, in that factors will be fixed or random. Very rarely will there be cases in which a sample is taken from a small number of possible levels of a factor.

We therefore deal only with this case, because the number of distinct situations which can arise is very large and it would be useless to attempt herein a description of even the cases which occur frequently. We therefore give a set of rules by which any particular case may be worked out. The algebra may be tedious but is rather straightforward if we use the relation that

$$\left(\sum_{i=1}^{n} x_i\right)^2 = \sum_{i=1}^{n} x_i^2 + \sum_{i=1}^{n} \sum_{i' \neq i} x_i x_{i'}$$

in various forms in which it may be needed.

In general a model will consist of four types of term:

1. A fixed number μ.
2. Terms (x) which are random for which $E(x) = 0$, $E(x^2) = \sigma_x^2$.
3. Terms (z say) which are fixed in the sense that repetitions of the experiment or observational setup will result in identical contributions. If the total number of such terms (z) of a particular type is a, so that there are terms $z_1, z_2, \cdots, z_a$, then we treat these as ordinary numbers and not as random variables. Hence

$$E(z_i) = z_i$$
$$E(z_i^2) = z_i^2$$
$$E(z_i z_{i'}) = z_i z_{i'}$$

4. Terms, u_{ij} say, which are like $(vp)_{ij}$ in our variety–place example, which arise from the interaction of a factor with fixed levels and a factor with random levels. If i denotes the level of the fixed factor with a levels in all and j the level of the random factor, we have

$$\underset{j}{E} u_{ij} = 0$$

where $\underset{j}{E}$ is the expectation over the levels of the random factor.

We can get the expectation by using this relation, if ensuing computations are thereby reduced, with the following complete set of necessary relationships:

$$E(u_{ij}) = 0, \qquad E(u_{ij}^2) = \frac{a-1}{a} \sigma_u^2, \qquad E(u_{ij}\, u_{ij'}) = 0$$

$$E(u_{ij}\, u_{i'j}) = -\frac{1}{a} \sigma_u^2, \qquad E(u_{ij}\, u_{i'j'}) = 0$$

where i' is unequal to i and j' is unequal to j.

We may further note that the interaction arising from two or more random factors is a random term with properties given under (2) above. The interaction arising from two or more fixed factors is a fixed term which is not a random variable. The interaction arising from some fixed factors and some random factors has properties which are the natural extension of those given under (4) above. In fact, we may regard a combination of levels of fixed factors as a level of a superfactor whose levels are all the possible combinations of the fixed factors. A combination of levels of random factors may be likewise regarded as a level of a superfactor whose levels are all possible combinations of the levels of the random factors. There are, however, certain qualifications on the latter statement, because, if for example factors a, b are fixed factors with A, B levels, respectively, and factors c and d are random factors, and the four-factor interaction contribution is denoted by

$$(abcd)_{ijkl}$$

then

$$\sum_i (abcd)_{ijkl} = \sum_j (abcd)_{ijkl} = 0$$

The exact rules may be worked out, and we shall merely give an example of the general result, which will serve as a guide for any situation.

First we should note that, for the case when varieties are completely fixed and places are random in our variety–place illustration, the following properties hold:

$$E(v_i) = v_i, \qquad E(v_i^2) = v_i^2, \qquad E(v_i v_{i'}) = v_i v_{i'}$$

$$E(p_j) = 0, \qquad E(p_j^2) = \sigma_p^2, \qquad E(p_j p_{j'}) = 0$$

$$E(vp)_{ij} = 0, \qquad E[(vp)_{ij}^2] = \frac{v-1}{v} \sigma_{vp}^2, \qquad E[(vp)_{ij}(vp)_{ij'}] = 0$$

$$E[(vp)_{ij}(vp)_{i'j}] = -\frac{1}{v} \sigma_{vp}^2, \qquad E[(vp)_{ij}(vp)_{i'j'}] = 0$$

In our example above, under assumptions of homogeneity of any component of variance within combinations of fixed factors, we find

$$E[(abcd)_{ijkl}] = 0, \qquad E[(abcd)_{ijkl}^2] = \left(\frac{A-1}{A}\right)\left(\frac{B-1}{B}\right) \sigma_{abcd}^2$$

$$E[(abcd)_{ijkl}(abcd)_{ijkl'}] = 0$$

$$E[(abcd)_{ijkl}(abcd)_{ijk'l}] = 0$$

$$E[(abcd)_{ijkl}(abcd)_{ijk'l'}] = 0$$

$$E[(abcd)_{ijkl}(abcd)_{ij'kl}] = -\left(\frac{A-1}{A}\right)\frac{1}{B} \sigma_{abcd}^2$$

$$E[(abcd)_{ijkl}(abcd)_{i'jkl}] = -\frac{1}{A}\left(\frac{B-1}{B}\right) \sigma_{abcd}^2$$

$$E[(abcd)_{ijkl}(abcd)_{i'j'kl}] = \frac{1}{A}\frac{1}{B} \sigma_{abcd}^2$$

and all other covariances are zero.

The general rule is therefore obvious. There is non-zero covariance between terms $(abcd)_{ijkl}$ and $(abcd)_{i'j'k'l'}$ only if

$$k = k'$$
$$l = l'$$

The coefficients of σ_{abcd}^2 is the product of two numbers, one for the fixed factor a and one for the fixed factor b. The number for factor a is

$$\frac{A-1}{A} \quad \text{if} \quad i = i'$$

$$-\frac{1}{A} \quad \text{if} \quad i \neq i'$$

Similarly, for factor b, the number is

$$\frac{B-1}{B} \quad \text{if} \quad j = j'$$

$$-\frac{1}{B} \quad \text{if} \quad j \neq j'$$

A single composite rule for getting the covariance (or, of course, the variance) of terms $(abcde \cdot \cdot)_{ijklm} \ldots$ and $(abcde \cdot \cdot)_{i'j'k'l'm'n'} \ldots$ is as follows: Make up the product of a number for each factor, which is as follows:

> Unity if the factor is random and the subscripts are equal
> Zero if the factor is random and the subscripts are unequal
> $(X-1)/X$ if the factor is fixed and the subscripts are equal
> $-1/X$ if the factor is fixed and the subscripts are unequal

where X is the number of levels of the fixed factor.

13.6 COMPONENTS OF COVARIANCE

Suppose we have two observations, y and z say, on each individual instead of only one as in the previous parts of this chapter. We can obviously consider the compound observation $y+z$ for each individual and make the same analysis of variance for this compound observation as for each basic observation y and z. Exactly the same formulas will hold for the expectations of mean squares, the components of variance being those for $y+z$ rather than for y or z. Also we know that

$$V(y + z) = V(y) + V(z) + 2 \operatorname{Cov}(y, z)$$

so we can write

$$\sigma^2_{h(y+z)} = \sigma^2_{hy} + \sigma^2_{hz} + 2\sigma_{hyz}$$

where

$\sigma^2_{h(y+z)}$ is the component of variance for $y+z$ attributable to the source of variation h

σ^2_{hy} is the component of variance for y attributable to the source of variation h

σ^2_{hz} is the component of variance for z attributable to the source of variation h

σ_{hyz} is the component of covariance for y and z attributable to the source of variation h

This last item is the new facet of the situation. We can imagine the case when we have an indefinitely large number of observations and can obtain the true averages of y and z for the levels of the h source of variation. Denote these by $(\bar{y}_1, \bar{z}_1), (\bar{y}_2, \bar{z}_2), \cdots (\bar{y}_H, \bar{z}_H)$, where there are H levels for the h source of variation. Then the component of covariance is equal to

$$\frac{1}{H-1} \sum_{i=1}^{H} (\bar{y}_i - \text{av } \bar{y}_i)(\bar{z}_i - \text{av } \bar{z}_i)$$

where av $\bar{y}_i$, av $\bar{z}_i$ denote population averages of $\bar{y}_i$ and $\bar{z}_i$.

The estimate of σ_{hyz} will be obtained as

$$\frac{\hat{\sigma}^2_{h(y+z)} - \hat{\sigma}^2_{hy} - \hat{\sigma}^2_{hz}}{2}$$

the three variance component estimates being obtained by equating observed mean squares and expected mean squares, or otherwise, as indicated earlier in this chapter.

The above procedure serves completely to define the estimation of components of covariance, provided we add the rider that, if within a particular level of classification there is no correspondence between the y and z values, we pair them in an arbitrary way and take the component of covariance within that level to be zero (see below).

The simplest example of this sort of thing is the computation of a genotypic covariance and correlation. Suppose the situation is that described at the beginning of this chapter with varieties, except that we have two attributes for each variety say yield y and per cent protein z. Let u equal $y + z$. Then our analyses of variance for z and u are of the same form as Table 13.1 with z and u in place of y. We can then form Table 13.10.

TABLE 13.10

ANALYSIS OF COVARIANCE

Source	d.f.	Mean Squares			Mean Product
		y	z	$u = y+z$	$y \times z$
Among varieties	$n-1$	V_y	V_z	V_u	$V_{yz} = \frac{1}{2}(V_u - V_y - V_z)$
Within varieties	$n(r-1)$	E_y	E_z	E_u	$E_{yz} = \frac{1}{2}(E_u - E_y - E_z)$
Total	$nr-1$				

Clearly we have

$$E(V_u) = \sigma_{eu}^2 + r\sigma_{gu}^2$$
$$E(V_y) = \sigma_{ey}^2 + r\sigma_{gy}^2$$
$$E(V_z) = \sigma_{ez}^2 + r\sigma_{gz}^2$$
$$E(E_u) = \sigma_{eu}^2$$
$$E(E_y) = \sigma_{ey}^2$$
$$E(E_z) = \sigma_{ez}^2$$

where for instance

σ_{eu}^2 is the error component of variance for attribute u

σ_{gy}^2 is the variety component of variance for attribute y

From the above we therefore have

$$E(V_{yz}) = E[\tfrac{1}{2}(V_u - V_y - V_z)]$$
$$= \tfrac{1}{2}(\sigma_{eu}^2 - \sigma_{ey}^2 - \sigma_{ez}^2) + \tfrac{1}{2}r(\sigma_{gu}^2 - \sigma_{gy}^2 - \sigma_{gz}^2)$$
$$E(E_{yz}) = \tfrac{1}{2}(\sigma_{eu}^2 - \sigma_{ey}^2 - \sigma_{ez}^2)$$

and, since $u = y + z$,

$$E(V_{yz}) = \sigma_{eyz} + r\sigma_{gyz}$$
$$E(E_{yz}) = \sigma_{eyz}$$

Hence we have estimates as follows:

$$\hat{\sigma}_{gy}^2 = \frac{1}{r}(V_y - E_y), \qquad \hat{\sigma}_{ey}^2 = E_y$$

$$\hat{\sigma}_{gz}^2 = \frac{1}{r}(V_z - E_z), \qquad \hat{\sigma}_{ez}^2 = E_z$$

$$\hat{\sigma}_{gyz} = \frac{1}{r}(V_{yz} - E_{yz}), \qquad \hat{\sigma}_{eyz} = E_{yz}$$

We may now estimate the correlation of the true variety means for y and z as

$$\hat{\rho}_{gyz} = \frac{\hat{\sigma}_{gyz}}{(\hat{\sigma}_{gy}^2 \hat{\sigma}_{gz}^2)^{1/2}}$$

and the error correlation of y and z as

$$\hat{\rho}_{eyz} = \frac{\hat{\sigma}_{eyz}}{(\hat{\sigma}_{ey}^2 \hat{\sigma}_{ez}^2)^{1/2}}$$

It should be noted that the observed correlation of variety means is a hodge-podge of the intrinsic paremeters in the situation, for we have

$$\hat{\rho}_{\bar{y}\bar{z}} = \frac{V_{yz}}{(V_y V_z)^{1/2}}$$

$$\sim \frac{(\sigma_{eyz} + r\sigma_{gyz})}{[\sigma_{ey}^2 + r\sigma_{gy}^2)(\sigma_{ez}^2 + r\sigma_{gz})]^{1/2}}$$

where $\sim$ means "is a consistent estimate of."

This observed correlation of variety means gives little indication of the correlation of the true variety means unless we can assume that σ_{eyz} is small, in which case the observed correlation will tend to be of the same sign but lower in absolute magnitude than the true correlation. It is possibly worth noting that most of the correlations reported in the 30's are "observed correlations" in the above sense and that the intrinsic correlations should be evaluated. There are undoubtedly many cases in which the worker computed the observed correlation and decided it was too low to be of interest or utility.

The adjustment of observed correlations to the correlation of true values is the same procedure as "adjustment for attenuation" used mainly by psychologists. In a similar manner regressions can be adjusted for "attenuation."

The rider attached to the procedure above may be illustrated by the following example. Suppose we had r plots for each variety on which we obtained the yield and an independent set of r plots on which we obtained the per cent protein. There would be no correspondence of individual values of y and z, and we would therefore take E_{yz}, σ_{eyz}, and $\hat{\sigma}_{eyz}$ to be zero. The true covariance would be estimated by the covariance of variety means.

An important question is the reliability of estimates of components of covariance and intrinsic correlations derived from them. The particular case of a genetic correlation has been examined by Rae (1950) and Reeve (1955).

REFERENCES

Fisher, R. A. 1925. *Statistical methods for research workers*, and succeeding editions. Oliver and Boyd, Edinburgh.

Kempthorne, Oscar. 1952. *The design and analysis of experiments*. John Wiley & Sons, New York.

Lush, J. L. 1937. *Animal breeding plans*. Iowa State College Press, Ames.

Rae, A. L. 1950. Genetic variation and covariation in productive characters of New Zealand Romney Marsh sheep. Ph.D. Thesis. Iowa State College Library.

Reeve, E. C. R. 1955. The variance of the genetic correlation coefficient. *Biometrics*, **11**, 357–374.

268   THE PARTITION OF VARIANCE

Wilk, M. B., and O. Kempthorne. 1955. Fixed, mixed, and random models. *J. Amer. statist. Ass.*, **50**, 1144–1167.
Wilk, M. B., and O. Kempthorne. 1956. Some aspects of the analysis of factorial experiments in a completely randomized design. *Ann. math. Statist.*, **27**, 950–985.

FURTHER READING

Anderson, R. L., and T. A. Bancroft. 1952. *Statistical theory in research.* McGraw-Hill Book Co., New York.
Bross, Irwin. 1950. Fiducial intervals for variance components. *Biometrics*, **6**, 136–144.
Comstock, R. E., and H. F. Robinson. 1951. Consistency of estimates of variance components. *Biometrics*, **7**, 75–82.
Comstock, R. E. 1955. Theory of quantitative genetics: synthesis. *Cold Spr. Harb. Symp. quant. Biol.*, **20**, 93–102.
Cornfield, J., and J. W. Tukey. 1956. Average values of mean squares in factorials. *Ann. math. Statist.*, **27**, 907–949.
Crump, S. L. 1946. The estimation of variance components in analysis of variance. *Biomet. Bull.*, **2**, 7–11.
Crump, S. L. 1951. The present status of variance component analysis. *Biometrics*, **7**, 1–16.
Fieller, E. C., and C. A. B. Smith. 1951. Note on the analysis of variance and intraclass correlation. *Ann. Eugen. Lond.*, **16**, 97–104.
Ganguli, M. 1941. A note on nested sampling. *Sankhyā*, **5**, 449–452.
Henderson, C. R. 1953. Estimation of variance and covariance components. *Biometrics*, **9**, 226–252.
Lowry, Dorothy C. 1955. Variance components with reference to genetic population parameters. *Biometrics*, **11**, 136–148.
Osborne, R., and W. S. B. Paterson. 1952. On the sampling variance of heritability estimates derived from variance analysis. *Proc. roy. Soc. Edinb. B*, **64**, 456–461.
Robertson, A. 1951. The analysis of heterogeneity in the binomial distribution. *Ann. Eugen. Lond.*, **16**, 1–14.
Satterthwaite, F. E. 1946. An approximate distribution of estimates of variance components. *Biomet. Bull.* **2**, 110–114.
Scheffé, H. 1956. Alternative models for the analysis of variance. *Ann. math. Statist.* **27**, 251–271.
Schultz, E. F. 1955. Rules of thumb for determining expectations of mean squares in analysis of variance. *Biometrics*, **11**, 123–135.
Smith, C. A. B. 1951. A test for heterogeneity of proportions. *Ann. Eugen. Lond.*, **16**, 16–25.
Smith, C. A. B. 1952. A simplified heterogeneity test. *Ann. Eugen. Lond.*, **17**, 35–36.
Smith, C. A. B. 1953. The linear function maximising intraclass correlation. *Ann. Eugen. Lond.*, **17**, 286–292.
Wright, Sewall. 1917. The average correlation within subgroups of a population. *J. Wash. Acad. Sci.*, **7**, 532–535.

PROBLEMS

1. Derive directly the expectations of the mean squares in Table 13.5.
2. Derive the estimate of the variance of the intraclass correlation of two random individuals from the whole population with the same sire for the case represented in Table 13.5.

3. Verify the expectations of $(vp)_{ij}^2$ and of cross products of the $(vp)_{ij}$.

4. Verify the expectation of the ABC mean square in Table 13.9.

5. Verify the expectation of the B mean square in Table 13.9.

6. Suppose we have v varieties, which are to be regarded as fixed, p places to be regarded as random, and r observations on each variety–place combination from a completely randomized design at each place. Construct the orthogonal analysis of variance, and evaluate the expectations of mean squares.

7. Suppose for the case of problem 6 we have $r_j(>0)$ observations on each variety at place j ($j = 1, 2, \cdots, p$). Construct the analysis of variance of variety–place means and for variety–place combinations and error, and find the expectations of mean squares.

8. Work out a procedure for the case of problem 6 when the number of observations on variety i and place j is $r_{ij} > 0$, all i, j).

9. Consider the case of s sires, d dams per sire, and n individuals per sire. Let the variance components be σ_s^2, σ_d^2, and σ_e^2. Obtain the variance of the estimate of

$$\sigma_s^2/(\sigma_s^2+\sigma_d^2+\sigma_e^2)$$

10. For the case of problem 9, obtain the variance of the estimate of

$$\sigma_d^2/(\sigma_s^2+\sigma_d^2+\sigma_e^2)$$

11. For the case of problem 9, obtain the variance of the estimate of

$$(\sigma_s^2+\sigma_d^2)/(\sigma_s^2+\sigma_d^2+\sigma_e^2)$$

CHAPTER 14

Multiple Regression, Correlation, the Adjustment of Data, and Path Analysis

In this chapter, we shall be concerned with the relationships between variables in a population, for instance, how one variable x_1 depends on the other variables x_2, x_3, $\cdots$, x_n, or the multiple correlation between x_1, and x_2, x_3, $\cdots$, x_n, which measures in some sense how the variability in x_1 may be explained in terms of the variability of x_2, x_3, $\cdots$, x_n.

14.1 MULTIPLE REGRESSION; POPULATION THEORY

Suppose that we have a population of individuals each of which has n characteristics, say, x_1, x_2, $\cdots$, x_n; for instance, with human beings we might have heights (x_1), weight (x_2), girth (x_3). The whole population may be thought of as forming a cluster in a space with n dimensions, just as we have a perfectly definite and perceivable cluster with two variables x_1 and x_2, for example. There is a whole branch of statistics which is concerned with such populations, known as multivariate analysis. We shall concern ourselves with simpler aspects of the situation.

Frequently we are interested in questions of the type: How much of the variation of x_1 can be attributed to the variation in x_2, x_3, $\cdots$, x_n? Or to put the matter in another form: What can we say about the x_1 for an individual, given that it has specified values for x_2, x_3, $\cdots$, x_n? Looked at in this way we consider what function of x_2, x_3, $\cdots$, x_n say should be used to predict x_1 say, and what the error of such a prediction will be. We confine ourselves to linear predictors of the form

$$x_1 = \alpha + \beta_2 x_2 + \beta_3 x_3 + \cdots + \beta_n x_n$$

because (1) such predictors can be handled with fair ease and (2) polynomial predictors are included as a special case, since we could have x_3 equals x_2^2 and so on. In other words there may, if we desire, be functional relations between the x's.

It is reasonable to define the best predictor of x_1 from $x_2, x_3, \cdots, x_n$ as that linear function

$$\alpha + \beta_2 x_2 + \beta_3 x_3 + \cdots + \beta_n x_n$$

which is such that the average value of

$$(x_1 - \alpha - \beta_2 x_2 - \beta_3 x_3 - \cdots - \beta_n x_n)^2$$

is a minimum. This is the predictor which will result in minimum mean square error of prediction. To obtain the values of $\alpha, \beta_2, \cdots, \beta_n$ we have to minimize

$$Q = E(x_1 - \alpha - \beta_2 x_2 - \beta_3 x_3 \cdots - \beta_n x_n)^2$$

Setting the derivative with respect to α equal to zero, and denoting $E(x_i)$ by μ_i, we have

$$\mu_1 - \alpha - \beta_2 \mu_2 - \beta_3 \mu_3 - \cdots - \beta_n \mu_n = 0$$

so that

$$\alpha = \mu_1 - \beta_2 \mu_2 - \beta_3 \mu_3 - \cdots - \beta_n \mu_n$$

If we insert this value into Q, we obtain

$$E(X_1 - \beta_2 X_2 - \beta_3 X_3 - \cdots \beta_n X_n)^2$$

where $X_i = x_i - \mu_i$, and this is equal to

$$\sigma_{11} + \sum_{j=2}^{n} \beta_j^2 \sigma_{jj} + \sum_{j' \neq j = 2}^{n} \beta_j \beta_{j'} \sigma_{jj'} - 2 \sum_{j=2}^{n} \beta_j \sigma_{1j}$$

where σ_{jj} equals $E(X_j^2)$ and $\sigma_{jj'}$ equals $E(X_j X_{j'})$.

Again differentiating with respect to the quantities $\beta_2, \beta_3, \cdots, \beta_n$ and setting the derivatives equal to zero, we get $n-1$ equations, of which the one obtained by differentiating with respect to β_j is

$$\beta_j \sigma_{jj} + \sum_{j' \neq j} \beta_{j'} \sigma_{jj'} = \sigma_{1j}, \qquad j = 2, 3, \cdots, n \qquad (1)$$

If we have variables $x_1, x_2, x_3,$ and x_4, the three equations are

$$\beta_2 \sigma_{22} + \beta_3 \sigma_{23} + \beta_4 \sigma_{24} = \sigma_{12}$$
$$\beta_2 \sigma_{32} + \beta_3 \sigma_{33} + \beta_4 \sigma_{34} = \sigma_{13}$$
$$\beta_2 \sigma_{42} + \beta_3 \sigma_{43} + \beta_4 \sigma_{44} = \sigma_{14}$$

Note that $\sigma_{jj'}$ equals $\sigma_{j'j}$, so that the equations are symmetric. We have three equations in three unknowns which can be solved for these. The resulting predictor is

$$X_1 = \beta_2 X_2 + \beta_3 X_3 + \cdots + \beta_n X_n$$

For some purposes it is desirable to keep distinct the whole set of regression equations or predictors we could obtain. For instance, we might be concerned with the prediction of x_1 from x_2, x_3, $\cdots$, x_{n-1} and would have an equation

$$X_1 = \beta_2 X_2 + \beta_3 X_3 + \cdots \beta_{n-1} X_{n-1}$$

Now the corresponding β's in the two cases will not necessarily, or in fact usually, be the same, so that it may be confusing to use the same subscripts to denote them. Yule devised a notation which is exemplified by the following two equations:

$$X_1 = \beta_{12.34 \, \ldots \, n} X_2 + \beta_{13.24 \, \ldots \, n} X_3 + \cdots + \beta_{1n.23 \, \ldots \, (n-1)} X_n$$
$$X_1 = \beta_{12.34 \, \ldots \, (n-1)} X_2 + \beta_{13.24 \, \ldots \, (n-1)} X_3$$
$$+ \cdot \quad \cdot + \beta_{1(n-1).23 \, \ldots \, (n-2)} X_{n-1}$$

the first of which describes the prediction of x_1 from x_2, x_3, $\cdots$, x_n, while the second describes the prediction of x_1 from x_2, x_3, $\cdots$, x_{n-1}. The subscripts on any β are divided into three groups as follows: The first subscript denotes the variable being predicted; the second the particular variable of which the contribution is the β times its value; the third group which is separated from the first and second by a decimal dot specifies the other variables which are included in the predicting equation. The first two subscripts are called primary subscripts and the subscripts after the dot are called secondary subscripts. It may be noted that the ordering of the primary subscripts is essential while the secondary subscripts may be written out in any order.

The equations (1) which give the partial regression coefficients may be presented in a form which is sometimes more useful. Note that we may write $\sigma_{22} = \sigma_2^2$, $\sigma_{33} = \sigma_3^2$, etc., $\sigma_{12} = \rho_{12}\sigma_1\sigma_2$, $\sigma_{13} = \rho_{13}\sigma_1\sigma_3$, $\sigma_{23} = \rho_{23}\sigma_2\sigma_3$, etc. Then, if we define

$$\beta_2' = \beta_2 \frac{\sigma_2}{\sigma_1}, \qquad \beta_3' = \beta_3 \frac{\sigma_3}{\sigma_1}, \qquad \text{etc.}$$

the equations may be written as

$$\beta_2' \quad + \beta_3'\rho_{23} + \cdots + \beta_n'\rho_{2n} = \rho_{12}$$
$$\beta_2'\rho_{32} + \beta_3' \quad + \cdots + \beta_n'\rho_{3n} = \rho_{13}$$
$$\beta_2'\rho_{42} + \beta_3'\rho_{43} + \cdots + \beta_n'\rho_{4n} = \rho_{14}$$
$$\cdot \quad \cdot \quad \cdot \quad \cdot \quad \cdot \quad \cdot \quad \cdot \quad \cdot \quad \cdot \quad \cdot \quad \cdot \quad \cdot$$
$$\beta_2'\rho_{n2} + \beta_3'\rho_{n3} + \cdots + \beta_n' \quad = \rho_{1n}$$

Here of course ρ_{ij} equals ρ_{ji}.

The solution to these equations may be written out by the use of Cramer's rule as follows. Let W be the matrix

$$W = \begin{pmatrix} 1 & \rho_{12} & \rho_{13} & \cdots & \rho_{1n} \\ \rho_{12} & 1 & \rho_{23} & \cdots & \rho_{2n} \\ \rho_{13} & \rho_{23} & 1 & \cdots & \rho_{3n} \\ \cdot & \cdot & \cdot & \cdots & \cdot \\ \rho_{1n} & \rho_{2n} & \rho_{3n} & \cdots & 1 \end{pmatrix}$$

Let W_{11} be the determinant of the array resulting by eliminating the first row and first column; let W_{ij} be the determinant of the array resulting by eliminating the ith row and jth column multiplied by $(-1)^{i+j+1}$. Then by Cramer's rule

$$\beta_2' = \frac{W_{12}}{W_{11}}, \quad \beta_3' = \frac{W_{13}}{W_{11}}, \quad \cdots, \quad \beta_n' = \frac{W_{1n}}{W_{11}}$$

Hence we have the predicting equation

$$X_1 = \frac{W_{12}}{W_{11}} \frac{\sigma_1}{\sigma_2} X_2 + \frac{W_{13}}{W_{11}} \frac{\sigma_1}{\sigma_3} X_3 + \cdots + \frac{W_{1n}}{W_{11}} \frac{\sigma_1}{\sigma_n} X_n$$

which we may write in an entirely symmetrical form as

$$\frac{X_1}{\sigma_1} = \frac{W_{12}}{W_{11}} \frac{X_2}{\sigma_2} + \frac{W_{13}}{W_{11}} \frac{X_3}{\sigma_3} + \cdots + \frac{W_{1n}}{W_{11}} \frac{X_n}{\sigma_n}$$

If we standardized all the variates by dividing each one by its standard deviation, and denoted the standardized variates by x_1', x_2', etc.,* the predicting equation would be

$$x_1' = \frac{W_{12}}{W_{11}} x_2' + \frac{W_{13}}{W_{11}} x_3' + \cdots + \frac{W_{1n}}{W_{11}} x_n'$$

By the use of this terminology we can write down the predictor for any variate. That for x_3 in terms of $x_1, x_2, x_4, \cdots, x_n$ would be in standardized form

$$x_3' = \frac{W_{31}}{W_{33}} x_1' + \frac{W_{32}}{W_{33}} x_2' + \frac{W_{34}}{W_{33}} x_4' + \cdots + \frac{W_{3n}}{W_{33}} x_n'$$

* It will be noted that we use x (lower-case) for original variates, X (capital) for deviates around the mean, and x' (lower-case and primed) for standardized variates, unless otherwise noted.

As we have mentioned, the variates in such equations are called standardized variates, and the coefficients of these variates are called standard partial regression coefficients. Many statistical texts describe the process for obtaining partial regression coefficients by first obtaining the standard partial regression coefficients.

Finally it may be shown that the variance of the predicted variable x_j, when predicted from all the other x's, is equal to

$$\sigma_j^2 \frac{|W|}{W_{jj}}$$

where $|W|$ here is the determinant of the matrix W given above. The notation for this variance devised by Yule is exemplified by

$$\sigma_{1.23\cdots n}^2$$

denoting the variance in

$$x_1 \text{ minus its value predicted from } x_2, x_3, \cdots, x_n$$

This residual variance serves to define the multiple correlation of x_1 with $x_2, x_3, \cdots, x_n$ by the formula

$$\sigma_{1.23\cdots n}^2 = \sigma_1^2(1 - R^2)$$

so

$$R^2 = 1 - \frac{|W|}{W_{11}}$$

14.2 PARTIAL CORRELATION COEFFICIENTS

Suppose we have three variates x_1, x_2, and x_3. Then we may be interested in answering the following question. A certain amount of the variation in x_1 can be attributed to a linear statistical dependence of x_1 on x_3, and likewise a certain amount of variation in x_2 can be attributed to a linear statistical dependence of x_2 on x_3. The question is then: What is the correlation between the residual variation of x_1 and the residual variation of x_2? Yule's notation in this is as follows:

Let the regression of x_1 on x_3 be β_{13}; then the deviation of x_1 from the value for x_1 predicted from the value of x_3 is

$$X_1 - \beta_{13}X_3$$

and this Yule denotes by $x_{1.3}$. Similarly

$$x_{2.3} = X_2 - \beta_{23}X_3$$

Now we wish to determine the correlation between $x_{1.3}$ and $x_{2.3}$. We may as well suppose that the variances of x_1, x_2, x_3 in our population (or sample) are unity and their means are zero. We can do this of course by dividing x_1 by σ_{x_1}, etc. We have

$$\rho(x_{1.3}x_{2.3}) = \rho_{12.3} = \frac{E(x_{1.3}x_{2.3})}{[E(x_{1.3}^2)\,E(x_{2.3}^2)]^{1/2}}$$

$$E(x_{1.3}x_{2.3}) = E(X_1 - \beta_{13}X_3)(X_2 - \beta_{23}X_3)$$
$$= \rho_{12} - \beta_{13}\rho_{23} - \beta_{23}\rho_{13} + \beta_{13}\beta_{23}$$

But

$$\beta_{13} = \frac{E(X_1 X_3)}{E(X_3^2)} = \rho_{13}, \quad \text{etc}$$

so

$$E(x_{1.3}x_{2.3}) = \rho_{12} - \rho_{13}\rho_{23}$$

Similarly

$$E(x_{1.3}^2) = E(X_1 - \beta_{13}X_3)^2 = E(X_1^2 - 2\beta_{13}X_1X_3 + \beta_{13}^2 X_3^2)$$
$$= 1 - 2\beta_{13}\rho_{13} + \beta_{13}^2$$
$$= 1 - 2\rho_{13}^2 + \rho_{13}^2$$
$$= 1 - \rho_{13}^2$$

and

$$E(x_{2.3}^2) = 1 - \rho_{23}^2$$

so that finally

$$\rho_{12.3} = \frac{\rho_{12} - \rho_{13}\rho_{23}}{[(1 - \rho_{13}^2)(1 - \rho_{23}^2)]^{1/2}}$$

This formula may be extended to the case where we want say $\rho_{12 \cdot qr}$, q being any set of subscripts from $3, 4, \cdots m$, and r another one of these subscripts, by the formula

$$\rho_{12 \cdot qr} = \frac{\rho_{12 \cdot q} - \rho_{1r \cdot q}\rho_{2r \cdot q}}{[(1 - \rho_{1r \cdot q}^2)(1 - \rho_{2r \cdot q}^2)]^{1/2}}$$

For example, it may be verified that $\rho_{12.34}$ is as follows:

$\rho_{12.34}$
$$= \frac{\rho_{12} - \rho_{13}\rho_{23} - \rho_{14}\rho_{24} - \rho_{12}\rho_{43}^2 + \rho_{13}\rho_{24}\rho_{43} + \rho_{14}\rho_{23}\rho_{34}}{(1 - \rho_{23}^2 - \rho_{34}^2 - \rho_{24}^2 + 2\rho_{24}\rho_{23}\rho_{34})^{1/2}(1 - \rho_{13}^2 - \rho_{14}^2 - \rho_{34}^2 + 2\rho_{13}\rho_{14}\rho_{43})^{1/2}}$$

These formula became very simple in the particular case when there are non-zero correlations between X_1 and $X_2, \cdots, X_n$, between X_2 and X_1, $X_3, \cdots, X_n$, but the correlations among $X_3, X_4, \cdots, X_n$ are zero. Let us obtain the result directly.

We have

$$X_1 = \beta_{13}X_3 + \beta_{14}X_4 + \cdots + \beta_{1n}X_n$$

where the β_{ij}'s satisfy

$$E[X_j(X_1 - \beta_{13}X_3 - \beta_{14}X_4 \cdots - \beta_{1n}X_n)] = 0, \qquad j = 3, 4, \cdots, n$$

Hence, since $E(X_jX_k) = 0$, where j and k are any two different subscripts out of $3, 4, \cdots, n$,

$$E(X_jX_1) = \beta_{1j}$$

or

$$\beta_{1j} = \rho_{1j}$$

Similarly, if

$$X_2 = \beta_{23}X_3 + \beta_{24}X_4 + \cdots \beta_{2n}X_n$$

$$\beta_{2j} = \rho_{2j}$$

Also

$$\begin{aligned}
E(x_{1.34\cdots n}x_{2.34\cdots n}) &= E(X_1 - \beta_{13}X_3 - \beta_{14}X_4 \cdots \beta_{1n}X_n) \\
&\quad (X_2 - \beta_{23}X_3 - \beta_{24}X_4 - \cdots - \beta_{2n}X_n) \\
&= \rho_{12} + \beta_{13}\beta_{23} + \beta_{14}\beta_{24} + \cdots + \beta_{1n}\beta_{2n} \\
&\quad - \beta_{13}\rho_{23} - \beta_{14}\rho_{24} - \cdots - \beta_{1n}\rho_{2n} \\
&\quad - \beta_{23}\rho_{13} - \beta_{24}\rho_{14} - \cdots - \beta_{2n}\rho_{1n} \\
&= \rho_{12} - \rho_{13}\rho_{23} - \rho_{14}\rho_{24} - \cdots - \rho_{1n}\rho_{2n}
\end{aligned}$$

$$\begin{aligned}
E(x_{1.34\cdots n}^2) &= E(X_1 - \beta_{13}X_3 - \beta_{14}X_4 - \cdots - \beta_{1n}X_n)^2 \\
&= 1 + \beta_{13}^2 + \beta_{14}^2 + \cdots + \beta_{1n}^2 \\
&\quad - 2\beta_{13}\rho_{13} - 2\beta_{14}\rho_{14} - \cdots - 2\beta_{1n}\rho_{1n} \\
&= 1 - \rho_{13}^2 - \rho_{14}^2 - \cdots - \rho_{1n}^2
\end{aligned}$$

and

$$E(x_{2.34\cdots n}^2) = 1 - \rho_{23}^2 - \rho_{24}^2 - \cdots - \rho_{2n}^2$$

Hence

$$\rho_{12.34\cdots n} = \frac{\rho_{12} - \rho_{13}\rho_{23} - \rho_{14}\rho_{24} - \cdots - \rho_{1n}\rho_{2n}}{[(1 - \rho_{13}^2 - \rho_{14}^2 - \cdots - \rho_{1n}^2)(1 - \rho_{23}^2 - \rho_{24}^2 - \cdots - \rho_{2n}^2)]^{1/2}}$$

A consequence of this is that, if

$$X_1 = \beta_{13}X_3 + \beta_{14}X_4 + \cdots + \beta_{1n}X_n + e_1$$

$$X_2 = \beta_{23}X_3 + \beta_{24}X_4 + \cdots + \beta_{2n}X_n + e_2$$

where the e_1's and e_2's are uncorrelated and $x_3, x_4, \cdots, x_n$ are all mutually uncorrelated, then the correlation of e_1 and e_2 is given by

$$\rho_{12} = \rho_{13}\rho_{23} + \rho_{14}\rho_{24} + \cdots + \rho_{1n}\rho_{2n}$$

14.3 SAMPLE REGRESSION AND CORRELATIONS

The formulas we have given above are also used to give multiple regression equations, and correlations, partial correlations, and multiple correlations for a sample. For purposes of tests of significance, however, a different but equivalent form of description is to be preferred. Detailed description and derivation of procedure is given in Kempthorne (1952, Chapter 5), and we shall give here only a condensed outline of the matter.

Consider the following situation: We have n observations y_k, $k = 1, 2, \cdots, n$ and know variables $x_1, x_2, \cdots, x_p$ for each observation, the value of x_j for the kth observation being x_{kj}. Then the multiple regression situation is that we postulate the equation or model

$$y_k = x_{k1}\beta_1 + x_{k2}\beta_2 + \cdots + x_{kp}\beta_p + e_k$$

where $\beta_1, \beta_2, \cdots, \beta_p$ are unknown constants, usually called regression coefficients, and the e_k's are deviations which are usually thought of as errors which follow certain distributions. For purposes of estimation, which will be described first, the e_k's will be assumed to have expectations of zero, to be uncorrelated, and to have the same variance σ^2. Note that this model includes such situations as the model

$$y_k = \alpha + \beta x_k + e_k$$

where there are two regression coefficients α and β. The quantities x_{k1} are all equal to unity, while x_{k2} is equal to x_k.

If we denote the sum of products of x_{ki} and x_{kj} by s_{ij}, i.e.

$$\sum_{k=1}^{n} x_{ki}x_{kj} = s_{ij} = s_{ji}$$

least squares leads to the following normal equations:

$$s_{11}\beta_1 + s_{12}\beta_2 + \cdots + s_{1p}\beta_p = \sum_k x_{k1}y_k = P_1 \quad \text{say}$$

$$s_{12}\beta_1 + s_{22}\beta_2 + \cdots + s_{2p}\beta_p = \sum_k x_{k2}y_k = P_2 \quad \text{say}$$

$$\cdots \cdots \cdots \cdots \cdots \cdots \cdots \cdots$$

$$s_{1p}\beta_1 + s_{2p}\beta_2 + \cdots + s_{pp}\beta_p = \sum_k x_{kp}y_k = P_p \quad \text{say}$$

These are p linear equations in p quantities $\beta_1, \beta_2, \cdots, \beta_p$, and the estimates of these are taken to be the solutions of the equations. The whole matter of obtaining the solutions is a computational one. The reader should consult computational texts (e.g. Dwyer, 1951) for detailed computational procedures. The following is one method which is not the quickest but is easy to follow and has certain advantages to be described later.

Consider the set of equations:

$$s_{11}c_1 + s_{12}c_2 + \cdots + s_{1p}c_p = 1$$
$$s_{12}c_1 + s_{22}c_2 + \cdots + s_{2p}c_p = 0$$
$$\cdots \cdots \cdots \cdots \cdots$$
$$s_{1p}c_1 + s_{2p}c_2 + \cdots + s_{pp}c_p = 0$$

These may be solved. Denote the solutions for $c_1, c_2, \cdots, c_p$ by $c_{11}, c_{21}, \cdots, c_{p1}$, respectively. Now form equations with the same left-hand sides, but with right-hand sides as 0, 1, 0, $\cdots$, 0 reading downward. Denote the solutions $c_1, c_2, \cdots, c_p$ of these by $c_{12}, c_{22}, \cdots, c_{p2}$, respectively. Then make up a third set of equations with unity as the right-hand side of the third equation and zero as the right-hand side for the other equations, and solve these. Continue in this fashion with unity occurring once as the right-hand side of each equation. In all there will be p sets of p linear equations in p unknowns, and the solutions $c_1, c_2, \cdots, c_p$ for the case when unity is the right-hand side of the jth equation are denoted by $c_{j1}, c_{j2}, \cdots, c_{jp}$, respectively. Then it is a mathematical fact that the solutions of the normal equations are

$$\hat{\beta}_1 = \sum_k c_{1k}P_k$$

$$\hat{\beta}_2 = \sum_k c_{2k}P_k$$

etc.

or, in general,

$$\hat{\beta}_j = \sum_k c_{jk}P_k$$

Furthermore the variances and covariances of the estimates under the error assumptions made are as follows:

$$V(\hat{\beta}_j) = c_{jj}\sigma^2, \qquad \text{Cov}\,(\hat{\beta}_j, \hat{\beta}_k) = c_{jk}\sigma^2$$

There remains the question of the estimation of σ^2, and this is easily done by taking

$$\frac{1}{(n-p)}\,(\textstyle\sum y_k^2 - \hat{\beta}_1 P_1 - \hat{\beta}_2 P_2 - \cdots \hat{\beta}_p P_p) = s^2$$

say. Estimated variances of the estimates of the regression coefficients are then formed by inserting s^2 in place of σ^2.

Sometimes we are interested in testing the significance of any one $\hat{\beta}_j$, and, for this to be strictly valid, the errors must also be normally distributed. In that case we can take

$$t = \frac{\hat{\beta}_j}{(c_{jj}s^2)^{1/2}}$$

and compare this to the t distributions with $(n-p)$ degrees of freedom. If the magnitude of the computed t exceeds the tabulated 5 per cent point, then the conclusion is drawn that $\hat{\beta}_j$ is significantly different from zero at the 5 per cent level.

There remains one other topic in this area, namely that the experimenter may wish to make a test of significance for several $\hat{\beta}_j$'s jointly. Let us suppose that he wishes to test $\hat{\beta}_1, \hat{\beta}_2, \cdots, \hat{\beta}_r$ jointly, where r is less than (or equal to) p, of course. This is done by an analysis of variance. Define the quantity $R(\beta_1, \beta_2, \cdots, \beta_p)$ to be $\hat{\beta}_1 P_1 + \hat{\beta}_2 P_2 + \cdots + \hat{\beta}_p P_p$. Now consider the estimates of $\beta_{r+1}, \beta_{r+2}, \cdots, \beta_p$ when $\beta_1, \beta_2, \cdots, \beta_r$ are taken to be zero in the model. These will be given by $(p-r)$ linear equations in $(p-r)$ unknowns:

$$S_{r+1,\,r+1}\,\beta_{r+1} + S_{r+1,\,r+2}\,\beta_{r+2} + \cdots + S_{r+1,\,p}\,\beta_p = P_{r+1}$$
$$S_{r+1,\,r+2}\,\beta_{r+1} + S_{r+2,\,r+2}\,\beta_{r+2} + \cdots + S_{r+2,\,p}\,\beta_p = P_{r+2}$$
$$\cdots \cdots \cdots \cdots \cdots \cdots \cdots \cdots \cdots \cdots$$
$$S_{r+1,\,p}\,\beta_{r+1} + S_{r+2,\,p}\,\beta_{r+2} + \cdots + S_{p,\,p}\,\beta_p = P_p$$

Denote the solution of these equations by

$$\tilde{\beta}_{r+1}, \tilde{\beta}_{r+2}, \cdots, \tilde{\beta}_p$$

and then set

$$R(\beta_{r+1}, \beta_{r+2}, \cdots, \beta_p) = \tilde{\beta}_{r+1} P_{r+1} + \tilde{\beta}_{r+2} P_{r+2} + \cdots + \tilde{\beta}_p P_p$$

The analysis of variance given in Table 14.1 may now be constructed.

TABLE 14.1

ANALYSIS OF VARIANCE FOR JOINT TEST OF SIGNIFICANCE

Source	d.f.	S.S.	M.S.
Fitting $\beta_{r+1}, \beta_{r+2}, \cdots, \beta_p$ alone	$p-r$	$R(\beta_{r+1}, \beta_{r+2}, \cdots, \beta_p)$	
Difference for testing $\beta_1, \cdots, \beta_r$	r	Difference	T
Fitting $\beta_1, \beta_2, \cdots, \beta_p$	p	$R(\beta_1, \beta_2, \cdots, \beta_p)$	
Residual	$n-p$	Difference	E
Total	n	$\sum y_k^2$	

Note that the table is filled out by making two subtractions. Mean squares are then obtained by dividing sums of squares by degrees of freedom. Finally F equal to T/E is computed, and the significance level obtained by looking at the percentage values given in the F table for r and $(n - p)$ degrees of freedom. Normality of errors is necessary for this test.

Some final notes on this process just described are desirable or necessary. First, as we indicated by example, the procedure described gives rules for fitting equations such as

$$y = \alpha + \beta x + \gamma z \quad \text{etc.}$$

where y is the dependent variable, x, z, etc. are the independent variables, and α, β, γ are the regression coefficients corresponding to the β_j's in our description. If we are fitting such an equation, we should first get the solution for α in terms of the other regression coefficients and the observed values and then substitute for α in the other equations. This has the following net effects:

1. $\hat{\alpha}$ is equal to $\bar{y} - \hat{\beta}\bar{x} - \bar{\gamma}\bar{z}$, etc.
2. The normal equations for β, γ, etc. are written down immediately by replacing the quantities S_{ii}, S_{ij}, P_j by the same sum of squares or products, as the case may be, but around the means instead of around zero.

Second, the above procedures must not be applied directly if there is dependence among the x_{kj}'s. By a dependence we mean that there exist numbers, say a_1, a_2, $\cdots$, a_p, such that $a_1 x_{k1} + a_2 x_{k2} + \cdots + a_p x_{kp} = $ a constant the same for all k.

Thus for example we could not use the procedures to fit for β_1 and β_2 in this following case, say

$$y_1 = \beta_1 + \beta_2 + e_1$$
$$y_2 = 2\beta_1 + 2\beta_2 + e_2$$
$$y_3 = 3\beta_1 + 3\beta_2 + e_2$$

In this case where x_{k1} is the coefficient of β_1 and x_{k2} is the coefficient of β_2, x_{k1} equals x_{k2} for all k and we can clearly estimate only $\beta_1 + \beta_2$.

In the case of the model

$$y_1 = \alpha + \beta_1 + e_1$$
$$y_2 = \alpha + \beta_1 + e_2$$
$$y_3 = \alpha + \beta_2 + e_3$$
$$y_4 = \alpha + \beta_2 + e_4$$

The coefficient of α is equal to the sum of the coefficients of β_1 and β_2. Only two functions of the parameters, namely, $\alpha+\beta_1$ and $\alpha+\beta_2$ may be estimated, or any linear function of these, such as for instance

$$(\alpha + \beta_1) - (\alpha + \beta_2) = \beta_1 - \beta_2$$

These two cases are examples of what is known as hypotheses which are not of full rank. Such cases are of very frequent occurrence because, as we shall see in the next section, they arise in the analysis of data which have a cross classification structure.

Third, some indication of the utility of the procedures should be given. Frequently genetic data are of one of two forms:

Form 1. The data consist of observations on individuals subject to various doses of some stimuli, and it is considered that the response is related linearly to the doses. In that case the procedures can be used to estimate the dependence of response on doses and to test the significance of the effects of each of the stimuli.

Form 2. The data are either observational, i.e. not completely planned, or arise in an experiment in which such factors as age or body weight have varied and introduced variation in the response. In that case it may be considered desirable to obtain adjustments for age or body weight, so that we attempt to make comparisons between groups for animals of the same age and body weight, and with the effects of the variations in these characteristics removed from the error. The procedures can be used to derive correction or adjustment factors. Such adjustments are biased unless the equation by which the adjustments are fitted is the true one.

14.4 MODIFICATION OF GENERAL REGRESSION PROCEDURE FOR CROSS CLASSIFICATION DATA

In the previous chapter, models for classification data were derived and examined. A model for classification data expresses each observation as the sum of effects arising from each class at each level of the classification. Thus for example we may have the model

$$y_{ijk} = \mu + a_i + b_j + e_{ijk}$$

in which the observation y_{ijk} is assumed to be composed additively of a constant μ, an effect a_i common to individuals in the ith a class, an effect b_j common to individuals in the jth b class, and an error e_{ijk}. Suppose that the quantities a_i and b_j are fixed effects and not random variables. Then we have a regression problem analogous to that discussed earlier in this chapter. The quantities μ, a_i, and b_j may be regarded as regression coefficients. To illustrate this point let us consider six observations,

y_{111}, y_{112}, y_{121}, y_{122}, y_{211}, y_{221}; the model for these can be written out as follows:

$$y_{111} = \mu \times 1 + a_1 \times 1 + a_2 \times 0 + b_1 \times 1 + b_2 \times 0 + e_{111}$$
$$y_{112} = \mu \times 1 + a_1 \times 1 + a_2 \times 0 + b_1 \times 1 + b_2 \times 0 + e_{112}$$
$$y_{121} = \mu \times 1 + a_1 \times 1 + a_2 \times 0 + b_1 \times 0 + b_2 \times 1 + e_{121}$$
$$y_{122} = \mu \times 1 + a_1 \times 1 + a_2 \times 0 + b_1 \times 0 + b_2 \times 1 + e_{122}$$
$$y_{211} = \mu \times 1 + a_1 \times 0 + a_2 \times 1 + b_1 \times 1 + b_2 \times 0 + e_{211}$$
$$y_{221} = \mu \times 1 + a_1 \times 0 + a_2 \times 1 + b_1 \times 0 + b_2 \times 1 + e_{221}$$

Here we have each y expressed as a *known* linear function of unknown parameters, μ, a_1, a_2, b_1, b_2, plus an error, and this is exactly the standard regression situation. But there is one particular feature of the present case which must be noted. Suppose we let x be an "independent" variate of which μ is the regression coefficient, let u_1, u_2 be "independent" variates corresponding to a_1 and a_2, and let v_1, v_2 be "independent" variates corresponding to b_1 and b_2. Then the values for the "independent" variates for the six observations are:

x	u_1	u_2	v_1	v_2
1	1	0	1	0
1	1	0	1	0
1	1	0	0	1
1	1	0	0	1
1	0	1	1	0
1	0	1	0	1

Note that x is equal to $u_1 + u_2$ for every observation and that x is equal to $v_1 + v_2$ for every observation. This means that the "independent" variates are not independent in the sense that, given u_1, say, we know without looking at the structure of the observations what the value of u_2 is, and similarly for v_1 and v_2.

It is a mathematical consequence that the normal equations cannot be solved uniquely, and that the matrix (c_{ij}) of the previous sections does not exist. This can be overcome very simply by imposing in this case two conditions, say that

$$a_1 + a_2 = 0$$
$$b_1 + b_2 = 0$$

or what are simpler operationally to use

$$a_2 = 0$$
$$b_2 = 0$$

In general for the $r \times s$ classification we can take one parameter for each way of classification to be zero. The equations can then be solved in the standard manner without any trouble. For multiple classification situations we solve for the constants of one factor in terms of the constants of the other factors, and so on.

Tests of significance will again require the assumption of normality of the residuals, and, given that assumption, are performed in the standard manner.

A very common difficulty in the application of classification models to applied genetic data arises because absence of a record is the result of culling based on a previous record or records. This introduces bias. A treatment of this is given by Kempthorne and von Krosigk (to be published).

14.5 CORRELATION AND CAUSATION

The preceding sections of this chapter have dealt with the prediction of one variable from a set of variables and with the correlations among sets of variables. The uses of these methods are rather strictly confined. We may wish to predict one variable from the other variables: i.e. to answer the question—given that an individual has x_2 equal to 6, x_3 equal to 9, what is our best guess of the value of x_1 for the individual, assuming that he is a random member of the population? Another application which is essentially a different aspect of the one just mentioned, but is worth emphasizing separately, is to answer the questions of the following type: The value of x_1 for an individual with x_2 equal to 1 is 9, what would the value of x_1 have been if x_2 were equal to 0? In this sense the methodology is useful for the adjustment of data to a common basis, such as for instance adjustment of the female records of a bunch of individuals of the two sexes to what the records would have been if these females had been males. Such adjustment obviously depends rather crucially on the choice of an equation to represent the records of the two sexes. We might for instance use the model:

$$y_m = m + e$$
$$y_f = m + s + f$$

where y_m, y_f are the records for male and females, m is the mean of all possible male records, and $m+s$ is the mean of all possible female records, so that s is an additive sex effect. Alternatively we might have the model

$$y_m = m + e$$
$$y_f = sm + f$$

where s is now the multiplicative sex effect. For instance the effect of sex on the body weight of sheep may be multiplicative so that individuals who are male at three months weigh 60 pounds and at six months weigh 100 pounds, whereas the respective weights for females are 57 and 95 pounds (5 per cent less). In such a case the procedure for adjusting female weights to male weights would be to multiply the female weights by 100/95 and not to add a certain number of pounds. The basis on which choice of a formula for adjustment must be made is the validity of the formula over a wide range of other conditions such as age, level of nutrition, sire and dam, and so on.

In this latter application we move into a branch of inquiry not hitherto considered, in that the adjustment of data should be based on knowledge of how the factor which is being adjusted for actually produces its effect. An arbitrarily chosen adjustment formula may introduce bias rather than remove the systematic difference. It is this fact which tends to vitiate the uses of the analysis of covariance recommended in most books on the analysis of experiments.

We now turn to the question of examining possible patterns of causality which give rise to a given set of observed correlations. Let us suppose we have three variables: x, y, and z. It is possible to indicate a large number of ways in which the observed correlations may arise. We shall indicate that x causes y by an arrow pointing from x to y, thus: $x \to y$. Other possible forces in the situation will be denoted by letters a, b, c, etc. We give in Figure 14.1 some of the possible ways in which the attributes x, y, and z may arise. In $(1a)$ for instance y is a function of x and z is a function of y and hence also a function of x. If the functions were linear functions all correlations would be unity in absolute values. In $(1b)$, $(2a)$, $(2b)$, $(3a)$, $(3b)$, merely the order of attributes is changed. In diagram $(4a)$ a force a and the force which produces x combine to produce y, and then z is a function of y. If the relationships are linear and also a and y are uncorrelated in their occurrence we would have $\rho_{xy} < 1$, $\rho_{zy} = 1$, $\rho_{zx} = \rho_{yx}$. Diagrams $(4b)$, $(5a)$, $(5b)$, $(6a)$, $(6b)$ are merely permutations of diagram $(4a)$. In diagram (7) force a and the force which produces x (or force x for brevity) jointly produce y, and then these forces combine with force b to produce z; note however that force x produces its effect on z through y. In diagram (8) we have forces a and x producing y and forces b, y, and x producing z, and in this case force x has an effect on z directly and an indirect effect through y.

The reader can probably think of many examples which may fall into one of the possible patterns listed or more complex ones. A simple one in economics is the supply of a food and the demand for that food expressed by the community in their purchases. The supply is the result of various forces such as current weather, the weather last year, the occurrence of disease, and also the price which the supplier can receive.

The amount purchased depends on the incomes of the consumers, their tastes, their alternatives, and the price. Note here that there is at least one common element, namely the price. The price affects the output of the supplier and the purchases of the consumer, but the price depends on the amount people wish to buy. If people are keen to buy the food, the price will be raised. Hence price and the amount purchased cause each other jointly, and one cannot be said to cause the other.

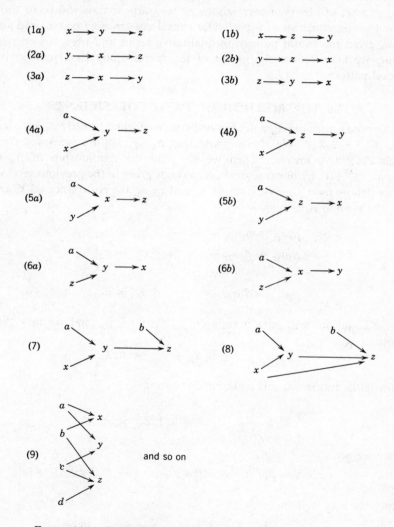

FIGURE 14.1. Some of the possible ways in which correlations among x, y, z may arise.

Strictly speaking correlation analysis and the prediction of variables make no use of the causal pattern in which the variables arose, and this fact perhaps more than any other has led to the decay of the use of the correlation coefficient in statistical inference. The adjustment of data should be based on the causal pattern, because otherwise the adjusted data may be biased.

We have considered a few of the possible causal patterns which can give rise to a set of observed correlations. Our purpose now will be to show how the consequences of a particular causal pattern may be assessed and how, given the causal pattern in qualitative terms and observed correlations, we may deduce the extent of the forces along each path in the causal pattern.

14.6 THE METHOD OF PATH COEFFICIENTS

Suppose a variable X_0 is determined completely and linearly by variables $X_1, X_2, \cdots, X_n$. We also suppose that X_0, X_1, X_2 are measured from their respective means. Then we can find the relationship of X_0 to $X_1, X_2, \cdots, X_n$ by linear regression methods given in the previous section. If we denote by σ_{ii} the variance of x_i, and by σ_{ij} the covariance of X_i and X_j, the normal equations are

$$\beta_1 \sigma_{11} + \beta_2 \sigma_{12} + \cdots + \beta_n \sigma_{1n} = \sigma_{10}$$

$$\beta_1 \sigma_{12} + \beta_2 \sigma_{22} + \cdots + \beta_n \sigma_{2n} = \sigma_{20}$$

$$\text{etc.}$$

$$\beta_1 \sigma_{1n} + \beta_2 \sigma_{2n} + \cdots + \beta_n \sigma_{nn} = \sigma_{n0}$$

These equations will have a solution $\beta_1, \beta_2, \cdots, \beta_n$, and we may then write

$$X_0 = \beta_1 X_1 + \beta_2 X_2 + \cdots + \beta_n X_n$$

Now let us transform this equation by writing

$$x_i' = \frac{X_i}{\sigma_{ii}^{1/2}}, \qquad i = 0, 1, 2, \cdots n$$

Then we get

$$x_0' \sigma_{00} = \beta_1 x_1' \sigma_{11}^{1/2} + \beta_2 x_2' \sigma_{22}^{1/2} + \cdots + \beta_n x_n' \sigma_{nn}^{1/2}$$

which we may write as

$$x_0' = \beta_1 \frac{\sigma_{11}^{1/2}}{\sigma_{00}} x_1' + \beta_2 \frac{\sigma_{22}^{1/2}}{\sigma_{00}} x_2' + \cdots + \beta_n \frac{\sigma_{nn}^{1/2}}{\sigma_{00}} x_n'$$

or as
$$x_0' = \gamma_1 x_1' + \gamma_2 x_2' + \cdots + \gamma_n x_n'$$
where
$$\gamma_i = \beta_i \left(\frac{\sigma_{ii}}{\sigma_{00}} \right)^{1/2}$$

The γ's are standard partial regression coefficients, but, now that we know $X_1, X_2, \cdots, X_n$ cause X_0, we define them to be path coefficients. We note that a path coefficient is always a standard partial regression coefficient. A standard partial regression coefficient of X_0 on X_i is a path coefficient only under the circumstances (1) that X_i is a cause more or less remote in the chains of causation leading to X_0, (2) that the other variables included in the prediction equation are also causes of X_0, possibly interconnected with each other and X_i, and (3) that all relevant variables are included.

We have thus indicated why we introduce this term "path coefficient" and now need to show in what way the coefficients are useful.

Consider the case when $x_1, x_2, \cdots, x_n$ are uncorrelated. Then we have
$$V(x_0') = \gamma_1^2 V(x_1') + \gamma_2^2 V(x_2') + \cdots \gamma_n^2 V(x_n')$$

but, since $V(x_i') = 1$, because all the variables are standardized, this becomes
$$1 = \gamma_1^2 + \gamma_2^2 + \cdots + \gamma_n^2$$

Now suppose that $x_2, x_3, \cdots, x_n$ are kept constant, and that x_1 maintains the same variability as before. It is rather questionable whether this can happen, because X_1 may be caused by $X_2, X_3, \cdots, X_n$. In that case we would have to presuppose some conceptual force which produced the same variation in X_1 as in the original population with $X_2, X_3, \cdots, X_n$ kept constant. If we skip over this difficulty (which does not appear to me to have been dealt with adequately by Wright, 1921), then the variance in x_0' would be γ_1^2, or the variance in X_0 would be $\sigma_{X_0}^2 \gamma_1^2$. In this sense γ_i^2 measures the proportion of the variability of X_0 which is directly attributable to X_1, and our equation specifies the proportions of the variability of X_0 attributable to $X_1, X_2, \cdots, X_n$. The quantities γ_i^2 are called coefficients of determination and are denoted as $d_{X_i \cdot X_0}^2$ by Wright. In the case when the forces are uncorrelated, the square of the path coefficient from X_i to X_0 measures the proportion of the variance of X_0 which is attributable to X_i.

Another use of path coefficients is to calculate the correlation between any X_i and X_0, for then we have
$$\rho_{X_i X_0} = \rho_{x_i' x_0'} = \gamma_1 \rho_{1i} + \gamma_2 \rho_{2i} + \cdots + \gamma_i + \gamma_{i+1} \rho_{i+1, i} + \cdots + \gamma_n \rho_{ni}$$

since the variables x_i' have unit variance.   This is simply seen from Figure 14.2.   The formula states that to get the correlation between x_i and x_0 we consider all paths from x_i to x_0, of which there are one direct one and $(n-1)$ via each of the other x's.

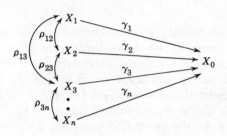

FIGURE 14.2

Actually in this case as in all the other cases discussed in the literature, the path diagrams appear unnecessary except insofar as they provide a visual picture of the causal forces in the situation.   The actual equations in standardized variates seem to be easier to manipulate and lay bare the quantitative nature of the causal relationships assumed.

Now we turn to the case in which x_0 is not completely determined by $x_1, x_2, \cdot \cdot \cdot, x_n$.   We may then consider the regression equation

$$X_0 = \beta_1 X_1 + \beta_2 X_2 + \cdot \cdot \cdot + \beta_n X_n + E$$

or in standardized form

$$x_0' = \gamma_1 x_1' + \gamma_2 x_2' + \cdot \cdot \cdot + \gamma_n x_n' + e \tag{A}$$

The errors, e, are uncorrelated with $x_1, x_2, \cdot \cdot \cdot, x_n$.

The variance of e is the variance of

$$x_0' - \gamma_1 x_1' - \gamma_2 x_2' \cdot \cdot \cdot - \gamma_n x_n'$$

which is

$$V(e) = 1 - \gamma_1^2 - \gamma_2^2 - \cdot \cdot \cdot - \gamma_n^2 - \sum_{\substack{i,j \\ i \neq j}} \gamma_i \gamma_j \rho_{ij}$$

Hence, if the standardized variate x_{n+1}' is introduced, defined by the equation

$$x_{n+1}' = \frac{e}{[V(e)]^{1/2}}$$

then

$$x_0' = \gamma_1 x_1' + \gamma_2 x_2' + \cdot \cdot \cdot + \gamma_n x_n' + \gamma_{n+1} x_{n+1}'$$

where

$$\gamma_{n+1} = [V(e)]^{1/2}$$

The complete determination of x_0 by $x_1, x_2, \cdots, x_n, x_{n+1}$ is expressed by taking variances of the left-hand side and right-hand side of (A), giving

$$1 = \gamma_1^2 + \gamma_2^2 + \cdots \gamma_n^2 + \sum_{\substack{i,j \\ i \neq j}} \gamma_i \gamma_j \rho_{ij} + \gamma_{n+1}^2$$

which is clearly true by definition of γ_{n+1}.

Hence we see that a situation in which there is not complete determination can be transformed into one in which there is complete determination by introducing a dummy variable with zero mean and unit variance which is uncorrelated with the variables already specified in the situation.

14.7 THE EFFECTS OF COMMON CAUSES

Consider two variables X and Y which are the result of a number of common causes B, C, D, and cause A which affects X only and cause E which affects Y only. All causes are assumed to be uncorrelated. The

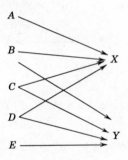

FIGURE 14.3

path diagram in this case is given in Figure 14.3. Let all the variates be standardized. Then we may write

$$X = aA + bB + cC + dD$$
$$Y = \qquad eB + fC + gD + hE$$

where a is $p_{X.A}$, b is $p_{X.B}$, etc., e is $p_{Y.B}$, etc. Then, since the A, B, C, D, E are assumed to be uncorrelated, we have $p_{X.A} = a = \gamma_{XA}$, etc. The correlation between X and Y is clearly

$$\rho_{XY} = be + cf + dg$$

In Wright's terminology, the general equation is

$$\rho_{XY} = p_{X.A}p_{Y.A} + p_{X.B}p_{Y.B} + p_{X.C}p_{Y.C} + p_{X.D}p_{Y.D}$$

where $p_{X.A}$ is the path coefficient from A to X and so on. If we worked out the partial correlation of X and Y eliminating B, C, D, we would find that it is zero.

It is interesting to note that two variables may result from the same causes and be uncorrelated with each other. If in the above case both X and Y are completely determined by B, C, and D, the correlation γ_{XY} will be zero if

$$be + cf + dg = 0$$

14.8 SYSTEMS OF CORRELATED CAUSES

As a simple example to illustrate the situation let X and Y be the result of causes M and N which are correlated with correlation ρ_{MN} (Figure 14.4). Let all the variates be standardized to have mean zero and unit

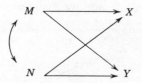

FIGURE 14.4

variance. The correlation between M and N is indicated by the two-headed arrow connecting M and N. We have

$$X = aM + bN, \qquad a^2 + b^2 + 2ab\rho_{MN} = 1$$
$$Y = cM + dN, \qquad c^2 + d^2 + 2cd\rho_{MN} = 1$$

then

$$\begin{aligned}
\rho_{XY} = E(XY) &= E[acM^2 + bdN^2 + (ad + bc)MN] \\
&= acE(M^2) + bdE(N^2) + (ad + bc)E(MN) \\
&= ac + bd + (ad + bc)\rho_{MN}
\end{aligned}$$

In Wright's terminology

$$\rho_{XY} = p_{X.M}p_{Y.M} + p_{X.N}p_{Y.N} + p_{X.M}\rho_{MN}p_{Y.N} + p_{X.N}\rho_{MN}p_{Y.M}$$

The general situation is covered by the following rule given by Wright: "The correlation between any two variables in a network of relations can be analyzed into contributions from all the possible paths by which the two variables are connected, such that the contribution from each path is the product of the path coefficients of the elementary paths or links of the path. If there are residual correlations represented by two-headed arrows, one and only one of the coefficients multiplied together to give the contribution of the connecting path may be a correlation coefficient." The truth of this statement is evident from the fact that, by means of equations such as

$$X = aM + bN$$

for the case when X is the result of M and N, the two attributes of which the correlation is sought, say U and V, can be expressed as linear functions of the primitive or unanalyzed variables of the system. Variables are said to be unanalyzed if there are no variables prior to these in the causal system. Thus, if the unanalyzed variables are A_1, A_2, $\cdot\cdot\cdot$, A_r, then U and V will be of the form

$$U = a_1A_1 + a_2A_2 + \cdot\cdot\cdot + a_rA_r$$
$$V = b_1A_1 + b_2A_2 + \cdot\cdot\cdot + b_rA_r$$

where a_1, a_2, $\cdot\cdot\cdot$, a_r, b_1, b_2, $\cdot\cdot\cdot$, b_r are either elementary path coefficients or products of elementary path coefficients. Obviously we then have

$$\rho_{UV} = a_1b_1 + a_2b_2 + \cdot\cdot\cdot + a_rb_r + \sum_{i \neq j} a_ib_j\rho_{A_iA_j}$$

It is clear that we cannot go in both directions along the same connecting path, and we cannot use a path through two variables more than once unless the two variables are correlated and not causally connected. Actually my experience is that the foolproof method of obtaining correlations is by writing out the standardized equations for all variables and expressing all variables in terms of unanalyzed variables. This may be tedious to an expert in looking at path diagrams, but it does not seem wise for the general worker in the field to clutter his mind with a cumbersome set of rules which are not easy to assimilate, when a simple direct primitive approach is possible as well as enlightening.

Uses of the Method of Path Coefficients

The uses of the method of path coefficients lie mainly in three directions:

1. In examining the consequences of forces which act linearly in which the result of the forces on X say is a linear combination of the results of the forces on variables occurring before X in the causal system.

2. In examining the feasibility of a pattern of causal forces in estimating the path coefficients of paths between forces whose direct results cannot be measured. Examples will be given below.

3. In making patently clear what can be deduced from a set of correlation coefficients.

14.9 EXAMPLES OF THE USE OF PATH COEFFICIENTS

We shall give in somewhat condensed form a few of the more interesting genetic examples from Wright's papers.

The Birth Weight of Guinea Pigs

Here the diagram used by Wright is given in Figure 14.5.

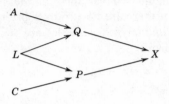

FIGURE 14.5

X = birth weight

Q = prenatal growth rate

P = gestation period

L = size of litter

A = hereditary and environmental factors which determine Q, apart from size of litter

C = factors determining gestation period apart from size of litter

We then have the equations in standardized form:

$$Q = aA + bL, \qquad a^2 + b^2 = 1$$
$$P = cL + dC, \qquad c^2 + d^2 = 1$$
$$X = eQ + fP$$
$$= eaA + ebL + fcL + fdC$$

The observed correlations and their values in terms of the path coefficients were as follows:

$$0.5547 = r_{XP} = ebc + fc^2 + fd^2$$
$$= ebc + f$$
$$-0.6758 = r_{XL} = eb + fc$$
$$-0.4444 = r_{PL} = c$$

Also

$$1 = e^2 + f^2 + 2ef\rho_{PQ}$$
$$= e^2 + f^2 + 2efbc$$

There are six equations with six unknowns, and the solutions were found to be

$$a = 0.80, \quad b = -0.59, \quad c = -0.44, \quad d = 0.90, \quad e = 0.86, \quad f = 0.33$$

It therefore appears, *if the path diagram is correct qualitatively*, that birth weight (X) is much more affected by variations in prenatal growth rate (Q) than by variations in gestation period (P) since $e^2 = 0.74$ and $f^2 = 0.11$. There is, however, some joint determination of X by P and Q since P and Q are correlated, and the partition of determination is reliable only if the causal factors are uncorrelated.

The analysis of determination plays a considerable role in Wright's development of path coefficients. However, I am in agreement with Tukey (1954) that the regression coefficients are of more value. These are obtained from the path coefficients which are standardized partial regression coefficients by "destandardizing" them. Thus the effect of size of litter (L) on X is equal to $(eb + fc)\sigma_X/\sigma_L$, which is the "destandardized" coefficient.

Two advantages of the "destandardized" path coefficients or path regression coefficients are given by Tukey.

The path regression coefficients tell us, within the limits of the analysis used of course, about the structural relationship between the variables whereas the path coefficients of Wright do not give this directly. Also the path regression coefficients are likely to be more stable. One reason for the stability is that the regression of one variable, say y, on another variable x is not affected by selection for the x variable if the regression is linear over the whole range. However the use of standardized partial regression coefficients or Wright's path coefficients leads to easy manipulation because all variables are standardized to have unit variance.

Heredity and Environment in Determining Human Intelligence

This example is taken from Wright (1934) who used data of Burks. The data consisted of intelligence tests on 104 California children and tests of their parents and grades of home environment. Similar data were obtained for 206 adopted children and their foster parents and home environments.

H = heredity of parents
P = mid-parent score
E = grade of home environment
O = child's score

The observed correlations adjusted for attenuation, were as follows:

	Own Children	Adopted Children
P–O	+0.61	+0.23
O–E	+0.49	+0.29
E–P	+0.86	?

The simplest diagram for interpretative purposes of the "own children" is given in Figure 14.6, where R represents the residual variation.   Note

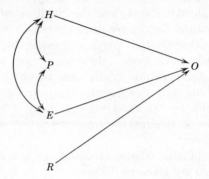

_{FIGURE 14.6}

that H, P, and E are represented as being correlated, it being impossible to specify a causal system for these variables.   We may write

$$O = aH + bE + cR \quad \text{with} \quad a^2 + b^2 + 2ab\rho_{HE} + c^2 = 1$$

and we have

$$\rho_{PE} = 0.86$$
$$\rho_{PO} = a\rho_{HP} + b\rho_{EP} = 0.61$$
$$\rho_{EO} = a\rho_{HE} + b = 0.49$$

so that we have four equations in six unknowns for which no unique solution exists.   The reader should note that here is a case where the path diagram way of representing the situation shows quite clearly that the information given, i.e. the three correlations plus the automatic equation in a, b, and c, is not sufficient to determine the magnitude of the forces along the paths.

One solution proposed by Wright (1934) is to use the same regression coefficient of O on E for own children as for adopted children (and this leads to a path coefficient from E to O of 0.27, i.e. a value of b equal to 0.27) and to amalgamate R with H. The diagrams are then as in Figure 14.7, the left one being for own children and the right for adopted children. The equations are

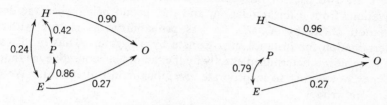

FIGURE 14.7

$$O = aH + bE$$
$$a^2 + b^2 + 2ab\rho_{HE} = 1$$
$$\rho_{PE} = 0.86$$
$$\rho_{PO} = a\rho_{HP} + b\rho_{EP} = 0.61$$
$$\rho_{EO} = a\rho_{HE} + b = 0.49$$

with $b = 0.27$.

These lead to the solutions: $a = 0.90$, $b = 0.27$, $\rho_{HP} = 0.42$, $\rho_{HE} = 0.24$, and $\rho_{PE} = 0.86$. Finally it is desirable to destandardize the equations so as to have some idea of the functional relationships deduced. We do not have the necessary variances to do it here.

A more extensive discussion of this example is given by Wright (1954).

14.10 NOTES ON WRIGHT'S USES OF PATH COEFFICIENTS

It is appropriate that we give an account of the path coefficient methodology of Wright (1921, 1934, 1954) because this methodology has been found very useful by many workers. What is given above contains in fact the background for the method and gives the same solution. Wright's procedure is not, however, to work in terms of the actual standardized equations but to omit writing these out explicitly and to reason entirely from the path diagram. We shall use the equations to derive the relationships between correlations and path coefficients. To quote from Wright (1954): "This method is based on the construction of a qualitative diagram in which the variables, whether actually measured or not, are represented as *additively* and *completely* determined by others, and these often in turn by more remote ones until an array of ultimate factors is arrived at, all correlations among which are assumed to be known." It has been shown above that, in the case when there are residuals in the (linear) determination of a variable X_0 by other variables (X_1, X_2, $\cdot\cdot\cdot$), we can introduce another independent factor which can be called the chance factor which results in complete determination of the variable y. There are two uses of this point, the first being when there are actual deviations from a linear relation, and the second being when the determination of X_0 by X_1, X_2, $\cdot\cdot\cdot$ is probabilistic as is true with the determination for instance of a gamete by a zygote. Thus in all cases the variable y is determined exactly by the factors introduced (even though we may not bother to incorporate *every* factor in a diagram). We can therefore write

$$x_0 = \sum_i^n p_{0i} x_i$$

where each x variable is standardized to have mean zero and unit variance. The quantity p_{0i} is the path coefficient from variable i to variable 0 and not the reverse as one might think offhand. The notation p_{0i} rather than $P_{X_0 \cdot X_i}$ for path coefficients has been used by Wright in recent years. The quantities p_{0i} are given by the regression of x_0 on x_1, x_2, $\cdot\cdot\cdot$, where one x, say x_n, is that due to the chance factor. The system can be represented as in Figure 14.8 in which the correlations among $x_1 \cdot\cdot\cdot x_n$ are

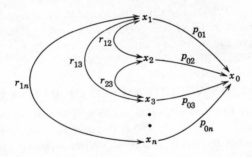

FIGURE 14.8

represented by two-headed arrows. It is immediately obvious that the normal equations are as follows:

$$p_{01} + p_{02} r_{12} + p_{03} r_{13} + \cdot\cdot\cdot + p_{0n} r_{1n} = r_{01}$$
$$p_{01} r_{12} + p_{02} + p_{03} r_{23} + \cdot\cdot\cdot + p_{0n} r_{2n} = r_{02}$$
$$p_{01} r_{1n} + p_{02} r_{2n} + p_{03} r_{3n} + \cdot\cdot\cdot + p_{0n} = r_{0n}$$

The values for the correlations of x_0 with any x_i are immediately read off the path diagram by the rule that the correlation is made up of parts, one for each path leading from x_i to x_0, a path running directly to x_0 from x_i or to x_0 through a variable x_j which is correlated with x_i. It is also clear that, if x_0 is perfectly determined by $x_1, x_2, \cdots, x_n$ (with the possibility of course that one of these is a pseudovariable, the chance factor mentioned above), then, since the sum of squares removed by a regression is the sum of products of estimates and right-hand sides of the normal equations, we have

or

$$p_{01}r_{01} + p_{02}r_{02} + \cdots + p_{0n}r_{0n} = 1$$

$$
\begin{aligned}
p_{01}^2 &+ 2p_{01}p_{02}r_{12} + 2p_{01}p_{02}r_{13} + \cdots \\
&+ p_{02}^2 + 2p_{02}p_{03}r_{23} + \cdots \\
&+ p_{03}^2 + 2p_{03}p_{04}r_{34} + \cdots \\
&+ \text{etc.} \qquad\qquad = 1
\end{aligned}
$$

In the case, when there are no correlations among $x_1, x_2, \cdots, x_n$, we have

$$p_{01}^2 + p_{02}^2 + \cdots + p_{0n}^2 = 1$$

The quantities p_{01}^2, p_{02}^2, etc. are called coefficients of determination by Wright and are denoted by $d_{0.1}$, $d_{0.2}$, etc.

If similarly we have a number of standardized variables $y_1, y_2, \cdots, y_m$ which are completely determined by variables $x_1, x_2, \cdots, x_n$, then of course

$$y_1 = p_{y_1x_1}x_1 + p_{y_1x_2}x_2 + p_{y_1x_3}x_3 + \cdots + p_{y_1x_n}x_n$$

$$y_2 = p_{y_2x_1}x_1 + p_{y_2x_2}x_2 + \cdots + p_{y_2x_n}x_n$$

etc., and algebraically we deduce immediately, because all the variates are standardized,

$$
\begin{aligned}
r_{y_1y_2} &= p_{y_1x_1}p_{y_2x_1} + p_{y_1x_2}p_{y_2x_2} + \cdots + p_{y_1x_n}p_{y_2x_n} \\
&+ \sum_{\substack{ij \\ i \neq j}} p_{y_1x_i}p_{y_2x_j}r_{ij}
\end{aligned}
$$

This formula can be written simply as

$$r_{y_1y_2} = \sum_{i,j} p_{y_1x_i}p_{y_2x_j}r_{ij}$$

with of course r_{ij} equal to unity if i and j are the same subscript. This relationship is easily read off the path diagram in Figure 14.9, by considering all the compound paths from Y_1 to Y_2. In the particular case when the x's are uncorrelated we have

$$r_{y_1 y_2} = \sum_i p_{y_1 x_i} p_{y_2 x_i}$$

which is a particularly simple relationship to use.

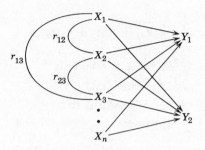

FIGURE 14.9

A third primitive case is that in which variables $Z_1, \cdot \cdot \cdot, Z_t$ result in $X_1, \cdot \cdot \cdot, X_n$ which in turn result in $Y_1, \cdot \cdot \cdot, Y_m$. Here algebraically we have

$$x_j = \sum_k p_{x_j z_k} z_k$$

$$y_l = \sum_i p_{y_l x_i} x_i$$

so

$$y_l = \sum_i p_{y_l x_i} \sum p_{x_i z_k} z_k$$

$$= \sum_k \left(\sum_i p_{y_l x_i} p_{x_i z_k} \right) z_k$$

$$= \sum_k p_{y_l z_k} z_k$$

This equation says that the total effect of z_k on y_l, or the compound of path coefficients from z_k to y_l, is equal to the sum over all combined paths of the compound path coefficient of any one path from z_k to y_l, denoted by $p_{y_l z_k}$, this compound path coefficient being the product of the elementary path coefficients of the elementary paths in the compound path. It is clear also that the correlation of y_l and y_u can be evaluated by the formula given above.

In the solution of problems Wright proceeds from typical equations of the following sort:

(1)
$$d_{0.1} = p_{01}^2$$

(2) if we denote $2p_{01}p_{02}r_{12}$ by $d_{0.\overline{12}}$, then

$$\sum_j d_{0.j} + \sum_{jk} d_{0.\overline{jk}} = 1$$

and

(3)
$$r_{00'} = \sum_j p_{0j}p_{0'j}$$

We have seen, however, that in many cases we need merely write down the equations in standardized form and we are led unerringly to the result. Wright would probably think, with his tremendous experience in the use of the method, that the equations are unnecessary and are implicit in the diagram (as indeed they are). However, I find some confusion arising in my own mind concerning the interpretation of Wright's statement that we follow all the paths including correlations, represented by two-headed arrows, "without going back after going forward along any arrow, and without passing through any variable twice in the same path · · ·. One, but not more of (these) elementary paths may be represented by a two-headed arrow without violating the rule against going back after going forward" (Wright, 1954).

A final note of caution should be made. The method of path coefficients is designed to deal with additive systems *only*. Any application to a situation in which non-additivity of factors (e.g. with dominance) may therefore lead to the wrong result.

14.11 THE PATH COEFFICIENT APPROACH TO INBREEDING THEORY

This approach is made in terms of scores of individuals based on their genotypes, the score for an individual being made up additively of a score from each gamete. Wright's original work (1921) was in terms of actual characteristics of individuals, with the case of inbreeding being covered by any one gene A of an allelic series carrying a score of unity and all others of the series a score of zero. The concepts inherent in the approach are:

1. The path coefficient from zygote to resultant gamete.
2. The path coefficient from gamete to resultant zygote.
3. The correlation between zygotic (or genotypic) scores of individuals or gametic scores within the individual.

We shall illustrate the approach with diploid individuals.

Let the genotypic value of any individual be made up additively of scores for each of the genes the individual possesses. Consider now an individual or zygote I' with score y' in a generation, the gamete G with score z handed on by the individual, and the resulting zygote I with score y which results from this gamete and the gamete which unites with it. Let I' contain genes a, b with effects α, β. Then

$$y' = \alpha + \beta$$

$z = \alpha$ or β each with probability $\frac{1}{2}$

$y = z + \gamma$ where γ is the score of the gamete which unites with z

Let

$$V(\alpha) = \frac{\sigma^2}{2} = V(\beta), \qquad \rho_{\alpha\beta} = F'_w$$

where $V(\alpha)$ is the variance of α, etc., and the subscript w on F is inserted to distinguish this F from the F defined in terms of identity by descent. Then

$$V(y') = \frac{\sigma^2}{2} + \frac{\sigma^2}{2} + 2\frac{\sigma^2}{2}F'_w = \sigma^2(1 + F'_w)$$

$$V(z) = \tfrac{1}{2}V(\alpha) + \tfrac{1}{2}V(\beta) \qquad = \frac{\sigma^2}{2} = V(\alpha) = V(\beta)$$

Also with no selection

$$V(\gamma) = \frac{\sigma^2}{2}$$

Then

$$\operatorname{Cov}(y', z) = \tfrac{1}{2}\operatorname{Cov}(y', \alpha) + \tfrac{1}{2}\operatorname{Cov}(y', \beta)$$

$$= \tfrac{1}{2}[V(\alpha) + \operatorname{Cov}(\alpha, \beta)] + \tfrac{1}{2}[V(\beta) + \operatorname{Cov}(\alpha, \beta)]$$

$$= \frac{\sigma^2}{2}(1 + F'_w)$$

and

$$V(y) = V(z) + V(\gamma) + \operatorname{Cov}(z, \gamma)$$

$$= \frac{\sigma^2}{2} + \frac{\sigma^2}{2} + 2F_w\frac{\sigma^2}{2}$$

$$= \sigma^2(1 + F_w)$$

where F_w is the correlation between the scores of uniting gametes in the later generation. Then we have

$$z = \frac{\operatorname{Cov}(y', z)}{V(y')}y' + \text{error}$$

and, standardizing the variables z and y', we have

$$\frac{z}{[V(z)]^{1/2}} = \left[\frac{V(y')}{V(z)}\right]^{1/2} \frac{\text{Cov}\,(y',z)}{V(y')} \frac{y'}{[V(y')]^{1/2}} + \text{error}$$

So $p_{zy'}$, the path coefficient from y' to z or from zygote to gamete, is equal to

$$\left[\frac{V(y')}{V(z)}\right]^{1/2} \frac{\text{Cov}\,(y',z)}{V(y')} = \frac{\text{Cov}\,(y',z)}{[V(z)\,V(y')]^{1/2}} = [\tfrac{1}{2}(1+F_w')]^{1/2}$$

Wright denotes this by b, with primes for the different generations.
 Also $y = z + \gamma$; so

$$P_{yz} = \left[\frac{V(z)}{V(y)}\right]^{1/2} = \left[\frac{\sigma^2}{2\sigma^2(1+F_w)}\right]^{1/2} = \left[\frac{1}{2(1+F_w)}\right]^{1/2}$$

is the path coefficient from gamete to zygote which Wright denotes by a, with primes to indicate the generation. In all cases the generation is the generation of the zygote, so that the path coefficient from gamete in one generation to gamete in the next generation involves a of the generation producing the original gamete and b of the next generation. The compounded path coefficient is therefore

$$ba' = \left[\frac{1}{2(1+F_w)}\right]^{1/2} [\tfrac{1}{2}(1+F_w)]^{1/2} = \frac{1}{2}$$

regardless of F_w. Also by a simple diagram we see that the correlation between the scores of uniting gametes is equal to $F_w = b^2m$, where m is the correlation of the parents with regard to genotypic or zygotic scores, of course.

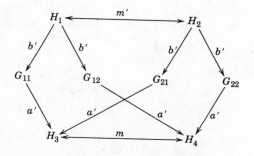

FIGURE 14.10. Simplified path diagram for full-sibbing. H_1 and H_2 denote parents in a generation, $G_{11}, G_{12}, G_{21}, G_{22}$ the gametes they produce, and H_3, H_4 the resulting progeny.

As an example of the use of these concepts consider the case of full-sibbing which, neglecting environmental effects, can be represented by Figure 14.10. We have

$$m = a'b'b'a' + a'b'm'b'a' + a'b'm'b'a' + a'b'b'a'$$
$$= 2(a'b')^2(1 + m')$$
$$= 2a'^2(b'^2 + F_w') \quad \text{since} \quad F_w = mb^2$$

Also

$$b^2 = \tfrac{1}{2}(1 + F_w'), \qquad b'^2 = \tfrac{1}{2}(1 + F_w''), \qquad a'^2 = \frac{1}{2(1 + F_w')}$$

So

$$m = 2 \frac{1}{2(1 + F_w')} [F_w' + \tfrac{1}{2}(1 + F_w'')]$$

and

$$F_w = mb^2 = \frac{m}{2}(1 + F_w') = \frac{1 + 2F_w' + F_w''}{4}$$

To convert this result into probability of heterozygosity we may consider as indicated above that a score of unity is attached to one allele A and zero to all other alleles. Since there is assumed to be no selection, we can use p for the frequency of A, and q for the frequency of the others for all generations. We then have the following table:

		$\male$		
		0	1	
	0	x	$q-x$	q
$\female$	1	$q-x$	$p-q+x$	p
		q	p	

and

$$F_w = \frac{p - q + x - p^2}{pq} = \frac{x - q^2}{pq}$$

so

$$x = q^2 + F_w pq$$

and

$$p - q + x = p^2 + F_w pq$$

The proportion of individuals heterozygous for A is $2(q-x)$ which equals $2pq(1-F_w)$.   In previous generations this will be $2pq(1-F_w')$, $2pq(1-F_w'')$, and so on.

In the present case of full-sibbing we have

$$(1 - F_w) = \tfrac{1}{2}(1 - F_w') + \tfrac{1}{4}(1 - F_w'')$$

so, if P is the proportion of individuals heterozygous for A,

$$P = \tfrac{1}{2}P' + \tfrac{1}{4}P''$$

14.12 RELATION OF PATH COEFFICIENT APPROACH TO PROBABILITY APPROACH

One way of seeing the relation of path coefficients and probability in inbreeding is as follows.   Let us consider an individual gene in the original population, and let us score it and all genes which are copies of it by unity, all other genes in any generation receiving a score of zero.   Consider now an individual X resulting from inbreeding with genes U, V which have scores u and v, respectively.   Then we can make up the following table:

		v		
		0	1	
u	0	$q-p+P(U=V)$	$p-P(U=V)$	q
	1	$p-P(U=V)$	$P(U=V)$	p
		q	p	

in which p is the frequency of the original gene, which will be $1/2N$ where N is the number of individuals in the original generation.   This frequency will stay constant under pure inbreeding without selection.   Then we have

$$F_w = \frac{P(U = V) - p^2}{pq}$$

so that

$$P(U=V) = p^2 + F_w pq$$

The left-hand side is the probability that the two genes of X are identical by descent from the original gene.   It is obvious therefore that the homogeneous recurrence equations involving F_x equals $P(U=V)$ and F_w, respectively, will be the same, where by "homogeneous" we mean "not involving terms independent of generation."   The same will be true for recurrence equations in the panmictic index and $(1 - F_w)$, respectively.

Note that, if F_w equals zero, $P(U = V)$ equals p^2, as we would expect under random mating.

14.13 A METHOD OF PARTIALLY DETERMINING CAUSES OF VARIATION

We have seen above that, given a linear system which is fully determined apart from pure random variation and given a path diagram which gives the qualitative nature of the causality, we can, following Wright (1921, 1934), obtain the path coefficients. Wright has used the squares of these path coefficients, simple or compound as they may be, as coefficients of determination intended to measure the extent to which the particular path determines the variable being analyzed. This aspect of the method is open to criticism, and it is therefore appropriate to mention an alternative. The following is not intended to be a complete answer if only for the reason that a complete answer cannot exist.

The procedure which I advocate for the case of an independent variable y and two dependent variables x_1 and x_2 is to make the partition of sum of squares given in Table 14.2. The idea is that we can attribute definitely

TABLE 14.2

PARTITION OF SUM OF SQUARES

Source	S.S.
x_1 after x_2	$R(x_1, x_2) - R(x_2) = S(x_1; x_2)$
x_2 after x_1	$R(x_1, x_2) - R(x_1) = S(x_2; x_1)$
x_1 and x_2 jointly	$R(x_1, x_2) - S(x_1; x_2) - S(x_2; x_1) = S(x_1, x_2)$
Residual	$\sum y^2 - R(x_1, x_2)$
Total	$\sum y^2$

to x_1 only the sum of squares due to x_1 after fitting for x_2, and this is denoted by $S(x_1; x_2)$, and likewise for x_2. The difference between that absolutely attributable to x_1 and that absolutely attributable to x_2 and the amount attributable to both x_1 and x_2 cannot be partitioned except with some knowledge of causality into a part due to x_1 and a part due to x_2. Note that this difference is said to be "due to x_1, x_2 jointly" and is equal to

$$R(x_1, x_2) - S(x_1; x_2) - S(x_2; x_1)$$

or

$$R(x_1) + R(x_2) - R(x_1, x_2)$$

where $R(\ )$ denotes the reduction in sum of squares due to fitting the variables in the parentheses. If the variates are standardized and the correlations of y with x_1 and x_2 are ρ_{1y}, ρ_{2y}, respectively, and that of x_1 and x_2 is ρ_{12}, we have

$$R(x_1, x_2) = \left(\frac{\rho_{1y}^2 + \rho_{2y}^2 - 2\rho_{1y}\rho_{2y}\rho_{12}}{1 - \rho_{12}^2} \right)$$

$$R(x_1) = \rho_{1y}^2$$

$$R(x_2) = \rho_{2y}^2$$

so that

$$S(x_1; x_2) = \left[\frac{\rho_{1y} - \rho_{2y}\rho_{12}}{(1 - \rho_{12}^2)^{1/2}} \right]^2 = \rho_{1y\cdot2}^2 \left(1 - \rho_{2y}^2 \right)$$

$$S(x_2; x_1) = \rho_{2y\cdot1}^2 \left(1 - \rho_{1y}^2 \right)$$

and

$$S(x_1, x_2) = -\left[\frac{\rho_{1y}^2\rho_{12}^2 + \rho_{2y}^2\rho_{12}^2 - 2\rho_{1y}\rho_{2y}\rho_{12}}{1 - \rho_{12}^2} \right]$$

For this example if the causal pattern were presumed to be as in Figure 14.11, in which a, b are the path coefficients, then we would find

$$b = \frac{\rho_{2y} - \rho_{1y}\rho_{12}}{1 - \rho_{12}^2}$$

$$a = \frac{\rho_{1y} - \rho_{2y}\rho_{12}}{1 - \rho_{12}^2}$$

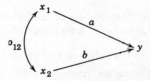

FIGURE 14.11

and the analysis of determination of Wright would be as follows:

Cause	Proportion
x_1	a^2
x_2	b^2
x_1 and x_2 jointly	$2ab\rho_{12}$

with a residual unexplained proportion.   In many cases the two partitions will be very similar.   Just what the method of Wright leads to with more complicated diagrams is as yet a moot point.   The alternative given above corresponds to the standard test of significance for an effect due to x_1 "independent" of x_2 and vice versa, and seems to give an answer which is meaningful and of scientific interest.

The extension of the alternative to more than two independent variables is straightforward.   With x_1, x_2, and x_3 we have the following partition:

Source	S.S.
x_1 after x_2, x_3	$R(x_1, x_2, x_3) - R(x_2, x_3) = S(x_1; x_2, x_3)$
x_2 after x_1 and x_3	$R(x_1, x_2, x_3) - R(x_1, x_3) = S(x_2; x_1, x_3)$
x_1 and x_2 jointly after x_3	$R(x_1, x_2, x_3) - R(x_3) - S(x_1; x_2, x_3)$ $- S(x_2; x_1, x_3) = S(x_1, x_2; x_3)$

and so on.   It should be stated that the notation $S(-; -)$ is not used generally.   The semicolon separates the variables considered from the other variables whose effects (assumed linear) are removed.

REFERENCES

Dwyer, P. S.   1951.   *Linear computations*.   John Wiley & Sons, New York.

Kempthorne, O.   1952.   *The design and analysis of experiments*.   John Wiley & Sons, New York.

Kempthorne, O., and M. von Krosigk.   1957.   The estimation of environmental and genetic trends from records subject to culling (to be published).

Tukey, J. W.   1954.   Causation, regression and path analysis.   Chapter 3 of *Statistics and mathematics in biology*, edited by O. Kempthorne et al.   Iowa State College Press, Ames.

Wright, Sewall.   1921.   Correlation and causation.   *J. agric. Res.*, **20**, 557–585.

Wright, Sewall.   1934.   The method of path coefficients.   *Ann. math. statist.*, **5**, 161–215.

Wright, Sewall.   1954.   The interpretation of multivariate systems.   Chapter 2 of *Statistics and mathematics in biology*.   Iowa State College Press, Ames.

FURTHER READING

Niles, Henry E.   1922.   Correlation, causation and Wright's theory of "path coefficients."   *Genetics*, **7**, 258–273.

Niles, Henry E.   1923.   The method of path coefficients—an answer to Wright.   *Genetics*, **8**, 256–260.

Wright, Sewall.   1923.   The theory of path coefficients—a reply to Niles's criticism.   *Genetics*, **8**, 239–255.

PROBLEMS

1.   Suppose we have x_1, x_2, x_3 and that their variance–covariance matrix is

$$\sigma_{ij} = \begin{pmatrix} 4 & 1 & 2 \\ 1 & 3 & 2 \\ 2 & 2 & 5 \end{pmatrix}$$

Evaluate

$$\beta_{12.3}, \beta_{23.1}, \beta'_{12.3}, \beta'_{23.1}, \beta_{12}, \beta'_{12}.$$

2. For the case of problem 1 evaluate $\sigma^2_{1.23}$ and $R^2_{1.23}$.

3. For the case of problem 1 evaluate $\rho_{12.3}$.

4. Suppose we have 5 observations as follows:

x_1	x_2	x_3
5	2	1
3	3	2
4	1	3
5	1	1
7	3	1

Fit the regression equation

$$x_1 = \alpha + \beta x_2 + \gamma x_3$$

and determine the true and estimated variances of α, β, γ.

5. For the case of problem 4 make a joint evaluation of the hypothesis $\beta = \gamma = 0$.

6. Suppose we have the following two-way classification of data

	a_1	a_2	a_3
b_1	8, 10	4	7, 6
b_2	6	3, 5	4
b_3	7, 8	6	—

where the numbers within the cells are the observations. Fit the model

$$y_{ijk} = \mu + a_i + b_j + e_{ijk}$$

CHAPTER 15

Inheritance of Quantitative Characters in a Random Mating Population

The previous chapters have provided us with the tools by which we may obtain shorthand descriptions of populations, in terms of means, variances, and covariances, regressions, and so on, and which have utility in problems quite distinct from genetic ones. It is now our job to examine how these concepts may be applied to a genetic population, that is, a population specified by the interaction in a general non-statistical sense of genotypes and environments.

Our procedure will be to examine the simplest situations first and then proceed to the complex ones, rather than to deal with the matter in full generality from the start. In this way the processes should be patently clear, and in this area, as in any other, belief in the results of a theory must be based on an understanding of the basic elements of the theory and of the processes by which the results are deduced in the theory. We shall start then with a population for which only one locus is variable, in which the mating has been, is, and will be random and in which the effect of environment may be discounted, in the sense that the value observed for an individual depends solely on the genotype of the individual. For simplicity we take first the case when there are two alleles at the locus. It must be emphasized that this is a particular case, the results of which have no general validity until proved so.

15.1 THE INHERITANCE OF EFFECTS WITH ONE VARIABLE LOCUS

In accordance with the previous paragraph we take a population whose specifications are as follows.

Genotype	Frequency	Genotypic Value	Coded Genotypic Value
AA	p^2	d	$d - \mu = i$
Aa	$2pq$	h	$h - \mu = j$
aa	q^2	r	$r - \mu = k$

The genotypic value is the constant value given by any individual with the genotype. The only assumption made is that the genotypic values are numbers. The mean for the population is denoted by μ where

$$\mu = p^2d + 2pqh + q^2r$$

and the deviations from this mean of the genotypic values are denoted by $i, j,$ and k, which therefore satisfy

$$p^2i + 2pqj + q^2k = 0$$

Now we wish to determine the extent to which the coded genotypic values can be explained in terms of gene effects; that is, we wish to fit

$$i = 2\alpha$$
$$j = \alpha + \beta$$
$$k = 2\beta$$

As in the general case of regression, we obtain the values for α and β by minimizing

$$Q = p^2(i - 2\alpha)^2 + 2pq(j - \alpha - \beta)^2 + q^2(k - 2\beta)^2$$

The normal equations, as usual, are

$$\frac{1}{2}\frac{\partial Q}{\partial \alpha} = 0$$

$$\frac{1}{2}\frac{\partial Q}{\partial \beta} = 0$$

or, in this case,

$$2p^2(i - 2\alpha) + 2pq(j - \alpha - \beta) = 0$$
$$2pq(j - \alpha - \beta) + 2q^2(k - 2\beta) = 0$$

or

$$4p^2\alpha + 2pq(\alpha + \beta) = 2p^2i + 2pqj$$
$$2pq(\alpha + \beta) + 4q^2\beta = 2pqj + 2q^2k$$

Adding these two equations, we get

$$(4p^2 + 4pq)\alpha + (4q^2 + 4pq)\beta = 2(p^2i + 2pqj + q^2k) = 0$$

so that

$$4p\alpha + 4q\beta = 0$$

and

$$p\alpha = -q\beta$$

Let $p\alpha = \gamma$, so that $\alpha = \gamma/p$, $\beta = -\gamma/q$; then

$$4p\gamma + 2pq \left(\frac{\gamma}{p} - \frac{\gamma}{q}\right) = 2p^2 i + 2pqj$$

or

$$2p\gamma + 2q\gamma = 2p^2 i + 2pqj$$

or

$$\gamma = p^2 i + pqj$$

Hence

$$\alpha = \frac{p^2 i + pqj}{p}, \qquad \beta = -\frac{p^2 i + pqj}{q} = \frac{pqj + q^2 k}{q}$$

or

$$\alpha = pi + qj, \qquad \beta = pj + qk$$

The effect of changing an a gene into an A gene is then $\alpha - \beta$ which is equal to

$$(pi + qj) - (pj + qk) \qquad \text{or} \qquad p(i - j) + q(j - k)$$

This is *defined* to be the effect of the gene substitution, A for a.

The sum of squares removed by the regression of α and β is equal to the sum of products of estimates and the right-hand sides of the normal equations: i.e.

$$\alpha(2p^2 i + 2pqj) + \beta(2pqj + 2q^2 k)$$

which equals

$$(pi + qj)2p(pi + qj) + (pj + qk)2q(pj + qk)$$
$$= 2p(pi + qj)^2 + 2q(pj + qk)^2 = 2p\alpha^2 + 2q\beta^2$$

Alternatively it is equal to

$$\left(\frac{p^2 i + pqj}{p}\right) 2(p^2 i + pqj) + \left(\frac{p^2 i + pqj}{q}\right) 2(p^2 i + pqj) = \frac{2}{pq}(p^2 i + pqj)^2$$

Another form is obtained by noting that

$$2pqj = -p^2 i - q^2 k$$

so that, substituting for j, we get

$$\frac{1}{2pq}(p^2 i - q^2 k)^2$$

Again another form is obtained by noting that

$$p^2 i + pqj = \gamma$$

and

$$\alpha - \beta = \frac{\gamma}{p} + \frac{\gamma}{q} = \frac{\gamma}{pq}$$

so that the sum of squares removed is $(2/pq)[pq(\alpha - \beta)]^2$ or $2pq(\alpha - \beta)^2$.

Fisher (1930) uses α instead of our $(\alpha - \beta)$, so that he obtains $2pq\alpha^2$. To avoid confusion we denote $\alpha - \beta$ by α_A and then have the formula, $2pq\alpha_A^2$.

The sum of squares removed by the regression on the gene content of the genotypes is *defined* to be the additive genetic variance. Hence we have the following forms for the additive genetic variance:

(1) $\qquad \dfrac{2}{pq}(p^2i + pqj)^2$

(2) $\qquad \dfrac{1}{2pq}(p^2i - q^2k)^2$

(3) $\qquad 2p\alpha^2 + 2q\beta^2$

(4) $\qquad 2pq(\alpha - \beta)^2 = 2pq[p(i - j) + q(j - k)]^2$

(5) $\qquad 2pq\alpha_A^2$

The reader will of course have to obtain the definitions of the quantities in the formulas from the previous pages. Throughout this text the additive genetic variance will be denoted by σ_A^2.

15.2 NOTES ON ADDITIVE GENETIC VARIANCE

We now give some notes, more or less unrelated, on the results of the previous section.

Let us first give an example of the use of the formulas. Consider the following population:

Genotype	Frequency	Genotypic Value
AA	p^2	2
Aa	$2pq$	1
aa	q^2	0

Here the mean is $2p^2 + 2pq$ which equals $2p$. The average effect of substituting the A gene for the a gene is $p(i - j) + q(j - k)$ which is equal to $p(d - h) + q(h - r)$, so that in the present case we get

$$p(2 - 1) + q(1 - 0)$$
$$= p + q$$
$$= 1$$

and this is equal to α_A. Hence the additive genetic variance is equal to $2pq$.

The total variance in the population is equal to

$$p^2 \times 4 + 2pq \times 1 - (2p)^2$$

which equals $2pq$, so that in the present case the additive genetic variance comprises the whole of the genotypic or hereditary variance.

Diagrammatically this can be seen in the following way. Let us plot the genotypic value against the number of A genes (Figure 15.1).

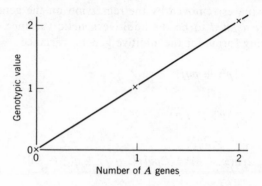

FIGURE 15.1.   Geometric representation of no dominance.

We see that the genotypic values lie on a straight line so that, regardless of gene frequency, a straight line may be fitted perfectly to the three points. This illustrates a facet of the matter, namely that the additive genetic variance *in the case when there are two alleles* is equal to the sum of squares removed by fitting a straight line weighted by genotypic frequencies in the figure. The effect of the gene substitution A for a is the slope of the best fitting straight line. The analogue of this when there are more than two alleles at a locus will be given later.

We have then an example of a population in which the additively genetic variance comprises the whole of the variance in the population.

Now let us consider a population in which *none* of the variance is additive genetic. Consider form (2) of the formulas for additive genetic variance. If p equals q, and i equals k, then clearly $p^2i - q^2k$ equals zero, and the additive genetic variance is then zero. Hence the following population:

Genotype	Frequency	Genotypic Value
AA	$\frac{1}{4}$	*u*
Aa	$\frac{1}{2}$	*v*
aa	$\frac{1}{4}$	*u*

where u and v are any numbers, has zero additive genetic variance. Of course, a population with these genotypic values but different gene frequencies would have additive genetic variance.

Another form of the additive genetic variance formula is used sometimes. Let the genotypic values for AA, Aa, and aa be denoted by a, d, and $-a$, respectively. Then the additive genetic variance is equal, using form (4) above, to

$$2pq[p(a - d) + q(d + a)]^2$$

which equals

$$2pq[a - (p - q)d]^2$$

15.3 THE CHANGE IN POPULATION MEAN DUE TO A SMALL CHANGE IN GENE FREQUENCY

Let us suppose that the random mating population $p^2AA + 2pqAa + q^2aa$, in which the gene frequency for A is p, and for a is q, is changed so that the gene frequency for A is $p + \Delta p$, and for q is therefore $q - \Delta p$, and random mating structure is maintained. What will be the change in the population mean? Originally the mean is

$$p^2d + 2pqh + q^2r$$

and after the change it is

$$(p + \Delta p)^2d + 2(p + \Delta p)(q - \Delta p)h + (q - \Delta p)^2r$$

or, neglecting the terms involving $(\Delta p)^2$, it is

$$(p^2 + 2p \, \Delta p)d + 2[pq + (q - p)\Delta p]h + (q^2 - 2q \, \Delta p)r$$
$$= p^2d + 2pqh + q^2r + [pd + (q - p)h - qr]2\Delta p$$

Hence the change in mean is

$$2\Delta p[pd + (q - p)h - qr]$$
$$= 2\Delta p[p(d - h) + q(h - r)]$$
$$= 2\Delta p[p(i - j) + q(j - k)]$$
$$= 2\Delta p(\alpha - \beta)$$
$$= 2\Delta p\alpha_A$$

The average effect of a gene substitution has therefore a very simple role n the case of a random mating population: namely that the change in population mean is equal to 2 × effect × (change in gene frequency for A). The effect of weak selection is therefore predictable from the change in gene frequency and the average effects of the genes. This is true only providing the change in gene frequency for A is small, and the best way of stating the result is that the rate of change in the population mean is equal to twice the average effect times the change in gene frequency. This is true only for random mating populations as we shall see in the next chapter.

15.4 THE DOMINANCE VARIANCE

In the case of one locus with two alleles there are three genotypes. As is general with the case of three observations, there are two degrees of freedom among the three observations. One of these two belongs to the average effect and has an appropriate sum of squares which we have evaluated and called the additive genetic variance. The residual sum of squares which is equal to

[Total sum of squares about mean minus additive genetic variance]

has one degree of freedom and is called the dominance variance. It will be denoted by σ_D^2. The explicit expression for the dominance variance is obtained as follows:

$$\text{Total variance} = p^2 i^2 + 2pq j^2 + q^2 k^2$$

$$= p^2 i^2 + q^2 k^2 + \frac{1}{2pq}(p^2 i + q^2 k)^2$$

$$\text{Additive genetic variance} = \frac{1}{2pq}(p^2 i - q^2 k)^2$$

Hence

$$\text{Dominance variance} = p^2 i^2 + q^2 k^2 + \frac{1}{2pq}[(p^2 i + q^2 k)^2 - (p^2 i - q^2 k)^2]$$

$$= p^2 i^2 + q^2 k^2 + \frac{1}{2pq}(4p^2 q^2 ik)$$

$$= p^2 i^2 + q^2 k^2 + 2pq ik$$

$$= (pi + qk)^2$$

An alternative form of the dominance form may be obtained by noting that

$$pi + qk = (p^2 + pq)i + (pq + q^2)k$$

$$= pqi + pqk + (p^2 i + q^2 k)$$

$$= pqi + pqk - 2pq j$$

$$= pq(i - 2j + k)$$

so that the dominance variance is equal to

$$p^2q^2(i - 2j + k)^2$$

It should also be noted that

$$\sigma_D^2 = \sum_{i,j} p_i p_j (y_{ij} - \alpha_i - \alpha_j)^2$$

that is, equal to the sum of squares of deviations of genotypic values from predicted genotypic values.

It may be noted that the forms for additive genetic variance and for dominance variance that are most useful are the following:

$$\sigma_A^2 = \text{additive genetic variance} = 2pq[p(i - j) + q(j - k)]^2$$
$$\sigma_D^2 = \text{dominance variance} \quad = p^2q^2(i - 2j + k)^2$$

because these formulas do not change if i, j, k are measured about different origins. Note that, if we put $i = I + v, j = J + v, k = K + v$, then the formulas are the same except that I, J, K replace i, j, k.

In view of the fact that several different notations for genotypic values have been used in the literature, it will be of use to record these and the corresponding expressions for the two variances.

Fisher's Model

Fisher (1918) takes the genotypic values of AA, Aa, and aa to be a, d, and $-a$, respectively. Hence we have:

$$\sigma_A^2 = \text{additive genetic variance} = 2pq[p(a - d) + q(d + a)]^2$$
$$= 2pq[a - (p - q)d]^2$$
$$\sigma_D^2 = \text{dominance variance} \quad = p^2q^2(a - 2d - a)^2$$
$$= 4p^2q^2d^2.$$

This form shows that, if d equals zero the dominance variance is zero.

Comstock and Robinson's Model

Comstock and Robinson (1948) take the genotypic values of AA, Aa, and aa to be u, au, and $-u$, respectively. Hence we have

$$\sigma_A^2 = \text{additive genetic variance} = 2pq[p(u - au) + q(au + u)]^2$$
$$= 2pqu^2[p(1 - a) + q(1 + a)]^2$$
$$= 2pqu^2[1 - (p - q)a]^2$$
$$\sigma_D^2 = \text{dominance variance} \quad = p^2q^2(u - 2au - u)^2$$
$$= 4p^2q^2a^2u^2$$

15.5 PARTICULAR POPULATIONS

It is of interest to note the values for the components of genotypic variance for a few particular populations.

Complete Dominance

Here the genotypic values for AA, Aa, and aa may be denoted by a, a, b. Then, by using form (4), we get:

$$\sigma_A^2 = \text{additive genetic variance} = 2pq[p(a - a) + q(a - b)]^2$$
$$= 2pq^3(a - b)^2$$

$$\sigma_D^2 = \text{dominance variance} \quad = p^2q^2(a - 2a + b)^2$$
$$= p^2q^2(a - b)^2$$

If the particular values $a = 1$, $b = 0$ are used, which amounts only to a change in scale, then

$$\sigma_A^2 = 2pq^3$$
$$\sigma_D^2 = p^2q^2$$

The ratio $\sigma_A^2/(\sigma_A^2 + \sigma_D^2)$ will be of particular interest. In the case we are considering $\sigma_A^2 + \sigma_D^2$ is equal to the total genotypic variance. The ratio is the proportion of genotypic variance which is additive. In the present case it is equal to $2q/(p+2q)$ or $2q/(1+q)$. It is worth noting also that, when q equals $1/2$, this becomes $2/3$, or twice $1/3$. This ratio $1/3$ was found to have genetic significance first by Pearson (1904).

An Overdominant Population

A population exhibiting overdominance was originally defined to be one in which the homozygote AA has a genotypic value greater than the homozygote aa and the heterozygote Aa has a genotypic value greater than that of AA. Presumably this notion goes back to notions of physiological stimulation, with gene a denoting absence of a stimulus and gene A presence of a stimulus. The reader will find many references to the absence–presence notion in the genetical writings before about 1930. It is now clear that such a notion is too restrictive and for very elementary reasons. An attribute is anything we care to measure, and we should think of measurement as comparing a length or a distance with a measuring stick which is divided into units. There is no reason why the measuring stick should be divided into units in a particular way. We can for instance think of measuring the length of individuals with a rule graduated in feet so that, if x is the length in feet, we read off the number x, or we can think of the measuring stick being so graduated as to give us $1/x$ or $\sqrt{x}$

or any other function of x. This then leads us to the point that $1/x$ is a perfectly reasonable attribute as well as x itself. If AA is greater than aa with respect to x, then AA will be less than aa with respect to $1/x$.

It is high time, in my opinion, to use the phrase "overdominance", or a similar word, to denote the case when the heterozygote is not between the homozogotes with respect to the character. If we do not use a general definition such as this, we are forced to use at least two terms: overdominance and underdominance. The term superdominance has also been used. Perhaps an entirely new term should be coined, leaving the term overdominance to have its original meaning. This is not easy from two points of view. First, it is doubted if unanimity could be reached on the original meaning. Second, if a term has been used vaguely in the past, a definition which includes past usages should be acceptable to all. It is worth noting in passing that the term "heterosis" is subject to exactly the same types of difficulty, and no unanimity on an operational definition of it exists.

From the point of view of evolutionary theory, what is said above is not entirely appropriate. This serves further to point the need for agreement on words.*

We therefore define a population with genotypic values d, h, r for AA, Aa, aa, respectively, to be an overdominant population if h is outside the range d to r. The scale of measurement can be chosen so that r is zero, and we then have

$$\sigma_A^2 = 2pq[p(d - h) + q(h)]^2$$
$$\sigma_D^2 = p^2q^2(d - 2h)^2$$

A very particular population is one in which d equals r; i.e. AA and aa have the same genotypic value, and Aa has a different genotypic value. In that case we can put d equal to zero also, and we have

$$\sigma_A^2 = 2pq(p - q)^2h^2$$
$$\sigma_D^2 = 4p^2q^2h^2$$

We note that σ_A^2 is zero for this population only if p equals q; i.e., $p = q = \frac{1}{2}$, and the genotypic variance is then entirely dominance variance. The proportion of genotypic variance which is additive in the population with p unequal to q is

$$\frac{2pq(p - q)^2}{2pq(p - q)^2 + 4p^2q^2} = \frac{(p - q)^2}{p^2 + q^2}$$

* I am a firm believer in operational definitions and dislike euphonic phrases and sentences which cannot be based on such definitions.

15.6 GENERALIZATION TO A POPULATION WITH
s ALLELES

Let us now examine the situation with the population with genotypic array

$$\sum_{i,j=1}^{s} p_i p_j A_i A_j \quad \text{or} \quad \sum_{i} p_i^2 A_i A_i + \sum_{\substack{i,j=1 \\ i \neq j}}^{s} p_i p_j A_i A_j$$

We shall denote the genotypic value of $A_i A_j$ measured from the population mean by y_{ij}, which will be equal to y_{ji}, the genotypic value of $A_j A_i$. We introduce $\alpha_1, \alpha_2, \cdots, \alpha_s$ for the effects of genes $A_1, A_2, \cdots, A_s$. Then these are given as the values for $\alpha_1, \alpha_2, \cdots, \alpha_s$ which minimize

$$Q = \sum_{i,j=1}^{s} p_i p_j (y_{ij} - \alpha_i - \alpha_j)^2$$

The normal equations are

$$\frac{d}{d\alpha_m} (\tfrac{1}{2}Q) = 0, \qquad m = 1, 2, \cdots, s$$

i.e. by

$$\sum_{i=1}^{s} p_i p_m (y_{im} - \alpha_i - \alpha_m) + \sum_{j=1}^{s} p_m p_j (y_{mj} - \alpha_m - \alpha_j) = 0$$

or

$$2 \sum_{i=1}^{s} p_i p_m (y_{im} - \alpha_i - \alpha_m) = 0$$

since $y_{mj} = y_{jm}$

or

$$2 \sum_{i=1}^{s} p_i p_m \alpha_i + 2 \sum_{i=1}^{s} p_i p_m \alpha_m = 2 \sum_{i=1}^{s} p_i p_m y_{im}$$

or

$$2 p_m \left(\sum_{i=1}^{s} p_i \alpha_i \right) + 2 p_m \alpha_m = 2 p_m \sum_{i=1}^{s} p_i y_{im}, \qquad m = 1, 2, \cdots, s$$

When we add these m equations, we get

$$2 \left(\sum_{m} p_m \right) \left(\sum_{i=1}^{s} p_i \alpha_i \right) + 2 \sum_{m} p_m \alpha_m = 2 \sum_{m} \sum_{i} p_m p_i y_{im}$$

or

$$4 \sum_m p_m \alpha_m = 0$$

since

$$\sum_m p_m = 1, \quad \sum_m p_m \alpha_m = \sum_i p_i \alpha_i, \quad \text{and} \quad \sum_{m,i} p_m p_i y_{im} = 0$$

Hence

$$\sum_{i=1}^s p_i \alpha_i = 0$$

and

$$2 p_m \alpha_m = 2 p_m \sum_{i=1}^s p_i y_{im}$$

or

$$\alpha_m = \sum_{i=1}^s p_i y_{im}$$

The range over which summations extend will not be specified in the rest of this section, because it will by now be clear to the reader.

As before, the additive genetic variance is *defined* to be the part of the total variance of the population which is removed by the fitting of parameters, one for each allele. It is, as usual, the sum of products of estimates and right-hand sides of the normal equations. The right-hand side of the normal equation is

$$2 p_m \sum_i p_i y_{im} = 2 p_m \alpha_m$$

The additive genetic variance is therefore

$$\sigma_A^2 = 2 \sum_m p_m \alpha_m^2$$

or

$$\sigma_A^2 = 2 \sum_m p_m \left(\sum_i p_i y_{im} \right)^2$$

The total genotypic variance is

$$\sum_{i,j} p_i p_j y_{ij}^2$$

in which, it will be recalled, the y_{ij}'s are measured around the population mean. Hence the dominance variance is given by

$$\sigma_D^2 = \sum_{i,j} p_i p_j y_{ij}^2 - 2 \sum_m p_m \alpha_m^2$$

and also

$$\sigma_D^2 = \sum_{i,j} p_i p_j (y_{ij} - \alpha_i - \alpha_j)^2$$

Note that, if $y_{ij} = \alpha_i + \alpha_j$ for all i and j, the dominance variance is zero. In that case

$$\alpha_i = y_{ii}/2, \qquad i = 1, 2, \cdots, m$$

The formulas given above are easily adjusted if the y_{ij} are not measured from the population mean. Let z_{ij} be the uncoded genotypic value, so that

$$z_{ij} = \mu + y_{ij}$$

where

$$\mu = \sum_{i,j} p_i p_j z_{ij}$$

Then

$$\alpha_m = \sum_i p_i y_{im} = \sum_i p_i (z_{im} - \mu) = \sum_i p_i z_{im} - \mu$$

and

$$\sigma_A^2 = 2 \sum_m p_m \alpha_m^2 = 2 \sum_m p_m \left(\sum_i p_i z_{im} - \mu \right)^2$$

$$= 2 \sum_m p_m \left(\sum_i p_i z_{im} \right)^2 - 2\mu^2$$

and

$$\sigma_D^2 = \sum_{i,j} p_i p_j (z_{ij} - \mu - \alpha_i - \alpha_m)^2$$

$$= \sum_{i,j} p_i p_j z_{ij}^2 - \mu^2 - \sigma_A^2$$

It is of interest to note the geometric analogue of the fitting of a straight line with two alleles. Suppose for illustration we have three alleles, say O, A, B. Then the genotypic values may be represented in three dimensions as in Figure 15.2. The two axes on the plane give the number of A genes and the number of B genes in the genotype, any residual genes being, of course, O genes. Each genotypic value is represented by a point on the vertical through the point representing the genotype at a height equal to the genotypic value. The procedure is to represent the six points by the best-fitting plane. The slope of the plane in the direction of the A axis is the effect of substituting gene A for gene O, in the direction of the B axis it is the effect of substituting gene B for gene O, and in the direction at 45 degrees to each of the A and B axes is the effect of substituting B for A (or vice versa, depending on the direction chosen). The dominance variance is the (weighted) sum of squares about the best-fitting plane.

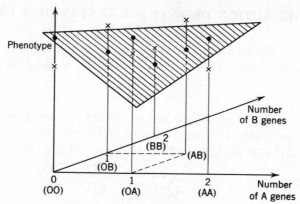

× Indicates actual phenotype

• Indicates prediction of phenotype by plane

FIGURE 15.2. Representation of genotypes with three alleles at the locus. Genotypic values are represented by x.

Example of a Three-Allele Population

The procedure will be illustrated by finding σ_A^2 and σ_D^2 for a population with genotypes aa, ab, ac, bb, bc, and cc with genotypic values 6, 5, 8, 3, 12, and 14, respectively, and gene frequencies, for a, $p_1 = 0.3$, for b, $p_2 = 0.2$, for c, $p_3 = 0.5$. The genotypic values may be represented by Table 15.1 which also contains the necessary partial sums.

TABLE 15.1

COMPUTATION OF COMPONENTS OF GENOTYPIC VARIANCE

i \ j	1	2	3	$\sum_m p_m z_{im}$
1	6	5	8	6.8
2	5	3	12	8.1
3	8	12	14	11.8
$\sum_m p_m z_{mj}$	6.8	8.1	11.8	$\mu = 9.56$

$$\sigma_A^2 + \sigma_D^2 = 103.60 - 91.3936 = 12.2064$$
$$\sigma_A^2 = 2[96.614 - 91.3936] = 10.4408$$
$$\sigma_D^2 = 12.2064 - 2(5.2204) = 1.7656$$

15.7 THE NOTION OF AVERAGE EXCESS OF A GENE SUBSTITUTION

We have already defined the average effect of a gene substitution. The notion is due to Fisher (1930), and for the case of two alleles his definition was

$$\alpha - \beta$$

where α, β are the effects of the genes. In the case of more than two alleles, it is preferable to define a number of average effects equal to the number of alleles as we have already done, so that the average effect of allele m is

$$\sum_i p_i y_{im}$$

Fisher also introduced the notion of average excess for the case of two alleles, the generalization being fairly obvious. Let us first give Fisher's definition for his particular case. He states that we should divide the population into two parts, one part containing all the homozygotes of one type and half of the heterozygotes, and the other part containing the remainder. We should then consider the mean genotypic value for each part or variety into which the population is divided and take the difference. This difference he defines to be the average excess associated with the gene substitution. In the case of the population $p^2 AA + 2pq Aa + q^2 aa$ the two parts are $p^2 AA + pq Aa$ and $pq Aa + q^2 aa$ with means equal to

$$\frac{p^2 d + pqh}{p^2 + pq} \quad \text{and} \quad \frac{pqh + q^2 r}{pq + q^2}$$

or

$$pd + qh \quad \text{and} \quad ph + qr$$

The average excess is then

$$(pd + qh) - (ph + qr)$$
$$= p(d - h) + q(h - r)$$

It is therefore equal to the average effect of the gene substitution. This is, however, true only for a random mating population.

In the case of s alleles we will define s average excesses, that associated with the mth allele being

$$\frac{p_1 p_m y_{1m} + p_2 p_m y_{2m} + p_m^2 y_{mm} + \cdots + p_s p_m y_{sm}}{p_1 p_m + p_2 p_m + \cdots + p_s p_m}$$
$$= p_1 y_{1m} + p_2 y_{2m} + \cdots + p_s y_{sm}$$
$$= \sum p_i y_{im}$$

It arises by dividing the population into s parts, the mth part consisting of individuals with genotype $A_m A_m$ and half of the individuals which are heterozygous with A_m as one of their genes. In the case of a random mating population the average excess as we have defined it is equal to the average effect.

15.8 THE COMPOSITION OF THE GENOTYPIC VALUE OF AN INDIVIDUAL

Consider an individual X with genotype $A_i A_j$. If the genes are additive in their effects, the genotypic value of X is equal to $\mu + \alpha_i + \alpha_j$, where α_i and α_j are the effects of genes A_i and A_j. In general, we call $(\alpha_i + \alpha_j)$ the additive genotypic value of individual X, and we call $(y_{ij} - \alpha_i - \alpha_j)$ the dominance deviation of individual X, all of course with reference to a particular attribute. If we denote the dominance deviation by d_{ij}, we have

$$y_{ij} = \alpha_i + \alpha_j + d_{ij}$$

or, if we use genotypic values which are not coded about the population mean μ,

$$z_{ij} = \mu + \alpha_i + \alpha_j + d_{ij}$$

Now we shall show some properties of the additive effects and the dominance deviations. First, the additive values are made up of two parts α_i and α_j, and, if an individual is chosen at random from the population, the two parts are uncorrelated. This is seen because (1) the average value of any one part is zero since $\sum_i p_i \alpha_i = 0$; (2) the covariance of the two parts is $\sum_{ij} p_i p_j \alpha_i \alpha_j$, which is equal to $\left(\sum_i p_i \alpha_i \right) (\sum p_j \alpha_j)$, which equals zero. Second, the average value of the dominance deviation is zero, since $E(y_{ij}) = 0$, $E(\alpha_i + \alpha_j) = 0$. Third, the additive component of the genotypic value and the dominance deviation are uncorrelated, for the covariance is

$$\sum_i \sum_j p_i p_j (\alpha_i + \alpha_j)(y_{ij} - \alpha_i - \alpha_j)$$

$$= \sum_i \sum_j p_i p_j \alpha_i y_{ij} + \sum_{ij} p_i p_j \alpha_j y_{ij} - \sum_{ij} p_i p_j (\alpha_i + \alpha_j)^2$$

$$= \sum_i p_i \alpha_i \cdot \alpha_i + \sum_j p_j \alpha_j \cdot \alpha_j - \sum_{ij} p_i p_j \alpha_i^2 - 2 \sum_{ij} p_i p_j \alpha_i \alpha_j - \sum_{ij} p_i p_j \alpha_j^2$$

$$= 2 \sum p_i \alpha_i^2 - \sum p_i \alpha_i^2 - 0 - \sum p_j \alpha_j^2$$

$$= 0$$

We may therefore express the genotypic value of an individual by the equation

$$G = A + D$$

where A is the sum of average effects of the genes and D is the dominance deviation. We have shown that A and D are uncorrelated so that

$$\sigma_G^2 = \sigma_A^2 + \sigma_D^2$$

which was the equation by which we obtained σ_D^2.

15.9 GENERALIZATION TO INCLUDE ENVIRONMENTAL EFFECTS

The previous sections of this chapter have been based on the assumption that the observation on a genotype is independent of the environment, of course within a population of environments. There are a number of attributes which exhibit this property, but the more general situation is that the observation on an individual depends on both the genotype of the individual and the environment in which the individual lives [see for example Bonnier and Hansson (1948) and Osborne (1952)]. The observed value of an attribute of an individual will be called the phenotypic value of the individual and will be denoted by P, with a variance σ_P^2 in the joint population of individuals and environments. It would be nice to deal with the effects of environment in a general way, but, with possibly only one exception (Wright, 1935) which has special characteristics to make solution easy, the only way in which the effects of environment have been handled is to suppose that the genotype and the environment are additive in their effects: in symbols

$$P = G + E$$

where P = phenotypic value

   G = genotypic value

   E = environmental contribution

It is assumed also that genotypes and environments are associated at random within the population of environments considered. In a planned experiment for instance, with plants to be grown in a field, we can achieve this by assigning plants to random positions in the fields. In the analysis of observational data, with some exceptions, an assumption of lack of association of genotype and environment must be made in order to apply the theory and methodology which will be described.

If our equation $P = G + E$ holds and G and E are uncorrelated, then

$$\sigma_P^2 = \sigma_G^2 + \sigma_E^2$$

and the partition of genotypic variance σ_G^2 into the components σ_A^2 and σ_D^2 proceeds as described in the previous sections except that, wherevei the words "total variance" were used, the words "total genotypic variance" should be substituted. The environmental contributions to phenotypic value will make no contribution to either σ_A^2 or σ_D^2 because they are uncorrelated with the genotypic values, and their regression on gene number will be zero.

15.10 THE CORRELATIONS BETWEEN RELATIVES

We shall now find the theoretical values of the correlations between relatives for an arbitrary attribute in the simple random mating population

$$\sum p_i p_j A_i A_j$$

Essentially all the results were given first by Fisher (1918).

There are two ways by which these may be obtained, and both ways are instructive. The first way is a direct one of considering two relatives X and Y and the genotypic arrays of X and Y. The other way uses the concept of coefficient of parentage due to Malécot (1948) described in Chapter 5.

In both ways the important part of the problem is to find the covariance between the relatives, because ρ_{XY} is given by

$$\rho_{XY} = \frac{\text{Cov}(X, Y)}{[V(X)\,V(Y)]^{1/2}}$$

and, at least for the present, X and Y are each random members of the population, though they are of course correlated. It should perhaps be noted that we use X and Y to denote the two individuals being correlated and the values of the attributes for these individuals. There should not result any confusion.

15.10.1 The Direct Method

Let us illustrate this by obtaining ancestral correlations. Consider an individual X drawn at random from the population and a random offspring of X, arising from X mating a random member of the population. In view of our assumption about environmental effects we need only consider genotypic values, since there will be no environmental covariance. In any applications of the theory of the present chapter to a real-world problem of course such an assumption must not be too freely or too glibly accepted. The probability that X has genotype $A_i A_j$ is $p_i p_j$. Now, when X mates with a random member of the population, he contributes the gametic array $\frac{1}{2}A_i + \frac{1}{2}A_j$. The random member of the population contributes the gametic array $\sum p_m A_m$ to the offspring. Hence the genotypic array of the offspring of X is

$$(\tfrac{1}{2}A_i + \tfrac{1}{2}A_j)(\sum p_m A_m)$$

or

$$\tfrac{1}{2}\sum_m p_m A_i A_m + \tfrac{1}{2}\sum_m p_m A_j A_m$$

Now the genotypic value of X is y_{ij}. The average genotypic value of the offspring of X is

$$\tfrac{1}{2}\sum_m p_m y_{im} + \tfrac{1}{2}\sum_m p_m y_{jm}$$

and from the earlier work in this chapter this is equal to $\tfrac{1}{2}(\alpha_i + \alpha_j)$. Hence we have to find the covariance of y_{ij} and $\tfrac{1}{2}(\alpha_i + \alpha_j)$ which is equal to

$$E[y_{ij}\cdot\tfrac{1}{2}(\alpha_i + \alpha_j)]$$
$$= E[(A + D)\tfrac{1}{2}A]$$
$$= \tfrac{1}{2}\sigma_A^2 \quad \text{since } D \text{ and } A \text{ are uncorrelated.}$$

Hence the parent offspring covariance is $\tfrac{1}{2}\sigma_A^2$, and the parent offspring regression, assuming no selection, is

$$\frac{1}{2}\frac{\sigma_A^2}{\sigma_P^2}$$

For grandchildren, great grandchildren, etc. the argument is very similar and easy to follow. Let us consider kth-degree offspring, $k = 2$ for grandchildren, $k = 3$ for great grandchildren, etc. Then the gametic array contributed by the $(k-1)$th degree of offspring is

$$\frac{1}{2^{k-1}}[\tfrac{1}{2}(A_i + A_j)] + \left(1 - \frac{1}{2^{k-1}}\right)(\sum p_m A_m)$$

and the gametic array contributed by the population to the kth-degree offspring is $(\sum p_m A_m)$. Hence the genotypic array of the kth-degree offspring is

$$\left\{\frac{1}{2^{k-1}}[\tfrac{1}{2}(A_i + A_j)] + \left(1 - \frac{1}{2^{k-1}}\right)(\sum p_m A_m)\right\}(\sum p_m A_m)$$

$$= \frac{1}{2^{k-1}}\left(\frac{1}{2}\sum_m p_m A_i A_m + \frac{1}{2}\sum_m p_m A_j A_m\right) + \left(1 - \frac{1}{2^{k-1}}\right)(\sum p_m p_n A_m A_n)$$

The mean genotypic value of these offspring is

$$\frac{1}{2^{k-1}} \left(\frac{1}{2} \sum_m p_m y_{im} + \frac{1}{2} \sum_m p_m y_{jm} \right) + \left(1 - \frac{1}{2^{k-1}} \right) (\Sigma p_m p_n y_{mn})$$

$$= \frac{1}{2^{k-1}} \left[\tfrac{1}{2}(\alpha_i + \alpha_j) \right]$$

Hence the covariance of X and his kth-degree offspring is

$$E \left[y_{ij} \cdot \frac{1}{2^k} (\alpha_i + \alpha_j) \right]$$

$$= E \left[(A + D) \cdot \frac{1}{2^k} A \right] = \frac{1}{2^k} \sigma_A^2$$

The correlation is therefore $\dfrac{1}{2^k} \dfrac{\sigma_A^2}{\sigma_P^2}$.

We will work out just one other covariance by the above methodology, because the methodology is interesting (in the author's opinion at least). Consider now the case of full-sibs. We shall find the covariance between an individual X and his full-sibs. Let X have genotype $A_r A_s$, the gene A_r coming from the sire and the gene A_s coming from the dam. Then the genotypic array of sires which can contribute a gene A_r is

$$\frac{1}{p_r} \left(p_r^2 A_r A_r + \sum_{t \neq r} p_r p_t A_r A_t \right) = \sum_{t=1}^s p_t A_r A_t$$

Similarly the genotypic array of the dams which can contribute A_s is

$$\sum_{u=1}^s p_u A_s A_u$$

Hence the array of sibships which contain an individual of genotype $A_r A_s$ is

$$\left[\sum_t p_t \tfrac{1}{2} (A_r + A_t) \right] \left[\sum_u p_u \tfrac{1}{2} (A_s + A_u) \right]$$

$$= \frac{1}{4} \sum_{t,u} p_t p_u (A_r + A_t)(A_s + A_u)$$

$$= \frac{1}{4} \sum_{t,u} p_t p_u (A_r A_s + A_r A_u + A_t A_s + A_t A_u)$$

The mean genotypic value of the array of sibs is

$$\frac{1}{4} \sum_{t,u} p_t p_u (y_{rs} + y_{ru} + y_{ts} + y_{tu})$$

$$= \frac{1}{4} \left(y_{rs} + \sum_u p_u y_{ru} + \sum_t p_t y_{ts} + \sum_{t,u} p_t p_u y_{tu} \right)$$

$$= \tfrac{1}{4}(y_{rs} + \alpha_r + \alpha_s)$$

Hence the covariance of full-sibs is

$$E[y_{rs} \cdot \tfrac{1}{4}(y_{rs} + \alpha_r + \alpha_s)]$$

$$= \tfrac{1}{4}E(y_{rs}^2) + \tfrac{1}{4}E[y_{rs}(\alpha_r + \alpha_s)]$$

$$= \tfrac{1}{4}(\sigma_A^2 + \sigma_D^2) + \tfrac{1}{4}\sigma_A^2$$

$$= \tfrac{1}{2}\sigma_A^2 + \tfrac{1}{4}\sigma_D^2$$

This result was obtained precisely first by Fisher (1918) by a different method. The result was indicated by Weinberg (1908, 1910). An interesting result obtained by Weinberg is implicit in the above derivation, and it will be given in Weinberg's terms. Let T be the genotypic value of an individual, F_1 be the mean genotypic value of the offspring of the individual, and C the mean genotypic value of the full-sibs of the individual, measured in all cases from the population mean. Then the above states

$$C = \tfrac{1}{4}(T + 2F_1)$$

since

$$F_1 = \tfrac{1}{2}(\alpha_r + \alpha_s)$$

or

$$4C - T - 2F_1 = 0$$

It is appropriate here to comment on the results given above. We have seen that with one locus and a random mating population the total genotypic variance σ_G^2 is the sum of two parts σ_A^2 and σ_D^2. The covariance of parent and offspring is $\tfrac{1}{2}\sigma_A^2$, and of full-sibs is $\tfrac{1}{2}\sigma_A^2 + \tfrac{1}{4}\sigma_D^2$. The latter is necessarily greater than the former since σ_D^2 is greater than or equal to zero. These results lead to procedure for estimating the components of variance in the simple case where we know an attribute P is due to the additive effects of a genotype involving one locus and environmental effects distributed at random. For we shall have

$$\sigma_P^2 = \sigma_G^2 + \sigma_E^2$$

$$\sigma_G^2 = \sigma_A^2 + \sigma_D^2$$

$$\text{Cov}(P, O) = \tfrac{1}{2}\sigma_A^2$$

$$\text{Cov}(F. S) = \tfrac{1}{2}\sigma_A^2 + \tfrac{1}{4}\sigma_D^2$$

where $\mathrm{Cov}\,(P, O)$ equals the covariance of parent and offspring and $\mathrm{Cov}\,(F.\,S)$ equals the covariance of full-sibs. These equations may be used to estimate the components by the following equations, where the $\widehat{}$ denotes "estimate of":

$$\widehat{\sigma_A^2} = 2\,\mathrm{Cov}\,(P, O)$$

$$\widehat{\sigma_D^2} = 4[\mathrm{Cov}\,(F.\,S) - \mathrm{Cov}\,(P, O)]$$

$$\widehat{\sigma_E^2} = \widehat{\sigma_P^2} - \widehat{\sigma_A^2} - \widehat{\sigma_D^2}$$

with $\widehat{\sigma_P^2}$ equal to the total variance of the attribute in the parental generation. The use of these formulas depend on:

1. The conditions already stated, i.e. genotype and environment additive in their effects and randomly associated, and the genotype arising from segregation at one locus.

2. The population having random mating structure and matings being at random, with equal viability of all genotypes and no selection.

It will be seen in a later chapter that the same formulas may be used under the circumstance that there is an arbitrary number of loci involved, if a certain condition is satisfied.

The results are sometimes stated in regression terms. We have

$$\beta_{OP} = \text{regression of offspring on parent} = \frac{\mathrm{Cov}\,(P, O)}{V(P)} = \frac{\frac{1}{2}\sigma_A^2}{\sigma_P^2}$$

Hence twice the regression of offspring on parent is σ_A^2/σ_P^2. This ratio is known as the heritability of the attribute (see for example Lush, 1937 and following editions, and Lerner, 1950). It is sometimes added that selection of the parents does not affect the estimation of the estimates of the ratios, on the basis that selection of an independent variable x does not bias the estimation of the regression of y on x; i.e., the estimate obtained from regressing y values on their x values which were chosen not at random is an unbiased estimate of the true regression. This will be true only if the regression of y on x is linear throughout the range of x. In the present case this will be true if there are no dominance deviations. Hence doubling the parent–offspring regression when there is selection of parents gives an unbiased estimate of heritability *only* in the case when there are no dominance deviations. A proof of a statement contrary to this would be of interest (and a surprise!) to the author. It will be remembered that all the results given above are stated only for the case of a single locus.

15.10.2 The General Method

It would be extremely tedious to follow the above direct method for all cases. Some simplification is desirable and is given by the following general method. We have to find the covariance of two individuals X and Y which are a random pair of members of the population with a certain pattern of relationship, e.g. cousins, half-sibs, double first cousins, and so on. Let X have the genotype $A_{x_s}A_{x_d}$, and Y the genotype $A_{y_s}A_{y_d}$. Then the phenotypic values of X and Y are

$$X = \mu + \alpha_{x_s} + \alpha_{x_d} + d_{x_s x_d} + e$$
$$Y = \mu + \alpha_{y_s} + \alpha_{y_d} + d_{y_s y_d} + f$$

where e and f are environmental errors uncorrelated with each other and with the genotypic values. We revert for the moment to the earlier equation for the genotypic value of an individual with genotype $A_r A_s$:

$$y_{rs} = \alpha_r + \alpha_s + d_{rs}$$

Consider an individual Z chosen at random from the population with genotype $A_{z_s}A_{z_d}$: Then the probability that z_s equals r is p_r, that z_d equals s is p_s; so in the model

$$Z = \alpha_{z_s} + \alpha_{z_d} + d_{z_s z_d}$$

the average value or expectation of α_{z_s} is $\sum p_r \alpha_r$ which is zero. Similarly, using E to denote expectation, we have

$$E(\alpha_{z_s} \alpha_{z_d}) = 0$$

$$E(d_{z_s z_d}) = 0 \quad \text{since} \quad \sum_{rs} p_r p_s d_{rs} = \sum_r p_r \sum_s p_s d_{rs}$$

$$= \sum_r p_r \left[\sum_s p_s (y_{rs} - \alpha_r - \alpha_s) \right]$$

$$= \sum_r p_r \left(\sum_s p_s y_{rs} - \alpha_r - 0 \right)$$

$$= \sum_r p_r (\alpha_r - \alpha_r) = 0$$

$$E(\alpha_{z_s} d_{z_s z_d}) = \sum_{rs} p_r \alpha_r p_s d_{rs}$$

$$= \sum_r p_r \alpha_r \sum_s p_s d_{rs}$$

$$= 0$$

The individual X is a random member of the population, and Y is a random member of the population having the particular relationship with X. Hence

$$\text{Cov}(X, Y) = E[(\alpha_{x_s} + \alpha_{x_d} + d_{x_s x_d})(\alpha_{y_s} + \alpha_{y_d} + d_{y_s y_d})]$$
$$= E(\alpha_{x_s}\alpha_{y_s}) + E(\alpha_{x_s}\alpha_{y_d}) + E(\alpha_{x_s}d_{y_s y_d}) + E(\alpha_{x_d}\alpha_{y_s})$$
$$+ E(\alpha_{x_d}\alpha_{y_d}) + E(\alpha_{x_d}d_{y_s y_d}) + E(d_{x_s x_d}\alpha_{y_s})$$
$$+ E(d_{x_s x_d}\alpha_{y_d}) + E(d_{x_s x_d}d_{y_s y_d})$$

Now consider each of these terms. Let $P(x_s = y_s)$ equal the probability that genes A_{x_s} and A_{y_s} are identical by descent. Then

$$E(\alpha_{x_s}\alpha_{y_s}) = \sum_r p_r \alpha_r \left\{ P(x_s = y_s)\alpha_r + [1 - P(x_s = y_s)] \sum_u p_u \alpha_u \right\}$$

$$= P(x_s = y_s) \times \sum_r p_r \alpha_r^2, \quad \text{the second term giving zero}$$

$$= P(x_s = y_s) \times \frac{\sigma_A^2}{2}$$

Hence the terms involving only α's gives

$$\tfrac{1}{2}\sigma_A^2 [P(x_s = y_s) + P(x_s = y_d) + P(x_d = y_s) + P(x_d = y_d)]$$
$$= \tfrac{1}{2}\sigma_A^2 4r_{XY} = 2r_{XY}\sigma_A^2$$

where r_{XY} is the coefficient of parentage of X and Y.

Turning to terms such as $E(\alpha_{x_s}d_{y_s y_d})$, we shall first make the assumption that $P(y_s = y_d) = P(x_s = x_d) = 0$, which is equivalent to assuming that neither individual X nor Y is inbred. If they were inbred, the expectation of terms like $d_{x_s x_d}$ would not be zero: In fact, it would be

$$\sum_r [p_r P(x_s = x_d)d_{rr}] + [1 - P(x_s = x_d)] \sum_{rs} p_r p_s d_{rs} = P(x_s = x_d) \sum_r p_r d_{rr}$$

which is not zero. In a later chapter we shall see what can be done about deducing results for the general case. Under our assumption it is not difficult to complete the reasoning because, if x_s and y_s are unrelated in the sense of having zero probability of being identical by descent, then $P(x_s = y_s = y_d) = 0$. Hence

$$E(\alpha_{x_s}d_{y_s y_d}) = \sum p_r \alpha_r \left[P(x_s = y_s) \sum_u d_{ru} p_u \right] = 0$$

and similarly for all other terms involving both an α term and a d term. Finally we are left with the term

$$E(d_{x_s x_d}d_{y_s y_d})$$

which is equal to

$$\sum_{uv} p_u p_v d_{uv} d_{uv} P(x_s{=}y_s,\, x_d{=}y_d) + \sum_{uv} p_u p_v d_{uv} d_{vu} P(x_s{=}y_d,\, x_d{=}y_s)$$

$$= [P(x_s{=}y_s,\, x_d{=}y_d) + P(x_s{=}y_d,\, x_d{=}y_s)]\sigma_D^2$$

where $P(x_s{=}y_s,\, x_d{=}y_d)$ is the probability that A_{x_s} and A_{y_s} are identical by descent *and* A_{x_d} and A_{y_d} are identical by descent.

In the particular case when we may identify x_s, y_s as genes contributed to X and Y on one chromosome and x_d, y_d as genes contributed to X and Y on the other chromosome, with no relationship between the two chromosomes received by X or by Y, then we may write

$$P(x_s{=}y_s) = \phi$$
$$P(x_d{=}y_d) = \phi'$$
$$P(x_s{=}y_d) = 0$$
$$P(x_d{=}y_s) = 0$$
$$P(x_s{=}y_s,\, x_d{=}y_d) = \phi\phi'$$
$$P(x_s{=}y_d,\, x_d{=}y_s) = 0$$

and the covariance becomes

$$\left(\frac{\phi + \phi'}{2}\right)\sigma_A^2 + \phi\phi'\sigma_D^2$$

which is the result given by Malécot (1948). We may, in evaluating ϕ and ϕ', think about x_s and y_s being the sire genes of X and Y, and x_d and y_d as the dam genes of X and Y, as an aid in comprehending the situation.

The general result for the covariance between $X = (A_{x_s} A_{x_d})$, and $Y = (A_{y_s} A_{y_d})$ is therefore

$$[P(x_s{=}y_s) + P(x_d{=}y_s) + P(x_s{=}y_d) + P(x_d{=}y_d)]\frac{\sigma_A^2}{2}$$

$$+ [P(x_s{=}y_s,\, x_d{=}y_d) + P(x_s{=}y_d,\, x_d{=}y_s)]\,\sigma_D^2$$

15.10.3 Examples

1. *Parent–offspring.* Let $X = (a, b)$ and $Y = (c, d)$ with gene d being contributed by the mate of X; then $P(c{=}a) = \frac{1}{2}$, $P(c{=}b) = \frac{1}{2}$, $P(d{=}a) = 0$, $P(d{=}b) = 0$, $P(a{=}c,\, b{=}d) = 0$, $P(a{=}d,\, b{=}c) = 0$ and hence Cov $(P, O) = \frac{1}{2}\sigma_A^2$.

2. *Full-sibs.* Using Figure 15.3, we may as well regard U as the sire and V as the dam. In that case

$$\phi = P(e=g) = P(a=e=g) + P(b=e=g) = \tfrac{1}{4} + \tfrac{1}{4} = \tfrac{1}{2}$$

Similarly

$$\phi' = \tfrac{1}{2}$$

and

$$\phi\phi' = \tfrac{1}{4}$$

so that

$$\text{Cov}\,(F.\,S) = \tfrac{1}{2}\sigma_A^2 + \tfrac{1}{4}\sigma_D^2$$

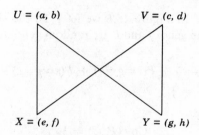

FIGURE 15.3

3. *Half-sibs.* Now use Figure 15.4, and let U be the common parent. Here $P(c=e) = \tfrac{1}{2} = \phi$, and ϕ' is zero, and hence $\text{Cov}\,(H.\,S) = \tfrac{1}{4}\sigma_A^2$.

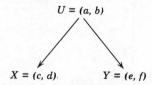

FIGURE 15.4

4. *Uncle–nephew.* Let $U = (a, b)$, $V = (c, d)$ be the parents; then the diagram is given in Figure 15.5. Let W be, for purposes of argument, the sire of Y. Then h is a random gene of the population. Since

$$P(e=g) + P(f=g) + P(e=h) + P(f=h) = P(e=g) + P(f=g) = \tfrac{1}{2}$$

and

$$P(e=g, f=h) + P(e=h, f=g) = 0$$
$$\text{Cov}\,(U,\,N) = \tfrac{1}{4}\sigma_A^2$$

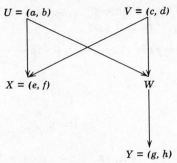

FIGURE 15.5

5. *First cousins.* In Figure 15.6 we let P be the sire of X and Q the sire of Y. Then the genes f and h are random genes from the population. Hence

$$\phi = P(e=g=a) + P(e=g=b) + P(e=g=c) + P(e=g=d)$$
$$= 4 \times \tfrac{1}{16} = \tfrac{1}{4}$$

and $\phi' = 0$. Hence

$$\text{Cov } (F.\ C) = \tfrac{1}{8}\sigma_A^2$$

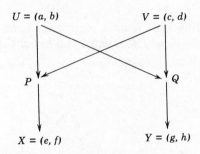

FIGURE 15.6

6. *Double first cousins.* With reference to Figure 15.7, let the individuals U, V provide the sire genes of both X and Y, with P, Q providing the dam genes of both X and Y. Then

$$\phi = 4 \times \tfrac{1}{16} = \tfrac{1}{4}$$
$$\phi' = \tfrac{1}{4}$$

so

$$\text{Cov } (D.\ F.\ C) = \tfrac{1}{4}\sigma_A^2 + \tfrac{1}{16}\sigma_D^2$$

We could continue indefinitely with examples, but by now the methodology should be clear to the reader, and miscellaneous results are given as problems at the end of the chapter. It is, however, worth noting that a fraction of σ_A^2 is involved in all the possible covariances, but the com-

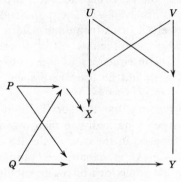

FIGURE 15.7

ponent σ_D^2 does not enter into the covariance of X and Y unless there is a non-zero probability that the two genes of X are identical by descent with the two genes of Y. If this probability is zero, then the covariance is simply $2r_{XY}\sigma_A^2$ where r_{XY} is the coefficient of parentage of X and Y, and $2r_{XY}$ is the intuitive degree of relationship of X and Y.

15.11 MATERNAL EFFECTS

While we are considering genotypic values determined by the genes at one locus, it behooves us to consider the case of maternal effects which are genetically determined.* We assume that the genotypic value of an individual is determined additively by the joint effect of the genes possessed by the individual and by the effect of the maternal genotype. Thus for instance we may consider the following table of genotypic values:

		Genotype of Mother		
		AA	Aa	aa
Genotype of Individual	AA	$D+d$	$H+d$	$R+d$
	Aa	$D+h$	$H+h$	$R+h$
	aa	$D+r$	$H+r$	$R+r$

We note that certain combinations can be achieved only by mutation or implantation. Such genetic control of the phenotype of an individual is

---

* Maternal effects which are not genetically determined present no problem, as they merely constitute an environmental correlation of full-sibs and maternal half-sibs.

quite likely in the case of all mammals. The situation is under the control of one locus, but there are nine "genotypic" values, and criticism of the term "genotypic value" can be made. It will be recalled that the genotypic value was defined to be the average of the phenotypic values of a large number of individuals of the particular genotype grown over the population of environments of relevance. The population of environments could of course be conceived of as including maternal environment, and in that case there would be no difficulty. It is, however, of great interest to examine the logical consequences of the system specified above. Perhaps some new term should be used here such as "true phenotypic value".

It may be noted in passing that the survival and hence reproductive value of humans may depend markedly on their own genotype in relation to their mother's genotype, as in the case of the Rh factor.

We do not propose to make an exhaustive examination of the present situation but merely to get some idea of the possibilities inherent in it.

The quantities D, H, R and d, h, r are assumed to be defined around means of zero, so that

$$p^2D + 2pqH + q^2R = 0$$
$$p^2d + 2pqh + q^2r = 0$$

The complete array of parents and offspring is given in Table 15.2.

TABLE 15.2

FREQUENCIES OF MATINGS, OFFSPRING AND VALUES OF OFFSPRING WITH MATERNAL EFFECTS

Sire	Dam	Frequency of Mating	Mean of Offspring	Mean of Sire	Mean of Dam
AA	AA	p^4	$D+d$	$pD+qH+d$	$pD+qH+d$
AA	Aa	$2p^3q$	$H+\frac{1}{2}(d+h)$	$pD+qH+d$	$\frac{1}{2}[pD+(p+q)H+qR]+h$
AA	aa	p^2q^2	$R+h$	$pD+qH+d$	$pH+qR+r$
Aa	AA	$2p^3q$	$D+\frac{1}{2}(d+h)$	$\frac{1}{2}[pD+(p+q)H+qR]+h$	$pD+qH+d$
Aa	Aa	$4p^2q^2$	$H+\frac{1}{4}(d+2h+r)$	$\frac{1}{2}[pD+(p+q)H+qR]+h$	$\frac{1}{2}[pD+(p+q)H+qR]+h$
Aa	aa	$2pq^3$	$R+\frac{1}{2}(h+r)$	$\frac{1}{2}[pD+(p+q)H+qR]+h$	$pH+qR+r$
aa	AA	p^2q^2	$D+h$	$pH+qR+r$	$pD+qH+d$
aa	Aa	$2pq^3$	$H+\frac{1}{2}(h+r)$	$pH+qR+r$	$\frac{1}{2}[pD+(p+q)H+qR]+h$
aa	aa	q^4	$R+r$	$pH+qR+r$	$pH+qR+r$

The mean value of either parent is obtained by noting that AA individuals have a genotypic array of parents

$$\frac{1}{p^2}(p^4AA + p^3qAA + p^3qAa + p^2q^2Aa)$$

$$= p^2AA + pqAA + pqAa + q^2Aa$$

$$= pAA + qAa$$

Similarly the genotypic array of parents of Aa individuals is

$$\tfrac{1}{2}[pAA + (p + q)Aa + qaa]$$

and of parents of aa individuals is

$$pAa + qaa$$

We now proceed to the evaluation of variances and covariances of offspring and sire, and of offspring and dam. We find that the variance in population is

$$p^4(D + d)^2 + p^3q[(H + d)^2 + (H + h)^2] + \text{etc.}$$

$$= (p^2D^2 + 2pqH^2 + q^2R^2) + (p^2d^2 + 2pqh^2 + q^2r^2)$$

$$+ 2p^2D(pd + qh) + 2pqH[pd + (p + q)h + qr] + 2q^2R(ph + qr)$$

This can be simplified in the following way:

(1) $p^2D^2 + 2pqH^2 + q^2R^2 = $ total variance in maternal contributions

$$= \sigma^2_{G_m} \quad \text{say}$$

(2) $p^2d^2 + 2pqh^2 + q^2r^2 = $ total variance in genotype effects

$$= \sigma^2_{G_d}$$

(3) Let $\left.\begin{array}{l} pD + qH = \alpha_1 \\ pH + qR = \alpha_2 \end{array}\right\}$ the additive components effects of the maternal contributions

$\left.\begin{array}{l} pd + qh = \beta_1 \\ ph + qr = \beta_2 \end{array}\right\}$ the additive components of the genotype effects

with

$$\left.\begin{array}{l} D = 2\alpha_1 + d_{11} \\ H = \alpha_1 + \alpha_2 + d_{12} \\ R = 2\alpha_2 + d_{22} \end{array}\right\} \quad \text{so that} \quad \begin{array}{l} pd_{11} + qd_{12} = 0 \\ pd_{12} + qd_{22} = 0 \end{array}$$

Then the variance is

$$\sigma^2_{G_m} + \sigma^2_{G_d} + 2p(pD + qH)(pd + qh) + 2q(pH + qR)(ph + qr)$$
$$= \sigma^2_{G_m} + \sigma^2_{G_d} + 2p\alpha_1\beta_1 + 2q\alpha_2\beta_2$$

or, if further we let

$\alpha_1 - \alpha_2 = \alpha$ the so called effect of the gene substitution A for a

$\beta_1 - \beta_2 = \beta$ likewise

we find that the variance in true phenotypic values

$$= \sigma^2_{G_m} + \sigma^2_{G_d} + 2pq\alpha\beta$$
$$= \sigma^2_{A_m} + \sigma^2_{D_m} + \sigma^2_{A_d} + \sigma^2_{D_d} + 2pq\alpha\beta$$
$$= 2pq\alpha^2 + 2pq\beta^2 + 2pq\alpha\beta + \sigma^2_{D_m} + \sigma^2_{D_d}$$

where $\sigma^2_{A_m}$ $\sigma^2_{A_d}$ are the additive variances of maternal and direct effects
and $\sigma^2_{D_m}$, $\sigma^2_{D_d}$ are the respective dominance variances.   It is of interest to
note that the covariance of maternal and direct effects enters only with
regard to their additive values.   This is to be expected.

Now we consider the sire–offspring covariance.   Table 15.2 may be condensed to Table 15.3.

TABLE 15.3

SIRE–OFFSPRING RELATIONSHIP

Frequency	Value	Sire	Mean of Offspring
p^2	$\alpha_1 + d$	AA	β_1
$2pq$	$\frac{1}{2}(\alpha_1 + \alpha_2) + h$	Aa	$\frac{1}{2}(\beta_1 + \beta_2)$
q^2	$\alpha_2 + r$	aa	β_2

Hence, with $d = 2\beta_1 + e_{11}$, $h = \beta_1 + \beta_2 + e_{12}$, $r = 2\beta_2 + e_{22}$, the
sire–offspring covariance is equal to

$$p^2(\alpha_1 + 2\beta_1 + e_{11})\beta_1 + 2pq[\tfrac{1}{2}(\alpha_1 + \alpha_2) + \beta_1 + \beta_2 + e_{12}][\tfrac{1}{2}(\beta_1 + \beta_2)]$$
$$+ q^2(\alpha_2 + 2\beta_2 + e_{22})\beta_2$$

$$= p^2\alpha_1\beta_1 + \frac{pq}{2}(\alpha_1 + \alpha_2)(\beta_1 + \beta_2) + q^2\alpha_2\beta_2 + 2p^2\beta_1^2 + pq(\beta_1 + \beta_2)^2$$

$$+ 2q^2\beta_2^2$$

$$= \frac{pq}{2}\alpha\beta + pq\beta^2 = \text{Cov}\,(S, O)$$

We note that, if α equals zero and $\sigma^2_{D_m}$ equals zero, we get the standard result.

For the dam–offspring covariance we find

$$\text{Cov}(D, O) = p^2(\alpha_1 + d)(D + \beta_1) + 2pq[\tfrac{1}{2}(\alpha_1 + \alpha_2) + h][H + \tfrac{1}{2}(\beta_1 + \beta_2)]$$
$$+ q^2(\alpha_2 + r)(R + \beta_2)$$
$$= pq\alpha^2 + pq\beta^2 + \tfrac{5}{2}pq\alpha\beta + \text{Cov}(d_{ij}, e_{ij})$$

where $\text{Cov}(d_{ij}, e_{ij})$ is the covariance of the dominance deviations of the maternal and direct effects. This is a rather peculiar result with respect to the covariance of additive maternal and direct effects.

It is interesting to note that the covariance of dominance deviations of the maternal and direct effects does not enter into the variance in the population, but does enter into the dam–offspring covariance.

The full-sib covariance turns out to be

$$\text{Cov}(F.S) = \sigma^2_{A_m} + \sigma^2_{D_m} + \tfrac{1}{2}\sigma^2_{A_d} + \tfrac{1}{4}\sigma^2_{D_d} + 2pq\alpha\beta$$

The whole situation requires the knowledge of seven parameters: the environmental variance, the additive and dominance variances of the maternal effects and of the direct effects, the covariance of the additive effects, and the covariance of the dominance deviations.

It is not within our present scope to cover this matter exhaustively. The above is sufficient, however, to indicate that the situation cannot be understood from the total variance, sire–offspring, dam–offspring, and full-sib covariances. It may happen for example that the covariances of sire and offspring and of dam and offspring are of the same order of magnitude when there are maternal effects with a particular structure.

We note that additive maternal effects were considered by Dickerson (1947).

15.12 SEX-LINKED GENES

It is necessary that we consider the role of sex-linked genes in quantitative inheritance (Bohidar and Kempthorne, 1957). We shall give only some short notes on the problem here, leaving exhaustive treatment to a later publication. We take the male to be heterogametic and the female homogametic. In view of the marked way in which sex can affect the expression of genes, we suppose that the genotypic values are as follows:

Genotypic value of male $A_i = u_i$

Genotypic value of female $A_i A_j = v_{ij}$

with, of course,

$$\sum p_i u_i = 0$$
$$\sum p_i p_j v_{ij} = 0$$

The genotypic variance of males is $\sum p_i u_i^2$, which we denote by σ_{MG}^2, and of females is $\sum p_i p_j v_{ij}^2$, which we denote by σ_{FG}^2. It is found that additive effects in the females are intrinsic, these being equal to

$$\alpha_i = \sum_j p_j v_{ij}$$

The genotypic covariance of sire and son is zero. The genotypic covariance of sire and daughter is equal to

$$\sum p_i u_i \alpha_i$$

which for brevity we denote by C. The covariance of dam and son is also equal to C. The covariance of dam and daughter is equal to

$$\sum p_i \alpha_i^2$$

which is one-half of the additive variance in the females. The covariance of full brothers is $\frac{1}{2}\sigma_{\text{MG}}^2$. The covariance of full brother and sister is $\frac{1}{2}C$. The covariance of full sisters is the usual formula for the autosomal case, namely $\frac{1}{2}$ of the additive variance plus $\frac{1}{4}$ of the dominance variance on the female side. These results are sufficient to examine the bias in certain procedures for estimating components of genotypic variance.

REFERENCES

Bohidar, N. R., and O. Kempthorne. 1957. The role of sex-linked genes in quantitative inheritance (to be published).

Bonnier, G., and H. Hansson. 1948. Identical twin genetics in cattle. *Heredity*, **2**, 1–27.

Comstock, R. E., and H. F. Robinson. 1948. The components of genetic variance in populations of biparental progenies and their use in estimating the average degree of dominance. *Biometrics*, **14**, 254–266.

Dickerson, G. E. 1947. Composition of hog carcasses as influenced by heritable differences in rate and economy of gain. *Res. Bull. Ia. agric. Exp. Sta.*, **354**, 489–524.

Fisher, R. A. 1918. On the correlation between relatives on the supposition of Mendelian inheritance. *Trans. roy. Soc. Edinb.*, **52**, 399–433.

Fisher, R. A. 1930. *The genetical theory of natural selection.* Clarendon Press, Oxford.

Fisher, R. A. 1941. Average excess and average effect of a gene substitution. *Ann. Eugen. Lond.*, **11**, 53–63.

Lerner, I. M. 1950. *Population genetics and animal improvement.* University Press, Cambridge.

Lush, J. L. 1937. *Animal breeding plans* and succeeding editions. Iowa State College Press, Ames.

Malécot, G. 1948. *Les mathématiques de l'hérédité.* Masson et Cie. Paris.

Osborne, R. 1952. Sexual maturity in Brown Leghorns. The interactions of genotype and environment. *Proc. roy. Soc. Edinb. B*, **64**, 445–455.

Pearson, F. 1904. On a generalized theory of alternative inheritance with special reference to Mendel's laws. *Phil. Trans. A*, **203**, 53–86.

Weinberg, W.   1908.   Uber Vererbungsgesetze beim Menschen.   *Z. indukt. Abstamm. -u. VererbLehre*, **1**, 377–392, 443–460; **2**, 276–330.

Weinberg, W.   1910.   Weitere Beitrage zur Theorie der Vererbung.   *Arch. Rass.-u. GesBiol.*, **7**, 35–49, 169–173.

Wright, Sewall.   1935.   The analysis of variance and the correlations between relatives with respect to deviations from an optimum.   *J. Genet.*, **30**, 243–256.

FURTHER READING

Bonnier, G., and A. Hansson.   1948.   Identical twin genetics in cattle.   *Heredity*, **2**, 1–27.

Bonnier, G., A. Hansson, and H. Skjervold.   1948.   Studies on monozygotic cattle twins.   IX.   The interplay of heredity and environment on growth and yield.   *Acta agric. suec.*, **3**, 1–57.

Crow, J. F.   1948.   Alternative hypotheses of hybrid vigor.   *Genetics*, **33**, 477–487.

Crow, J. F.   1952.   Dominance and overdominance.   Chapter 18 of *Heterosis*, edited by J. W. Gowen, Iowa State College Press, Ames.

Gardner, C. O., P. H. Harvey, R. E. Comstock, and H. F. Robinson.   1953.   Dominance of genes controlling quantitative characters in maize.   *Agron. J.*, **45**, 186–191.

Gowen, J. W.   1919.   A biometrical study of crossing over.   *Genetics*, **4**, 205–250.

Gowen, J. W.   1934.   The influence of inheritance and environment on the milk production and butterfat percentage of Jersey cattle.   *J. agric. Res.*, **49**, 433–465.

Gowen, J. W.   1952.   Hybrid vigor in *Drosophila*.   Chapter 29 of *Heterosis*, Iowa State College Press, Ames.

Hogben, L.   1933.   *Nature and nurture.*   London.

Lewis, D.   1954.   Gene-environment interaction: the relationship between dominance, heterosis, phenotypic stability and variability.   *Heredity*, **8**, 333–356.

Osborne, R.   1954.   Sex-linked association of egg weight and body weight in Brown Leghorns.   *Proc. roy. Soc. Edinb.*, **65**, 317–326.

Pearson, Karl.   1909a.   On the ancestral gametic correlations of a Mendelian population mating at random.   *Proc. roy. Soc. Lond. B*, **81**, 225–229.

Pearson, Karl.   1909b.   The theory of ancestral contributions in heredity.   *Proc. roy. Soc. Lond. B*, **81**, 219–224.

Robertson, F. W., and E. C. R. Reeve.   1952.   Heterozygosity, environmental variation and heterosis.   *Nature*, **170**, 286.

Robinson, H. F., R. E. Comstock, and P. H. Harvey.   1949.   Estimates of heritability and the degree of dominance in corn.   *Agron. J.*, **41**, 353–359.

Robinson, H. F., T. J. Mann, and R. E. Comstock.   1954.   An analysis of quantitative variability in *Nicotiana tabacum*.   *Heredity*, **8**, 365–376.

Spuhler, J. N.   1954.   Some problems in the study of quantitative inheritance in man.   *Amer. J. hum. Genet.*, **6**, 130–156.

"Student."   1934.   A calculation of the minimum number of genes in Winter's selection experiment.   *Ann. Eugen. Lond.*, **6**, 77–82.

Wright, Sewall.   1920.   The relative importance of heredity and environment in determining the piebald pattern of guinea pigs.   *Proc. nat. Acad. Sci.*, **6**, 320–322.

Wright, Sewall.   1921.   Systems of mating.   I.   The biometric relation between parent and offspring.   *Genetics*, **6**, 111–123.

PROBLEMS

1. For the case of complete dominance obtain the genotypic variance, additive variance, and dominance variance as functions of the gene frequency.   Plot

the ratio (additive variance/total genotypic variance) as a function of gene frequency.

2. For the case of "perfect" overdominance in which the two homozygotes have the same genotypic value different from that of the heterozygote, plot the ratio (additive variance/total genotypic variance) as a function of gene frequency.

3. Evaluate the additive and dominance variance for the case of a random mating population with three alleles a, b, c for which the gene frequencies are 0.3, 0.2 and 0.5, respectively, and the genotypic values for aa, ab, ac, bb, bc, and cc are, respectively, 5, 3, 2, 1, 0, 1.

4. Do as in question 3 when the genotypic values are, respectively, 5, 5, 4, 5, 4, 2.

5. Plot the ratio (dominance variance/additive variance) for question 1.

6. Plot the ratio (dominance variance/additive variance) for the population of question 2.

7. Plot the ratio (dominance variance/additive variance) for the population of question 3.

8. Plot the ratio (dominance variance/additive variance) for the population of question 4.

9. Work out the covariance of parent and offspring for the populations of questions 1, 2, 3, and verify the general formula.

10. Find the regression of genotypic value of an individual on the mid-parent value and the mean value of the full-sibs of the individual *jointly*.

11. Obtain the covariance of sire and offspring, of dam and offspring and of full-sibs, with maternal effects, for a random population $p^2AA + 2pqAa + q^2aa$, $p = 0.3$, $q = 0.7$, and

$$D = 2, \qquad d = 4$$
$$H = 1, \qquad h = 2$$
$$R = 0, \qquad r = 0$$

12. Do problem 11 with

$$D = 2, \qquad d = 0$$
$$H = 1, \qquad h = 1$$
$$R = 0, \qquad r = 0$$

13. Do problem 11 with

$$D = 0, \qquad d = 0$$
$$H = 1, \qquad h = 2$$
$$R = 1, \qquad r = 0$$

CHAPTER 16

Non-random Mating Diploid Populations with One Locus Segregating

16.1 EFFECTS AND VARIANCES

Now let us consider the population

$$PAA + 2QAa + Raa$$

in which Q^2 is not equal to PR. If Q^2 equals PR, then we can write $P = p^2$, $R = q^2$, and $Q = pq$, and we have a population which has the random mating structure.

Again we use i, j, k for the genotypic values of AA, Aa, and aa, respectively, these being defined around the mean so that

$$Pi + 2Qj + Rk = 0$$

The additive effects are now obtained by minimizing

$$P(i - 2\alpha)^2 + 2Q(j - \alpha - \beta)^2 + R(k - 2\beta)^2$$

The normal equations are

$$2P(i - 2\alpha) + 2Q(j - \alpha - \beta) = 0$$
$$2Q(j - \alpha - \beta) + 2R(k - 2\beta) = 0$$

or, in the usual form,

$$4P\alpha + 2Q(\alpha + \beta) = 2(Pi + Qj)$$
$$2Q(\alpha + \beta) + 4R\beta = 2(Qj + Rk)$$

Adding these two equations, we get

$$4(P + Q)\alpha + 4(Q + R)\beta = 2(Pi + 2Qj + Rk) = 0$$

and by definition $P + Q$ equals p, the frequency of gene A, and $Q + R$ equals q, the frequency of gene a. Hence

$$p\alpha + q\beta = 0 \text{ as in the random mating case.}$$

343

Proceeding as in that case, we put

$$p\alpha = \gamma = -q\beta$$

so that

$$\alpha = \frac{\gamma}{p}, \quad \beta = \frac{-\gamma}{q}$$

and

$$\alpha - \beta = \gamma\left(\frac{1}{p} + \frac{1}{q}\right) = \frac{\gamma}{pq}$$

Hence the sum of squares removed by the regression on gene content is equal to

$$2\frac{\gamma}{p}(Pi + Qj) - \frac{\gamma}{q}2(Qj + Rk)$$

$$= 2\gamma\left(\frac{Pi + Qj}{p} - \frac{Qj + Rk}{q}\right)$$

Fisher calls $(\alpha - \beta)$ the average effect of a gene substitution and the quantity

$$\frac{Pi + Qj}{p} - \frac{Qj + Rk}{q}$$

which equals

$$\frac{Pi + Qj}{P + Q} - \frac{Qj + Rk}{Q + R}$$

the average excess of the gene substitution. He uses α for our $(\alpha - \beta)$, but we have used α_A to avoid confusion. Likewise we denote the average excess by a_A, and, since $\alpha_A = \alpha - \beta = \gamma/pq$, $\gamma = pq\alpha_A$, we find that the additive genetic variance in the population is $2pq\alpha_A a_A$.

It is of interest to consider the change in population mean resulting from a small change Δp in the frequency of gene A, with a consequent change of $-\Delta p$ in the frequency of gene a. In fact, this change will be

$$\Delta Pi + 2\Delta Qj + \Delta Rk$$

which, because $Pi + 2Qj + Rk = 0$, we may write as

$$\Delta Pi + 2\Delta Qj - \frac{\Delta R}{R}(Pi + 2Qj)$$

$$= \left(\Delta P - \frac{P\,\Delta R}{R}\right)i + 2\left(\Delta Q - \frac{Q\,\Delta R}{R}\right)j$$

Also we find, substituting for α, β in terms of γ in the first normal equation, that

$$\gamma = \frac{Pi + Qj}{2\dfrac{P}{p} + \dfrac{Q}{p} - \dfrac{Q}{q}}$$

so that $2\Delta p(\alpha - \beta)$ equals

$$2\frac{\Delta p}{pq}\left[\frac{Pi + Qj}{2\dfrac{P}{p} + \dfrac{Q}{p} - \dfrac{Q}{q}}\right]$$

If the change in population mean is to equal the change to be expected from the change in gene frequency and the average effect, we must have

$$\Delta P - \frac{P\,\Delta R}{R} = \left[\frac{2}{2\dfrac{P}{p} + \dfrac{Q}{p} - \dfrac{Q}{q}}\right]\frac{P\,\Delta p}{pq}$$

$$2\Delta Q - 2Q\frac{\Delta R}{R} = \left[\frac{2}{2\dfrac{P}{p} + \dfrac{Q}{p} - \dfrac{Q}{q}}\right]\frac{Q\,\Delta p}{pq}$$

or we must have

$$\frac{\Delta P}{P} - \frac{\Delta R}{R} = 2\frac{\Delta Q}{Q} - 2\frac{\Delta R}{R}$$

or

$$\frac{\Delta P}{P} + \frac{\Delta R}{R} = 2\frac{\Delta Q}{Q}$$

This equation then prescribes how the population genotypic frequencies must change in order that the change in population mean be equal to the sum of products of changes in gene frequency and average gene effects. This equation can be integrated to give

$$\log P + \log R = 2\log Q + \text{constant}$$

so that PR/Q^2 is equal to a constant, or, as Fisher (1941) puts it, Q^2/PR must equal some number λ.

This then prescribes in a definite manner the interpretation to be made of average gene effects in a population with non-random mating structure.

16.2 THE TWO-ALLELE CASE IN WRIGHT'S NOTATION

We have seen in Chapter 5 that, if the random mating population

$$p^2AA + 2pqAa + q^2aa, \qquad p + q = 1$$

is inbred regularly, then the resultant population is

$$[Fp + (1 - F)p^2]AA + 2(1 - F)pqAa + [Fq + (1 - F)q^2]aa$$

By "inbred regularly" we mean that either the coefficient of inbreeding of all individuals in the resulting population is F or that the original population was divided into parts at random, each of which was inbred to a constant inbreeding coefficient, the value for F then being the weighted average of the inbreeding coefficients of the separate parts. Let us now translate the results of the previous section into this symbolism. We have

$$P = Fp + (1 - F)p^2 = p^2 + Fpq$$
$$Q = \qquad (1 - F)pq$$
$$R = Fq + (1 - F)q^2 = q^2 + Fpq$$

Now the normal equations could be written

$$(4P + 2Q)\alpha + 2Q\beta = 2(Pi + Qj)$$
$$2Q\alpha + (2Q + 4R)\beta = 2(Qj + Rk)$$

and

$$4P + 2Q = 4p^2 + 4Fpq + 2(1 - F)pq$$
$$= 4p^2 + 2(1 + F)pq$$
$$2Q = \qquad 2(1 - F)pq$$
$$2Q + 4R = \qquad 4q^2 + 2(1 + F)pq$$

Hence the normal equations become

$$[4p^2 + 2(1 + F)pq]\alpha + 2(1 - F)pq\beta = 2[(p^2 + Fpq)i + (1 - F)pqj]$$
$$2(1 - F)pq\alpha + [4q^2 + 2(1 + F)pq]\beta = 2[(1 - F)pqj + (q^2 + Fpq)k]$$

When we divide the upper equation by $2p$ throughout and the bottom equation by $2q$ throughout, we get

$$[2p + (1 + F)q]\alpha + (1 - F)q\beta = (p + Fq)i + (1 - F)qj$$
$$(1 - F)p\alpha + [2q + (1 + F)p]\beta = (1 - F)pj + (q + Fp)k$$

or, since

$$2p + (1 + F)q = 1 + F + (1 - F)p$$

and

$$2q + (1 + F)p = 1 + F + (1 - F)q$$

we have

$$(1 + F)\alpha + (1 - F)(p\alpha + q\beta) = (p + Fq)i + (1 - F)qj$$
$$(1 + F)\beta + (1 - F)(p\alpha + q\beta) = (1 - F)pj + (q + Fp)k$$

Since $p\alpha + q\beta = 0$, as proved in the previous section,

$$\alpha = [(p + Fq)i + (1 - F)qj]/(1 + F)$$

and

$$\beta = [(1 - F)pj + (q + Fp)k]/(1 + F)$$

and

$$\alpha_A = \alpha - \beta = a_A/(1 + F)$$

where α_A is the average effect of the gene substitution and a_A is the average excess associated with the gene substitution. Hence the additive genetic variance σ_A^2 is given by

$$\sigma_A^2 = 2pq\alpha_A a_A = 2pqa_A^2/(1 + F) = (1 + F)2pq\alpha_A^2$$

It is clear from the derivation that this should *not* be interpreted to state that the additive genetic variance in the inbred population is $(1+F)$ times the additive genetic variance in the original population. In more detail, let us drop the subscript A on the α's and a's and use the symbol α_R, a_R for the average effect and excess in the original random mating population, α_F, a_F for the average effect and excess in the inbred population, and σ_{AR}^2 and σ_{AF}^2 for the additive genetic variance in the two cases. Then

$$\sigma_{AR}^2 = 2pq\alpha_R a_R = 2pq\alpha_R^2$$
$$\sigma_{AF}^2 = 2pq\alpha_F a_F = 2pq\alpha_F(1 + F)\alpha_F = (1 + F)2pq\alpha_F^2$$

Now we have to take account of the fact that the mean of the inbred population is not the same as the mean of the random mating population. The genotypic values of the genotypes will be the same [under all the circumstances we consider, though one could imagine these changing]. When we revert to our previous notation of d, h, r for the genotypic values of AA, Aa, and aa, we have, using subscripts R and F to indicate the random mating population and the inbred population, respectively,

$$\mu_R = p^2 d + 2pqh + q^2 r$$
$$\mu_F = (p^2 + Fpq)d + 2(1 - F)pqh + (q^2 + Fpq)r$$
$$= \mu_R + Fpq(d - 2h + r)$$

The average effect in the inbred case is

$$\alpha_F = \frac{(p+Fq)(d-\mu_F)+(1-F)q(h-\mu_F)-(1-F)p(h-\mu_F)-(q+Fp)(r-\mu_F)}{1+F}$$

$$= \frac{(p+Fq)d+(1-F)qh-(1-F)ph-(q+Fp)r}{1+F}$$

$$= \frac{(pd+qh-ph-qr)+F(qd-qh+ph-pr)}{1+F}$$

$$= \frac{\alpha_R+F[q(d-h)+p(h-r)]}{(1+F)}$$

$$= \frac{\alpha_R+F\{[(d-h)+(h-r)]-[p(d-h)+q(h-r)]\}}{1+F}$$

$$= \alpha_R\left(\frac{1-F}{1+F}\right)+\frac{F}{1+F}(d-r)$$

$$= \alpha_R+\frac{F}{1+F}(d-r-2\alpha_R)$$

Hence α_F equals α_R if and only if $d-r=2\alpha_R$, which holds only if $p=q$ for any dominance or if there is no dominance. Under these circumstances then, $\sigma^2_{AF}=(1+F)\sigma^2_{AR}$, but in general this is not true. For example the population

$$p^2AA + 2pqAa + q^2aa$$

with genotypic values $d=2$, $h=h$, $r=0$ has zero additive genetic variance if

$$p = \frac{h}{2h-2}$$

When this population is completely inbred, its structure is

$$pAA + qaa$$

with total genotypic variance equal to additive genetic variance and equal to $4p-4p^2=4pq$. In this example the additive genetic variance initially is zero, and with degree of inbreeding F it is $8pqF^2/(1+F)$.

In the case of complete dominance, with say $d=h=1, r=0$, we have

$$\alpha_R = p(1-1)+q(1-0) = q$$

$$\alpha_F = q+\frac{F}{1+F}(1-2q) = \frac{q+pF}{1+F}$$

and α_R equals α_F only if $1 - 2q = 0$, or $q = \frac{1}{2}$. Also $\sigma_{AR}^2 = 2pq^3$, and

$$\sigma_{AF}^2 = 2pq \frac{(q + pF)^2}{1 + F}$$

It is interesting to note that, if and only if $p = q$, does $\sigma_{AF}^2 = (1 + F)\sigma_{AR}^2$. The cases in which the relationship

$$\sigma_{AF}^2 = (1 + F)\sigma_{AR}^2$$

namely, no dominance, or any dominance and $p = q = \frac{1}{2}$, must be regarded as *very special* cases, and the use of the above equation to adjust the additive variance in the inbred population to the additive variance in the original population must be regarded in general as questionable.

16.3 GENERALIZATION OF RESULTS TO ARBITRARY NUMBER OF ALLELES

Consider the population $\sum P_{ij}A_iA_j$, where i and j run from 1 to s, the number of alleles, with P_{ij} equal to P_{ji}. The frequency of the A_iA_j genotype is $2P_{ij}$ for i not equal to j. Let the genotypic value of A_iA_j measured from the population mean be y_{ij}, so that $\sum_{ij} P_{ij}y_{ij} = 0$. Then the average effects are defined as the values for α_i, $i = 1, 2, \cdots, s$ which minimize $\sum_{ij} P_{ij}(y_{ij} - \alpha_i - \alpha_j)^2$. The normal equations are as follows, wherein we let p_i equal $\sum_j P_{ij}$, the gene frequency of the ith allele:

$$2(p_1 + P_{11})\alpha_1 + 2P_{12}\alpha_2 + \cdots + 2P_{1s}\alpha_s = 2\sum_j P_{1j}y_{1j}$$

$$2P_{12}\alpha_1 + 2(p_2 + P_{22})\alpha_2 + \cdots + 2P_{2s}\alpha_s = 2\sum_j P_{2j}y_{2j}$$

$$2P_{1s}\alpha_1 + 2P_{2s}\alpha_2 + \cdots + 2(p_s + P_{ss})\alpha_s = 2\sum_j P_{sj}y_{sj}$$

The quantities $\left(\sum_j P_{ij}y_{ij}\right)\Big/p_i$ are defined to be the average excesses associated with the genes, and will be denoted by a_i. It may be noted that a_i is the mean genotypic value of the individuals A_iA_i and half of the individuals A_iA_j as a deviation from the population mean. The right-hand sides of the normal equations are therefore $2p_ia_i$, $i = 1, 2$,

$\cdots, s$. The sum of squares removed by the regression which by definition is the additive genetic variance is equal to

$$2 \sum_i p_i \alpha_i a_i$$

No general solution of the normal equations exists, though in special circumstances a simple solution can be found. If the population has arisen by regular inbreeding, then

$$P_{ii} = Fp_i + (1 - F)p_i^2$$
$$P_{ij} = (1 - F)p_i p_j$$

It then follows, merely by summing the normal equations, that

$$\sum p_i \alpha_i = 0$$

The ith normal equation, after dividing by 2 throughout, is now

$$[(1 + F)p_i + (1 - F)p_i^2]\alpha_i + \sum_{i' \neq i} (1 - F)p_i p_{i'} \alpha_{i'} = p_i a_i$$

or

$$(1 + F)p_i \alpha_i + (1 - F)p_i \left(\sum_i p_i \alpha_i \right) = p_i a_i$$

so that

$$\alpha_i = a_i/(1 + F)$$

Under these circumstances then the additive variance is

$$2 \sum_i p_i \alpha_i^2 (1 + F)$$

Again it should be noted that the α_i here is not the same as it would be in a random mating population with the same gene frequency. In fact we have

$$(\alpha_i)_R = \frac{1}{p_i} \sum_j p_i p_j y_{ij} = \sum_j p_j y_{ij}$$

$$(1 + F)(\alpha_i)_F = \frac{1}{p_i} \left\{ [Fp_i + (1 - F)p_i^2]y_{ii} + \sum_{j \neq i} (1 - F)p_i p_j y_{ij} \right\}$$

$$= Fy_{ii} + (1 - F) \sum_j p_j y_{ij}$$

$$= Fy_{ii} + (1 - F)(\alpha_i)_R$$

It follows that $(\alpha_i)_F$ equals $(\alpha_i)_R$ if and only if y_{ii} equals $2(\alpha_i)_R$, i.e., if there is no dominance.

Reverting to the general normal equations, we may write them matrix-wise, after deleting the factor of 2, as

$$\mathbf{A\alpha = R}$$

so that

$$\mathbf{\alpha = A^{-1}R}$$

where $\mathbf{A^{-1}}$ is the inverse of $\mathbf{A}$.   More fully

$$\alpha_i = \sum_j A^{ij}R_j$$

where A^{ij} is the (ij)th element of $\mathbf{A^{-1}}$.

The result of the previous section may be generalized as follows.   In the case of the random mating population $\sum_{ij} p_i p_j A_i A_j$ the change in mean $\Delta\mu$ resulting from changes Δp_i in the gene frequencies is

$$\sum_{ij}(p_i + \Delta p_i)(p_j + \Delta p_j)y_{ij} - \sum_{ij} p_i p_j y_{ij}$$

$$= \sum_{ij} p_i\,\Delta p_j y_{ij} + \sum_{ij} p_j\,\Delta p_i y_{ij}, \text{ neglecting terms of order } \Delta^2$$

$$= 2\sum_i \Delta p_i \alpha_i$$

Thus the change in mean is the simple function of effects and changes in gene frequency we would expect.   Now let us see what would happen in the case of the non-random mating population.   We now have

$$\Delta\mu = \sum_{ij}(\Delta P_{ij})y_{ij}$$

The change in mean depends on genotypic frequencies as well as changes in gene frequency.   We therefore find the circumstances under which the equation

$$\Delta\mu = 2\sum_i \Delta p_i \alpha_i$$

holds identically in the y_{ij}'s.   We have

$$\Delta\mu = 2\sum_i \Delta p_i \sum_j A^{ij}R_j$$

$$= 2\sum_i \Delta p_i \sum_j A^{ij} \sum_k P_{jk}y_{jk}$$

$$= 2\sum_{jk}\left(\sum_i \Delta p_i A^{ij}\right)P_{jk}y_{jk}$$

This must equal

$$\sum_{jk} \Delta P_{jk} y_{jk}$$

Hence

$$\frac{\Delta P_{jj}}{P_{jj}} = 2 \sum_i \Delta p_i A^{ij}$$

$$\frac{\Delta P_{kk}}{P_{kk}} = 2 \sum_i \Delta p_i A^{ik}$$

$$(\Delta P_{jk} + \Delta P_{kj}) = 2P_{jk} \sum_i \Delta p_i A^{ij} + 2P_{kj} \sum_i \Delta p_i A^{ik}$$

so that, if we let $2Q_{jk} = P_{jk} + P_{kj} = 2P_{jk}$ which is the total frequency of the genotype $A_j A_k$, then $2\Delta Q_{jk} = \Delta P_{jk} + \Delta P_{kj}$ and $\Delta P_{jj}/P_{jj} + \Delta P_{kk}/P_{kk} = 2(\Delta Q_{jk}/Q_{jk})$ or

$$\Delta \log P_{jj} + \Delta \log P_{kk} = 2\Delta \log Q_{jk}$$

or

$$P_{jj} P_{kk} = \lambda_{jk} Q_{jk}^2$$

If the changes in population mean were such that they must, by reason of some other force, be equal to

$$2 \sum_i \Delta p_i \alpha_i$$

the relations between genotypic frequencies given above must hold. It is interesting to speculate about the existence of such a force and the path which the population would follow. This path can be visualized in the case of three alleles, by the use of triangular coordinates.

16.4 THE CHANGE IN POPULATION MEAN UNDER SELECTION

We have

$$\lambda_{jk} = \frac{P_{jk}^2}{P_{jj} P_{kk}}$$

so that

$$\log \lambda_{jk} = 2 \log P_{jk} - \log P_{jj} - \log P_{kk}$$

and

$$\frac{1}{\lambda_{jk}} \Delta \lambda_{jk} = \frac{2}{P_{jk}} \Delta P_{jk} - \frac{1}{P_{jj}} \Delta P_{jj} - \frac{1}{P_{kk}} \Delta P_{kk}$$

Hence

$$\frac{1}{P_{jk}} \Delta P_{jk} = \frac{1}{2} \left(\frac{1}{P_{jj}} \Delta P_{jj} + \frac{1}{P_{kk}} \Delta P_{kk} + \frac{1}{\lambda_{jk}} \Delta \lambda_{jk} \right)$$

and the changes in frequencies of heterozygotes are expressible in terms of changes in the frequencies of homozygotes and of the λ's.

It is interesting to note that the changes in genotypic frequencies can be expressed in terms of the changes in gene frequencies Δp_i and changes in the λ's, $\Delta\lambda_{jk}$.   For we have

$$\Delta P_{jj} + \sum_{k \neq j} \Delta P_{jk} = \Delta p_j$$

so

$$\Delta P_{jj} + \frac{1}{2}\sum_{k \neq j} P_{jk}\left(\frac{1}{P_{jj}}\Delta P_{jj} + \frac{1}{P_{kk}}\Delta P_{kk} + \frac{1}{\lambda_{jk}}\Delta\lambda_{jk}\right) = \Delta p_j$$

or

$$\Delta P_{jj}\left(1 + \frac{1}{2}\frac{\sum_{k \neq j} P_{jk}}{P_{jj}}\right) + \frac{1}{2}\sum_{k \neq j}\frac{P_{jk}}{P_{kk}}\Delta P_{kk} = \Delta p_j - \frac{1}{2}\sum_{k \neq j}\frac{P_{jk}}{\lambda_{jk}}\Delta\lambda_{jk}$$

or, if we let

$$\frac{\Delta P_{jj}}{P_{jj}} = v_j$$

$$\tfrac{1}{2}v_j(p_j + P_{jj}) + \frac{1}{2}\sum_{k \neq j} P_{jk}\,v_k = \Delta p_j - \frac{1}{2}\sum_{k \neq j}\frac{P_{jk}}{\lambda_{jk}}\Delta\lambda_{jk}$$

This equation can be written matrix-wise as

$$\mathbf{A}\mathbf{v} = \mathbf{T}$$

where

$$\mathbf{A} = \begin{pmatrix} p_1 + P_{11} & P_{12} & \cdots & P_{1s} \\ P_{12} & p_2 + P_{22} & \cdots & P_{2s} \\ \cdot & \cdot & \cdots & \cdot \\ \cdot & \cdot & \cdots & \cdot \\ \cdot & \cdot & \cdots & \cdot \\ P_{1s} & P_{2s} & \cdots & p_s + P_{ss} \end{pmatrix}, \qquad v = \begin{pmatrix} v_1 \\ v_2 \\ \cdot \\ \cdot \\ \cdot \\ v_s \end{pmatrix}$$

$$\mathbf{T} = \begin{pmatrix} 2\Delta p_1 - \sum_{k \neq 1}\dfrac{P_{1k}}{\lambda_{1k}}\Delta\lambda_{1k} \\ 2\Delta p_2 - \sum_{k \neq 2}\dfrac{P_{2k}}{\lambda_{2k}}\Delta\lambda_{2k} \\ \cdot \\ \cdot \\ \cdot \\ 2\Delta p_s - \sum_{k \neq s}\dfrac{P_{sk}}{\lambda_{sk}}\Delta\lambda_{sk} \end{pmatrix} = \begin{pmatrix} T_1 \\ T_2 \\ \cdot \\ \cdot \\ \cdot \\ T_s \end{pmatrix}$$

It is interesting that the matrix $\mathbf{A}$ is the matrix which occurred in the previous section in connection with the effects in the general non-random mating population.   Hence

$$\begin{pmatrix} \nu_1 \\ \nu_2 \\ \cdot \\ \nu_s \end{pmatrix} = (\mathbf{A}^{-1})\mathbf{T}$$

or

$$\nu_j = \sum_k A^{jk}T_k$$

Now consider the change in the population mean.   It is equal to

$$\sum_{ij} \Delta P_{ij}y_{ij} = \sum_i \Delta P_{ii}y_{ii} + \sum_{\substack{i,j \\ i \neq j}} \Delta P_{ij}y_{ij}$$

$$= \sum_i \Delta P_{ii}y_{ii} + \sum_{\substack{i,j \\ i \neq j}} P_{ij} \frac{\Delta P_{ij}}{P_{ij}} y_{ij}$$

$$= \sum_i \Delta P_{ii}y_{ii} + \frac{1}{2}\sum_{\substack{i,j \\ i \neq j}} P_{ij} \left(\frac{\Delta P_{ii}}{P_{ii}} + \frac{\Delta P_{jj}}{P_{jj}} + \frac{1}{\lambda_{ij}}\Delta\lambda_{ij} \right) y_{ij}$$

$$= \sum_i \nu_i P_{ii}y_{ii} + \frac{1}{2}\sum_{\substack{i,j \\ i \neq j}} P_{ij} \left(\nu_i + \nu_j + \frac{1}{\lambda_{ij}}\Delta\lambda_{ij} \right) y_{ij}$$

$$= \sum_i \nu_i p_i a_i + \frac{1}{2}\sum_{\substack{i,j \\ i \neq j}} P_{ij} \frac{\Delta\lambda_{ij}}{\lambda_{ij}} y_{ij}$$

But

$$\sum_i \nu_i p_i a_i = \sum_i \sum_k A^{ik}T_k p_i a_i$$

$$= \sum_k \left(\sum_i A^{ik}p_i a_i \right) T_k$$

$$= \sum_k \alpha_k T_k$$

Hence

$$\sum_{ij} \Delta P_{ij}y_{ij} = \sum_k \alpha_k \left(2\Delta p_k - \sum_{j \neq k} P_{kj} \frac{\Delta\lambda_{kj}}{\lambda_{kj}} \right) + \frac{1}{2}\sum_{\substack{i,j \\ i \neq j}} P_{ij} \frac{\Delta\lambda_{ij}}{\lambda_{ij}} y_{ij}$$

$$= \sum_k 2\Delta p_k \alpha_k + \frac{1}{2}\sum_{\substack{i,j \\ i \neq j}} P_{ij} \frac{\Delta\lambda_{ij}}{\lambda_{ij}} (y_{ij} - \alpha_i - \alpha_j)$$

Hence, if we denote $y_{ij} - \alpha_i - \alpha_j$ which is the dominance deviation attached to the genotype $A_i A_j$ by d_{ij}, we have

$$\Delta\mu = 2\sum_k \Delta p_k \alpha_k + \frac{1}{2}\sum_{\substack{i,j \\ i \neq j}} P_{ij} \frac{\Delta\lambda_{ij}}{\lambda_{ij}} d_{ij}$$

We note that, if d_{ij} equals zero for all i, j which are unequal, then there is no dominance, and

$$\Delta\mu = 2\sum_k \Delta p_k \alpha_k$$

In general the change in population mean consists of two parts; the first part, $2\sum_k \Delta p_k \alpha_k$, is that which can be attributed to the changes in gene frequency, and the second part, $\frac{1}{2}\sum_{i \neq j} P_{ij} \frac{\Delta\lambda_{ij}}{\lambda_{ij}} d_{ij}$, is that which can be attributed to the mating system.   The second part depends on the dominance deviations.   If there is no dominance, the change in mean is attributable solely to the changes in gene frequency.   If the changed population were obtained by some sort of selection in a random mating population followed by random mating of selected individuals, the change in mean would be equal exactly to $2\sum_k \Delta p_k \alpha_k$ because the λ_{jk}'s would be unity and would not change.   If on the other hand the changed population arises by some sort of assortative mating with differential reproduction, as seems likely in many selection situations, then the change in population mean cannot be inferred from the changes in gene frequency.   I regard the above equation for $\Delta\mu$ as the fundamental or basic equation of selection theory.   The equation can be extended.

The proof given above is possibly tedious to the reader.   It is the one by which I originally obtained the result and it appeals to me as an exercise in matrix manipulation.   Dr. Kimura (private communication) has developed a simpler proof based on quantities he has devised called "coefficients of departure from random mating" given by

$$\theta_{ij} = P_{ij}/p_i p_j$$

It seems possible that these quantities are more intrinsic to the behavior of non-random mating populations, and we look forward to publications by Dr. Kimura.

16.5 FISHER'S FUNDAMENTAL THEOREM OF NATURAL SELECTION

Fisher (1930, 1941) has made an ingenious application of the theory given in this chapter to the theory of natural selection.   It will be the purpose of this section to develop the fundamental theorem Fisher obtained.   We shall present a proof from first principles for the case of one locus and two alleles.

Consider the population $PAA + 2QAa + Raa$ where there are no restrictions about P, Q, and R except that they be non-negative and that $P + 2Q + R$ equals unity.   Suppose that, crediting each parent with one half of its actual offspring, each AA individual has $(1+m_{AA})$ offspring, each Aa individual has $(1+m_{Aa})$ offspring and each aa individual has $(1+m_{aa})$ offspring.   The quantities m_{AA}, m_{Aa}, and m_{aa} may be called the reproductive values of individuals of the respective genotypes.   We assume these reproductive values to remain constant at least over the period in the history of the population that will be considered.   The resulting population will contain

and

$$[2P(1 + m_{AA}) + 2Q(1 + m_{Aa})] \ A \text{ genes}$$

$$[2Q(1 + m_{Aa}) + 2R(1 + m_{aa})] \ a \text{ genes}$$

and we are concerned with the reproductive value of this resulting population.   It is quite obvious, since individual genes per se do not have reproductive values, that we can say nothing in general about the average reproductive value of the population without specifying how these genes are combined into genotypes.   Furthermore, how they are combined into genotypes depends on the mating system which the population follows. An exception to this would be the case when m_{AA}, m_{Aa}, and m_{aa} exhibit no dominance, for then we could attach a reproductive value to each gene, and the average reproductive value would be twice the average induced reproductive value of the genes.

Let

and

$$p = P + Q, \quad \text{the original frequency of } A$$

with

$$q = Q + R, \quad \text{the original frequency of } a$$

$$p + q = 1$$

Let μ denote the mean reproductive value of the original population, so that

$$\mu = Pm_{AA} + 2Qm_{Aa} + Rm_{aa}$$

Let

$$m_{AA} = \mu + 2\alpha_A + d_{AA}$$
$$m_{Aa} = \mu + \alpha_A + \alpha_a + d_{Aa}$$
$$m_{aa} = \mu + 2\alpha_a + d_{aa}$$

where

α_A is the average effect of A on reproductive value

α_a is the average effect of a on reproductive value

and the d's are dominance deviations.

It follows from the earlier part of this chapter that α_A and α_a are given by the two equations,

$$(2P + Q)\alpha_A + Q\alpha_a = pa_A$$
$$Q\alpha_A + (Q + 2R)\alpha_a = qa_a$$

where

$$a_A = \frac{1}{p}(Pm_{AA} + Qm_{Aa}) - \mu, \quad \text{the excess associated with } A$$

and

$$a_a = \frac{1}{q}(Qm_{Aa} + Rm_{aa}) - \mu, \quad \text{the excess associated with } a$$

Also, as a consequence of the definitions by least squares of α_A and α_a, we have

$$Pd_{AA} + Qd_{Aa} = 0$$
$$Qd_{Aa} + Rd_{aa} = 0$$

with, of course,

$$Pd_{AA} + 2Qd_{Aa} + Rd_{aa} = 0$$

If we let p', q' denote the frequencies of A, a, respectively, in the resulting population, we have

$$p' = \frac{P(1 + m_{AA}) + Q(1 + m_{Aa})}{1 + \mu}$$

$$q' = \frac{Q(1 + m_{Aa}) + R(1 + m_{aa})}{1 + \mu}$$

or, using the values for the m's in terms of mean, effects, and dominance deviations,

$$p' = \frac{(P + Q) + p(\mu + a_A)}{1 + \mu} = p + \frac{pa_A}{1 + \mu}$$

$$q' = \frac{(Q + R) + q(\mu + a_a)}{1 + \mu} = q + \frac{qa_a}{1 + \mu}$$

Hence, if we write

$$p' = p + \Delta p$$
$$q' = q + \Delta q$$

we have

$$\Delta p = \frac{pa_A}{1 + \mu} = -\Delta q = - \frac{qa_a}{1 + \mu}$$

Now suppose the resulting population is

$$P'AA + 2Q'Aa + R'aa$$

Then the mean reproductive value, μ' equal to $\mu + \delta\mu$, is equal to

$$P'(\mu + 2\alpha_A + d_{AA}) + 2Q'(\mu + \alpha_A + \alpha_a + d_{Aa}) + R'(\mu + 2\alpha_a + d_{aa})$$

$$= \mu + 2(P' + Q')\alpha_A + 2(Q' + R')\alpha_a + P'd_{AA} + 2Q'd_{Aa} + R'd_{aa}$$

$$= \mu + 2p'\alpha_A + 2q'\alpha_a + P'd_{AA} + 2Q'd_{Aa} + R'd_{aa}$$

$$= \mu + 2p\alpha_A + 2q\alpha_a + \frac{2pa_A\alpha_A + 2qa_a\alpha_a}{1 + \mu} + P'd_{AA} + 2Q'd_{Aa} + R'd_{aa}$$

$$= \mu + \frac{\sigma_A^2(m)}{1 + \mu} + P'd_{AA} + 2Q'd_{Aa} + R'd_{aa}$$

where $\sigma_A^2(m)$ is the additive variance of the reproductive values. If there is no dominance for the reproductive values, then the d's are zero, and we have the simple relationship

$$\delta\mu = \frac{\sigma_A^2(m)}{1 + \mu}$$

A result quite similar to this is quoted by Crow and Kimura (1955) from dittoed material by Wright. Instead of working with the reproductive values as defined here, we could work with fitness denoted by f, where the functional relation between f and m is

$$e^f = 1 + m$$

Let the mean of f in the original population be v and in the resulting population $v + \Delta v$. Then

$$e^f = e^{v+f-v} \cong e^v[1 + (f - v)] = 1 + \mu + (m - \mu)$$

approximately, so that small changes are related as follows:

$$\Delta m = e^v \, \Delta f = (1 + \mu) \, \Delta f$$

Hence

$$\sigma_A^2(m) = (1 + \mu)^2 \, \sigma_A^2(f)$$

and

$$\Delta v = \frac{\Delta\mu}{1 + \mu} = \frac{\sigma_A^2(m)}{(1 + \mu)^2} = \sigma_A^2(f)$$

In this simple case the change in mean of fitness is equal to the additive variance in fitness. This result has been shown by the above argument to hold regardless of the mating system if there is no dominance in reproductive value and hence fitness. In this case, of course, the additive variance is equal to the total genotypic variance. It must not be supposed that it is necessary that there be no dominance in order that this result should hold.

In fact, we see that the result will hold if and only if

$$P'd_{AA} + 2Q'd_{Aa} + R'd_{aa} = 0$$

or

$$\Delta Pd_{AA} + 2\Delta Qd_{Aa} + \Delta Rd_{aa} = 0$$

It seems to me that Fisher exhibited great insight in recognizing that this condition could hold over a wider class of circumstances. I have found Fisher (1930, 1941) entirely obscure with regard to his derivation of the result. The following simple argument, however, appears to be correct.

In order that the result may hold, we must delimit the possible solutions to the following equation:

$$\Delta Pd_{AA} + 2\Delta Qd_{Aa} + \Delta Rd_{aa} = 0$$

But by definition of the dominance deviations

$$Pd_{AA} + Qd_{Aa} = 0$$
$$Qd_{Aa} + Rd_{aa} = 0$$

so

$$d_{AA} = -\frac{Q}{P}d_{Aa}, \qquad d_{aa} = -\frac{Q}{R}d_{Aa}$$

so

$$\Delta Pd_{AA} + 2\Delta Qd_{Aa} + \Delta Rd_{aa}$$

$$= \left[\Delta P\left(-\frac{Q}{P}\right) + 2\Delta Q + \Delta R\left(-\frac{Q}{R}\right)\right]d_{Aa}$$

$$= \left[\frac{2\Delta Q}{Q} - \frac{\Delta P}{P} - \frac{\Delta R}{R}\right]Qd_{Aa}$$

The change in population mean fitness is therefore equal to the additive variance in fitness if

$$\frac{2\Delta Q}{Q} = \frac{\Delta P}{P} + \frac{\Delta R}{R}$$

or

$$Q^2 = \lambda PR$$

We have therefore completed the derivation of Fisher's fundamental theorem of natural selection that

The rate of increase of fitness of a species is equal to the additive variance in fitness, provided *that the mating system is such that Q^2/PR remains constant*.

It seems appropriate to give some notes on this result. The theorem was first stated by Fisher (1930) without the condition, and it seemed to me that one could easily be led to the conclusion that it was universally true, at least as regards non-random mating. The result for a random mating population which is inherent in the theorem as stated above, since Q^2/PR is then always equal to unity, has been proved in other ways by Wright. The limiting condition was given by Fisher (1941), with the statement that, only if Q^2/PR, which he denoted by λ, remains constant, can the changes in genotypic frequencies be ascribed to the changes in gene frequency.

The above derivation is of value in indicating that, if the theorem is to hold, the changes in P, Q, R must be related to the dominance deviations d_{AA}, d_{Aa}, and d_{aa} in a particular way. For example,

$$\Delta Q = \frac{d_{aa} - d_{AA}}{2d_{Aa} - d_{AA} - d_{aa}} \, \Delta p$$

A complete statement of the change in mean reproductive value can be derived from the general equation of the previous section, which holds for any measurable attribute, namely:

$$\Delta \mu = 2 \sum_k \Delta p_k \alpha_k + \frac{1}{2} \sum_{\substack{ij \\ i \neq j}} P_{ij} \frac{\Delta \lambda_{ij}}{\lambda_{ij}} d_{ij}$$

We may let the measurable attribute be reproductive value. If we let m_{ij} be the reproductive value of the genotype $A_i A_j$, the changes in gene frequency are given by

$$\Delta p_i = \frac{\sum_j P_{ij}(1 + m_{ij})}{1 + \mu} - p_i$$

$$= \frac{\sum_j P_{ij} m_{ij} - p_i \mu}{1 + \mu}$$

$$= \frac{p_i a_i}{1 + \mu}$$

Hence

$$\Delta\mu = \frac{2 \sum_k p_k a_k \alpha_k}{1 + \mu} + \frac{1}{2} \sum_{\substack{ij \\ i \neq j}} P_{ij} \frac{\Delta\lambda_{ij}}{\lambda_{ij}} d_{ij}$$

$$= \frac{\sigma_A^2(m)}{1 + \mu} + \frac{1}{2} \sum_{\substack{ij \\ i \neq j}} P_{ij} \frac{\Delta\lambda_{ij}}{\lambda_{ij}} d_{ij}$$

and, translating into terms of fitness, we have

$$\Delta v = \sigma_A^2(f) + \frac{1}{2} \sum_{\substack{ij \\ i \neq j}} P_{ij} \frac{\Delta\lambda_{ij}}{\lambda_{ij}} d_{ij}(f)$$

where $d_{ij}(f)$ is the dominance deviation for fitness.

It is interesting to speculate on the possible extension of the result to the case of more than one locus.   It is likely that, if the appropriate λ quantities remain constant, the rate of increase in fitness will involve both additive and additive × additive (see Chapter 19) components of genotypic variance of fitness.

Fisher's derivation which I have been unable to follow was in terms of Malthusian parameters of fitness, which are based on the survival and reproductive rates of individuals of the possible ages.   He also used the concept of the present value of future offspring of an individual which, it seems, must depend on the gene with which the genes of the individual combine, and hence on the mating system.   However, if the derivation given above is acceptable, this concept need not be introduced.

The range of validity of the mathematical result per se can be inferred from the derivation above.   It is clear that the population must be such that reproductive values or fitnesses do not change with infinitesimal changes in genotypic frequency, and this seems highly likely.   It is possible, of course, that, if a population changes markedly in genotypic frequencies and there is assortative mating, the mating possibilities and hence reproductive values of individuals with some genotypes may change markedly. One can imagine, for instance, that humans with particular attributes find it increasingly difficult with time to find mates.

The derivation given above has utilized non-overlapping generations, but we may assume safely that it will hold with overlapping generations.

It is surprising that little comment has been made in the literature on the theorem.   Its utility for random mating populations is entirely clear. One may wonder, however, to what extent it is applicable to real biological populations, in which some sort of assortative mating is probably quite general.   That a population should change in genotypic frequencies in such a way that Q^2/PR, or its multi-allelic analogues, should remain constant seems unlikely.   On the other hand, the deviations from random mating may be such as to make these quantities nearly constant.   In this connection the reader should consult Chapter 22 in which some results by Fisher on mild assortative mating are given.

The reader is referred to Crow and Kimura (1955) for detailed discussion of the whole question from other points of view.   They give a derivation of the theorem for random mating populations.   The work by the present author referred to in their paper is that of this chapter.   They include also the cases when the population mean fitness changes with time and when there are small mutational effects on fitness.   They also go into the stochastic examination of the matter in which random sampling variations are given their proper role.   The 1941 paper by Fisher contains an interesting example in which intense selection occurs with no change in average fitness of the species.   Fisher's 1930 book contains extensive discussion of the implications of the theorem.

REFERENCE

Crow, J. F., and M. Kimura.   1955.   Some genetic problems in natural populations.   *Proc. 3rd Birk. Symp. on Math. Stat. Prob.*, **4**, 1–22.

Fisher, R. A.   1930.   *The genetical theory of natural selection.*   Clarendon Press, Oxford.

Fisher, R. A.   1941.   Average excess and average effect of a gene substitution.   *Ann. Eugen. Lond.*, **11**, 53–63.

PROBLEMS

1. Consider the population

$$0.4AA + 0.4Aa + 0.2aa$$

What are its additive variance and its dominance variance when the genotypic values are as follows: AA, 2; Aa, 1; aa, 0?

2. Suppose the genotypic values in question 1 are 1, 1, and 0, respectively, for AA, Aa, and aa.   Do likewise.

3. Specify the way in which the population in question 1 would change with changing gene frequency if λ stays constant.

4. From the result of question 3 evaluate the additive effect and the excess of the substitution A for a at gene frequencies for A of 0.2, 0.25, and 0.3, and relate these to the change in population mean.

5. Consider the population

$$0.3AA + 0.4Aa + 0.3aa$$

with genotypic values of 1, 1, 0, for AA, Aa, and aa.   Evaluate the effect of the substitution A for a.   Suppose the gene frequency of A changes to 0.6 but the value of λ stays constant.   What is the effect of the substitution in the resultant population?   Comment on the result.

6. Consider the following population:

Genotype	Frequency	Genotypic Value
aa	0.45	3
ab	0.10	3
ac	0.10	2
bb	0.15	2
bc	0.15	1
cc	0.05	0

Evaluate the additive variance and the dominance variance for this population.

7. What would be the genotypic frequencies of the population which results from the population in question 6 by changing the gene frequencies to 0.5, 0.3, and 0.2 for a, b, and c, respectively, under the condition that the λ's remain constant?

8. Consider the random mating population

$$p^2 AA + 2pqAa + q^2 aa$$

with genotypic values d, h, r for AA, Aa, aa, respectively, and the population resulting from this one by selfing for 1, 2, 3, $\cdots$ generations. Obtain the following as they are related to generations of selfing:

> Additive variance
> Dominance variance
> Genotypic variance
> Additive variance/genotypic variance
> Dominance variance/additive variance

What happens in the special case $d - h = h - r$? What happens in the case $p = q$? Discuss the results.

9. Consider the population

$$p^2 AA + 2pqAa + q^2 aa$$

and suppose it is inbred by successive selfing. Plot F and λ against the generation number, and λ against F.

10. Discuss the relative merits of λ and F for describing the progress of a population under selfing.

11. Do as in question 10 for full-sibbing.

CHAPTER 17

Correlations between Relatives under Inbreeding with One Locus Segregating

17.1 INTRODUCTION

In previous chapters we have dealt with the partition of variance in random mating populations and the correlations between relatives expressed in terms of the components of phenotypic variance. It will be recalled that we do in fact restrict our results on correlations between relatives to the case in which there is no inbreeding, that is, the case when there is zero probability that the two genes possessed by an individual are identical by descent.

The results on random mating populations are of value in indicating the sort of things that can happen in a real population. It will be remembered that the term "random mating" should be regarded in general as including:

1. Actual mating at random occurs; i.e., every male in the population has the same probability of mating with every female, regardless of their respective genotypes.

2. Every mating has the same distribution of number of offspring.

3. The offspring are a random sample of the formal genetic possibilities of the cross.

4. Offspring are equally viable; for example, there are no lethal or semilethal genes.

5. There is no selection among parents or among offspring.

All these aspects lead, of course, to the two relationships:

Prob (A_iA_j mates with A_kA_l) = Prob (individual is A_iA_j)

$$\times \text{Prob (individual is } A_kA_l)$$

and

Offspring array of the mating $A_iA_j \times A_kA_l$

$$= \tfrac{1}{4}A_iA_k + \tfrac{1}{4}A_iA_l + \tfrac{1}{4}A_jA_k + \tfrac{1}{4}A_jA_l$$

We know that these conditions are rarely if ever satisfied, and we can expect that in a real population there is homogamy or associative mating maybe of like to like, or in domesticated animals at times mating of unlikes, and selection both with respect to which individuals become parents and also among the offspring, and inbreeding in which matings are based partially at least on consanguinity.

Our solutions for random mating populations must then be regarded as solutions for an idealized situation which real populations approximate to a greater or less degree. It may perhaps be asked why we should spend so much time on a particular situation and then proceed to describe all the limitations of the applicability of the solution to real populations. The answer is twofold: First, the random mating situation can be regarded as a limiting situation which will give an approximate solution to real situations, and second, the random mating situation is one that can be worked out and yields readily comprehensible results, whereas other situations are more difficult. It is to be hoped that the next fifty years will see the examination of many simple situations which correspond in an intuitive sense more closely to the real world.

In this chapter we consider what happens when there is mating of individuals on the basis of consanguinity rather than at random.

We can distinguish between two cases. In one case we have a population which is at equilibrium under a mating system which includes partial mating at random and partial mating by consanguinity. Here we are brought to an abrupt stop very quickly because in our present state of knowledge we know little about what mating systems lead to equilibrium,[*] and we may also anticipate that there are several mating systems which have as their result a population whose genotypic array is constant from generation to generation and for which the inbreeding coefficient is constant. In the second case we can envisage an initial population from which populations are developed by particular systems of inbreeding. We shall consider the second case and, to be more specific, shall take the case in which the population

$$p^2 AA + 2pqAa + q^2 aa, \qquad p + q = 1$$

is mated at random initially and then subsequent generations are obtained by selfing, by full-sib mating, and by parent–offspring matings. The level of generality here considered may strike many readers as being too low, and the only answer we can make is that the level of generality at which a problem is tackled depends on how the results fall out. If it is easy to get results on this level of generality, then we would be unsatisfied with them and would attempt a higher level of generality. If on the other hand

---

[*] Except for simple mixtures of pure inbreeding systems.

the results at this level are not easy to obtain and comprehend, we shall not pursue the matter further. It is to be hoped, of course, that other workers will find a "key" which will unlock the door to results of increasing generality.

17.2 GENERAL RESULTS FOR ANY SYSTEM OF INBREEDING

Initially the results given below were worked out with genotypic values for AA, Aa, aa taken to be d, h, and r, respectively, but in all cases it comes out that the results are in a reasonably simple form in terms of $d - r$ and $d - 2h + r$. We therefore use coded genotypic values as follows:

Genotype	Coded Genotypic Value
AA	y
Aa	$(y-x)/2$
aa	0

In this case

$$y = d - r$$

and

$$x = d + r - 2h$$

From Chapter 5 we know that the genotypic array after n generations of inbreeding is as given in Table 17.1. The total genotypic mean in generation n is therefore equal to

$$(p^2 + F_n pq)y + 2(1 - F_n)\, pq(y - x)/2$$
$$= py - (1 - F_n)pqx = \mu_n \quad \text{say}$$

TABLE 17.1

Genotype	Genotypic Value	Frequency
AA	y	$p^2 + F_n pq$
Aa	$(y-x)/2$	$2(1 - F_n)pq$
aa	0	$q^2 + F_n pq$

The genotypic variance in generation n is equal to

$$(p^2 + F_n pq)y^2 + 2(1 - F_n)\, pq \frac{(y - x)^2}{4} - \mu_n^2$$
$$= \left(\frac{1 + F_n}{2}\right) pqy^2 + (1 - F_n)(p - q)\, pqxy + \left(\frac{1 - F_n}{2}\right) pqx^2$$
$$- (1 - F_n)^2 p^2 q^2 x^2$$
$$= V_n, \quad \text{say}$$

The above representation of the situation is useful in that if there is no dominance, a case of possibly unlikely occurrence, but nevertheless one of interest, then x is zero, and we would then have

$$\mu_n = py$$

$$V_n = \left(\frac{1 + F_n}{2}\right) pqy^2$$

If further we let $y = 2a$, then the variance in generation n is $V_n = (1 + F_n)$ $\times 2pqa^2$. It will be recalled that under the present circumstances the genotypic variance in the original population is $2pqa^2$.

The formulas of Chapter 16 may be used to show that the partition of genotypic variance in generation n is as follows:

Additive variance $= (1 + F_n)2pq\alpha^2$ where α is the average effect of the gene substitution in generation n

$$= \left(\frac{1 + F_n}{2}\right) pqy^2 + (1 - F_n)(p - q)pqxy$$

$$+ \frac{(1 - F_n)^2}{2(1 + F_n)} pq(p - q)^2 x^2$$

and

Dominance variance $= \left(\frac{1 - F_n}{1 + F_n}\right) [F_n + (1 - F_n)^2 pq] \, pqx^2$

It is of interest to note for future reference what happens with p equal to q, i.e. p equal to $\frac{1}{2}$. This case arises when the original population is an F_2 resulting from two completely inbred lines. For this case we have

$$\text{Additive variance} = \left(\frac{1 + F_n}{8}\right) y^2$$

and

$$\text{Dominance variance} = \frac{(1 - F_n^2)}{16} x^2$$

If for example the genotypic values for AA, Aa, and aa are 2, $1+k$, 0, respectively, then y equals 2, and x equals $2 - 2(1 + k)$ or $-2k$, so that

$$\text{Additive variance} = \frac{1 + F_n}{2}$$

and

$$\text{Dominance variance} = \frac{(1 - F_n^2)}{4} k^2$$

If again we denote genotypic values by u, au, and $-u$, respectively, for the genotypes AA, Aa, and aa, respectively, then with, of course, gene frequency of variable loci equal to one half

$$\text{Additive variance} = \left(\frac{1 + F_n}{2}\right) u^2$$

and

$$\text{Dominance variance} = \frac{(1 - F_n^2)}{4} a^2 u^2$$

The quantity a here has been termed by Comstock and Robinson (1952) and others who have worked with it as the degree of dominance. It has been applied as we shall see later to the case of a number of factors among which there is no epistasis.

17.3 SELFING

The problem we consider here is that we have a population

$$p^2 AA + 2pq Aa + q^2 aa, \qquad p + q = 1$$

that matings in the initial or zeroth generation are made at random and then subsequent generations are obtained by selfing.

TABLE 17.2

ELEMENTARY ASPECTS OF SELFING

Parent	Genotypic Value	Sibship	Mean Genotypic Value of Offspring
AA	y	AA	y
Aa	$(y-x)/2$	$\frac{1}{4}AA + \frac{1}{2}Aa + \frac{1}{4}aa$	$\frac{1}{4}(2y-x)$
aa	0	aa	0

It is easy to see that, if by $\mathcal{G}_0$, $\mathcal{G}_1$, $\mathcal{G}_2$, etc., we denote the genotypic arrays in generations 0, 1, 2, etc., then

$$\mathcal{G}_0 = p^2 AA + 2pq Aa + q^2 aa$$

$$\mathcal{G}_1 = \left(p^2 + \frac{pq}{2}\right) AA + pq Aa + \left(q^2 + \frac{pq}{2}\right) aa$$

$$\mathcal{G}_2 = (p^2 + \tfrac{3}{4}pq) AA + \tfrac{1}{2}pq Aa + (q^2 + \tfrac{3}{4}pq) aa$$

$$\cdots \cdots \cdots \cdots \cdots \cdots \cdots \cdots$$

$$\mathcal{G}_n = \left[p^2 + \left(1 - \frac{1}{2^n}\right)pq\right] AA + (\tfrac{1}{2})^n 2pq Aa + \left[q^2 + \left(1 - \frac{1}{2^n}\right)pq\right] aa$$

or $\mathcal{G}_n = (p^2 + F_n pq)AA + 2pq(1 - F_n)Aa + (q^2 + F_n pq)aa$

Hence we have the following covariances between relatives:

1. *Parent–offspring:* i.e. parent in generation n and offspring in generation $n+1$.

$$\text{Cov}(P, O) = (p^2 + F_n pq)y^2 + 2pq(1 - F_n)\frac{(y - x)(2y - x)}{8} - \mu_n\mu_{n+1}$$

$$= (p^2 + F_n pq)y^2 + pq(1 - F_n)\frac{(y - x)(2y - x)}{4}$$

$$- [py - (1 - F_n)pqx][py - (1 - F_{n+1})pqx]$$

$$= \left(\frac{1 + F_n}{2}\right)pqy^2 + \tfrac{3}{4}(1 - F_n)(p - q)pqxy + \frac{(1 - F_n)}{4}pqx^2$$

$$- \frac{(1 - F_n)^2}{2}p^2q^2x^2$$

using the fact that $1 - F_{n+1} = \tfrac{1}{2}(1 - F_n)$.

2. *Covariance of full-sibs in generation $n+1$.*

$$\text{Cov}(F.S) = (p^2 + F_n pq)y^2 + 2pq(1 - F_n)\tfrac{1}{16}(2y - x)^2 - \mu_{n+1}^2$$

$$= (p^2 + F_n pq)y^2 + \frac{pq}{8}(1 - F_n)(2y - x)^2$$

$$- [py - \tfrac{1}{2}(1 - F_n)pqx]^2$$

$$= \left(\frac{1 + F_n}{2}\right)pqy^2 + \left(\frac{1 - F_n}{2}\right)(p - q)pqxy + \left(\frac{1 - F_n}{8}\right)pqx^2$$

$$- \frac{(1 - F_n)^2}{4}p^2q^2x^2$$

3. *Covariance of parent in generation n and offspring in generation $n+s$.* This comes out to be

$$\text{Cov}(P, O_s) = \left(\frac{1 + F_n}{2}\right)pqy^2 + \left(\frac{1 - F_n}{2}\right)\left(1 + \frac{1}{2^s}\right)(p - q)pqxy$$

$$+ \frac{1}{2^{s+1}}(1 - F_n)pqx^2 - \frac{1}{2^s}(1 - F_n)^2p^2q^2x^2$$

4. *General formula.* In general we may consider the covariance of kth generation means of nth generation individuals, and kth generation means of n'th generation individuals within $(k-1)$th generation families (cf. Horner, 1951). Diagrammatically this can be represented as shown in Figure 17.1.

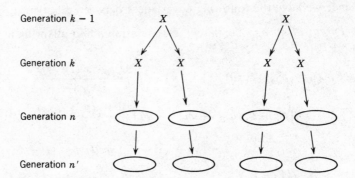

FIGURE 17.1 Diagrammatic representation of general situation with selfing: X's denote individuals, ⬭ denote populations, n' being greater than n (see text).

The basis of computations are given in Table 17.3.

The covariance which may be denoted by Cov $(X, X' | k, k-1; n, n')$ is equal to

$$2(1 - F_{k-1})\, pq \left[\tfrac{1}{4} y^2 + \frac{1}{2} \left(\frac{y}{2} - \frac{x}{2^{n-k+1}} \right) \left(\frac{y}{2} - \frac{x}{2^{n'-k+1}} \right) \right.$$

$$\left. - \left(\frac{y}{2} - \frac{x}{2^{n-k+2}} \right) \left(\frac{y}{2} - \frac{x}{2^{n'-k+2}} \right) \right]$$

$$= 2(1 - F_{k-1})\, pq \left(\tfrac{1}{8} y^2 + \frac{1}{2^{n+n'-2k+4}}\, x^2 \right)$$

TABLE 17.3

COMPUTATION OF GENERAL COVARIANCE (see text)

Generation $k-1$		Generation k Genotype	Mean of Generation n Individuals	Mean of Generation n' Individuals
Genotypes	Frequency			
AA	$p^2 + F_{k-1} pq$	AA	y	y
Aa	$2(1 - F_{k-1}) pq$	$\tfrac{1}{4} AA$	y	y
		$\tfrac{1}{2} Aa$	$\dfrac{y}{2} - \dfrac{x}{2^{n-k+1}}$	$\dfrac{y}{2} - \dfrac{x}{2^{n'-k+1}}$
		$\tfrac{1}{4} aa$	0	0
aa	$q^2 + F_{k-1} pq$	aa	0	0

Also because the system of inbreeding is selfing and F_{k-1} is the coefficient of inbreeding in the $(k-1)$th generation, the value of F_{k-1} is given by the relationship

$$(1 - F_{k-1}) = \tfrac{1}{2}(1 - F_{k-2}) = \quad \text{etc.}$$

So

$$(1 - F_{k-1}) = \frac{1}{2^{k-1}}$$

In the special case of an F_2 population† arising from two inbred lines, p equals q equals $\tfrac{1}{2}$, and the additive and dominance variance are, respectively,

$$\sigma_A^2 = 2pq[p(d - h) + q(h - r)]^2$$
$$= 2\,\tfrac{1}{2}\,\tfrac{1}{2}\,(\tfrac{1}{2}y)^2 = \tfrac{1}{8}y^2$$
$$\sigma_D^2 = p^2q^2(d - 2h + r)^2$$
$$= \tfrac{1}{4}\,\tfrac{1}{4}\,x^2 = \tfrac{1}{16}x^2$$

Hence in this case

$$\text{Cov}\,(X, X' | k, k-1; n, n') = \frac{1}{2^k}\,\sigma_A^2 + \frac{1}{2^{n+n'-k}}\,\sigma_D^2$$

To convert this formula into the language of the plant geneticist who works with F_2, F_3, F_4, F_N populations obtained by successive selfing, we merely note that

$$N = n + 2, \qquad N' = n' + 2, \qquad K = k + 2$$

and the formula for the covariance of F_K means of F_N individuals and $F_{N'}$ individuals within F_{K-1} families is

$$\frac{1}{2^{K-2}}\,\sigma_A^2 + \frac{1}{2^{N+N'-K-2}}\,\sigma_D^2$$

The particular values of this formula for early generations of selfing of an F_2 population are given in Table 17.4 adapted from Horner, Comstock, and Robinson (1955).

As an example of the interpretation of Table 17.4, the entry under $N = 4$, $N' = 4$, $K = 4$ is the covariance of individuals of the F_4 population with individuals of the F_4 population, these individuals being classified by the F_4 population, within the F_3 population. Hence it is the variance of F_4 individuals within F_3 families. The entry $N = 4$, $N' = 5$, $K = 3$, is the covariance of the F_4 progeny means of F_3 individuals with the F_5

---

† It may be a bit confusing to some readers to see F_2 as the coefficient of inbreeding in generation 2 and as the designation of a particular population.

TABLE 17.4

COVARIANCES OF MEANS OF F_N INDIVIDUALS AND $F_{N'}$ INDIVIDUALS FOR F_K INDIVIDUALS WITHIN F_{K-1} FAMILIES (VARIANCES GIVEN BY $KN = N'$)

The first number of the doublet is the coefficient of σ_A^2 and the second number the coefficient of σ_D^2

		N'			
N	K	2	3	4	5
2	2	$(1, 1)$	$(1, \frac{1}{2})$	$(1, \frac{1}{4})$	$(1, \frac{1}{8})$
3	2		$(1, \frac{1}{4})$	$(1, \frac{1}{8})$	$(1, \frac{1}{16})$
3	3		$(\frac{1}{2}, \frac{1}{2})$	$(\frac{1}{2}, \frac{1}{4})$	$(\frac{1}{2}, \frac{1}{8})$
4	2			$(1, \frac{1}{16})$	$(1, \frac{1}{32})$
4	3			$(\frac{1}{2}, \frac{1}{8})$	$(\frac{1}{2}, \frac{1}{16})$
4	4			$(\frac{1}{4}, \frac{1}{4})$	$(\frac{1}{4}, \frac{1}{8})$
5	2				$(1, \frac{1}{64})$
5	3				$(\frac{1}{2}, \frac{1}{32})$
5	4				$(\frac{1}{4}, \frac{1}{16})$
5	5				$(\frac{1}{8}, \frac{1}{8})$

progeny means of the same F_3 individuals within F_2 families. Also it may be noted that the variances (or covariances) of F_k progeny means evaluated in particular generations within F_{k-2} families is equal to the variance (or covariance) of F_k progeny means within F_{k-1} families plus the variance or covariance of F_{k-1} means with F_{k-2} families, and so on. Hence, for example, the variance of F_4 progeny means of F_5 individuals within F_2 families is equal to $\frac{1}{4}\sigma_A^2 + \frac{1}{16}\sigma_D^2$ (the variance of F_4 means within F_3 families) plus $\frac{1}{2}\sigma_A^2 + \frac{1}{32}\sigma_D^2$ (the variance of F_3 means within F_2 families), i.e. is equal to $\frac{3}{4}\sigma_A^2 + \frac{3}{32}\sigma_D^2$.

17.4 UTILITY OF ABOVE RESULTS

It is clear, if we have a population with one variable locus with two alleles which has random mating structure and is inbred by selfing, that we can estimate the quantities

$$pqy^2$$

$$(p-q)pqxy$$

$$pqx^2$$

and

$$p^2q^2x^2$$

Hence we can estimate pq, y^2, $(p-q)xy$, and x^2, and hence the additive and dominance variance in the original population. It is not of course necessary to take recourse to selfing to estimate the original additive and dominance variances: We need merely to obtain the parent–offspring and full-sib covariances. The degree of dominance is defined as

$$\frac{Aa - aa}{\frac{1}{2}(AA - aa)} - 1$$

which takes the value of zero with no dominance, and the value of unity with complete dominance; it is equal to $\left[\left(\dfrac{y - x}{2}\right)\Big/\dfrac{y}{2}\right] - 1 = -\dfrac{x}{y}$ and is estimated apart from sign by $(x^2/y^2)^{1/2}$. The fact that this is especially easy with populations in which gene frequency is one half does not limit the result to such populations. The result can be obtained with arbitrary gene frequency. A special reason why the methodology is applicable to F_2 populations arising from two inbred lines is that under such circumstances there will be exactly two alleles at a locus.

It is clear that it would be desirable to remove the limitation that there should be two alleles at the locus, as well as the already removed limitation that the gene frequency be equal to one half. The restriction to one variable locus is at present one imposed by our order of presentation. It is rather clear intuitively that, if one has an arbitrary number of loci which are segregating independently and between which there is no epistacy, the results may be extended merely by summation over all the loci. This aspect will be covered in a later chapter, wherein also some of the effects of linkage and epistacy will be discussed.

It may be noted finally that Mather (1949) has covered some of the topics discussed above. His notation is to use d, h, and $-d$ for the genotypic values of AA, Aa, and aa, respectively, so that our y becomes $2d$ in Mather's notation and our x becomes $-2h$ in Mather's notation. He uses D for $\frac{1}{8}y^2(=d^2/2)$ and H for $\frac{1}{16}x^2(=h^2/4)$. It is unfortunate that there are so many different notations in the field. The history of notations as the author knows it is as follows:

	AA	Aa	aa
Fisher, 1918	a	d	$-a$
Mather, 1949 (and in earlier papers)	d	h	$-d$
Comstock and Robinson, 1952 (and in earlier papers)	u	au	$-u$

The notation the author has used in many places is d, h, and r, respectively, so as to avoid possible confusion with the above which are already well represented in the literature. In the present chapter these are replaced by

y, $(y-x)/2$, and 0, respectively. It is true that the case of no dominance is dealt with easily in all cases: With Fisher's notation we put $d = 0$, with Mather's $h = 0$, with Comstock et al.'s notation we put $a = 0$, and with the one adopted here we put $x = 0$. The notations given above suffer from a suggestiveness that the homozygote AA is always greater than the homozygote aa because some people will tend to regard a, d, or u, as the case may be, as a positive number. Mather's choice of symbols for variances suffers from the defect that the letter D will tend to be associated with dominance in the minds of at least initial students. It is awkward to have to remember that D in Mather's terminology denotes "additive," while H which could easily (and is in fact used so) denote "heritable," denotes "dominance." With regard to Comstock et al.'s notation there is one defect (which is possibly to be regarded as esoteric): that it makes no provision for the two homozygotes to have the same genotypic value, and the heterozygote a different one, except by the artifice of letting u tend to zero and a tend to infinity.

17.5 SOME GENERAL CONSIDERATIONS‡

We consider for the moment the population

$$\sum_{ij} p_i p_j A_i A_j$$

with the genotypic value of $A_i A_j$ denoted by y_{ij}. The y_{ij} will be coded so that the mean of the original population is zero, i.e. so that

$$\sum_i p_i^2 y_{ii} + 2 \sum_{i<j} p_i p_j y_{ij} = 0$$

After n generations of regular inbreeding the population structure will be

$$\sum [F_n p_i + (1 - F_n) p_i^2] A_i A_i + 2(1 - F_n) \sum_{i<j} p_i p_j A_i A_j$$

We have seen in a previous chapter that the total variance is

$$\sigma_G^2 = \sum_i [F_n p_i + (1 - F_n) p_i^2] y_{ii}^2 + 2(1 - F_n) \sum_{i<j} p_i p_j y_{ij}^2$$

which can be expressed as

$$\sigma_{GR}^2 + F(\sigma_{I\infty}^2 - \sigma_{GR}^2) + F(1 - F)(\mu_{I\infty} - \mu_R)^2$$

‡ This section is possibly of little use, and can be ignored. It is included because it "tickles the fancy" of the author.

with obvious definitions of symbols; that is, $\sigma_{I\infty}^2$ is the genotypic variance in the homozygous population, and $\mu_{I\infty}$ its mean, while μ_R is the mean in the original random mating population. The additive variance is

$$\sigma_A^2 = 2 \sum_i p_i \alpha_i^2 (1 + F_n)$$

where

$$\alpha_i = \frac{1}{1 + F_n} \left[F_n y_{ii} + (1 - F_n) \sum_m p_m y_{im} \right]$$

and the dominance variance is

$$\sigma_D^2 = \sigma_G^2 - \sigma_A^2$$

It is of interest and may possibly be useful later to record another form for the dominance deviations. It will be recalled that the dominance variance of the random mating population

$$p^2 AA + 2pq Aa + q^2 aa$$

is

$$p^2 q^2 (2Aa - AA - aa)^2$$

or

$$p^2 q^2 (2y_{12} - y_{11} - y_{22})^2$$

or $p^2 q^2 x^2$ where x is as defined earlier in this chapter. We examine whether this formula extends to the case of more than two alleles, for random mating populations. It will be recalled that the average effect of gene i, α_i, is

$$\sum_m p_m y_{im}$$

when the y_{im}'s are the genotypic values defined about the population mean. If we use z_{ij} as the genotypic value with arbitrary mean, then

$$\alpha_i = \sum_m p_m z_{im} - \mu$$

where

$$\mu = \sum_{i,j} p_i p_j z_{ij}$$

Then the dominance deviation attached to the genotypic value of $A_i A_j$ is equal to

$$d_{ij} = z_{ij} - \mu - \alpha_i - \alpha_j$$

$$= z_{ij} - \sum_m p_m z_{im} - \sum_m p_m z_{jm} + \mu$$

Now let us define $\epsilon_{ij} = 2z_{ij} - z_{ii} - z_{jj} = 2y_{ij} - y_{ii} - y_{jj}$ for all unequal i and j. The ϵ's are what a biologist might regard as dominance deviations. Then it can be verified directly by substitution that

$$d_{ij} = \sum_{\substack{r,s \\ r<s}} \lambda_{rs}^{ij} \epsilon_{rs}$$

where

$$2\lambda_{rs}^{ij} = \delta_{ri}\delta_{sj} + 2p_r p_s - \delta_{ri}p_s - \delta_{si}p_r - \delta_{rj}p_s - \delta_{sj}p_r \qquad (r < s)$$

where

$$\delta_{ri} = 1 \text{ if } r \text{ and } i \text{ are equal and is zero otherwise}$$
$$\delta_{sj} = 1 \text{ if } s \text{ and } j \text{ are equal and is zero otherwise}$$

and likewise for δ_{rj} and δ_{si}. For instance, with two alleles with frequencies p_1 and p_2,

$$d_{11} = \tfrac{1}{2}(2p_1 p_2 - 2p_2)\epsilon_{12} = -p_2^2 \epsilon_{12} \quad \text{since} \quad p_1 + p_2 = 1$$
$$d_{12} = \tfrac{1}{2}(1 + 2p_1 p_2 - p_1 - p_2)\epsilon_{12} = +p_1 p_2 \epsilon_{12}$$
$$d_{22} = \tfrac{1}{2}(2p_1 p_2 - 2p_1)\epsilon_{12} = -p_1^2 \epsilon_{12}$$

where of course $\epsilon_{12} = 2y_{12} - y_{11} - y_{22}$. The dominance variance is therefore $[p_1^2(-p_2^2)^2 + 2p_1 p_2(p_1 p_2)^2 + p_2^2(-p_1^2)^2]\epsilon_{12}^2$, which is readily seen to be equal to $p_1^2 p_2^2 \epsilon_{12}^2$, which is the standard result.

As another example suppose we have three alleles, with gene frequencies p_1, p_2, p_3; then we have

$$d_{11} = (p_1 p_2 - p_2)\epsilon_{12} + (p_1 p_3 - p_3)\epsilon_{13} + p_2 p_3 \epsilon_{23}$$
$$d_{12} = (p_1 p_2 + \tfrac{1}{2}p_3)\epsilon_{12} + (p_1 p_3 - \tfrac{1}{2}p_3)\epsilon_{13} + (p_2 p_3 - \tfrac{1}{2}p_3)\epsilon_{23}$$
$$d_{13} = (p_1 p_2 - \tfrac{1}{2}p_2)\epsilon_{12} + (p_1 p_3 + \tfrac{1}{2}p_2)\epsilon_{13} + (p_2 p_3 - \tfrac{1}{2}p_2)\epsilon_{23}$$
$$d_{22} = (p_1 p_2 - p_1)\epsilon_{12} + p_1 p_3 \epsilon_{13} + (p_2 p_3 - p_3)\epsilon_{23}$$
$$d_{23} = (p_1 p_2 - \tfrac{1}{2}p_1)\epsilon_{12} + (p_1 p_3 - \tfrac{1}{2}p_1)\epsilon_{13} + (p_2 p_3 + \tfrac{1}{2}p_1)\epsilon_{23}$$
$$d_{33} = p_1 p_2 \epsilon_{12} + (p_1 p_3 - p_1)\epsilon_{13} + (p_2 p_3 - p_2)\epsilon_{23}$$

With four alleles typical terms are as follows:

$$d_{12} = \tfrac{1}{2}(1 + 2p_1 p_2 - p_1 - p_2)\epsilon_{12} + (p_1 p_3 - \tfrac{1}{2}p_3)\epsilon_{13}$$
$$+ (p_1 p_4 - \tfrac{1}{2}p_4)\epsilon_{14} + (p_2 p_3 - \tfrac{1}{2}p_3)\epsilon_{23} + (p_2 p_4 - \tfrac{1}{2}p_4)\epsilon_{24} + p_3 p_4 \epsilon_{34}$$

Another form of the equation giving dominance deviations is

$$2d_{ij} = (1 + 2p_i p_j - p_i - p_j)\epsilon_{ij} + \sum_{m \neq j} (2p_i p_m - p_m)\epsilon_{im}$$

$$+ \sum_{m \neq i} (2p_m p_j - p_m)\epsilon_{mj} + \sum_{\substack{r,s \\ r \neq i, s \neq j}} 2p_r p_s \epsilon_{rs}$$

This is not at all a nice-looking expression, and the dominance variance which will be a quadratic form in the ϵ's does not appear to have a simple formula. It is to be noted, however, that the ϵ's enter the dominance variance in products as well as squares.

We may note in passing that with one locus (or by the obvious extension with an arbitrary number of non-interacting loci) the population mean under inbreeding is a linear function of the coefficient of inbreeding F, being equal in fact to μ_I where

$$\mu_I = F \sum_i p_i y_{ii} + (1 - F) \sum_{ij} p_i p_j y_{ij}$$

$$= F\mu_{I\infty} + (1 - F)\mu_R$$

$$= \mu_R + F(\mu_{I\infty} - \mu_R)$$

where $\mu_{I\infty}$ is the mean of the completely inbred population and μ_R of the original population (cf. Wright, 1951). This is presumably the basis according to which observations are sometimes adjusted linearly by the inbreeding coefficient.

17.6 THE DOMINANCE DEVIATIONS IN INBRED POPULATIONS

We have seen that the mean of the inbred population is

$$\mu_I = F \sum_s p_s y_{ss}$$

when the y_{ij}'s are the genotypic values coded so that

$$\sum_{i,j} p_i p_j y_{ij} = 0$$

The genotypic values expressed about the mean of the inbred population are

$$y'_{ij} = y_{ij} - \mu_I$$

and the effect of gene A_i is α_{iI}, where

$$(1 + F)\alpha_{iI} = Fy'_{ii} + (1 - F) \sum_j p_j y'_{ij}$$

Hence the dominance deviation attached to the individual with genotype A_iA_j in the inbred population is

$$y'_{ij} - \frac{1}{(1 + F)}\left[Fy'_{ii} + (1 - F)\sum_s p_s y'_{is} + Fy'_{jj} + (1 - F)\sum_s p_s y'_{js}\right]$$

$$= y_{ij} - \mu_I - \frac{1}{(1 + F)}\left[Fy_{ii} - F\mu_I + (1 - F)\sum_s p_s y_{is} - (1 - F)\mu_I\right.$$

$$\left. + Fy_{jj} - F\mu_I + (1 - F)\sum_s p_s y_{js} - (1 - F)\mu_I\right]$$

$$= y_{ij} - \mu_I - \frac{1}{(1 + F)}[F(y_{ii} + y_{jj}) + (1 - F)(\alpha_i + \alpha_j) - 2\mu_I]$$

where α_i, α_j are the effects in the original random mating population,

$$= \frac{(1 - F)(y_{ij} - \alpha_i - \alpha_j) + 2F(y_{ij} - \tfrac{1}{2}y_{ii} - \tfrac{1}{2}y_{jj}) + (1 - F)\mu_I}{1 + F}$$

$$= \frac{(1 - F)d_{ij} + 2Fe_{ij}}{1 + F} + \left(\frac{1 - F}{1 + F}\right)\mu_I$$

where d_{ij} is the dominance deviation in the original population and e_{ij} is given by

$$e_{ij} = y_{ij} - \tfrac{1}{2}y_{ii} - \tfrac{1}{2}y_{jj}$$

a quantity of biological interest, being the deviation of the heterozygote from the mean of the corresponding homozygotes. The dominance deviation ϵ in the inbred population can also be expressed as

$$e_{ij} + \left(\frac{1 - F}{1 + F}\right)(d_{ij} - e_{ij}) + \left(\frac{1 - F}{1 + F}\right)[F(\mu_{I\infty} - \mu_R) + \mu_R]$$

where $\mu_{I\infty}$ is the mean of the infinitely inbred population, i.e.

$$\mu_{I\infty} = \sum_s p_s y_{ss}$$

and μ_R is the mean of the initial random mating population.

We see therefore that the dominance deviations in inbred populations are linear functions of the dominance deviations in a nearly homozygous population (F nearly 1), the dominance deviations in the original population, and the means of these two populations.

This suggests that there is likely to be little utility in working with dominance deviations, defined by least squares, in inbred populations. It is possible, however, that some use will be found for them in such situations.

17.7 THE GENERAL SOLUTION FOR SELFING WITH ONE LOCUS

The purpose of the succeeding section is to exhibit another way of looking at the problems of selfing (Kempthorne, 1956). The solution that will be given is general in the sense that the number of alleles at the locus is assumed to be arbitrary. It will be assumed that there is no selection. Only the diploid case will be discussed.

Consider an individual with genotype A_iA_j. Then its progeny array will be $\frac{1}{4}(A_iA_i + 2A_iA_j + A_jA_j)$, whether or not, of course, genes A_i and A_j are the same. The basic fact resulting from this, which gives us the clue to the understanding of covariances and correlations between relatives, is that if the genotypic value of A_iA_j is denoted by y_{ij}, and we denote the operation of selfing by placing an S before y_{ij}; then§

$$Sy_{ij} = y_{ij} - \epsilon_{ij} \tag{1}$$

where

$$\epsilon_{ij} = \tfrac{1}{4}(2y_{ij} - y_{ii} - y_{jj})$$

and

$$S\epsilon_{ij} = \tfrac{1}{2}\epsilon_{ij} \tag{2}$$

Thus we have

$$S(A_iA_j) = \tfrac{1}{4}(A_iA_i + A_jA_j + 2A_iA_j)$$

so

$$\begin{aligned}
S(y_{ij}) &= \tfrac{1}{4}(y_{ii} + y_{jj} + 2y_{ij}) \\
&= y_{ij} - \tfrac{1}{4}(2y_{ij} - y_{ii} - y_{jj}) \\
&= y_{ij} - \epsilon_{ij}
\end{aligned}$$

Also

$$S\left(\frac{2A_iA_j - A_iA_i - A_jA_j}{4}\right) = \frac{1}{2}\left(\frac{2A_iA_j + A_iA_i + A_jA_j}{4}\right) - \frac{A_iA_i}{4} - \frac{A_jA_j}{4}$$

so

$$\begin{aligned}
S(\epsilon_{ij}) &= \tfrac{1}{2}(y_{ij} - \epsilon_{ij}) - \tfrac{1}{4}y_{ii} - \tfrac{1}{4}y_{jj} \\
&= \epsilon_{ij} - \tfrac{1}{2}\epsilon_{ij} \\
&= \tfrac{1}{2}\epsilon_{ij}
\end{aligned}$$

Note in the above that the ϵ quantity for a homozygote A_iA_i is zero, automatically; i.e.,

$$\epsilon_{ii} = \tfrac{1}{4}(y_{ii} + y_{ii} - 2y_{ii}) = 0$$

§ The quantity ϵ_{ij} in this section is one-quarter of the quantity denoted by the same symbol in the previous section.

We take an arbitrary initial population, whose genotypic array is

$$\sum_{\substack{i,j \\ i \le j}} P_{ij}^{(0)} A_i A_j$$

The mean of this population is

$$\mu^{(0)} = \sum_{\substack{i,j \\ i \le j}} P_{ij}^{(0)} y_{ij} \tag{3}$$

and we suppose that the y_{ij}'s are coded so that this is zero.

Now we consider the mean genotypic value of the offspring of an individual with genotype $A_i A_j$ after k generations of selfing. We have

$$Sy_{ij} = y_{ij} - \epsilon_{ij}$$
$$S\epsilon_{ij} = \tfrac{1}{2}\epsilon_{ij}$$

so

$$S^2 y_{ij} = S(Sy_{ij}) = y_{ij} - \epsilon_{ij} - \tfrac{1}{2}\epsilon_{ij}$$
$$= y_{ij} - \tfrac{3}{2}\epsilon_{ij}$$
$$S^3 y_{ij} = S(S^2 y_{ij}) = y_{ij} - \epsilon_{ij} - \tfrac{3}{4}\epsilon_{ij}$$
$$= y_{ij} - \tfrac{7}{4}\epsilon_{ij}$$

and in general

$$S^r y_{ij} = y_{ij} - 2\left(1 - \frac{1}{2^r}\right)\epsilon_{ij} \tag{4}$$

The population mean in generation r is

$$\sum_{\substack{ij \\ i \le j}} P_{ij}^{(0)} S^r y_{ij} = -2\left(1 - \frac{1}{2^r}\right)\sum_{\substack{ij \\ i < j}} P_{ij}^{(0)} \epsilon_{ij} \tag{5}$$

We shall denote $\sum P_{ij}^{(0)} \epsilon_{ij}$ by μ_ϵ, and the population mean in generation r by μ_r, so that

$$\mu_r = -2\left(1 - \frac{1}{2^r}\right)\mu_\epsilon \tag{6}$$

We now consider variances and covariances in the populations of individuals which arise by repeated selfing. First we consider ancestral covariances. The covariances of rth generation offspring and sth generation offspring of individuals in the original population is

$$\text{Cov}\,(S^r y_{ij}, S^s y_{ij}) = \text{Cov}\,(y_{ij} - K_r \epsilon_{ij}, y_{ij} - K_s \epsilon_{ij})$$

where $K_r = 2(1 - 1/2^r)$, $K_s = 2(1 - 1/2^s)$. This equals

$$\sum_{\substack{ij \\ i \le j}} P_{ij}^{(0)}[y_{ij} - K_r(\epsilon_{ij} - \mu_\epsilon)][y_{ij} - K_s(\epsilon_{ij} - \mu_\epsilon)]$$

$$= \sigma_G^2 - (K_r + K_s) \operatorname{Cov}(y_{ij}, \epsilon_{ij}) + K_r K_s V(\epsilon_{ij}) \qquad (7)$$

We obtain somewhat more symmetry in the result if we follow standard statistical notation in denoting σ_G^2 by σ_{GG}, $\operatorname{Cov}(y_{ij}, \epsilon_{ij})$ by σ_{GH}, and $V(\epsilon_{ij})$ by σ_{HH}. The result then becomes

$$\sigma_{GG} - (K_r + K_s)\sigma_{GH} + K_r K_s \sigma_{HH} \qquad (7a)$$

We use the subscript H for the ϵ_{ij}, because the ϵ_{ij} measure the deviation of heterozygotes from their two corresponding homozygotes.

It is also of interest to generalize the covariance of the rth generation offspring and the sth generation offspring of kth generation individuals, *within* $(k-1)$th generation individuals given in a previous section. This is readily obtained in the following way. Let the genotypic array in generation $(k-1)$ be

$$\sum_{\substack{i,j \\ i \le j}} P_{ij}^{(k-1)} A_i A_j$$

Then clearly

$$P_{ii}^{(k)} = P_{ii}^{(k-1)} + \frac{1}{4} \sum_{\substack{j \\ j \ne i}} P_{ij}^{(k-1)}$$

$$P_{ij}^{(k)} = \tfrac{1}{2} P_{ij}^{(k-1)}$$

$$P_{jj}^{(k)} = P_{jj}^{(k-1)} + \frac{1}{4} \sum_{\substack{i \\ i \ne j}} P_{ij}^{(k-1)}$$

Hence

1. $P_{ii}^{(k-1)}$ individuals of genotype $A_i A_i$ in generation $(k-1)$ lead to $A_i A_i$ individuals thereafter.

2. $P_{ij}^{(k-1)}$ individuals of genotype $A_i A_j$ in generation $(k-1)$ lead to $\tfrac{1}{4} A_i A_i + \tfrac{1}{2} A_i A_j + \tfrac{1}{4} A_j A_j$ individuals in generation k. The mean offspring in the rth and sth generations of these k generation individuals are given in Table 17.5.

TABLE 17.5

kth Generation Individual	Genotypic Value	Mean Value of Offspring in Generation	
		r	s
$A_i A_i$	y_{ii}	y_{ii}	y_{ii}
$A_i A_j$	y_{ij}	$y_{ij} - K_{r-k}\epsilon_{ij}$	$y_{ij} - K_{s-k}\epsilon_{ij}$
$A_j A_j$	y_{jj}	y_{jj}	y_{jj}
Mean	$y_{ij} - \epsilon_{ij}$	$y_{ij} - K_{r-k+1}\epsilon_{ij}$	$y_{ij} - K_{s-k+1}\epsilon_{ij}$

Hence the required covariance is

$$\sum_{\substack{i,j \\ i<j}} P_{ij}^{(k-1)}[\tfrac{1}{4}y_{ii}^2 + \tfrac{1}{4}y_{jj}^2 + \tfrac{1}{2}(y_{ij} - K_{r-k}\epsilon_{ij})(y_{ij} - K_{s-k}\epsilon_{ij})$$
$$- (y_{ij} - K_{r-k+1}\epsilon_{ij})(y_{ij} - K_{s-k+1}\epsilon_{ij})] \tag{8}$$

$$= \sum_{\substack{ij \\ i<j}} P_{ij}^{(k-1)}[\tfrac{1}{4}y_{ii}^2 + \tfrac{1}{4}y_{jj}^2 - \tfrac{1}{2}y_{ij}^2 - \tfrac{1}{2}K_{r-k}\epsilon_{ij}y_{ij} - \tfrac{1}{2}K_{s-k}\epsilon_{ij}y_{ij}$$
$$+ K_{r-k+1}\epsilon_{ij}y_{ij} + K_{s-k+1}\epsilon_{ij}y_{ij} + (\tfrac{1}{2}K_{r-k}K_{s-k} - K_{r-k+1}K_{s-k+1})\epsilon_{ij}^2]$$

But

$$K_{m+1} - \tfrac{1}{2}K_m = 1 \quad \text{for all } m$$

Hence the covariance reduces to

$$\sum_{\substack{ij \\ i<j}} P_{ij}^{(k-1)}[\tfrac{1}{4}y_{ii}^2 + \tfrac{1}{4}y_{jj}^2 - \tfrac{1}{2}y_{ij}^2 + 2\epsilon_{ij}y_{ij} + (-1 - \tfrac{1}{2}K_{r-k} - \tfrac{1}{2}K_{s-k}$$
$$+ \tfrac{1}{4}K_{r-k}K_{s-k})\epsilon_{ij}^2]$$

$$= \sum_{\substack{i,j \\ i<j}} P_{ij}^{(k-1)}[\tfrac{1}{4}y_{ii}^2 + \tfrac{1}{2}y_{ij}^2 + \tfrac{1}{4}y_{jj}^2 - (y_{ij} - \epsilon_{ij})^2$$
$$+ (-\tfrac{1}{2}K_{r-k} - \tfrac{1}{2}K_{s-k} + \tfrac{1}{4}K_{r-k}K_{s-k})\epsilon_{ij}^2$$

$$= \sum_{\substack{i,j \\ i<j}} P_{ij}^{(k-1)} \left[[\tfrac{1}{4}y_{ii}^2 + \tfrac{1}{2}y_{ij}^2 + \tfrac{1}{4}y_{jj}^2 - (y_{ij} - \epsilon_{ij})^2 - \epsilon_{ij}^2 + \frac{1}{2^{r+s-2k}}\epsilon_{ij}^2 \right] \tag{9}$$

Now

$$\tfrac{1}{4}y_{ii}^2 + \tfrac{1}{2}y_{ij}^2 + \tfrac{1}{4}y_{jj}^2 - (y_{ij} - \epsilon_{ij})^2 - \epsilon_{ij}^2$$
$$= \tfrac{1}{4}y_{ii}^2 + \tfrac{1}{2}y_{ij}^2 + \tfrac{1}{4}y_{jj}^2 - \left(\frac{2y_{ij} + y_{ii} + y_{jj}}{4}\right)^2 - \left(\frac{2y_{ij} - (y_{ii} + y_{jj})}{4}\right)^2$$
$$= \tfrac{1}{4}y_{ii}^2 + \tfrac{1}{2}y_{ij}^2 + \tfrac{1}{4}y_{jj}^2 - 2\left(\frac{2y_{ij}}{4}\right)^2 - 2\left(\frac{y_{ii} + y_{jj}}{4}\right)^2$$
$$= \tfrac{1}{4}y_{ii}^2 + \tfrac{1}{4}y_{jj}^2 - \tfrac{1}{8}(y_{ii} + y_{jj})^2$$
$$= \tfrac{1}{8}(y_{ii} - y_{jj})^2$$

We therefore get

$$\sum_{\substack{i,j \\ i<j}} P_{ij}^{(k-1)} \left[\tfrac{1}{8}(y_{ii} - y_{jj})^2 + \frac{1}{2^{r+s-2k}}\epsilon_{ij}^2 \right] \tag{9a}$$

Using

$$P_{ij}^{(k-1)} = \frac{1}{2^{k-1}} P_{ij}^{(0)}$$

and denoting

$$\sum_{\substack{i,j \\ i \le j}} P_{ij}^{(0)} \tfrac{1}{8} (y_{ii} - y_{jj})^2$$

by σ_1^2, the final expression for the covariance reduces to

$$C_{k,r,s} = \frac{1}{2^{k-1}} \sigma_1^2 + \frac{1}{2^{r+s-k-1}} (\sigma_\epsilon^2 + \mu_\epsilon^2) \tag{9b}$$

There seems little point in deriving the correlations between relatives, because the way one should examine data arising by selfing is by means of analyses of variance and the evaluation of covariances.

General Discussion of One-Locus Case

It is interesting to note that, in the case of two alleles with equal frequency and random mating in the original population, the covariance $C_{k,r,s}$ is expressible very simply in terms of the additive and dominance variance as defined by Fisher (1918). It is easily seen from the present development that this will not be true in general. We need only note

1. The term which leads to the contribution involving the additive variance in the special case is

$$\sum_{\substack{i,j \\ i < j}} P_{ij}^{(0)} \tfrac{1}{8} (y_{ii} - y_{jj})^2$$

an expression which is functionally independent of the genotypic values of the heterozygotes.

2. The dominance variance does not reduce in general to the expression

$$2 \sum_{\substack{i,j \\ i < j}} P_{ij}^{(0)} \epsilon_{ij}^2 = 2 \sum_{\substack{i,j \\ i < j}} P_{ij}^{(0)} \frac{(2y_{ij} - y_{ii} - y_{jj})^2}{16}$$

because this expression does not involve the frequencies of homozygous genotypes.

We have seen that the concepts of additive and dominance variance are of utility in describing covariances and correlations between relatives only in random mating populations. The results given above demonstrate that different quadratic functions of the genotypic values enter into the covariances between relatives under selfing for the general case. It is curious, though the reasons are obvious from what is given above, that in the special case of an F_2 population the description of covariances involves the same parameters for random mating or selfing.

17.8 COVARIANCES UNDER FULL-SIBBING

We shall give the solution only for the case of two alleles, A, a, and we shall suppose that we have initially the population

$$p^2 AA + 2pq Aa + q^2 aa$$

and that, after matings are made at random initially, all subsequent matings are between full-sibs (Kempthorne, 1955). We shall derive the covariance between full-sibs after n generations.

It is necessary to use the methodology of the generation matrix theory of inbreeding given in Chapter 6 (Fisher, 1949), and the reader should refresh his mind on that material before continuing. In that chapter, concern was only with mating types, where the matings $AA \times AA$ and $aa \times aa$ for instance are of the same type. We now need to consider all the possible matings with respect to the genotypes of the individuals in the matings. We therefore talk about kinds of matings. The use of the phrase "kind of mating" here is purely a convenience, and some other phrase may be better. The kinds of matings with initial frequencies are given in Table 17.6.

TABLE 17.6

Mating		Initial Frequency
$AA \times AA$	(1)	p^4
$AA \times Aa$	(2)	$4p^3q$
$AA \times aa$	(3)	$2p^2q^2$
$Aa \times Aa$	(4)	$4p^2q^2$
$Aa \times aa$	(5)	$4pq^3$
$aa \times aa$	(6)	q^4

We let the frequencies of the kinds of matings in generation n be $f_1^{(n)}, f_2^{(n)}, \cdots, f_6^{(n)}$. Then we have the equations

$$f_1^{(1)} = f_1^{(0)} + \tfrac{1}{4}f_2^{(0)} + \tfrac{1}{16}f_4^{(0)}$$

$$f_2^{(1)} = \tfrac{1}{2}f_2^{(0)} + \tfrac{1}{4}f_4^{(0)}$$

$$f_3^{(1)} = \tfrac{1}{8}f_4^{(0)}$$

$$f_4^{(1)} = \tfrac{1}{4}f_2^{(0)} + f_3^{(0)} + \tfrac{1}{4}f_4^{(0)} + \tfrac{1}{4}f_5^{(0)}$$

$$f_5^{(1)} = \tfrac{1}{4}f_4^{(0)} + \tfrac{1}{2}f_5^{(0)}$$

$$f_6^{(1)} = \tfrac{1}{16}f_4^{(0)} + \tfrac{1}{4}f_5^{(0)} + f_6^{(0)}$$

or, in matrix form,

$$\mathbf{f}^{(1)} = \mathbf{A}\mathbf{f}^{(0)}$$

where $\mathbf{f}^{(1)}$ and $\mathbf{f}^{(0)}$ are column matrices and $\mathbf{A}$ is a 6×6 matrix. The roots of the matrix are denoted in the following by

$$\lambda_1 = 1, \ \lambda_2 = \tfrac{1}{2}, \ \lambda_3 = \tfrac{1}{4}, \ \lambda_4 = \epsilon = \tfrac{1}{4}(1+\sqrt{5}), \ \lambda_5 = \epsilon' = \tfrac{1}{4}(1-\sqrt{5}), \ \lambda_6 = 1$$

and principal components corresponding to these roots are

$$
\begin{aligned}
g_1 &= f_1 + f_2 + && f_3 + && f_4 + f_5 + f_6 \\
g_2 &= && f_2 && && - f_5 \\
g_3 &= && f_2 - && 4f_3 - && f_4 + f_5 \\
g_4 &= && f_2 + (4 + 8\epsilon')f_3 - 4\epsilon'f_4 + f_5 \\
g_5 &= && f_2 + (4 + 8\epsilon)f_3 - 4\epsilon f_4 + f_5 \\
g_6 &= 4f_1 + 3f_2 + && 2f_3 + && 2f_4 + f_5
\end{aligned}
$$

$$g_1^{(n)} = g_1^{(0)}, \qquad g_2^{(n)} = (\tfrac{1}{2})^n g_2^{(0)}, \qquad g_3^{(n)} = (\tfrac{1}{4})^n g_3^{(0)},$$

$$g_4^{(n)} = \epsilon^n g_4^{(0)}, \qquad g_5^{(n)} = (\epsilon')^n g_5^{(0)}, \qquad g_6^{(n)} = g_6^{(0)}$$

Also, by solving for the f_i's in terms of the g_i's,

$$
\begin{pmatrix} f_1 \\ f_2 \\ f_3 \\ f_4 \\ f_5 \\ f_6 \end{pmatrix}
=
\begin{pmatrix}
0 & -\dfrac{1}{4} & -\dfrac{1}{20} & -\left(\dfrac{1}{8}+\dfrac{2\epsilon}{5}\right) & -\left(\dfrac{1}{8}+\dfrac{2\epsilon'}{5}\right) & \dfrac{1}{4} \\[2ex]
0 & \dfrac{1}{2} & \dfrac{1}{5} & \dfrac{1}{10}(1+2\epsilon) & \dfrac{1}{10}(1+2\epsilon') & 0 \\[2ex]
0 & 0 & -\dfrac{1}{10} & \dfrac{1}{20} & \dfrac{1}{20} & 0 \\[2ex]
0 & 0 & -\dfrac{1}{5} & \dfrac{2\epsilon}{5} & \dfrac{2\epsilon'}{5} & 0 \\[2ex]
0 & -\dfrac{1}{2} & \dfrac{1}{5} & \dfrac{1}{10}(1+2\epsilon) & \dfrac{1}{10}(1+2\epsilon') & 0 \\[2ex]
1 & \dfrac{1}{4} & -\dfrac{1}{20} & -\left(\dfrac{1}{8}+\dfrac{2\epsilon}{5}\right) & -\left(\dfrac{1}{8}+\dfrac{2\epsilon'}{5}\right) & -\dfrac{1}{4}
\end{pmatrix}
\begin{pmatrix} g_1 \\ g_2 \\ g_3 \\ g_4 \\ g_5 \\ g_6 \end{pmatrix}
$$

where we have used the matrix form of representing the results. In this equation

$$f_j = \sum_k C^{jk} g_k$$

where C^{jk} is the number in the jth row and kth column of the 6×6 array on the right-hand side.

Now the frequencies of kinds of mating are the frequencies of full-sib pairs, when the mating system is full-sibbing. Hence we merely have to find the g's in the initial generation and hence the g's in the nth generation and then find the f's. In fact we find

$$g_1^{(0)} = 1$$
$$g_2^{(0)} = 4pq(p - q)$$
$$g_3^{(0)} = 4pq(p^2 - 3pq + p^2)$$
$$g_4^{(0)} = 4pq$$
$$g_5^{(0)} = 4pq$$
$$g_6^{(0)} = 4p$$

so that

$$g_1^{(n)} = 1$$
$$g_2^{(n)} = (\tfrac{1}{2})^n 4pq(p^2 - q^2)$$
$$g_3^{(n)} = (\tfrac{1}{4})^n 4pq(p^2 - 3pq + q^2)$$
$$g_4^{(n)} = \epsilon^n 4pq$$
$$g_5^{(n)} = \epsilon'^n 4pq$$
$$g_6^{(n)} = 4p$$

The population genotypic array in any generation is equal to

$$(f_1 + \tfrac{1}{2}f_2 + \tfrac{1}{2}f_3)AA + (\tfrac{1}{2}f_2 + f_4 + \tfrac{1}{2}f_5)Aa + (\tfrac{1}{2}f_3 + \tfrac{1}{2}f_5 + f_6)aa$$

Now

$$f_1 + \tfrac{1}{2}f_2 + \tfrac{1}{2}f_3 = \left[-\tfrac{1}{4}g_2 - \tfrac{1}{20}g_3 - \left(\frac{1}{8} + \frac{2\epsilon}{5} \right)g_4 - \left(\frac{1}{8} + \frac{2\epsilon'}{5} \right)g_5 + \tfrac{1}{4}g_6 \right]$$
$$+ [\tfrac{1}{4}g_2 + \tfrac{1}{10}g_3 + \tfrac{1}{20}(1 + 2\epsilon)g_4 + \tfrac{1}{20}(1 + 2\epsilon')g_5]$$
$$+ (-\tfrac{1}{20}g_3 + \tfrac{1}{40}g_4 + \tfrac{1}{40}g_5)$$
$$= \left(-\frac{1}{20} - \frac{3\epsilon}{10} \right)g_4 + \left(-\frac{1}{20} - \frac{3\epsilon'}{10} \right)g_5 + \tfrac{1}{4}g_6$$

Hence, in generation n,

$$f_1^{(n)} + \tfrac{1}{2}f_2^{(n)} + \tfrac{1}{2}f_3^{(n)}$$
$$= \left(-\frac{1}{20} - \frac{3\epsilon}{10} \right)g_4^{(n)} + \left(-\frac{1}{20} - \frac{3\epsilon'}{10} \right)g_5^{(n)} + \tfrac{1}{4}g_6^{(n)}$$
$$= \left(-\frac{1}{20} - \frac{3\epsilon}{10} \right)\lambda_4^{(n)}g_4^{(0)} + \left(-\frac{1}{20} - \frac{3\epsilon'}{10} \right)\lambda_5^n g_5^{(0)} + \tfrac{1}{4}\lambda_6^n g_6^{(0)}$$
$$= \left(-\frac{1}{20} - \frac{3\epsilon}{10} \right)\epsilon^n 4pq + \left(-\frac{1}{20} - \frac{3\epsilon'}{10} \right)\epsilon'^n 4pq + \tfrac{1}{4} \cdot 1^n 4p$$
$$= p - pq(\tfrac{1}{5}\epsilon^n + \tfrac{1}{5}\epsilon'^n + \tfrac{6}{5}\epsilon^{n+1} + \tfrac{6}{5}\epsilon'^{n+1})$$

or, if we let

$$S_n = \epsilon^n + \epsilon'^n, \qquad S_{n+1} = \epsilon^{n+1} + \epsilon'^{n+1}$$

the frequency of AA individuals in generation n is

$$p - pq(\tfrac{1}{5}S_n + \tfrac{6}{5}S_{n+1})$$

Similarly the frequency of Aa in generation n is

$$2pq(\tfrac{1}{5}S_n + \tfrac{6}{5}S_{n+1})$$

and the frequency of aa is

$$q - pq(\tfrac{1}{5}S_n + \tfrac{6}{5}S_{n+1})$$

If now we let

$$\tfrac{1}{5}S_n + \tfrac{6}{5}S_{n+1} = 1 - F_n$$

the genotypic array in generation n is

$$[p - (1 - F_n)pq]AA + 2(1 - F_n)pqAa + [q - (1 - F_n)pq]aa$$

which is the standard result obtained by Wright (1921) and given in Chapter 5.

The mean in generation n using genotypic values of y, $(y-x)/2$, and 0 for the genotypes AA, Aa, and aa, respectively, is

$$\mu_n = py - (1 - F_n)pqx$$

The covariance between full-sibs in generation n is equal by definition to

$$f_1^{(n)}y^2 + f_2^{(n)}y \frac{(y - x)}{2} + f_4^{(n)} \frac{(y - x)^2}{4} - \mu_n^2$$

We now put everything in terms of F's by the use of the following equation,

$$S_{n+2} = \tfrac{1}{2}S_{n+1} + \tfrac{1}{4}S_n$$

which holds since ϵ and ϵ' are the roots of the equation

$$x^2 = \tfrac{1}{2}x + \tfrac{1}{4}$$

Also by definition

$$(1 - F_n) = \tfrac{1}{5}S_n + \tfrac{6}{5}S_{n+1}$$
$$= \tfrac{1}{5}S_n + \tfrac{6}{5}(\tfrac{1}{2}S_n + \tfrac{1}{4}S_{n-1})$$
$$= \tfrac{3}{10}S_{n-1} + \tfrac{4}{5}S_n$$

and

$$(1 - F_{n-1}) = \tfrac{1}{5}S_{n-1} + \tfrac{6}{5}S_n$$

Hence

$$S_{n-1} = 2 + 4F_{n-1} - 6F_n$$

and

$$S_n = \tfrac{1}{2} - \tfrac{3}{2}F_{n-1} + F_n$$

The final result for the covariance between full-sibs is

$$\text{Cov}\,(F.\,S) = \tfrac{1}{4}(1 + F_{n-1} + 2F_n)\,pqy^2 - (1 - F_n)^2 p^2 q^2 x^2$$
$$- (\tfrac{1}{2})^n pq(p - q)xy - \tfrac{1}{5}(\tfrac{1}{4})^n\,pq(p^2 - 3pq + q^2)x^2$$
$$+ (\tfrac{3}{10} + \tfrac{1}{10}F_{n-1} - \tfrac{2}{5}F_n)pqx^2 + (1 - F_n)\,pq(p-q)xy$$

Also the variance in generation n is

$$V(S) = \frac{pq}{2}(1 + F_n)y^2 - (1 - F_n)^2 p^2 q^2 x^2 + \tfrac{1}{2}(1 - F_n)pqx^2$$
$$+ (1 - F_n)\,pq(p - q)xy$$

The correlation between full-sibs is then

$$\text{Cov}\,(F.\,S)/V(S)$$

The problem considered above was worked out by Wright (1921) for the special case when there is no dominance. In that case we may put $d = 2a$, $h = a$, and $r = 0$, so that $x = d + r - 2h = 0$. This fact was the reason for the particular form in which the result is given above. A number of unpleasant terms drop out. In fact we have

$$\text{Cov}\,(F.\,S) = (1 + F_{n-1} + 2F_n)pqa^2$$

and

$$V(S) = 2(1 + F_n)pqa^2$$

and the correlation is

$$\frac{1}{2}\left(\frac{1 + F_{n-1} + 2F_n}{1 + F_n}\right) = \frac{1}{2}\left(1 + \frac{F_{n-1} + F_n}{1 + F_n}\right)$$

It may be noted also that the additive genetic variance in the original population is $2pqa^2$.

In the case, $p = q = \tfrac{1}{2}$, the term involving the root $\tfrac{1}{2}$ drops out. Also we shall use the Mather terminology for genotypic values, with $d = d$, $h = h$, $r = -d$. Then $y = 2d$ and $x = -2h$. We then find

$$\text{Cov}\,(F.\,S) = \tfrac{1}{4}(1 + F_{n-1} + 2F_n)d^2 - (1 - F_n)^2\,\frac{h^2}{4}$$

$$+ (\tfrac{3}{10} + \tfrac{1}{10}F_{n-1} - \tfrac{2}{5}F_n)h^2 + \tfrac{1}{20}(\tfrac{1}{4})^n\,h^2$$

$$V(S) = d^2 - \tfrac{1}{2}(1 - F_n)(d^2 - h^2) - (1 - F_n)^2\,\frac{h^2}{4}$$

$$= \left(\frac{1 + F_n}{2}\right)d^2 + \tfrac{1}{4}(1 - F_n^2)h^2$$

These formulas may be used for the case when two inbred lines are crossed in a way analogous to the use suggested by Mather (1949, pp. 55–58) for certain formulas he gives based on selfing. He denotes d^2 by D and h^2 by H.

Parent–Offspring Covariances under Full-Sibbing

Most of the work already done is useful in obtaining the covariance of parents in generation n with offspring in generation $n+1$. In fact this is equal to

$$f_1^{(n)}y^2 + f_2^{(n)}\left(\frac{3y-x}{4}\right)^2 + f_3^{(n)}\frac{y(y-x)}{4} + f_4^{(n)}\frac{(y-x)(2y-x)}{8}$$

$$+ f_5^{(n)}\left(\frac{y-x}{4}\right)^2 - \mu_n\mu_{n+1}$$

After some manipulation this reduces to

$$\mathrm{Cov}\,(P, O) = \frac{pq}{4}(1 + F_n + 2F_{n+1})y^2 - (1 - F_n)(1 - F_{n+1})p^2q^2x^2$$

$$- (\tfrac{1}{2})^{n+1}pq(p - q)xy + \frac{pq}{4}(1 - F_n)x^2 + \left(\frac{2 - F_n - F_{n+1}}{2}\right)pq(p - q)xy$$

Also we have

$$V(P) = pq\left(\frac{1 + F_n}{2}\right)y^2 + \tfrac{1}{2}(1 - F_n)pqx^2$$

$$- (1 - F_n)^2p^2q^2x^2 + (1 - F_n)\,pq(p - q)xy$$

and $V(O)$ is the same formula with F_{n+1} in place of F_n.

With no dominance we may put $d = 2a$, $h = a$, $r = 0$, $x = 0$, and we find

$$\mathrm{Cov}\,(P, O) = pqa^2(1 + F_n + 2F_{n+1})$$

$$V(P) = 2pqa^2(1 + F_n)$$

$$V(O) = 2pqa^2(1 + F_{n+1})$$

Hence

$$\rho_{PO} = \frac{1 + F_n + 2F_{n+1}}{2[(1 + F_n)(1 + F_{n+1})]^{1/2}}$$

$$\beta_{OP} = \frac{1 + F_n + 2F_{n+1}}{2(1 + F_n)} = \frac{1}{2} + \frac{F_{n+1}}{1 + F_n}$$

These results are in accord with those of Wright (1921).

In the special case of $p = q = \frac{1}{2}$, we have the following results after putting $d = d$, $h = h$, $r = -d$:

$$\text{Cov}(P, O) = \tfrac{1}{4}(1 + F_n + 2F_{n+1})d^2 + \frac{F_{n+1}}{4}(1 - F_n)h^2$$

This result could have applicability to populations resulting from the F_2 of two inbred lines.

17.9 THE GENERAL CASE OF AN ARBITRARY NUMBER OF ALLELES

The situation with an arbitrary number of alleles at the locus can be written down from Fisher's work (1949). Consider an initial mating $(ab) \times (cd)$ which is in general of type vii; if genes a and b are identical in state, the mating type will of course be type vi, and so on. Then the frequencies of Fisher's type i to type vii, from his pages 36 and 37, are as given in Table 17.7.

TABLE 17.7

Type	Frequency in Generation n
$aa \times aa$	$t_n = 1 - \tfrac{1}{10}(5S_n + 16S_{n+1}) + (\tfrac{1}{2})^n - \tfrac{1}{5}(\tfrac{1}{4})^n$
$aa \times ab$	$u_n = \tfrac{1}{5}(2S_n + 4S_{n+1}) - 2(\tfrac{1}{2})^n + \tfrac{4}{5}(\tfrac{1}{4})^n$
$ab \times ab$	$v_n = \tfrac{4}{5}S_{n+1} - \tfrac{4}{5}(\tfrac{1}{2})^n + \tfrac{4}{15}(\tfrac{1}{4})^n + \tfrac{2}{15}(-\tfrac{1}{8})^n$
$aa \times bb$	$w_n = \tfrac{1}{10}S_n - \tfrac{1}{5}(\tfrac{1}{2})^n + \tfrac{2}{15}(\tfrac{1}{4})^n - \tfrac{2}{15}(-\tfrac{1}{8})^n$
$ab \times ac$	$x_n = \tfrac{8}{5}(\tfrac{1}{2})^n - \tfrac{4}{3}(\tfrac{1}{4})^n - \tfrac{4}{15}(-\tfrac{1}{8})^n$
$aa \times bc$	$y_n = \tfrac{2}{5}(\tfrac{1}{2})^n - \tfrac{2}{3}(\tfrac{1}{4})^n + \tfrac{4}{15}(-\tfrac{1}{8})^n$
$ab \times cd$	$z_n = (\tfrac{1}{4})^n$

In the initial random mating $(ab) \times (cd)$, a, b, c, d will be alleles taken at random from the population so that

$$P(a=A) = p(b=A) = p(c=A) = p(d=A) = p_1$$

etc. Also the frequencies of the kinds of matings can be written down. For instance the mating type $(aa) \times (ab)$ will contain the following matings in equal proportions: $aa \times ab$, $aa \times ac$, $aa \times ad$, $bb \times ba$, $bb \times bc$, $bb \times bd$, $cc \times ca$, $cc \times cb$, $cc \times cd$, $dd \times da$, $dd \times db$, $dd \times dc$. Hence the frequency of each of these matings in generation n is equal to $u_n/12$. A similar argument may be applied to the other mating types. Finally the probabilities of the genes a, b, c, d being either of A_1, A_2, $\cdots$, A_m, the possible alleles at the locus, may be used to give the array of matings by genotype in the

nth generation. It turns out that these are as shown in Table 17.8 for an arbitrary generation where p_i is the gene frequency of A_i.

TABLE 17.8

Kind of Mating	Frequency
$A_iA_i \times A_iA_i$	$p_i t + p_i^2(u + v + w) + p_i^3(x + y) + p_i^4 z$
$A_iA_i \times A_iA_j$	$p_ip_j u + 2p_i^2 p_j x + 2p_i^2 p_j y + 4p_i^3 p_j z$
$A_iA_j \times A_iA_j$	$2p_ip_j v + (p_i^2 p_j + p_i p_j^2)x + 4p_i^2 p_j^2 z$
$A_iA_i \times A_jA_j$	$2p_ip_j w + (p_i p_j^2 + p_i^2 p_j)y + 2p_i^2 p_j^2 z$
$A_iA_j \times A_iA_k$	$2p_ip_jp_k x + 8p_i^2 p_j^2 z$
$A_iA_i \times A_jA_k$	$2p_ip_jp_k y + 4p_i^2 p_j p_k z$
$A_iA_j \times A_kA_l$	$8p_ip_jp_kp_l z$

17.10 COVARIANCES UNDER PARENT–OFFSPRING INBREEDING

Horner (1956) has found the following expressions for covariances under parent–offspring mating: The covariance of parent and offspring is given by

$$\text{Cov}(P_{n-1}, O_n) = (\tfrac{1}{4} + \tfrac{1}{4}F_{n-1} + \tfrac{1}{2}F_n)\, pqy^2$$
$$+ [(\tfrac{1}{2})^n - 1 + \tfrac{1}{2}F_{n-1} + \tfrac{1}{2}F_n]\, pq(q - p)xy$$
$$+ \tfrac{1}{4}(1 - F_{n-1})[(q - p)^2 + 4pqF_n]pqx^2$$

where P_{n-1} is the parent in generation $n-1$, and O_n is the offspring in generation n; and the covariance of full-sibs in generation n is given by

$$\text{Cov}(F.\,S_n) = (\tfrac{1}{8} + \tfrac{1}{8}0^{n-1} - \tfrac{1}{8}F_{n-1} + F_n)pqy^2$$
$$+ [(\tfrac{1}{2})^n - (1 - F_n)]\, pq(q - p)xy$$
$$+ [\tfrac{1}{4}pq\, 0^{n-1} + \tfrac{1}{4}(1 - F_n) - pq(1 - F_n)^2]pqx^2$$

The paper by Horner (1956) contains considerable discussion of the relationship between parent–offspring and full-sib correlations and generation of mating by parent–offspring mating. It also considers biasses of possible schemes for estimating additive variance from inbred material.

17.11 OTHER COVARIANCES UNDER INBREEDING

We may also consider the case when matings are made at random in the population

$$\sum p_i p_j A_i A_j$$

and then lines are formed independently by inbreeding from each mating. It will be appropriate to consider the covariance of parent and rth generation progeny mean, or the covariance of rth generation progeny mean and sth generation progeny mean, these tracing independently to the original mating.

Taking the first case, let a random mating be denoted by $A_i A_j \times A_k A_l$. Then under inbreeding this mating will lead in generation r to the subpopulation

$$F_r \sum (\tfrac{1}{4} A_i A_i + \tfrac{1}{4} A_j A_j + \tfrac{1}{4} A_k A_k + \tfrac{1}{4} A_l A_l)$$
$$+ (1 - F_r)(\tfrac{1}{16} A_i A_i + \tfrac{2}{16} A_i A_j + \tfrac{2}{16} A_i A_k + \tfrac{2}{16} A_i A_l + \tfrac{1}{16} A_j A_j$$
$$+ \tfrac{2}{16} A_j A_k + \tfrac{2}{16} A_j A_l + \tfrac{1}{16} A_k A_k + \tfrac{2}{16} A_k A_l + \tfrac{1}{16} A_l A_l)$$

This may be written as

$$\frac{1 - F_r}{4} \left(\frac{2 A_i A_j - A_i A_i - A_j A_j}{4} + \frac{2 A_i A_k - A_i A_i - A_k A_k}{4} \right.$$

$$+ \frac{2 A_i A_l - A_i A_i - A_l A_l}{4} + \frac{2 A_j A_k - A_j A_j - A_k A_k}{4}$$

$$\left. + \frac{2 A_j A_l - A_j A_j - A_l A_l}{4} + \frac{2 A_k A_l - A_k A_k - A_l A_l}{4} \right)$$

$$+ \tfrac{1}{4}(A_i A_i + A_j A_j + A_k A_k + A_l A_l)$$

Hence the genotypic mean of the rth generation progeny of the mating $A_i A_j \times A_k A_l$ is, with an obvious shorthand (see Section 17.5),

$$\tfrac{1}{4}(y_{ii} + y_{jj} + y_{kk} + y_{ll}) + \frac{1 - F_r}{4} (\epsilon_{ij} + \epsilon_{ik} + \epsilon_{il} + \epsilon_{jk} + \epsilon_{jl} + \epsilon_{kl})$$

The parental mean is $\tfrac{1}{2}(y_{ij} + y_{kl})$, or, since

$$y_{ij} = 2\epsilon_{ij} + \tfrac{1}{2}(y_{ii} + y_{jj})$$

the parental mean is

$$\tfrac{1}{4}(y_{ii} + y_{jj} + y_{kk} + y_{ll}) + \epsilon_{ij} + \epsilon_{kl}$$

We now proceed to find the covariance of the parental mean and the offspring mean. It should be noted that the form in which we have expressed the formulas is suggested by what we did about selfing earlier and is a useful form. Clearly the covariance is equal to

$$V(X) + \text{Cov}(X, Y) + \frac{1 - F_r}{4} \text{Cov}(X, Z) + \frac{1 - F_r}{4} \text{Cov}(Y, Z)$$

where $X = \frac{1}{4}(y_{ii} + y_{jj} + y_{kk} + y_{ll})$

$Y = \epsilon_{ij} + \epsilon_{kl}$

$Z = \epsilon_{ij} + \epsilon_{ik} + \epsilon_{il} + \epsilon_{jk} + \epsilon_{jl} + \epsilon_{kl}$

Or we may write it in shorter form as

$$K + \left(\frac{1 - F_r}{4}\right) L$$

where

$$K = V(X) + \text{Cov}(X, Y)$$
$$L = \text{Cov}(X, Z) + \text{Cov}(Y, Z)$$

Similarly the covariance of rth generation progeny means and sth generation progeny means, these being obtained from independent lines, is

$$V(X) + \left(\frac{1 - F_r}{4} + \frac{1 - F_s}{4}\right) \text{Cov}(X, Z) + \frac{(1 - F_r)(1 - F_s)}{16} V(Z)$$

Exactly the same results will be obtained if the mating system is parent–offspring inbreeding.

In this situation the intrinsic quantities are $V(X)$, $\text{Cov}(X, Y)$, $\text{Cov}(X, Z)$, $\text{Cov}(Y, Z)$, and $V(Z)$.

Before evaluating these, it is desirable to derive a few relationships among the ϵ's, the y_{ii}'s, the additive effects and variance in the original population. We have

(1) $$\mu_0 = \mu_R = \sum_i \sum_j p_i p_j y_{ij} = 0 \quad \text{by definition}$$

where μ_0 equals μ_R is the mean of the initial random mating population:

(2) $$E(\epsilon_{ij}) = \sum_{ij} p_i p_j \epsilon_{ij} = \frac{1}{4} \sum_{ij} p_i p_j (2y_{ij} - y_{ii} - y_{jj})$$

$$= \frac{1}{2} \sum_i p_i \left(\sum_j p_j y_{ij}\right) - \frac{1}{4} \sum p_i y_{ii} - \frac{1}{4} \sum p_j y_{jj}$$

$$= \frac{1}{2} \sum p_i \alpha_i - \frac{1}{2} \mu_\infty$$

where α_i is the additive effect of gene A_i in the original random mating population and μ_∞ is the mean of the completely inbred population.

Hence

$$\mu_\epsilon = E(\epsilon_{ij}) = -\tfrac{1}{2}\mu_\infty$$

(3) $\quad E(\epsilon_{ij}^2) = \dfrac{1}{16}\sum_{i,j} p_i p_j (2y_{ij} - y_{ii} - y_{jj})^2$

$$= \frac{1}{16}\sum_{ij} p_i p_j (4y_{ij}^2 + y_{ii}^2 + y_{jj}^2 - 4y_{ii}y_{ij} - 4y_{jj}y_{ij} + 2y_{ii}y_{jj})$$

$$= \tfrac{1}{16}\left[4\sigma_G^2 + 2(V_\infty + \mu_\infty^2) - 8\sum_i p_i \alpha_i y_{ii} + 2\mu_\infty^2\right]$$

where V_∞ is the variance in the completely inbred population; so

$$V(\epsilon_{ij}) = \tfrac{1}{4}\sigma_G^2 + \tfrac{1}{8}V_\infty - \frac{1}{2}\sum_i p_i \alpha_i y_{ii}$$

We may note here that

$$2\sum_i p_i \alpha_i y_{ii} = \sum_i p_i (2\alpha_i)y_{ii}$$

and is the covariance of the additive value of homozygous genotypes in the initial random mating population and the final completely inbred population.

(4) $\quad E(y_{ii}\epsilon_{ij}) = \sum_{ij} p_i p_j y_{ii}\epsilon_{ij}$

$$= \sum_i p_i y_{ii}\left(\sum_j p_j \epsilon_{ij}\right)$$

$$= \sum_i p_i y_{ii}\left[\sum_j p_j(\tfrac{1}{2}y_{ij} - \tfrac{1}{4}y_{ii} - \tfrac{1}{4}y_{jj})\right]$$

$$= \sum_i p_i y_{ii}(\tfrac{1}{2}\alpha_i - \tfrac{1}{4}y_{ii} - \tfrac{1}{4}\mu_\infty)$$

$$= \frac{1}{2}\sum_i p_i y_{ii}\alpha_i - \tfrac{1}{4}(V_\infty + \mu_\infty^2) - \tfrac{1}{4}\mu_\infty^2$$

$$= \frac{1}{2}\sum_i p_i y_{ii}\alpha_i - \tfrac{1}{4}V_\infty - \tfrac{1}{2}\mu_\infty^2$$

So

$$\text{Cov}(y_{ii}, \epsilon_{ij}) = \frac{1}{2}\sum_i p_i y_{ii}\alpha_i - \frac{1}{4}V_\infty$$

(5) $E(\epsilon_{ij}\epsilon_{ik}) = \displaystyle\sum_{ijk} p_i p_j p_k \epsilon_{ij}\epsilon_{ik}$

$$= \sum_i p_i \left(\sum_j p_j \epsilon_{ij}\right)\left(\sum_k p_k \epsilon_{ik}\right)$$

$$= \sum_i p_i(\tfrac{1}{2}\alpha_i - \tfrac{1}{4}y_{ii} - \tfrac{1}{4}\mu_\infty)^2$$

$$= \frac{1}{4}\sum_i p_i\alpha_i^2 + \tfrac{1}{16}(V_\infty + \mu_\infty^2) + \tfrac{1}{16}\mu_\infty^2 - \frac{1}{4}\sum_i p_i\alpha_i y_{ii} + \tfrac{1}{8}\mu_\infty^2$$

$$= \tfrac{1}{8}\sigma_A^2 + \tfrac{1}{16}V_\infty - \frac{1}{4}\sum_i p_i\alpha_i y_{ii} + \tfrac{1}{4}\mu_\infty^2$$

So

$$\text{Cov}(\epsilon_{ij}, \epsilon_{ik}) = \tfrac{1}{8}\sigma_A^2 + \tfrac{1}{16}V_\infty - \frac{1}{4}\sum_i p_i\alpha_i y_{ii}$$

Since the quantity $\displaystyle\sum_i p_i(2\alpha_i)y_{ii}$ appears to recur in many formulas, we shall use a special symbol C for it; i.e.

$$C = 2\sum_i p_i\alpha_i y_{ii}$$

We can now evaluate the terms of interest. We find

(1) $V(X) = \tfrac{1}{16}V(y_{ii} + y_{jj} + y_{kk} + y_{ll})$
$= \tfrac{1}{4}V_\infty$

(2) $\text{Cov}(X, Y) = \tfrac{1}{4}\text{Cov}(y_{ii}+y_{jj}+y_{kk}+y_{ll}, \epsilon_{ij}+\epsilon_{kl})$
$= \tfrac{1}{4}[4E(y_{ii}\epsilon_{ij}) + 4\mu_\infty\mu_\epsilon - 8\mu_\infty\mu_\epsilon]$
$= \text{Cov}(y_{ii}, \epsilon_{ij})$
$= \tfrac{1}{4}C - \tfrac{1}{4}V_\infty$

(3) $\text{Cov}(X, Z) = \tfrac{1}{4}\text{Cov}(y_{ii}+y_{jj}+y_{kk}+y_{ll}, \epsilon_{ij}+\epsilon_{ik}+\epsilon_{il}+\epsilon_{jk}+\epsilon_{jl}+\epsilon_{kl})$
$= 3\,\text{Cov}(y_{ii}, \epsilon_{ij})$
$= \tfrac{3}{4}C - \tfrac{3}{4}V_\infty.$

(4) $\text{Cov}(Y, Z) = E(YZ) - E(Y)E(Z)$

$$= E(YZ) - 12\mu_\epsilon^2$$

$$E(YZ) = 2E(\epsilon_{ij}^2) + 8E(\epsilon_{ij}\epsilon_{ik}) + 2\mu_\epsilon^2$$

$$\text{Cov}(Y, Z) = 2V(\epsilon_{ij}) + 8\,\text{Cov}(\epsilon_{ij}, \epsilon_{ik})$$

$$= \tfrac{1}{2}\sigma_G^2 + \tfrac{1}{4}V_\infty - \tfrac{1}{2}C + \sigma_A^2 + \tfrac{1}{2}V_\infty - C$$

$$= \tfrac{3}{2}(\sigma_A^2 - C) + \tfrac{1}{2}\sigma_D^2 + \tfrac{3}{4}V_\infty$$

(5) $V(Z) = 6V(\epsilon_{ij}) + 24\,\text{Cov}(\epsilon_{ij}, \epsilon_{ik})$ by similar reasoning

$$= \tfrac{3}{2}\sigma_G^2 + \tfrac{3}{4}V_\infty - \tfrac{3}{2}C + 3\sigma_A^2 + \tfrac{3}{2}V_\infty - 3C$$

$$= \tfrac{9}{2}(\sigma_A^2 - C) + \tfrac{3}{2}\sigma_D^2 + \tfrac{9}{4}V_\infty$$

Finally

$$K = V(X) + \text{Cov}(X, Y)$$

$$= \tfrac{1}{4}C$$

$$L = \text{Cov}(X, Z) + \text{Cov}(Y, Z)$$

$$= \tfrac{3}{2}\sigma_A^2 - \tfrac{3}{4}C + \tfrac{1}{2}\sigma_D^2$$

We may summarize the algebraic computations given above in the following statements. Suppose matings are made at random in the original population, these matings being the origin of lines; then, if the inbreeding within lines is carried to an extent measured by F_r, we have (1) the genotypic variance of line means in the generation with inbreeding F_r is

$$\tfrac{1}{4}V_\infty + \frac{(1 - F_r)}{2}(\tfrac{3}{4}C - \tfrac{3}{4}V_\infty) + \frac{(1 - F_r)^2}{16}(\tfrac{9}{2}\sigma_A^2 - \tfrac{9}{2}C + \tfrac{3}{2}\sigma_D^2 + \tfrac{9}{4}V_\infty)$$

where V_∞ = genotypic variance in homozygous resulting population

σ_A^2 = additive variance in original population

σ_D^2 = dominance variance in original population

C = covariance of additive values of homozygous genotypes in original and in completely homozygous populations

(2) the genotypic covariance of midparent and rth generation line mean is

$$\tfrac{1}{4}C + \frac{1 - F_r}{4}(\tfrac{3}{2}\sigma_A^2 - \tfrac{3}{4}C + \tfrac{1}{2}\sigma_D^2)$$

Also if rth generation individuals and sth generation individuals are obtained from independent samples of the gametes of the two individuals in original matings, we have (3) the genotypic covariance of rth generation line mean and sth generation line mean is

$$\tfrac{1}{4}V_\infty + \left(\frac{1 - F_r}{4} + \frac{1 - F_s}{4}\right)(\tfrac{3}{4}C - \tfrac{3}{4}V_\infty)$$

$$+ \frac{(1 - F_r)(1 - F_s)}{16}(\tfrac{9}{2}\sigma_A^2 - \tfrac{9}{2}C + \tfrac{3}{2}\sigma_D^2 + \tfrac{9}{4}V_\infty)$$

Just how useful the above formulas can be is an open question. It is clear that one can estimate σ_A^2, σ_D^2, C, and V_∞ with little trouble. The quantities which are of special interest here are C and V_∞, since we have already seen how σ_A^2 and σ_D^2 can be estimated. The quantity V_∞ appears to be of interest in that it tells us just what variance there would be among completely homozygous lines obtained from the original population. The quantity C tells us the extent of dominance in that, if C is equal to σ_A^2, there is no dominance. As in all the work in this chapter, the results are valid for an arbitrary number of loci, provided there is no epistacy and we interpret each component such as σ_A^2 as the total variance of that type in the population.

17.12 THE TESTING OF INBRED MATERIAL

We may, following Henderson (1954), consider what happens if we have the population

$$\sum_{i,j} p_i p_j A_i A_j$$

obtain an inbred population

$$\sum_i F p_i A_i A_i + (1 - F)\sum_{i,j} p_i p_j A_i A_j$$

and then test the individuals of the inbred population by the original population. Each individual of the inbred population will have a test value, which may be termed its general combining ability, and we may consider the variance of the test values or in other words the variance of general combining ability.

The frequency of an individual with genotype $A_i A_j$ is

$$F p_i \delta_{ij} + (1 - F)p_i p_j, \|$$

and, since the test population contributes a gametic array $\sum_s p_s A_s$, the test value or mean value of progeny is $\dfrac{1}{2}\sum_s p_s y_{is} + \dfrac{1}{2}\sum_s p_s y_{js}$ which, it

$\|$ δ_{ij} is the Kronecker delta which is unity if i equals j and is zero otherwise.

will be recalled, is equal to $\frac{1}{2}(\alpha_i + \alpha_j)$.   The mean value of progeny means is clearly zero; so the variance in general combining ability is

$$\frac{1}{4} \sum_{ij} [Fp_i\delta_{ij} + (1 - F)p_ip_j](\alpha_i + \alpha_j)^2$$

which equals

$$\frac{1}{4} \sum_i Fp_i(2\alpha_i)^2 + (1 - F) \sum_{i,j} p_ip_j(\alpha_i^2 + 2\alpha_i\alpha_j + \alpha_j^2)$$

$$= \tfrac{1}{4}[2F\sigma_A^2 + (1 - F)\sigma_A^2]$$

$$= \frac{1 + F}{4} \sigma_A^2$$

We shall see in the later chapter dealing with an arbitrary number of loci that this formula can be generalized easily.

REFERENCES

Comstock, R. E., and H. F. Robinson. 1952. Estimation of average dominance of genes. Chapter 30 of *Heterosis*, edited J. W. Gowen. Iowa State College Press, Ames.

Fisher, R. A. 1918. On the correlation between relatives on the supposition of Mendelian inheritance. *Trans. roy. Soc. Edinb.*, **52**, 399–433.

Fisher, R. A. 1949. *The theory of inbreeding*. Oliver and Boyd, Edinburgh.

Henderson, C. R. 1954. Effect of inbreeding on components of genetic variation. Paper presented at meeting of American Society of Animal Production.

Horner, T. W. 1951. Non-allelic gene interaction and the interpretation of quantitative genetic data. Ph.D. Thesis. North Carolina State College Library.

Horner, T. W. 1956. Parent–offspring and full-sib correlations under a parent–offspring mating system. *Genetics*, **41**, 460–468.

Horner, T. W., R. E Comstock and H. F. Robinson. 1956. Non-allelic gene interactions and the interpretation of quantitative genetic data. *Tech. Bull. N. C. agric. Exp. Sta.* **118**.

Kempthorne, O. 1955. The correlations between relatives in inbred populations. *Genetics*, **40**, 681–691.

Kempthorne, O. 1956. On the covariances between relatives under selfing with general epistacy. *Proc. roy. Soc. Lond.*, B, **145**, 100–108.

Malécot, G. 1948. *Les mathématiques de l'hérédité*. Masson et Cie, Paris.

Mather, K. 1949. *Biometrical genetics*. Methuen, London.

Morley, F. H. W. 1954. Selection for economic characters in Australian Merino sheep. IV. The effect of inbreeding. *Aust. J. agric. Res.*, **5**, 305–316.

Wright, Sewall. 1921. Systems of mating. II. The effects of inbreeding on the genetic composition of a population. *Genetics*, **6**, 124–143.

Wright, Sewall. 1951. The genetical structure of populations. *Ann. Eugen. Lond.*, **15**, 323–354.

FURTHER READING

Bateman, A. J., and K. Mather. 1951. The progress of inbreeding in barley. *Heredity*, **5**, 321–348.

Dickinson, A. G., and J. L. Jinks. 1956. A generalized analysis of diallel crosses. *Genetics*, **41**, 65–78.

Hayman, B. I. 1953. Components of variation under sib-mating. *Heredity*, **7**, 121–126.

Henderson, C. R. 1948. Estimation of general, specific, and maternal combining abilities in crosses among inbred lines of swine. Unpublished Ph.D. Thesis. Iowa State College Library.

Hogben, Lancelot. 1933. The effect of consanguineous parentage upon metrical characters of the offspring. *Proc. roy. Soc. Edinb.*, **52**, 239–251.

Jinks, J. L. 1956. The F_2 and backcross generations from a set of diallel crosses. *Heredity*, **10**, 1–30.

Robertson, Alan. 1952. The effect of inbreeding due to recessive genes. *Genetics*, **37**, 189–207.

Yates, F. 1947. The analysis of data from all possible reciprocal crosses between a set of parental lines. *Heredity*, **1**, 287–302.

PROBLEMS

1. Suppose we start with the population

$$p^2AA + 2pqAa + q^2aa$$

and obtain progeny by selfing. Obtain the following as functions of p:

> Variance of offspring
> Covariance of parent and offspring
> Correlation of parent and offspring

if the genotypic values for AA, Aa, and aa are 1, 1, 0, respectively.

2. Obtain the same results as in question 1 if the genotypic values are 3, 2, 1, respectively, by the shortest method you know.

3. Plot the covariance of parent in generation n and offspring in generation $n+1$ for the case of full-sibbing when the original population is random mating with two alleles A and a, the gene frequency of A is equal to (a) 0.5, (b) 0.9, and the genotypic values of AA, Aa, and aa, are respectively 1, 1, 0.

4. Do as in question 3 for the case of inbreeding with a parent–offspring mating system.

5. Evaluate directly the covariance of full-sibs when the parents are random members of the population

$$0.35AA + 0.30Aa + 0.35aa$$

and verify agreement with the general formula.

6. Consider a random mating population which is inbred to an extent F. What is the covariance of parent and offspring with random mating of the inbred population. Evaluate the results.

CHAPTER .18

One-Locus Polyploid Populations

In this chapter we take up the theory of quantitative inheritance in polyploid populations with a single locus segregating. The theory of course applies to the case where there is an arbitrary number of loci among which there is no epistacy or linkage, merely by supposing that all relevant quantities are defined for each locus separately and totaled over loci. We shall include in this chapter what is known on random mating and on inbreeding. In the case of diploid populations we have no theory of assortative matings in relation to quantitative inheritance, except that developed by Fisher and given in Chapter 22, and that developed by Wright (1921) which we regard as having too restrictive a basis. There appear to be no results on assortative mating in polyploid populations.

18.1 RANDOM MATING POPULATIONS

The results even in this case are complicated in general, and we have to take recourse to the work of Fisher (1943) and Mather (1936) on polysomic segregation to have a general treatment. The case of no dominance was worked out by Wright (1938). We shall consider only the case in which segregation is by chromosomes rather than by chromatids (Kempthorne, 1955a). In that case for an autotetraploid with genotype $abcd$, for example, the contributions to an offspring are ab, ac, ad, bc, bd, and cd, each with a probability of $\frac{1}{6}$.

18.2 THE BREAKDOWN OF GENOTYPIC VALUE

We suppose that the observed attribute P of an individual when averaged over the population of environments gives the genotypic value of the individual, G say, and we are concerned with the partition of G into meaningful components. We first deal with the case of autotetraploids.

Consider an individual with genotype $A_i A_j A_k A_l$. Then we have the identity

$$A_i A_j A_k A_l = \rho^4 + (A_i - \rho)\rho^3 + \rho(A_j - \rho)\rho^2 + (A_i - \rho)(A_j - \rho)\rho^2$$
$$+ \rho^2(A_k - \rho)\rho + (A_i - \rho)\rho(A_k - \rho)\rho + \rho(A_j - \rho)(A_k - \rho)\rho$$

$$+ (A_i - \rho)(A_j - \rho)(A_k - \rho)\rho + \rho^3(A_l - \rho) + (A_i - \rho)\rho^2(A_l - \rho)$$
$$+ \rho(A_j - \rho)\rho(A_l - \rho) + (A_i - \rho)(A_j - \rho)\rho(A_l - \rho)$$
$$+ \rho^2(A_k - \rho)(A_l - \rho) + (A_i - \rho)\rho(A_k - \rho)(A_l - \rho)$$
$$+ \rho(A_j - \rho)(A_k - \rho)(A_l - \rho) + (A_i - \rho)(A_j - \rho)(A_k - \rho)(A_l - \rho) \quad (1)$$

where ρ is equal to $\sum_{i=1}^{m} p_i A_i$. Now let us expand each of the terms on the right-hand side, and replace each genotype symbol by the genotypic value of that genotype. Using $A_i A_j A_k A_l$ also to denote the genotypic value of the genotype $A_i A_j A_k A_l$ on the left-hand side, we may write the result as

$$A_i A_j A_k A_l = \mu + \alpha_i + \alpha_j + \beta_{ij} + \alpha_k + \beta_{ik} + \beta_{jk} + \gamma_{ijk} + \alpha_l$$
$$+ \beta_{il} + \beta_{jl} + \gamma_{ijl} + \beta_{kl} + \gamma_{ikl} + \gamma_{jkl} + \delta_{ijkl} \quad (2)$$

where the terms are made to correspond one by one, and for instance μ is the population mean, α_i is equal to the expansion of $(A_i - \rho)\rho^3$ expressed in genotypic values; that is, it is equal to $\sum_{a,b,c} p_a p_b p_c y_{iabc}$ where y_{iabc} is the genotypic value of $A_i A_a A_b A_c$ measured around the mean, and so on.

We now state that the terms on the right-hand side of (2) have zero means and are uncorrelated in the population; that is: If we suppose that a random assignment of the numbers 1, 2, 3, 4 is made to the genes of each individual in the population, so as to give the genes an order, then the covariance of each term on the right-hand side between two random individuals is zero. The fact that the means are zero is obvious. A couple of examples are sufficient to exhibit orthogonality of terms. Consider the terms α_i and $\alpha_{i'}$ for two random individuals: then, for each, i and i' take the values a and $a' = 1, 2, \cdots, m$ with probability p_a and $p_{a'}$ independently. Hence

$$E(\alpha_i \alpha_{i'}) = \sum_{a} p_a[(A_a - \rho)\rho^3] \sum_{a'} p_{a'}[(A_{a'} - \rho)\rho^3]$$
$$= (\rho^4 - \rho^4)(\rho^4 - \rho^4)$$
$$= 0$$

Again take β_{ik} for one individual and γ_{ikl} for another. We have

$$E_{i,k,l} (\beta_{ik}\gamma_{ikl}) = E_{ik} \beta_{ik}(E_{l} \gamma_{ikl})$$
$$= E_{ik} \beta_{ik}(0)$$
$$= 0$$

We see therefore that the genotypic value of an individual tetraploid is made up additively of the following parts:

 1. μ the population mean.

 2. Four gene effects α_i, α_j, α_k, α_l which by analogy with diploid population may be called the additive effects of genes A_i, A_j, A_k, and A_l.

 3. Six terms arising from the interaction of two genes, β_{ij}, β_{ik}, β_{jk}, β_{il}, β_{jl}, β_{kl}, which are analogous to dominance deviations in the diploid case.

 4. Four terms arising from the interaction of three genes, γ_{ijk}, γ_{ijl}, γ_{jkl}, and γ_{ikl}, to which again there is no analogy in the diploid case.

 5. One term arising from the interaction of four genes, δ_{ijkl}, to which again there is no analogy in the diploid case.

The fact that the α_i's are the additively genetic effects of the genes A_i follows from the definition of additive genetic effects and the orthogonality or lack of correlation between the terms on the right-hand side of (2).

There appears to be no terminology established for terms like the γ's or δ's defined above. We might perhaps suggest that terms like β_{ij} should be called digene effects, terms like γ_{ijk} trigene effects, and terms like δ_{ijkl} quadrigene effects.

The values of the different contributions are exhibited in explicit form below.

Definitions

$$y_{ijkl} = \text{genotypic value as deviation from population mean}$$

$$\overline{A_i A_j A_k A_l} = y_{ijkl}$$

$$\overline{A_i A_j A_k} = \sum_a p_a y_{ijka}$$

$$\overline{A_i A_j} = \sum_a \sum_b p_a p_b y_{ijab}$$

$$\overline{A_i} = \sum_a \sum_b \sum_c p_a p_b p_c y_{iabc}$$

Contributions

$$\alpha_i = \overline{A_i}, \; \alpha_j = \overline{A_j}, \; \alpha_k = \overline{A_k}, \; \alpha_l = \overline{A_l}$$

$$\beta_{ij} = \overline{A_i A_j} - \alpha_i - \alpha_j$$

$$\beta_{ik} = \overline{A_i A_k} - \alpha_i - \alpha_k$$

$$\beta_{il} = \overline{A_i A_l} - \alpha_i - \alpha_l$$

$$\beta_{jk} = \overline{A_j A_k} - \alpha_j - \alpha_k$$

$$\beta_{jl} = \overline{A_j A_l} - \alpha_j - \alpha_l$$

$$\beta_{kl} = \overline{A_k A_l} - \alpha_k - \alpha_l$$

$$\gamma_{ijk} = \overline{A_i A_j A_k} - \beta_{ij} - \beta_{ik} - \beta_{jk} - \alpha_i - \alpha_j - \alpha_k$$

$$\gamma_{ijl} = \overline{A_i A_j A_l} - \beta_{ij} - \beta_{il} - \beta_{jl} - \alpha_i - \alpha_j - \alpha_l$$

$$\gamma_{ikl} = \overline{A_i A_k A_l} - \beta_{ik} - \beta_{il} - \beta_{kl} - \alpha_i - \alpha_k - \alpha_l$$

$$\gamma_{jkl} = \overline{A_j A_k A_l} - \beta_{jk} - \beta_{jl} - \beta_{kl} - \alpha_j - \alpha_k - \alpha_l$$

$$\delta_{ijkl} = \overline{A_i A_j A_k A_l} - \gamma_{ijk} - \gamma_{ijl} - \gamma_{ikl} - \gamma_{jkl} - \beta_{ij} - \beta_{ik} - \beta_{il}$$
$$- \beta_{jk} - \beta_{jl} - \beta_{kl} - \alpha_i - \alpha_j - \alpha_k - \alpha_l$$

Finally we can envisage the partition of genotypic variance by the equation

$$\sigma_G^2 = \sigma_A^2 + \sigma_D^2 + \sigma_T^2 + \sigma_F^2$$

where

$$\tfrac{1}{4}\sigma_A^2 = \sum_{1=l}^{m} p_i \alpha_i^2$$

$$\tfrac{1}{6}\sigma_D^2 = \sum_{i,j} p_i p_j \beta_{ij}^2$$

$$\tfrac{1}{4}\sigma_T^2 = \sum_{i,j,k} p_i p_j p_k \gamma_{ijk}^2$$

and

$$\sigma_F^2 = \sum_{ijkl} p_i p_j p_k p_l \delta_{ijkl}^2$$

These components of variance will be found useful in characterizing correlations between relatives.

In the general case of a $2r$-ploid individual (Kempthorne, 1955b) we know that

$$\left(\sum_{i=1}^{m} p_i A_i \right)^{2r}$$

is the genotypic array of a random mating population at equilibrium. As in the tetraploid case, we let

$$\rho = \sum_{i=1}^{m} p_i A_i$$

and

$$v_i = A_i - \rho$$

Then

$$A_i A_j A_k \cdots = [\rho + (A_i - \rho)][\rho + (A_j - \rho)][\rho + (A_k - \rho)] \cdots$$

or

$$A_i A_j A_k A_l \cdots = \rho^{2r} + v_i\rho^{2r-1} + v_j\rho^{2r-1} + v_k\rho^{2r-1} + v_l\rho^{2r-1} + \cdots$$
$$+ v_i v_j\rho^{2r-2} + v_i v_k\rho^{2r-2} + \cdots$$
$$+ v_i v_j v_k\rho^{2r-3} + \cdots$$
$$+ v_i v_j v_k v_l\rho^{2r-4} + \cdots$$
$$+ v_i v_j v_k v_l v_m\rho^{2r-5} + \cdots$$
$$+ \text{etc.}$$

Each separate symbol on the right-hand side is to be written out fully in terms of genotypic symbols, and then genotypic values are to be inserted. We let the genes of each individual in the population be numbered at random from 1 to $2r$, and consequently the probability that the gene numbered k is actually allele A_j is p_j independently over k. The relation above can then be written in the form:

Genotypic value

$$= \mu + \alpha_1 + \alpha_2 + (\alpha\alpha)_{12} + \alpha_3 + (\alpha\alpha)_{13} + (\alpha\alpha)_{23} + (\alpha\alpha\alpha)_{123}$$
$$+ \alpha_4 + (\alpha\alpha)_{14} + (\alpha\alpha)_{24} + (\alpha\alpha\alpha)_{124} + (\alpha\alpha)_{34} + (\alpha\alpha\alpha)_{134}$$
$$+ (\alpha\alpha\alpha)_{234} + (\alpha\alpha\alpha\alpha)_{1234} + \alpha_5$$
$$+ (\alpha\alpha)_{15} + (\alpha\alpha)_{25} + (\alpha\alpha\alpha)_{125} + (\alpha\alpha)_{35} + (\alpha\alpha\alpha)_{135}$$
$$+ (\alpha\alpha\alpha)_{235} + (\alpha\alpha\alpha\alpha)_{1235} + \cdots$$
$$+ (\alpha\alpha\alpha\alpha\alpha)_{12345} + \cdots$$
$$+ (\alpha\alpha\alpha\alpha\alpha\alpha)_{123456} + \cdots$$

where α_1 is equal to $v_1\rho^{2r-1}$ if gene 1 is A_1, $v_2\rho^{2r-1}$ if gene 1 is A_2, etc.; $(\alpha\alpha)_{13}$ for instance is $v_1 v_3\rho^{2r-2}$ if gene 1 is A_1 and gene 3 is A_3, and is $v_2 v_6\rho^{2r-2}$ if gene 1 is A_2 and gene 3 is A_6; $(\alpha\alpha\alpha)_{125}$ is $v_2 v_7 v_8\rho^{2r-3}$ if gene 1 is A_2, gene 2 is A_7, and gene 5 is A_8; and so on. In this way the genotypic value is made up of a combination corresponding to the gene numbered 1, the gene numbered 2, the pair of genes numbered 1 and 2, and so on.

We now state that the average value over the population of any contribution associated with any set of numbers is zero. For instance,

$$E(\alpha_1) = \sum_{i=1}^{m} p_i \nu_i \rho^{2r-1}$$

$$= \sum_{i=1}^{m} p_i (A_i - \sum p_s A_s) \rho^{2r-1}$$

$$= (\sum p_i A_i - \sum p_i A_i) \rho^{2r-1}$$

$$= 0$$

$$E(\alpha\alpha)_{12} = \underset{(1)}{E} \left\{ \underset{(2)}{E} \left[(\alpha\alpha)_{12} \right] \right\},$$

where for example $\underset{(1)}{E}$ denotes expectation over the first gene, $\underset{(2)}{E}$ expectation over the second gene and

$$\underset{(2)}{E}(\alpha\alpha)_{12} = \sum_{s=1}^{m} \nu_i \left(\sum_{j=1}^{m} p_j \nu_j \right) \rho^{2r-2} = 0$$

It is also easily seen that the terms of different origins are uncorrelated. For instance,

$$E[\alpha_1 (\alpha\alpha)_{12}] = \sum_{i=1}^{m} \sum_{j=1}^{m} p_i \nu_i \rho^{2r-1} p_j \nu_i \nu_j \rho^{2r-2}$$

$$= \sum_{i=1}^{m} p_i \nu_i \rho^{2r-1} \left[\nu_i \left(\sum_{j=1}^{m} p_j \nu_j \right) \rho^{2r-2} \right]$$

$$= 0 \quad \text{since} \quad \sum_j p_j \nu_j = 0$$

We now state that

(1) $\rho^{2r} = \mu$ is the population mean

(2) $\nu_i \rho^{2r-1}$ is the average effect of gene A_i

(3) $\nu_i \nu_j \rho^{2r-2}$ is the dominance deviation associated with genes A_i and A_j

(4) $\nu_i \nu_j \nu_k \rho^{2r-3}$ is the deviation, say trigenic, associated with genes A_i, A_j, A_k

and so on.

A genotypic value consists then of one constant μ, $2r$ average gene effects, $2r(2r-1)/2$ dominance deviations, $2r(2r-1)(2r-2)/2 \cdot 3$ trigenic deviations, and so on, with $(2r!/t!)(2r-t)!$ deviations due to sets of t genes. Of course these deviations are not necessarily all different for any one genotype. In the case of the genotype A^{2r} the genotypic value consists of μ, $2r$ times the effect of gene A, $2r(2r - 1)/2$ times the dominance deviation due to genes A and A, $2r(2r - 1)(2r - 2)/6$ times the trigenic deviation due to genes A, A, and A, and so on.

In view of the fact that all the terms are uncorrelated, the average value of the square of the genotypic value is equal to

$$\mu^2 + \sigma_A^2 + \sigma_D^2 + \sigma_T^2 + \sigma_F^2 + \cdots$$

where σ_A^2 is equal to $2r$ times the average value of the square of average gene effects, σ_D^2 is equal to $2r(2r - 1)/2$ times the average of the square of the dominance deviations, and so on; i.e.,

$$\sigma_A^2 = 2r\, E(\nu_i \rho^{2r-1})^2$$

$$\sigma_D^2 = \frac{2r(2r - 1)}{2}\, E(\nu_i \nu_j \rho^{2r-2})^2$$

$$\sigma_T^2 = \frac{2r(2r - 1)(2r - 2)}{6}\, E(\nu_i \nu_j \nu_k \rho^{2r-3})^2$$

up to a component which is the average value of the square of the deviation particular to every individual genotype.

18.3 THE GENOTYPIC COVARIANCES BETWEEN RELATIVES UNDER RANDOM MATING

Consider two individuals X and Y which are related in some way: Then their genotypic values G_X and G_Y, respectively, will be given by

$$G = \mu + \text{average gene effects} + \text{dominance deviations}$$
$$+ \text{trigenic deviations} + \text{etc.}$$

The different terms on the right-hand side are uncorrelated over the population, so that under random mating the only covariances that can arise have their origin in like terms for the two relatives. We let

$\rho_1 =$ probability that a random gene of X and a random gene of Y are identical by descent

$\rho_2 =$ probability that a random pair of genes of X are identical by descent to a random pair of genes of Y

$\rho_3 =$ probability that a random set of three genes of X are identical by descent to a random set of three genes of Y

and so on.

Then the genotypic covariance between X and Y is equal to

$$\rho_1 2r\sigma_A^2 + \rho_2 \frac{2r(2r-1)}{1 \cdot 2} \sigma_D^2 + \rho_3 \frac{2r(2r-1)(2r-2)}{1 \cdot 2 \cdot 3} \sigma_T^2 \cdots$$

$$+ \rho_k \frac{2r!}{k!(2r-k)!} \sigma_{L(k)}^2 + \cdots$$

where $\sigma_{L(k)}^2$ is the component of genotypic variance arising from the deviations common to all individuals which possess at least the same k genes.

In the case of genotypic covariance of an individual with itself the multipliers of the separate components are clearly unity. For parent–offspring covariances under the assumption that segregation is by chromosomes and not by chromatids, we have

$$\rho_1 = \frac{1}{2(2r)}, \qquad \rho_2 = \frac{r(r-1)}{2r(2r-1)} \times \frac{1 \cdot 2}{2r(2r-1)}$$

$$\rho_3 = \frac{r(r-1)(r-2)}{2r(2r-1)(2r-2)} \times \frac{1 \cdot 2 \cdot 3}{2r(2r-1)(2r-2)}$$

and in general

$$\rho_k = \frac{[(2r-k)!]^2 k! \, r!}{[(2r)!\,]^2 (r-k)!}$$

For tetraploids the covariance of parent and offspring is $\frac{1}{2}\sigma_A^2 + \frac{1}{6}\sigma_D^2$: for hexaploids it is $\frac{1}{2}\sigma_A^2 + \frac{1}{5}\sigma_D^2 + \frac{1}{20}\sigma_T^2$. Note that, for diploids, with $r = 1$, we get $\frac{1}{2}\sigma_A^2$ for the parent–offspring covariance.

In some cases the relationship between two individuals is such that half of the gene complement of each individual comes from one source and the other half comes from an independent source. Suppose for purposes of definiteness that the sire genes, i.e. genes contributed by the respective sire, of the two individuals are related, and that the dam genes are related but the sire and dam genes are independent. Let the sire genes be $A_{s1}, A_{s2}, \cdots, A_{sk}$. These are a random set of the totality of possible genes. Let Q_{s1} be the probability that both individuals I and II receive gene A_{s1}. Let

$$\phi = \sum_{\text{sire genes}} Q_{s1}$$

Let ψ equal the sum of the probabilities that individuals I and II receive each possible pair of sire genes, and so on. Let ϕ', ψ', etc. be defined likewise for the dam genes. Then it can be seen that the genotypic covariance of I and II is equal to

$$(\phi + \phi') \frac{1\sigma_A^2}{2r} + (\phi\phi' + \psi + \psi') \frac{\sigma_D^2}{2r(2r-1)/2} \quad \text{etc.}$$

In the case of autotetraploids the covariance is

$$(\phi + \phi') \frac{\sigma_A^2}{4} + (\phi\phi' + \psi + \psi') \frac{\sigma_D^2}{6} + (\phi\psi' + \phi'\psi) \frac{\sigma_T^2}{4} + \psi\psi'\sigma_F^2$$

These particular formulas hold only if the pattern of relationship is of the particular type. The formalization leads quickly to the results for parent–offspring, full-sib, double first cousin, and parent–grandoffspring covariances for example. In those cases the values of ϕ, ϕ', ψ, ψ' are as follows for tetraploids:

	ϕ	ϕ'	ψ	ψ'
Parent–offspring	2	0	1	0
Full-sib	1	1	$\frac{1}{6}$	$\frac{1}{6}$
Double first cousin	$\frac{1}{2}$	$\frac{1}{2}$	$\frac{8}{6^3}$	$-\frac{8}{6^3}$
Parent–grandoffspring	1	0	$\frac{1}{6}$	0

The covariances that have been worked out for autotetraploids are specified by K, L, M, N with

$$\text{Cov}(X, Y) = K\sigma_A^2 + L\sigma_D^2 + M\sigma_T^2 + N\sigma_F^2$$

and the values for K, L, M, N are given in Table 18.1. It is left as an exercise to the reader to evaluate the covariances for hexaploids and others.

TABLE 18.1

GENOTYPIC COVARIANCES OF RELATIVES

$$\text{Cov} = K\sigma_A^2 + L\sigma_D^2 + M\sigma_T^2 + N\sigma_F^2$$

Relationship	K	L	M	N
Identical twin	1	1	1	1
Parent–offspring	$\frac{1}{2}$	$\frac{1}{6}$	0	0
Parent–grandoffspring	$\frac{1}{4}$	$\frac{1}{36}$	0	0
Full-sib	$\frac{1}{2}$	$\frac{2}{9}$	$\frac{1}{12}$	$\frac{1}{36}$
Uncle–nephew	$\frac{1}{4}$	$\frac{2}{63}$	0	0
Half-sib	$\frac{1}{4}$	$\frac{1}{36}$	0	0
Double first cousin	$\frac{1}{4}$	$\frac{70}{6^4}$	$\frac{2}{6^3}$	$\frac{64}{6^6}$

It is to be emphasized that the methods and results given above are special and based on the assumption of segregation by chromosomes. The more general case has not been treated to our knowledge though we can guess that double reduction affects the results very little.

18.4 COVARIANCES UNDER INBREEDING IN POLYPLOID POPULATIONS

The case in which the genotypic value is determined exactly by additive effects of genes is easily disposed of. It is clear that, if r_{XY} is the coefficient of parentage of X and Y, and is the probability that a random gene of X and a random gene of Y are identical by descent, then the genotypic covariance of X and Y is $2k\sigma_A^2 \times r_{XY}$. The genotypic variance of individuals of the same amount of inbreeding as X is $2k\sigma_A^2 r_{XX}$ which from earlier material is equal to $\sigma_A^2\{1 + (2k - 1)F_X\}$. Note that with diploids k equals unity and we get as before $\sigma_A^2(1 + F_X)$.

We know of no work which takes account of dominance.

REFERENCES

Fisher, R. A. 1943. Allowance for double reduction in the calculation of genotypic frequencies with polysomic inheritance. *Ann. Eugen. Lond.*, **12**, 169–171.

Fisher, R. A. 1949. *The theory of inbreeding*. Oliver and Boyd, Edinburgh.

Kempthorne, O. 1955a. The correlation between relatives in a simple autotetraploid population. *Genetics*, **40**, 168–174.

Kempthorne, O. 1955b. The correlations between relatives in random mating populations. *Cold Spr. Harb. Symp. quant. Biol.*, **20**, 60–75.

Mather, K. 1936. Segregation and linkage in autotetraploids. *J. Genet.*, **32**, 287–314.

Wright, Sewall. 1921. Systems of mating. *Genetics*, **6**, 111–178.

Wright, Sewall. 1938. The distribution of gene frequencies in populations of polyploids. *Proc. nat. Acad. Sci. Wash.*, **24**, 372–377.

PROBLEMS

1. Suppose we have the population

$$(0.3A + 0.7a)^4$$

with genotypic values for A^4, A^3a, A^2a^2, Aa^3, and a^4 equal to 4, 4, 3, 2, 1. Obtain the numerical values of the components of genotypic variance and hence the covariances of parent and offspring and of full-sibs.

2. Develop some theory of the partition of genotypic variance in a partially inbred autotetraploid population.

3. Consider the population

$$(pA + qa)^4$$

Suppose it is inbred by full-sibbing for two generations and then matings are made at random. Obtain the covariance of parent and offspring.

CHAPTER 19

Diploid Populations with Arbitrary Number of Segregating Loci and Arbitrary Epistacy

19.1 INTRODUCTION

We have attempted in previous chapters to give the sum total of present knowledge on variability in populations in which one locus is segregating. The reader may feel that we have spent an undue amount of space on this problem, but we excuse ourselves on the basis that methodology by which results are obtained should be presented in some detail so that other workers and particularly students can see how problems are tackled and the methodology which is successful at least to some extent.

There is little doubt that most of the problems to which the theory of quantitative inheritance should present a guide involve more than one locus, and indeed, may involve hundreds of loci. We therefore consider the generalization of the single-locus results. Generalization has been achieved only with random mating populations or with a few special problems involving inbreeding. We omit here the extensive work by Fisher (1918) and some based on that, which we may term as infinitesimal theory. In this theory it as assumed that there is a large number of loci and that the genes have small effects. We shall take up this theory in Chapter 22.

The generalization from one to many loci involves two phenomena not by the nature of things occurring in the single-locus case, namely linkage and epistacy. There is no need to review the notion of linkage. In the case of epistacy (or epistasis, as some writers prefer), some discussion is necessary.

The term epistacy was introduced by Bateson in 1908, to describe the situation when there are two loci and the genes of one locus suppress the effect of genes at the other locus. The reader may find a description of epistacy from this point of view in Sinott, Dunn, and Dobzhansky (1950).

410

An example described by them occurs in summer squashes. The genotypes and phenotypes are as follows:

WWYY:	white	WwYY:	white	wwYY:	yellow
WWYy:	white	WwYy:	white	wwYy:	yellow
WWyy:	white	Wwyy:	white	wwyy:	green

Here, if we look at the effect of Yy versus yy, we find that, in the case
when the W locus is represented by WW or Ww, there is no effect, but,
when the W locus has genes ww, the effect is yellow versus green. Alternatively W suppresses the effect of Y, and Y is dominant to y. The table
can also be looked at horizontally. By either way the gene effects at one
locus depend on the genes present at the other locus.

There are various classical models of epistacy, and to represent them
we shall give tables showing the phenotype (perhaps coded as 0 or 1) in
terms of the number of one of the alleles at one locus and the number of
one of the alleles at the other locus. The case of complementary gene
action is represented by Table 19.1. The case of duplicate action is
represented in Table 19.2.

TABLE 19.1

EXAMPLE OF COMPLEMENTARY GENE ACTION

Locus 1

		2	1	0
	2	1	1	0
Locus 2	1	1	1	0
	0	0	0	0

TABLE 19.2

EXAMPLE OF DUPLICATE GENE ACTION

Locus 1

		2	1	0
	2	1	1	1
Locus 2	1	1	1	1
	0	1	1	0

A third simple case is given in Table 19.3 in which the effects are
multiplicative. Here the heterozygous phase results in multiplication by

TABLE 19.3

EXAMPLE OF MULTIPLICATIVE GENE ACTION

Locus 1

		2	1	0
	2	Kb_1b_2	Ke_1b_2	Kb_2
Locus 2	1	Kb_1e_2	Ke_1e_2	Ke_2
	0	Kb_1	Ke_1	K

e_1 or e_2, and the alternative homozygous phase in multiplication by b_1 or b_2. If the phenotypes are expressed logarithmically, there is no interaction in the table, and if in addition $e_1^2 = b_1$, $e_2^2 = b_2$, there would be no dominance.

The above are particular examples of epistacy, and the general form, more general than was envisaged by Bateson or presented in most elementary texts on genetics, is given in Table 19.4. In Table 19.4 there is epistacy if there is any interaction in the table: that is, if every entry is not representable by the mean plus a row effect plus a column effect.

TABLE 19.4

GENERAL TWO-FACTOR EPISTASIS

Locus 1

		2	1	0
	2	y_{22}	y_{12}	y_{02}
Locus 2	1	y_{21}	y_{11}	y_{01}
	0	y_{20}	y_{10}	y_{00}

We may anticipate that there will in general be epistacy as indicated by interaction in tables of the form exemplified above. In a similar way we can introduce a third locus by making up three or more tables in each of which the genotype at the third locus is constant, and, if there is interaction in one or more of the tables which is not the same for all the tables, there is epistacy involving the three factors. In general, if a general genotypic value is denoted by $A_{i_1}A_{i_2}B_{j_1}B_{j_2}C_{k_1}C_{k_2}\cdots$, then there is no epistacy if this can be represented as

$$\text{Constant} + a_{i_1i_2} + b_{j_1j_2} + c_{k_1k_2} + \cdots \text{ etc.}$$

There is two-factor epistacy only if it can be represented as

$$\text{Constant} + a_{i_1i_2} + b_{j_1j_2} + c_{k_1k_2} + (ab)_{i_1i_2j_1j_2} + (ac)_{i_1i_2k_1k_2}$$
$$+ (bc)_{j_1j_2k_1k_2} + \cdots + \text{etc.}$$

in which one or more of the (ab), (ac), or (bc) terms is not zero. There is three-factor epistasis if it can be represented as

$$\text{Constant} + a_{i_1 i_2} + b_{j_1 j_2} + c_{k_1 k_2} + (ab)_{i_1 i_2 j_1 j_2} + (ac)_{i_1 i_2 k_1 k_2}$$
$$+ (bc)_{j_1 j_2 k_1 k_2} + (abc)_{i_1 i_2 j_1 j_2 k_1 k_2} + \cdots + \text{etc.}$$

and one of the terms $(abc)_{i_1 i_2 j_1 j_2 k_1 k_2}$ is not zero. The ideas here are the standard ones of factorial experiments, the theory of which was largely developed by Fisher and Yates for any situation, although the ideas were until comparatively recently used almost only in agronomy.

Before taking up the general case we shall first deal with the case when there is no epistasis and no linkage.

19.2 MANY FACTORS WITH NO EPISTASIS AND NO LINKAGE

The basic result is that all formulas obtained for the case of one locus under random mating or inbreeding may be extended to the case of an arbitrary number of loci merely by redefining each component of variance as the total over loci of the component evaluated at each locus, providing there is no epistasis and no linkage. This result is intuitively obvious and has been used extensively in the literature.

The proof lies in the fact that the genotypic value of an individual is equal to the sum of components, one arising from the status of each locus. Also, because of the absence of linkage, what happens at any one locus is independent statistically of what happens at any other locus. It is well known that, if

$$y = A + B$$

and A and B are independent (or even uncorrelated), then

$$V(y) = V(A) + V(B)$$

and, if another y value, say y', is given by

$$y' = A' + B'$$

then

$$\text{Cov}(y, y') = \text{Cov}(A, A') + \text{Cov}(B, B')$$

since A, B' and B, A' are independent in the absence of linkage. The result therefore follows.

19.3 THE GENERAL CASE WITH RANDOM MATING AND INDEPENDENT ASSORTMENT

A notation to deal with an arbitrary number of loci, at each of which there is an arbitrary number of alleles, and among which there is arbitrary epistacy must necessarily be a little complex (Kempthorne, 1954, 1955a, b). If however the biologist reader makes sure to familiarize himself with the notation, he should have little trouble. If he is not interested in the derivations, he may skip to the two-loci case (p. 416) and the final results.

We denote loci by superscripts a running from 1 to n, an arbitrary pair of genes at locus a by $A_{i_a}^a$ and $A_{j_a}^a$. An arbitrary genotype is then

$$A_{i_1}^1 A_{j_1}^1 A_{i_2}^2 A_{j_2}^2 A_{i_3}^3 A_{j_3}^3 \cdots \quad \text{or} \quad \prod_{a=1}^{n} A_{i_a}^a A_{j_a}^a.$$

and we shall use *exactly* the same symbol to denote the genotypic value of an individual with this genotype. We shall suppose that the frequency of gene $A_{i_a}^a$ is $p_{i_a}^a$, and that the population is at equilibrium under random mating. It will be recalled from Chapter 2 that such equilibrium would be reached only asymptotically. The population genotypic array may be written as

$$\prod_{a=1}^{n} \sum_{i_a j_a} p_{i_a}^a p_{j_a}^a A_{i_a}^a A_{j_a}^a$$

It is essential to bear in mind that superscripts are not powers. Now make the formal definition

$$v_{i_a}^a = A_{i_a}^a - \sum_{s_a} p_{s_a}^a A_{s_a}^a$$

where the summation extends over all the alleles at the ath locus, and for brevity denote $\sum_{s_a} p_{s_a}^a A_{s_a}^a$ by ρ^a. From this we have formally

$$A_{i_a}^a = \rho^a + v_{i_a}^a$$

and hence

$$\prod_{a=1}^{n} A_{i_a}^a A_{j_a}^a = \prod_{a=1}^{n} (\rho^a + v_{i_a}^a)(\rho^a + v_{j_a}^a)$$

$$= \prod_{a=1}^{n} \rho^a \rho^a + \sum_{a} v_{i_a}^a \rho^a \prod_{a' \neq a} \rho^{a'} \rho^{a'} + \sum_{a} \rho^a v_{j_a}^a \prod_{a' \neq a} \rho^{a'} \rho^{a'}$$

$$+ \sum_{a} v_{i_a}^a v_{j_a}^a \prod_{a' \neq a} \rho^{a'} \rho^{a'} + \sum_{a,a'} v_{i_a}^a \rho^a v_{i_{a'}}^{a'} \rho^{a'} \prod_{a''} \rho^{a''} \rho^{a''}$$

$$+ \sum_{a,a'} v_{i_a}^a \rho^a \rho^{a'} v_{j_{a'}}^{a'} \prod_{a''} \rho^{a''} \rho^{a''} + \sum_{a,a'} v_{j_a}^a \rho^a v_{i_{a'}}^{a'} \rho^{a'} \prod_{a''} \rho^{a''} \rho^{a''}$$

$$+ \sum_{a,a'} \rho^a v_{j_a}^a \rho^{a'} v_{j_{a'}}^{a'} \prod_{a''} \rho^{a''} \rho^{a''}$$

$$+ \sum_{a,a'a''} v_{i_a}^a \rho^a v_{i_{a'}}^{a'} \rho^{a'} v_{i_{a''}}^{a''} \rho^{a''} \prod_{a'''} \rho^{a'''} \rho^{a'''} + \text{etc.} \qquad \text{(A)}$$

In any particular term on the right-hand side the possible values for a, a', a'', etc. are different. Now let each term on the right-hand side be expanded by writing, for example, $\rho^{a''}$ as $\sum_{s_{a''}} p^{a''}_{s_{a''}} A^{a''}_{s_{a''}}$ and $v^{a'}_{i_{a'}}$ as $A^{a'}_{i_{a'}} - \sum_{s_{a'}} p^{a'}_{s_{a'}} A^{a'}_{s_{a'}}$ and then multiplying the whole expression out. This will yield a linear function of genotypic symbols, and, if genotypic values are inserted in place of genotypic symbols, a single number will result.

We will illustrate the terminology by the case of two loci each with two alleles, say A, a and B, b, respectively. Then, denoting A by A^1_1, a by A^1_2, B by A^2_1 and b by A^2_2, we have

$$v^1_1 = A^1_1 - \rho^1 \qquad \rho^1 = p^1_1 A^1_1 + p^1_2 A^1_2$$

$$v^1_2 = A^1_2 - \rho^1 \qquad \rho^2 = p^2_1 A^2_1 + p^2_2 A^2_2$$

$$v^2_1 = A^2_1 - \rho^2$$

$$v^2_2 = A^2_2 - \rho^2$$

and, for example,

$$A^1_1 A^1_2 A^2_1 A^2_2 = (\rho^1 + v^1_1)(\rho^1 + v^1_2)(\rho^2 + v^2_1)(\rho^2 + v^2_2)$$

$$= \rho^1\rho^1\rho^2\rho^2 + v^1_1\rho^1\rho^2\rho^2 + v^1_2\rho^1\rho^2\rho^2 + \rho^1\rho^1 v^2_1\rho^2 + \rho^1\rho^1 v^2_2\rho^2$$

$$+ v^1_1 v^1_2\rho^2\rho^2 + \rho^1\rho^1 v^2_1 v^2_2 + v^1_1\rho^1 v^2_1\rho^2 + v^1_1\rho^1 v^2_2\rho^2$$

$$+ v^1_2\rho^1 v^2_1\rho^2 + v^1_2\rho^1 v^2_2\rho^2 + v^1_1 v^1_2 v^2_1\rho^2 + v^1_1 v^1_2 v^2_2\rho^2$$

$$+ v^1_1\rho^1 v^2_1 v^2_2 + v^1_2\rho^1 v^2_1 v^2_2 + v^1_1 v^1_2 v^2_1 v^2_2$$

A term on the right-hand side is exemplified by

$$v^1_1\rho^1 v^2_1\rho^2 = (A^1_1 - \rho^1)\rho^1(A^2_1 - \rho^2)\rho^2$$

$$= A^1_1\rho^1 A^2_1\rho^2 - \rho^1\rho^1 A^2_1\rho^2 - A^1_1\rho^1\rho^2\rho^2 + \rho^1\rho^1\rho^2\rho^2$$

$$= A^1_1(p^1_1 A^1_1 + p^1_2 A^1_2)\,A^2_1(p^2_1 A^2_1 + p^2_2 A^2_2)$$

$$- (p^1_1 A^1_1 + p^1_2 A^1_2)(p^1_1 A^1_1 + p^1_2 A^1_2)\,A^2_1(p^2_1 A^2_1 + p^2_2 A^2_2)$$

$$- A^1_1(p^1_1 A^1_1 + p^1_2 A^1_2)(p^2_1 A^2_1 + p^2_2 A^2_2)(p^2_1 A^2_1 + p^2_2 A^2_2)$$

$$+ (p^1_1 A^1_1 + p^1_2 A^1_2)(p^1_1 A^1_1 + p^1_2 A^1_2)(p^2_1 A^2_1 + p^2_2 A^2_2)(p^2_1 A^2_1 + p^2_2 A^2_2)$$

If the gene action were complementary with A^1_2 and A^2_2 as the recessive alleles, the number to which this term reduces is

$$1 - (1 - p^1_2 p^1_2) - (1 - p^2_2 p^2_2) + (1 - p^1_2 p^1_2)(1 - p^2_2 p^2_2) = p^1_2 p^1_2 p^2_2 p^2_2$$

We now state that the terms on the right-hand side of (A) are as follows:

$$\mu = \prod_{a=1}^{n} \rho^a \rho^a = \text{population genotypic mean}$$

$$\alpha_{i_a}^a = v_{i_a}^a \rho^a \prod_{a' \neq a} \rho^{a'} \rho^{a'} = \text{additive effect of gene } A_{i_a}^a$$

$$d_{i_a j_a}^a = v_{i_a}^a v_{j_a}^a \prod_{a' \neq a} \rho^{a'} \rho^{a'} = \text{dominance deviation associated with genes } A_{i_a}^a$$
$$\text{and } A_{j_a}^a \text{ of the } a\text{th locus}$$

$$(\alpha^a \alpha^{a'})_{i_a i_{a'}} = v_{i_a}^a \rho^a v_{i_{a'}}^{a'} \rho^{a'} \prod_{a'' \neq a, a'} \rho^{a''} \rho^{a''} = \text{additive} \times \text{additive deviation associ-}$$
$$\text{ated with genes } A_{i_a}^a \text{ and } A_{i_{a'}}^{a'} \text{ at loci } a \text{ and } a'$$

$$(d^a \alpha^{a'})_{i_a j_a i_{a'}} = v_{i_a}^a v_{j_a}^a v_{i_{a'}}^{a'} \rho^{a'} \prod_{a''} \rho^{a''} \rho^{a''} = \text{dominance} \times \text{additive deviation as-}$$
$$\text{sociated with genes } A_{i_a}^a \text{ and } A_{j_a}^a \text{ at locus } a \text{ and gene } A_{i_{a'}}^{a'} \text{ at}$$
$$\text{locus } a'$$

$$(d^a d^{a'})_{i_a j_a i_{a'} j_{a'}} = v_{i_a}^a v_{j_a}^a v_{i_{a'}}^{a'} v_{j_{a'}}^{a'} \prod_{a''} \rho^{a''} \rho^{a''} = \text{dominance} \times \text{dominance deviation}$$
$$\text{associated with genes } A_{i_a}^a \text{ and } A_{j_a}^a \text{ at locus } a \text{ and genes}$$
$$A_{i_{a'}}^a \text{ and } A_{j_{a'}}^{a'} \text{ at locus } a'$$

and so on. If the deviation involves additive with respect to a locus, the formal expression contains a factor like $v_{i_a}^a$, and, if the deviation involves dominance with respect to a locus, the formal expression contains a factor like $v_{i_a}^a v_{j_a}^a$. The total number of effects and deviations associated with a particular genotypic value is 2^n, corresponding to the fact that any deviation involves either a ρ-like factor or a v-like factor. The above may be taken to be the definitions of the various types of deviations. We can see that the additive effects correspond to the definitions for the single locus case because

$$v_{i_a}^a \rho^a = (A_{i_a}^a - \rho^a) \rho^a$$

$$= (A_{i_a}^a - \sum_{s_a} p_{s_a}^a A_{s_a}^a) \left(\sum_{s_a} p_{s_a}^a A_{s_a}^a \right)$$

$$= \sum_{s_a} p_{s_a} A_{i_a}^a A_{s_a}^a - \text{mean}$$

the ρ-like terms for other loci merely involving an average over these loci weighting of course by frequency.

In the case of two loci, say the A and B loci, a simpler notation can be used and one which is in many ways more expressive (Kempthorne, 1955a). Let y_{ijkl} be the genotypic value of the individual with genotype $A_i A_j B_k B_l$,

p_i be the frequency of A_i, and q_k the frequency of B_k. Define means as follows:

$$y_{i \cdot kl} = \sum_j p_j y_{ijkl}$$

$$y_{ij \cdot l} = \sum_k q_k y_{ijkl}$$

$$y_{i \cdot k \cdot} = \sum_l q_l y_{i \cdot kl} = \sum_{jl} p_j q_l y_{ijkl}$$

$$y_{ij \cdot \cdot} = \sum_l q_l y_{ij \cdot l} = \sum_{kl} q_k q_l y_{ijkl}$$

$$y_{\cdot \cdot kl} = \sum_{ij} p_i p_j y_{ijkl}$$

$$y_{i \cdot \cdot \cdot} = \sum_j p_j y_{ij \cdot \cdot} = \sum_{jkl} p_j q_k q_l y_{ijkl}$$

$$y_{\cdot j \cdot \cdot} = \sum_i p_i y_{ij \cdot \cdot}, \qquad y_{\cdot \cdot k \cdot} = \sum_i p_i y_{i \cdot k \cdot}$$

$$y_{\cdot \cdot \cdot l} = \sum_{ijk} p_i p_j q_k y_{ijkl}, \qquad y_{\cdot \cdot \cdot \cdot} = \sum_{ijkl} p_i p_j q_k q_l y_{ijkl}$$

with of course

$$y_{ijkl} = y_{ijlk} = y_{jikl} = y_{jilk}$$

and consequences of this with respect to the mean. Then

$$\mu = y_{\cdot \cdot \cdot \cdot}$$

$$\alpha_i^1 = y_{i \cdot \cdot \cdot} - \mu = y_{\cdot i \cdot \cdot} - \mu; \qquad \alpha_j^1 = y_{\cdot j \cdot \cdot} - \mu = y_{j \cdot \cdot \cdot} - \mu$$

$$\alpha_k^2 = y_{\cdot \cdot k \cdot} - \mu; \qquad \alpha_l^2 = y_{\cdot \cdot \cdot l} - \mu$$

$$d_{ij}^1 = y_{ij \cdot \cdot} - \mu - \alpha_i^1 - \alpha_j^1; \qquad d_{kl}^2 = y_{\cdot \cdot kl} - \mu - \alpha_k^2 - \alpha_l^2$$

$$(\alpha^1 \alpha^2)_{ik} = y_{i \cdot k \cdot} - \mu - \alpha_i^1 - \alpha_k^2 \quad \text{and similar terms}$$

$$(d^1 \alpha^2)_{ijk} = y_{ijk \cdot} - \mu - \alpha_i^1 - \alpha_j^1 - d_{ij}^1 - \alpha_k^2 - (\alpha^1 \alpha^2)_{ik} - (\alpha^1 \alpha^2)_{jk}$$

and similar terms

$$(d^1 d^2)_{ijkl} = y_{ijkl} - \mu - \alpha_i^1 - \alpha_j^1 - d_{ij}^1 - \alpha_k^2 - \alpha_l^2 - d_{kl}^2$$
$$- (\alpha^1 \alpha^2)_{ik} - (\alpha^1 \alpha^2)_{il} - (\alpha^1 \alpha^2)_{jk} - (\alpha^1 \alpha^2)_{jl}$$
$$- (d^1 \alpha^2)_{ijk} - (d^1 \alpha^2)_{ijl} - (\alpha^1 d^2)_{ikl} - (\alpha^1 d^2)_{jkl}$$

The reader should verify that the two formulations are in agreement.

We now revert to the general formulation. We suppose that the two genes at each locus of an arbitrary individual are ordered at random, the first being denoted with the subscript i_a and the second with the subscript j_a. Then we can say for our equilibrium population,

$$P(A^a_{i_a} = A^a_r) = p^a_r, \qquad a = 1, 2, \cdots, n$$

or in words: The probability that the first gene at locus a in an individual is the particular gene A^a_r is p^a_r, the frequency of the gene A^a_r. The genes possessed by a random individual are random with these probabilities, and we may correctly talk about averages or expectations. As usual we denote the operation of taking the expectation by E. We then have

$$E(\alpha^a_{i_a}) = \sum_{s_a} p^a_{s_a} \alpha^a_{s_a}$$

$$= \left(\sum_{s_a} p^a_{s_a} \nu^a_{s_a} \rho^a \right) \prod_{a' \neq a} \rho^{a'} \rho^{a'}$$

and

$$\sum_{s_a} p^a_{s_a} \nu^a_{s_a} = \sum_{s_a} p^a_{s_a} \left(A^a_{s_a} - \sum_{s_a} p^a_{s_a} A^a_{s_a} \right)$$

$$= \sum_{s_a} p^a_{s_a} A^a_{s_a} - \sum_{s_a} p^a_{s_a} A^a_{s_a} = 0$$

This says that the average value of an additive effect of a random gene over the whole population is zero. Similarly the expectation of any effect or deviation is zero, and also the covariance of any two different effects or deviations is zero. For example,

$$E(\alpha^a_{i_a} \alpha^a_{j_a}) = E(\alpha^a_{i_a})\, E(\alpha^a_{j_a}) = 0$$

$$E(\alpha^a_{i_a} d^a_{i_a j_a}) = \underset{i_a}{E}\left[\alpha^a_{i_a} \underset{j_a}{E}(d^a_{i_a j_a}) \right] = 0$$

where $\underset{i_a}{E}$ means expectation with respect to i_a. In fact the expectation of any effect or deviation with respect to any *one* of its subscripts is zero. Because all the terms on the right-hand side of equation A are uncorrelated, we have

$$V(y) = \sum_{\text{deviations}} V(\text{deviation})$$

and we proceed to put together deviations of the same nature. We define

$E(\alpha^{a\,2}_{i_a}) = \frac{1}{2}\sigma^2_{A(a)} =$ half the additive variance due to locus a

$E(d^{a\,2}_{i_a j_a}) = \sigma^2_{D(a)} =$ dominance variance due to locus a

$E[(\alpha^a \alpha^{a'})_{i_a i_{a'}}]^2 = \frac{1}{4}\sigma^2_{AA(aa')} = \frac{1}{4}$ additive $\times$ additive variance due to loci a and a'

$E[(\alpha^a \alpha^{a'} \alpha^{a''})_{i_a i_{a'} i_{a''}}]^2 = \frac{1}{8}\sigma^2_{AAA(aa'a'')} = \frac{1}{8}$ additive $\times$ additive $\times$ additive variance due to loci a, a', and a''

and, if X involves α for r loci and d for s loci,

$$E(X^2) = \frac{1}{2^r} \sigma^2_{A^r D^s} = \frac{1}{2^r} \overset{(r \text{ terms})}{\text{additive} \times \text{additive} \times \cdots \times \text{additive}}$$
$$\overset{(s \text{ terms})}{\times \text{ dominance} \times \text{dominance} \times \cdots \times \text{dominance}} \text{ variance due}$$
to the r loci and the s loci

Finally we may form

$$\sigma^2_A = \sum_a \sigma^2_{A(a)} = \text{the total additive variance in the population}$$

$$\sigma^2_D = \sum_a \sigma^2_{D(a)} = \text{the total dominance variance in the population}$$

$$\sigma^2_{AA} = \sum_{aa'} \sigma^2_{AA(aa')} = \text{the total additive} \times \text{additive variance in the population}$$

and so on, so that we merely sum any component over all possible sets of loci. The net result of these processes is the equation

$$\sigma^2_G = \sigma^2_A + \sigma^2_D + \sigma^2_{AA} + \sigma^2_{AD} + \sigma^2_{DD} + \sigma^2_{AAA} + \sigma^2_{AAD} + \sigma^2_{ADD}$$
$$+ \sigma^2_{DDD} + \cdots$$

in which the genotypic variance is partitioned into the different variance components on the right-hand side.

If we should wish to determine the variance components for a particular specified population, we would have to obtain means, as indicated above in the particular case of two loci, gene frequencies at which are given by p_i and q_k, and obtain weighted sums of squares of these means. In that case for instance,

$$\sum_i p_i y_i^2 \ldots = \mu^2 + \tfrac{1}{2}\sigma^2_{A(1)}$$

$$\sum_{ijk} p_i p_j q_k y_{ijk}^2 \cdot = \mu^2 + \sigma^2_{A(1)} + \tfrac{1}{2}\sigma^2_{A(2)} + \sigma^2_{D(1)} + \tfrac{1}{2}\sigma^2_{AA(12)} + \tfrac{1}{2}\sigma^2_{AD(21)}$$

The coefficients of the single loci components are easily written down, and coefficients of interaction components are products of coefficients of corresponding single loci components.

19.4 THE GENOTYPIC COVARIANCES BETWEEN RELATIVES

Here we shall make the assumption that there is no linkage, so that the loci are segregating independently. It would be nice to have a general solution for arbitrary linkages but such has not yet been obtained (see

Cockerham, 1956, for a special case). We shall also assume that there is no inbreeding; that is, there is zero probability that the two genes possessed by an individual at any locus are identical by descent. We shall obtain the covariance between the genotypic value of an individual X who is a random member of the population and an individual Y who is in a particular relationship to X.

Let the genes of X at the a locus be $i_a j_a$ and of Y be $k_a l_a$, and consider the covariance of an effect or deviation which involves the interaction of the additive effects at a set of r loci, say set I, and the dominance effects at a set of s loci, say set II. There are 2^{2r} terms of the same nature and origin in the genotypic expression for X which can give rise to non-zero covariance, and likewise for Y. Now a term gives zero covariance unless the subscripts are identical over and above the fact of being alike by chance. The coefficient of parentage of X and Y is defined to be r_{XY} where

$$4r_{XY} = P(i_a{=}k_a) + P(i_a{=}l_a) + P(j_a{=}k_a) + P(j_a{=}l_a)$$

and the compound events $i_a = k_a$, $i_a = l_a$ or $j_a = k_a$, $j_a = l_a$ are impossible (the equality sign denoting identical by descent) because these relations would imply that X and Y are inbred. The only possible relations are

$$i_a = k_a \quad \text{and/or} \quad j_a = l_a \quad \text{or neither}$$

or

$$i_a = l_a \quad \text{and/or} \quad j_a = k_a \quad \text{or neither}$$

If $i_a = k_a$ and independent conditions hold at relevant loci other than the a locus, a covariance of $(1/2^r)\sigma_{A^r}^2$ for the set of loci will arise, where A^r is short for $A \times A \times \cdots A$ with r terms. Similarly for each of $j_a = l_a$, $i_a = l_a$, and $j_a = k_a$, a covariance of $(1/2^r)\sigma_{A^r}^2$ will arise. This term arises for every case in which a gene of X and a gene of Y at each locus are identical by descent. With independent assortment the total covariance with regard to set I of loci will be $(4r_{XY})^r(1/2^r)\sigma_{A^r}^2$. With regard to loci of set II, the two genes at each locus of X must be identical by descent with those of Y. Let the probability of this for one locus be u_{XY}. With independent assortment the probability for s loci is u_{XY}^s. There is no divisor resulting from the dominance part of the deviation, so that the result as regards the particular loci is $\frac{1}{2}^r(4r_{XY})^r(u_{XY})^s\sigma_{A^rD^s}^2$. The covariance from different sets of loci are additive under our assumptions. We therefore have the final result

$$\text{Cov}\,(X, Y) = \sum_{r,s,r+s\geqslant 1} (2r_{XY})^r(u_{XY})^s\sigma_{A^rD^s}^2$$

the summation running up to all values of r and s such that $r + s$ equals n, the total number of loci which are segregating.

19.5 DISCUSSION OF RESULTS

We see then that, under the conditions of random mating in an equilibrium population with no selection and no linkage, the covariances between relatives are simply written down from the covariances in the one-locus case. The relationships which are likely to be of interest are given in Table 19.5.

TABLE 19.5

Relationship	$2r_{XY}$	u_{XY}
Identical twins	1	1
Full-sibs	$\frac{1}{2}$	$\frac{1}{4}$
Parent–offspring	$\frac{1}{2}$	0
Parent–kth degree offspring	$1/2^k$	0
Uncle–nephew	$\frac{1}{4}$	0
Cousins	$\frac{1}{8}$	0
Double first cousin	$\frac{1}{4}$	$\frac{1}{16}$

A fairly common genetic experiment is the following. We have s sires which for convenience we number from i equals 1 to s; each sire is mated to a random sample of dams, sire i to dams (ij) where j goes from 1 to m_i, and finally the mating sire i by dam ij produces n_{ij} progeny. A particular characteristic is then observed, such as 40-day weight of progeny. An analysis of variance of the resulting numbers is then made. It will be of the form in Table 19.6.

TABLE 19.6

ANALYSIS OF VARIANCE

Source	d.f.	Mean Square	Expectation of Mean Square
Sires	$s-1$	S	$\sigma_e^2 + k_2\sigma_d^2 + k_3\sigma_s^2$
Dams within sires	$\sum_i (m_i - 1)$	D	$\sigma_e^2 + k_1\sigma_d^2$
Progeny within dam and sire	$\sum_{ij} (n_{ij} - 1)$	E	σ_e^2
Total	$\sum_{ij} n_{ij} - 1$		

The expectations of mean squares can be obtained by noting that, if the observations are represented by

$$y_{ijk} = \mu + s_i + d_{ij} + e_{ijk}$$

in which

$$E(s_i) = E(d_{ij}) = E(e_{ijk}) = 0$$

and the s, d, and e quantities are uncorrelated and $E(s_i^2) = \sigma_s^2$, $E(d_{ij}^2) = \sigma_d^2$, and $E(e_{ijk}^2) = \sigma_e^2$, then

$$E(y_{ijk} - \mu)(y_{ijk'} - \mu) = \sigma_s^2 + \sigma_d^2 \qquad (k' \neq k)$$

and this must equal the covariance of full-sibs. Also, if j is not equal to j',

$$E(y_{ijk} - \mu)(y_{ij'k'} - \mu) = \sigma_s^2$$

is the covariance of half-sibs. Also

$$E(y_{ijk} - \mu)^2 = \sigma_s^2 + \sigma_d^2 + \sigma_e^2$$

is the variance of individual genotypic values and is σ_P^2. Hence

$$\sigma_e^2 = \sigma_P^2 - \text{Cov. } (F.\,S)$$
$$\sigma_d^2 = \text{Cov } (F.\,S) - \text{Cov } (H.\,S)$$
$$\sigma_s^2 = \text{Cov } (H.\,S)$$

Hence the situation can be represented by the equation or model

$$y_{ijk} = \mu + s_i + d_{ij} + e_{ijk}$$

with the terms having the properties enumerated above. Finally from Chapter 13 we have

$$k_1 = \frac{1}{m-s}\left(N_{..} - \sum_{ij} \frac{n_{ij}^2}{N_{i.}}\right), \qquad m = \sum m_i, \; N_{i.} = \sum_j n_{ij}$$

$$N_{..} = \sum_{ij} n_{ij}$$

$$k_2 = \frac{1}{s-1}\left(\sum_{ij} \frac{n_{ij}^2}{N_{i.}} - \sum_{ij} \frac{n_{ij}^2}{N_{..}}\right)$$

$$k_3 = \frac{1}{s-1}\left[N_{..} - \frac{\sum_i N_{i.}^2}{N_{..}}\right]$$

It is clear that we can estimate σ_s^2, σ_d^2, and σ_e^2 by equating observed mean squares to their expectations and solving the resulting equations. Hence we can estimate the covariance of half-sibs and of full-sibs and the phenotypic variance by the equations

$$\text{Cov}\,(H.\,S) = \hat{\sigma}_s^2$$
$$\text{Cov}\,(F.\,S) = \hat{\sigma}_d^2 + \hat{\sigma}_s^2$$
$$\sigma_P^2 = \hat{\sigma}_e^2 + \hat{\sigma}_d^2 + \hat{\sigma}_s^2$$

In order to equate the estimates of these covariances to the theoretical genotypic covariances deduced above, it is necessary to assume that environmental deviations are associated at random with genotypes and that the non-environmental part of the phenotype of an individual is determined solely by the genotype of the individual and not for instance partially by maternal effects or other causes which may be operating. Providing these assumptions can be made, we are in a position to estimate

$$\tfrac{1}{4}\sigma_A^2 + \tfrac{1}{16}\sigma_{AA}^2 + \tfrac{1}{64}\sigma_{AAA}^2 + \text{etc.} \quad \text{by Cov}\,(H.\,S)$$
$$\tfrac{1}{2}\sigma_A^2 + \tfrac{1}{4}\sigma_D^2 + \tfrac{1}{4}\sigma_{AA}^2 + \tfrac{1}{8}\sigma_{AD}^2 + \tfrac{1}{16}\sigma_{DD}^2 + \tfrac{1}{8}\sigma_{AAA}^2 + \text{etc.}$$
$$\text{by Cov}\,(F.\,S)$$

and

$$V(E) + \sigma_A^2 + \sigma_D^2 + \sigma_{AA}^2 + \sigma_{AD}^2 + \sigma_{DD}^2 + \text{etc.}$$
$$\text{by } \sigma_e^2 + \text{Cov}\,(F.\,S)$$

where $V(E)$ is the environmental variance. If there were no epistacy, the ratio

$$\frac{4\hat{\sigma}_s^2}{\hat{\sigma}_e^2 + \hat{\sigma}_d^2 + \hat{\sigma}_s^2}$$

would be a consistent estimate of

$$\frac{\sigma_A^2}{\sigma_P^2}$$

which is the expression for "heritability in the narrow sense" as defined by Lush (1937 and succeeding editions) and used widely in the theory and practice of animal breeding. The amount of bias in the presence of epistacy may be guessed to be small since the expected value of the denominator is the required denominator, and the expected value of the numerator is greater than the required value by only $\tfrac{1}{4}\sigma_{AA}^2 + \tfrac{1}{16}\sigma_{AAA}^2 +$ etc. Of course, if almost the whole of the phenotypic variance is genotypic variance and almost all of this is additive $\times$ additive, the indicated value of heritability will be near $\tfrac{1}{4}$ instead of 0.

Similarly the quantity $4\hat{\sigma}_d^2$ has been suggested as the numerator for the estimation of

$$\frac{\sigma_P^2 - V(E)}{\sigma_P^2}$$

which is by Lush's definition (1937) "heritability in the broad sense." Under our assumptions the expectation of $4\hat{\sigma}_d^2$ is

$$\sigma_A^2 + \sigma_D^2 + \tfrac{3}{4}\sigma_{AA}^2 + \tfrac{1}{2}\sigma_{AD}^2 + \tfrac{1}{4}\sigma_{DD}^2 + \tfrac{7}{16}\sigma_{AAA}^2 + \text{etc.}$$

so that the $4\hat{\sigma}_d^2$ is an underestimate of the total genotypic variance by an amount which depends on the size of the epistatic variance components.

The above considerations will be vitiated by the presence of maternal effects in an unknown way, if the maternal effects are genetically controlled. Also sex-linked factors will introduce a disturbance (Chapter 15). The role of genotype–environment interaction should also be considered.

19.6 A NUMERICAL EXAMPLE OF THE PARTITION OF GENOTYPIC VARIANCE

A numerical illustration of what results follows. Let there be three loci, each with two genes, denoted by A_1, A_2, and B_1, B_2 and C_1, C_2. Let the gene frequencies of A_1, B_1, and C_1 be 0.3, 0.4, and 0.5, respectively, and suppose the genotypic values are those given in Table 19.7.

TABLE 19.7

HYPOTHETICAL GENOTYPIC VALUES

	A_1A_1			A_1A_2			A_2A_2		
	B_1B_1	B_1B_2	B_2B_2	B_1B_1	B_1B_2	B_2B_2	B_1B_1	B_1B_2	B_2B_2
C_1C_1	0	2	1	1	1	3	2	4	5
C_1C_2	0	2	3	0	4	5	3	5	6
C_2C_2	0	3	4	3	4	6	2	4	5

It is found that the components are:

$$\sigma_A^2 = 1.965, \qquad \sigma_{AD}^2 = 0.158, \qquad \sigma_{AAD}^2 = 0.002$$
$$\sigma_D^2 = 0.189, \qquad \sigma_{DD}^2 = 0.049, \qquad \sigma_{ADD}^2 = 0.040$$
$$\sigma_{AA}^2 = 0.143, \qquad \sigma_{AAA}^2 = 0.011, \qquad \sigma_{DDD}^2 = 0.059$$

and the broad division of genotypic variance is

Additive	75.1%
Dominance	7.2%
Epistatic	17.7%
	100.0%

19.7 OTHER POSSIBLE EXPERIMENTS

It would be foolishly pretentious to attempt an enumeration of designs which may be of value in estimating the components of environmental and genotypic variance. The example given above of a random sample of sires mated with a random sample of dams is probably the simplest design. It does, however, suffer from the possibility of maternal effects, either genotypically or environmentally controlled, biasing the conclusions. The design is likely to be of most utility in plant research rather than animal research.

We note that the intrinsic property of the design, which incidentally was called Experiment I by Comstock and Robinson (1952), is that the phenotypic variance, full-sib covariance, and half-sib covariance are obtained by a single balanced setup. Comstock and Robinson have put forward another design in which both maternal half-sib and paternal half-sib covariances are obtained.

We may note that, ignoring the difference between maternal and paternal half-sibs, the essence of the design is given by Figure 19.1. In

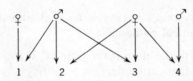

FIGURE 19.1. Essential nature of Experiment 1.

this figure the offspring are denoted by the numbers 1, 2, 3, 4, and we see that 1 and 4 are unrelated, 1 and 2 are half-sibs, as are 2 and 4, 3 and 4, and 1 and 3, while 2 and 3 are full-sibs. The only design problem here is to multiply the setup in a balanced way so that estimates of the covariances are easily obtained.

Figure 19.1 suggests the more extensive basic plan given in Figure 19.2. This plan will require three seasons or generations, and yields five different covariances in the second generation. With the plan indicated in Figure 19.2, covariances are obtained in the second generation and in the third generation, and also from the second and third generations. The co-variances in the second generation are as follows. Full-sib covariance between 3 and 4, half-sib covariance between 2 and 3, 2 and 4, 4 and 5, and 3 and 5,

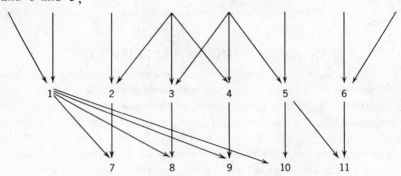

FIGURE 19.2. Essence of plan for estimating genotypic covariances.

and zero genotypic covariance between the other pairs. In generation 3 we may note that

$$2r_{XY} = \frac{\phi + \phi'}{2}$$

and

$$u_{XY} = \phi\phi'$$

where ϕ = probability that sire (say) gene of X and sire (say) gene of Y are identical by descent

and ϕ' = probability that dam (say) gene of X and dam (say) gene of Y are identical by descent

for the typical case in which X and Y are related by having sire genes in common and by having dam genes in common, the sire genes and the dam genes being independent. The computations are given in Table 19.8. There are four different non-zero relationships in Table 19.8, and the taking of a number of progeny from each mating will produce full-sib relationships in addition.

In addition, taking covariances between the second and third generation leads to the following relationships: 1 and 7, 1 and 8, 1 and 9, 1 and 10, 2 and 7, 3 and 8, 4 and 9, 5 and 10, 5 and 11, 6 and 11 are all parent–offspring relationships with $2r_{XY} = \frac{1}{2}$, $u_{XY} = 0$. We also have the following relationships: 2 and 8, 2 and 9, 3 and 7, 3 and 10, 3 and 11,

4 and 7, 4 and 10, 4 and 11, 5 and 8, 5 and 9,   have $2r_{XY} = \frac{1}{8}$ and $u_{XY} = 0$; 3 and 9, 4 and 8 have $2r_{XY} = \frac{1}{4}$, $u_{XY} = \frac{1}{16}$.

TABLE 19.8

COMPUTATION OF COVARIANCES OF RELATIVES IN FIGURE 19.2

	ϕ	ϕ'	$2r_{XY}$	u_{XY}
7 & 8	$\frac{1}{2}$	$\frac{1}{8}$	$\frac{5}{16}$	$\frac{1}{16}$
7 & 9	$\frac{1}{2}$	$\frac{1}{8}$	$\frac{5}{16}$	$\frac{1}{16}$
7 & 10	$\frac{1}{2}$	0	$\frac{1}{4}$	0
7 & 11	0	0	0	0
8 & 9	$\frac{1}{2}$	$\frac{1}{4}$	$\frac{3}{8}$	$\frac{1}{8}$
8 & 10	$\frac{1}{2}$	$\frac{1}{8}$	$\frac{5}{16}$	$\frac{1}{16}$
8 & 11	0	$\frac{1}{8}$	$\frac{1}{16}$	0
9 & 10	$\frac{1}{2}$	$\frac{1}{8}$	$\frac{5}{16}$	$\frac{1}{16}$
9 & 11	0	$\frac{1}{8}$	$\frac{1}{16}$	0
10 & 11	0	$\frac{1}{2}$	$\frac{1}{4}$	0

Thus the second and third generations lead to the following distinct relationships:

$$(\tfrac{1}{2}, \tfrac{1}{4}), \quad (\tfrac{1}{2}, 0), \quad (\tfrac{3}{8}, \tfrac{1}{8}), \quad (\tfrac{5}{16}, \tfrac{1}{16}), \quad (\tfrac{1}{4}, 0), \quad (\tfrac{1}{8}, 0), \quad \text{and} \quad (\tfrac{1}{16}, 0)$$

where the first member of the pair of numbers is the value of $2r_{XY}$ and the second is the value of u_{XY}. The general idea would be to replicate this plan say 100 times, or perhaps more. We would then be able to get a number of independent estimates of the covariance for each relationship. These could be examined for the possibility of their being represented only by within locus components of variance, σ_A^2 and σ_D^2, leaving six degrees of freedom for error of regression to be tested against the pure error between estimates of the same genotypic covariance. We would have to be careful to ensure that the estimates were of approximately the same accuracy before using a least-squares fit. Also we could examine the possibility of the covariances being explainable in terms of σ_A^2, σ_D^2, σ_{AA}^2, σ_{AD}^2, and σ_{DD}^2. Should either the former non-epistatic hypothesis or the latter dual epistatic hypothesis fit the data, we could then estimate σ_G^2 and then, since the variance among unrelated individuals is $\sigma_G^2 + \sigma_E^2$, we could estimate σ_E^2. There are various purely statistical questions of estimation which are not covered exhaustively here.

It will be in ways such as the above that we can find out the characteristics of the genetic population we are considering. The utility of the knowledge so obtained would lie in the fact that we would have a good idea of the breeding potentialities in the population, and it is this which will frequently be our ultimate aim. If we can show, for instance, that a population contains members whose yield is greater than some number L, and we can lay down a breeding system which will lead us to those members in a reasonable time, we can surely claim to have an understanding of the situation.

19.8 POLYPLOID POPULATIONS

It is not our aim to give a full description of polyploid populations analogous to what is given above for diploid populations. The only work on the subject (Kempthorne, 1955b) assumes that segregation is by chromosomes. We have seen that, for a one-locus tetraploid population, we have four components of genotypic variance, which were denoted by σ_A^2, σ_D^2, σ_T^2, σ_F^2. An argument exactly analogous to the diploid one presented above shows that a two-loci population has components with subscripts as follows: A, D, T, F, AA, AD, AT, AF, DD, DT, DF, TT, TF, and FF, or 14 in all. The number of components increases rapidly with number of loci. It can be seen, however, that the number of such components of variance is negligible compared to the number of distinct genotypes so that an economy is achieved. The reader is referred to Kempthorne (1955b) for the general picture and the covariances between relatives.

19.9 THE SPECIAL CASE OF TWO ALLELES PER LOCUS AND GENE FREQUENCY EQUAL TO ONE HALF

This case arises naturally when two homozygous lines are crossed and the resultant F_1 is selfed or mated at random. It is, however, essential to point out that this may well be an entirely unrealistic case from the point of view of applied genetics in particular. The usual situation will be that the breeder has a population of genetic material perhaps unhomogeneous in the sense of not having arisen by random mating of a single population. The plant breeder who is looking for guidance in his breeding plans is hardly likely to get such guidance from a pair of inbred lines from the original population and the populations derivable from that pair of inbred lines. Every possible pair of inbred lines will lead to an F_2 population which will have its particular genetic parameters σ_A^2, σ_D^2, σ_{AA}^2, σ_{AD}^2, σ_{DD}^2, etc., and possibly also environmental parameters. If we have an original population in which 20, say, loci are segregating, there will be at least 2^{20}, or approximately 1 million possible inbred lines, and hence of the order of 10^{12} possible pairs of inbred lines, and resultant F_2 and other populations. Each of these will have its particular parameters, and it is difficult to see how the intensive study of one of these 10^{12} F_2 populations will lead to an understanding of the original population. It could be that some reasonable sample of the 10^{12} or so F_2 populations would lead to useful information, but this seems to the author a moot point. In fact, the average properties of the 10^{12} F_2 populations are obtained by selfing the original population, because the quantities intrinsic to the behavior of the original population under selfing are quantities like

$$(AA - aa)^2$$
$$(AA - 2Aa + aa)^2$$

where genotypic values are inserted for the genotypic symbols (Chapter 17). These are precisely the intrinsic parameters of the resultant F_2 populations. The argument given above is not rigorous but can be made so in its essential features. If, however, we are concerned with genetical analysis in the sense of Mather (1949) the above arguments do not have the same force.

Notwithstanding the above, we shall give a little discussion of the special case, because it is somewhat illuminating with regard to what can happen under special circumstances, and also it is another example of the dangers of working with special cases, the results for which may be entirely misleading as indications of the general situation.

In the special case of two equally frequent alleles at every locus, there is a considerable simplification of the representation of the genotypic value in terms of additive effects, dominance deviations, and epistatic deviations. It will be recalled that any deviation is compounded of factors like

$$(A_i - \sum p_s A_s)(\sum p_s A_s)$$

and

$$(A_i - \sum p_s A_s)(A_j - \sum p_s A_s)$$

the former entering into a deviation if the deviation is an "additive" type with regard to the locus, and the latter if the deviation is a "dominance" type with respect to the locus. In the present case the possible additive factors are

$$[A_1 - \tfrac{1}{2}(A_1 + A_2)] [\tfrac{1}{2}(A_1 + A_2)]$$

and

$$[A_2 - \tfrac{1}{2}(A_1 + A_2)] [\tfrac{1}{2}(A_1 + A_2)]$$

The former is equal to

$$\tfrac{1}{4}(A_1 - A_2)(A_1 + A_2)$$

and the latter is

$$\tfrac{1}{4}(A_2 - A_1)(A_1 + A_2)$$

which is the negative of the former. In the case of the dominance factors, we have three possibilities

$$[A_1 - \tfrac{1}{2}(A_1 + A_2)] \, [A_1 - \tfrac{1}{2}(A_1 + A_2)]$$
$$[A_1 - \tfrac{1}{2}(A_1 + A_2)] \, [A_2 - \tfrac{1}{2}(A_1 + A_2)]$$

and

$$[A_2 - \tfrac{1}{2}(A_1 + A_2)] \, [A_2 - \tfrac{1}{2}(A_1 + A_2)]$$

These are equal, respectively, to

$$\tfrac{1}{4}(A_1 - A_2)(A_1 - A_2)$$
$$-\tfrac{1}{4}(A_1 - A_2)(A_1 - A_2)$$

and

$$\tfrac{1}{4}(A_1 - A_2)(A_1 - A_2)$$

Hence all deviations of a particular type, say for example additive $\times$ additive $\times$ dominance, with regard to an ordered set of three loci are the same in absolute magnitude. It follows that the genotypic value with n loci can be expressed in terms of 3^n parameters, and the coefficients on the parameters are obtained by simple multiplication of the coefficients attached to the single locus effects. Table 19.9 gives the situation for the nine genotypes possible with two loci.

TABLE 19.9

REPRESENTATION OF GENOTYPIC VALUES IN TERMS OF ADDITIVE, DOMINANCE, AND EPISTATIC CONTRIBUTIONS FOR THE CASE OF TWO LOCI WITH TWO EQUALLY FREQUENT ALLELES

Genotype	μ	α	$(\alpha\alpha)$	β	$(\beta\beta)$	$(\alpha\beta)$	$(\alpha\alpha\beta)$	$(\alpha\beta\beta)$	$(\alpha\alpha\beta\beta)$
AABB	1	2	1	2	1	4	2	2	1
AABb	1	2	1	0	−1	0	0	−2	−1
AAbb	1	2	1	−2	1	−4	−2	2	1
AaBB	1	0	−1	2	1	0	−2	0	−1
AaBb	1	0	−1	0	−1	0	0	0	1
Aabb	1	0	−1	−2	1	0	2	0	−1
aaBB	1	−2	1	2	1	−4	2	−2	1
aaBb	1	−2	1	0	−1	0	0	2	−1
aabb	1	−2	1	−2	1	4	−2	−2	1

In Table 19.9 we have denoted the additive effect of A as α, of B as β, the dominance deviation associated with the A locus as $(\alpha\alpha)$, the dominance deviation associated with the B locus as $(\beta\beta)$, the additive $\times$ dominance deviation associated with the ordered pair (AB) of the loci as $(\alpha\beta\beta)$, the additive $\times$ dominance deviation associated with the ordered pair (BA) of the loci as $(\beta\alpha\alpha)$, and the dominance $\times$ dominance deviation as $(\alpha\alpha\beta\beta)$. The coefficients are written down simply as follows: We first obtain the coefficient in the α column as 2, 0, or -2, according to whether the phase at the A locus is AA, Aa, or aa; the coefficient in the $(\alpha\alpha)$ column is 1, -1, or 1, according to whether the phase of the A locus is AA, Aa, or aa; we do likewise for the B locus; the coefficient in any other column is obtained by multiplication, as exemplified by that for $(\alpha\beta)$ which is the product of the coefficient in the α column and the coefficient in the β column; similarly the coefficient in the $(\alpha\alpha\beta)$ column is the product of the coefficient in the $(\alpha\alpha)$ column and the coefficient in the β column. It is difficult to imagine anything simpler than this scheme which is written down for the case of n loci in exactly the same way.

It is left as an exercise to the reader to verify that, if the genotypic frequencies are those resulting in an F_2 population from selfing or crossing the double heterozygote, with linkage absent, then the parameters are mutually orthogonal. The sum of products of any two columns weighted by genotypic frequency is equal to zero. If then the genotypic values are given, the values of the genetic parameters can be written down by the rule

$$\frac{\sum c_j(\text{genotypic value of the }j\text{th genotype})}{\sum c_j^2}$$

where c_j is the entry in the column corresponding to the parameter. It is this orthogonality property exemplified here for this particular situation which makes all computations of variances and covariances among non-inbred relatives so easy.

Hayman and Mather (1955) have given a scheme for representing epistatic deviations for the case of two loci. Their scheme does not have the property of full orthogonality referred to above, but this may not be of any particular disadvantage in general: that is, when one is going to apply the scheme to inbreeding as well as random mating. Their scheme uses, as must any scheme which can be considered for general use, a total of nine parameters for the case of two loci with two alleles at each locus. The parameter μ in the scheme presented above is not of course essential if we are considering variation, though it may be noted that it is the mean of the F_2 population. If we code this one to be zero, we are left with eight parameters. However, for general purposes we must retain this parameter and the one analogous to it. For Hayman and Mather's scheme we use ν as the parameter which gives the origin of the scale of measurement. Their scheme is given in Table 19.10.

TABLE 19.10

HAYMAN AND MATHER'S REPRESENTATION OF GENOTYPIC VALUES IN TERMS OF EPISTATIC PARAMETERS

Genotype	ν	d_a	h_a	d_b	h_b	$i_{ab/}$	$\frac{1}{2}j_{a/b}$	$\frac{1}{2}j_{b/a}$	$\frac{1}{4}l_{/ab}$
AABB	1	1	0	1	0	1	−1	−1	1
AABb	1	1	0	0	1	0	1	0	−1
AAbb	1	1	0	−1	0	−1	−1	1	1
AaBB	1	0	1	1	0	0	0	1	−1
AaBb	1	0	1	0	1	0	0	0	1
Aabb	1	0	1	−1	0	0	0	−1	−1
aaBB	1	−1	0	1	0	−1	1	−1	1
aaBb	1	−1	0	0	1	0	−1	0	−1
aabb	1	−1	0	−1	0	1	1	1	1

The similarity of Tables 19.9 and 19.10 will be readily apparent. To get from Table 19.9 to Table 19.10 we make the substitutions:

$$\mu = \nu + \tfrac{1}{2}h_a + \tfrac{1}{2}h_b$$
$$\alpha = \tfrac{1}{2}d_a, \qquad \beta = \tfrac{1}{2}d_b$$
$$(\alpha\alpha) = -\tfrac{1}{2}h_a, \qquad (\beta\beta) = -\tfrac{1}{2}h_b$$
$$(\alpha\beta) = \tfrac{1}{4}i_{ab/}$$
$$(\alpha\alpha\beta) = -\tfrac{1}{2}(\tfrac{1}{2}j_{b/a}) = -\tfrac{1}{4}j_{b/a}$$
$$(\alpha\beta\beta) = -\tfrac{1}{2}(\tfrac{1}{2}j_{a/b}) = -\tfrac{1}{4}j_{a/b}$$
$$(\alpha\alpha\beta\beta) = \tfrac{1}{4}l_{/ab}$$

We therefore see that there is the standard difference between the definitions of this book and Mather's definitions with regard to intralocus effects, but that there is no essential difference between the epistatic parameters introduced by Hayman and Mather (1955) and the epistatic parameters given by Kempthorne (1954, 1955), when these are defined on the basis of a population with two alleles and gene frequency equal to one half throughout. It is obvious that results in terms of the one system of notation can be translated into the other notation. For instance, the quantity $(i_{ab/})^2$ is in fact $64\sigma_{AA}^2$ of the F_2 population, since σ_{AA}^2 is $4(\alpha\beta)^2$. Likewise $2(\alpha\alpha\beta)^2$ is the dominance $(B) \times$ additive (A) variance and is equal to $\tfrac{1}{8}(j_{b/a})^2$; also $2(\alpha\beta\beta)^2$ equals $\tfrac{1}{8}(j_{a/b})^2$ and finally σ_{DD}^2 the dominance $\times$ dominance variance is $\tfrac{1}{16}(l_{/ab})^2$.

The author prefers the notation he has developed because Table 19.9 is so easy to construct and the Hayman–Mather terminology appears unhandy typographically. Also the extension of the latter notation to

the case of any number of loci is not obvious and could encounter difficulties with regard to writing down both coefficients and parameters.   It
would obviously be foolish to claim more biological significance for the
one set of epistatic parameters than the other.   Whether either system is
best for tackling certain problems remains to be seen.   It is the opinion
of the author that neither system is best for the expression of results under
inbreeding because the quantities intrinsic to inbreeding (*not* followed by
random mating) are not those intrinsic to random mating.   It will also
be recalled that even for random mating the terminology in terms of α,
$(\alpha\alpha)$, β, $(\beta\beta)$, $(\alpha\beta)$, $(\alpha\beta\beta)$, $(\alpha\alpha\beta)$, and $(\alpha\alpha\beta\beta)$ is a special case appropriate
for the two alleles per locus and that the generalization for arbitrary
number of alleles per locus has been given.

19.10 BRIEF HISTORICAL NOTE

The first treatment of epistacy was given by Fisher (1918).   This work
lay essentially unused for about thirty years.   Wright (1935) partially
developed the situation for a particular epistatic model.   Work started
at Iowa State College essentially contemporaneously by Cockerham (1952),
Anderson (1953) and by Anderson and Kempthorne (1954).   The terms
additive $\times$ additive, additive $\times$ dominance, etc. were first given by
Cockerham (1952, 1954) who worked out the case of two alleles per locus
with arbitrary gene frequency by a special device.   At about the same time,
Horner (1951) considered the case of 2 and 3 loci with certain symmetrical
models and with selfing, and examined the effects of the particular types
of epistacy on covariances between relatives in the inbred populations.
The symmetrical models considered were ones for which there are two
alleles at each locus and the genotypic value is a function of the numbers
of loci in the three possible phases.   This work was extended by Horner
(1952).   The solution given in the present chapter was obtained by
Kempthorne (1954) in the course of writing this book.   The reader is
referred to Hayman and Mather's paper (1955) for the details of their
development and the application to populations derived from inbred lines.
The reader is referred to Cockerham (1956) for an extension of the
procedure in the present chapter to the case of linkage.   The case of
symmetrical populations is discussed extensively by Horner and Kempthorne (1955) and by Horner (1956a, b).   What is quite possibly the best
application of random mating population theory is that of Morley (1951).

19.11 RELATIONSHIPS AMONG MEANS OF CROSSED
POPULATIONS

The problem we consider here is that we have populations $\prod_i$,
$i = 1, 2, \cdots, p$ say, and are concerned about the means of populations

derived by crossing these populations. We consider the case in which the populations $\prod_i$ have random mating structure and only one locus is segregating. Let there be m alleles, and let p_m^i be the frequency of the mth allele in the population; then the genotypic mean of population $\prod_i$ is

$$\mu_i = \sum_m \sum_{m'} p_m^i p_{m'}^i y_{mm'}$$

where $y_{mm'}$ is the genotypic value of the genotype with the m and m' alleles. Now consider $\prod_i \times \prod_j$ and suppose that the mating is *at random*. Then the mean of this population is

$$\mu_{ij} = \sum_{mm'} p_m^i p_{m'}^j y_{mm'}$$

which will bear no particular relationship to μ_i and μ_j unless the genes are additive in their effects, in which case

$$\mu_i = \sum_m \sum_{m'} p_m^i p_{m'}^i (\alpha_m + \alpha_{m'})$$

$$= 2 \sum_m p_m^i \alpha_m$$

$$\mu_j = 2 \sum_m p_m^j \alpha_m$$

and

$$\mu_{ij} = \sum_m p_m^i \alpha_m + \sum p_m^j \alpha_m$$

$$= \tfrac{1}{2} \mu_i + \tfrac{1}{2} \mu_j$$

It is interesting that this result is obtained under either Mendelian inheritance or blending inheritance. As we have stated, there will in general be no relationship among the above three means in the presence of dominance.

Now consider a problem of practical importance: namely the means of 3-way and 4-way crosses. For a 3-way cross say, $(\prod_i \times \prod_j) \times \prod_k$, we have the obvious result that the gametic output of $(\prod_i \times \prod_j)$ is equal to the sum of one half of the gametic output of $\prod_i$ and one half of the gametic output of $\prod_j$; so the genotypic array in $(\prod_i \times \prod_j) \times \prod_k$ is

$$[\tfrac{1}{2} \sum (p_m^i + p_m^j) A_m](\sum p_m^k A_m)$$

where the alleles are denoted by A_m. Hence the genotypic mean of $(\prod_i \times \prod_j) \times \prod_k$ is

$$\frac{1}{2} \sum_{m,m'} (p_m^i + p_m^j) p_m^k y_{mm'}$$

so that we have

$$\mu \left[(\prod_i \times \prod_j) \times \prod_k \right] = \tfrac{1}{2}\mu \left(\prod_i \times \prod_k \right) + \tfrac{1}{2}\mu \left(\prod_j \times \prod_k \right)$$

or

$$\mu_{(i \times j) \times k} = \tfrac{1}{2}\mu_{ik} + \tfrac{1}{2}\mu_{jk}$$

Similarly we see also that

$$\mu \left[(\prod_i \times \prod_j) \times (\prod_k \times \prod_l) \right] = \tfrac{1}{4}\mu \left(\prod_i \times \prod_k \right) + \tfrac{1}{4}\mu \left(\prod_i \times \prod_l \right)$$
$$+ \tfrac{1}{4}\mu \left(\prod_j \times \prod_k \right) + \tfrac{1}{4}\mu \left(\prod_j \times \prod_l \right)$$

or

$$\mu_{(i \times j) \times (k \times l)} = \tfrac{1}{4}\mu_{ik} + \tfrac{1}{4}\mu_{il} + \tfrac{1}{4}\mu_{jk} + \tfrac{1}{4}\mu_{jl}$$

The general result which follows from the fact that the gametic array produced by the population which arises by random mating of two populations is the average of the gametic arrays of the two populations. If any prediction formula involves the means of original populations, it will be valid only if those original populations have random mating structure. If this were the case, we would have for instance that the mean of the population $[(1 \times 2) \times 3] \times (1 \times 4)$ is equal to

$$\tfrac{1}{8}\mu_1 + \tfrac{1}{8}\mu_{12} + \tfrac{1}{4}\mu_{13} + \tfrac{1}{8}\mu_{14} + \tfrac{1}{8}\mu_{24} + \tfrac{1}{4}\mu_{34}$$

These prediction formulas hold only in the absence of epistasis. The presence of epistasis with or without linkage disturbs them in an unknown way.

This general result is of utility in breeding problems, as, for example, in the prediction of double-cross yields from single-cross yields (cf. Doxtator and Johnson, 1936; Millang and Sprague, 1939; Combs and Zuber, 1949). A more general use of the result could be as follows. Suppose we have 20 inbred lines and wish to determine various characteristics of the population made up from some or all of these lines. We would obtain the means of all the original populations and single-cross populations. Also we would make up a number of 3-way crosses involving some parent populations twice, and we would then be able to test if the 3-way cross population means can be represented in terms of the original population means and the single-cross means. This would necessitate replication of the 3-way cross population entries in order to get a pure estimate of the error of the estimated means, and to provide a denominator against which the deviations of estimated means from means predicted with the original population and single-cross means could be tested. If the result of this test should be negative in the sense that the deviations of predictions are not large relative to the estimate of pure error, we would be entitled to proceed on the basis that epistatic deviations which would invalidate the prediction formula are negligible. We would then estimate the mean of any possible population derivable from the original population. If on the other hand the deviations of predictions were appreciable, we should search for a transformation of the original data which makes them negligible and then proceed to estimate the means of derived populations on the transformed scale. The breeder will not of course be interested in means on the transformed scale, but we may be confident that the rank order of population means on the transformed scale and the untransformed scales will be essentially the same. This is the case because, if y is the observed value on the original scale of an individual, and x is equal to $f(y)$ is the observed value on the transformed scale, then approximately

$$\mu_x = f(\mu_y) + \left(\frac{d^2f}{dy^2}\right)_{\mu_y} \sigma_y^2$$

where μ_y, μ_x are the means on the respective scales, σ_y^2 is the variance in the population on the y scale, and

$$\left(\frac{\partial^2 f}{\partial y^2}\right)_{\mu_y}$$

is the second derivative of $f(y)$ with regard to y evaluated at y equal to μ_y. The essential parts of the error in ranking depend on the function $f(y)$ and on the variance in a calculable way.

REFERENCES

Anderson, V. L. 1953. A model for the study of quantitative inheritance. Ph.D. Thesis. Iowa State College Library.

Anderson, V. L., and O. Kempthorne. 1954. A model for the study of quantitative inheritance. *Genetics*, **39**, 883–898.

Cockerham, C. C. 1952. Genetic covariation among characteristics of swine. Ph.D. Thesis. Iowa State College Library.

Cockerham, C. C. 1954. An extension of the concept of partitioning hereditary variance for analysis of covariance among relatives when epistasis is present. *Genetics*, **39**, 859–882.

Cockerham, C. C. 1956. Effects of linkage on the covariances between relatives. *Genetics*, **41**, 138–141.

Comstock, R. E., and H. F. Robinson. 1952. Estimation of average dominance of genes. Chapter 30 of *Heterosis*, edited J. W. Gowen. Iowa State College Press, Ames.

Combs, J. B., and M. S. Zuber. 1949. Further use of punched card equipment in predicting the performance of double-crossed corn hybrids. *Agron. J.*, **41**, 485–486.

Doxtator, C. W., and I. J. Johnson. 1936. Prediction of double cross yields in corn. *J. Amer. Soc. Agron.*, **28**, 460.

Fisher, R. A. 1918. The correlation between relatives on the supposition of Mendelian inheritance. *Trans roy. Soc. Edinb.*, **52**, 399–433.

Hayman, B. I., and K. Mather. 1955. The description of genic interactions in continuous variation. *Biometrics*, **11**, 69–82.

Horner, T. W. 1951. The contribution of non-allelic gene interactions in populations of selfed lines. M.S. thesis, North Carolina State College.

Horner, T. W. 1952. Non-allelic gene interaction and the interpretation of quantitative genetic data. Ph.D. thesis, North Carolina State College.

Horner, T. W. 1956a. The components of variance in symmetrical random mating populations with the frequency of the more favourable allele the same at all loci. *Iowa St. Coll. J. Sci.*, **31**, 67–77.

Horner, T. W. 1956b. Full-sib and parent–offspring correlations in symmetrical random mating populations with the frequency of the more favourable allele the same at all loci. *Iowa St. Coll. J. Sci.* **31**, 55–64.

Horner, T. W., and O. Kempthorne. 1955. The components of variance and the correlations between relatives in symmetrical random mating populations. *Genetics*, **40**, 310–320.

Kempthorne, O. 1954. The correlations between relatives in a random mating population. *Proc. roy. Soc. Lond. B*, **143**, 103–113.

Kempthorne, O. 1955. The theoretical values of correlations between relatives in random mating populations. *Genetics*, **40**, 153–167.

Kempthorne, O. 1955a. The theoretical values of correlations between relatives in random mating populations. *Genetics*, **40**, 153–167.

Kempthorne, O. 1955b. The correlations between relatives in random mating populations. *Proc. XXth Cold Spr. Harb. Symp. quant. Biol.*, **20**, 60–78.

Mather, K. 1949. *Biometric Genetics*. Dover Publications, New York.

Millang, Amy, and G. F. Sprague. 1939. The use of punched card equipment in predicting the performance of double cross hybrids. Mimeographed paper. Iowa State College, Ames.

Morley, F. H. W. 1951. Selection for economic characters in Australian sheep. I. Estimates of phenotypic and genetic parameters. *N. S. Wales Dep. Agric. Sci. Bull.*, **73**.

Sinott, E. W., L. C. Dunn, and T. Dobzhansky. 1950. *Principles of genetics*. McGraw-Hill Book Co., New York.

Wright, Sewall. 1935. The analysis of variance and the correlations between relatives with respect to deviations from an optimum. *J. Genet.* **30**, 243–256.

FURTHER READING

Chapman, A. B. 1946. Genetic and nongenetic sources of variation in the weight response of the immature rat ovary to a gonadotrophic hormone. *Genetics*, **31**, 194–207.

Fisher, R. A., and H. Gray. 1938. Inheritance in man: Boas's data studied by the method of analysis of variance. *Ann. Eugen. Lond.*, **8**, 74–93.

438 ARBITRARY DIPLOID POPULATIONS

Hazel, L. N., and W. F. Lamoureux. 1947. Heritability, maternal effects and nicking in relation to sexual maturity and body weight in White Leghorns. *Poult. Sci.*, **26**, 508–514.

Kempthorne, O., and O. B. Tandon. 1953. The estimation of heritability by regression of offspring on parent. *Biometrics*, **9**, 90–100.

Knapp, B., Jr., and A. W. Nordskog. 1946. Heritability of growth and efficiency in beef cattle. *J. Anim. Sci.*, **5**, 62–70.

Robertson, A., and I. M. Lerner. 1949. The heritability of all-or-none traits: viability of poultry. *Genetics*, **34**, 395–411.

Wright, Sewall. 1952. The genetics of quantitative variability. Pp. 5–41 of *Quantitative inheritance*. Her Majesty's Stationery Office, London.

PROBLEMS

1. Suppose the phenotypes in the white–yellow–green summer squash situation are scored by 0 for white, 1 for yellow, and 2 for green, that the gene frequencies are $\frac{1}{2}$, and that we have a random mating population. Evaluate the components of genotypic variance.

2. Evaluate the components of variance for the case in Table 19.1, assuming gene frequencies of one-half and a random mating equilibrium population.

3. Do as in problem 2 for Table 19.2.

4. Do as in problem 2 for Table 19.3.

5. Construct a set of genotypic values for which the only effects are additive × additive.

6. Construct a set of genotypic values for which the only effects are additive × dominance.

7. Construct a set of genotypic values for which the only effects are dominance × dominance.

8. Derive the components of genotypic variance for the following set of genotypic values:

		C		c	
		B	b	B	b
A		4	3	1	2
a		2	1	3	4

with gene frequencies for A, B, and C equal to 0.6, 0.4, and 0.3, respectively.

CHAPTER 20

Inbreeding with an Arbitrary Diploid Population

20.1 INTRODUCTION

As in the previous chapters, we are concerned with the theory of quantitative inheritance and not with the probability theory of inbreeding per se. We shall give a very short account, which is all indeed that is necessary, of covariances among relatives when there is no epistacy and no linkage. Next we shall take up the case of inbreeding with arbitrary epistasis and with linkage absent. Our knowledge of the effects of linkage is restricted to the case of no epistacy and populations derived from homozygous lines and is given in Chapter 21.

20.2 NO EPISTACY AND NO LINKAGE

Here the situation is indeed simple. We merely have to apply what we already know, given in Chapter 17, on the case of one locus. The application consists of defining new components of variance and covariance as the sum over loci of the previously obtained components for a single locus.

In the case of two alleles for instance, we have given the covariances between full-sibs and between parent and offspring under full-sib and parent–offspring inbreeding systems. By denoting genotypic values as follows:

$$AA: \quad y$$
$$Aa: \quad (y - x)/2$$
$$aa: \quad 0$$

we found that these covariances were known linear functions of y^2, xy, and x^2. In the n-loci case we merely define y_s and x_s for the sth locus, and replace y^2, xy, and x^2 by $\sum_s y_s^2$, $\sum_s x_s y_s$, and $\sum x_s^2$, respectively, in the particular formula.   In the case of selfing we found that the covariances were expressible in terms of

$$(y_{ii} - y_{jj})^2 \quad \text{and} \quad \epsilon_{ij}$$

so that we merely have to define these quantities for each pair of alleles at each locus and after obtaining the result for a particular locus add over loci.

It is possible to make very general statements in the case when the genes are strictly additive in their effects.   We may under these circumstances apply the procedures for the analysis of additive systems.   If for example an individual has inbreeding coefficient F, then the variance of its phenotypic value is clearly

$$\sigma_G^2(1 + F) + \sigma_E^2$$

where of course σ_G^2 is equal to σ_A^2.   If two individuals X, Y have coefficient of parentage r_{XY}, then their covariance is $2r_{XY}\sigma_G^2$.   It is a straightforward process to obtain all variances and covariances for any system of inbreeding.   If two individuals X, Y have coefficients of inbreeding equal to F_X, F_Y, respectively, and coefficient of parentage r_{XY}, their correlation is

$$\frac{2r_{XY}\sigma_G^2}{[(1 + F_X)\sigma_G^2 + \sigma_E^2]^{1/2}[(1 + F_Y)\sigma_G^2 + \sigma_E^2]^{1/2}}$$

If we put σ_E^2 equal to zero, we have what is termed the genetic correlation of X and Y (Wright, 1951).

20.3 SELFING WITH ARBITRARY EPISTACY AND NO LINKAGE

We shall take up the simplest inbreeding system; namely, selfing (Kempthorne, 1956a).

Consider an arbitrary individual with genotype

$$\prod_{s=1}^{n} A_{i_s}^s A_{j_s}^s$$

with genes $A_{i_s}^s$ and $A_{j_s}^s$ at the sth locus.   On selfing for k generations with no linkage, the genotypic array becomes

$$\prod_{s=1}^{n} \left\{ A_{i_s}^s A_{j_s}^s - \frac{1}{2}\left(1 - \frac{1}{2^k}\right)[2A_{i_s}^s A_{j_s}^s - A_{i_s}^s A_{i_s}^s - A_{j_s}^s A_{j_s}^s] \right\}$$

$$= \prod_{s=1}^{n} (A_{i_s}^s A_{j_s}^s - K_k S_{i_s j_s}^s) \quad \text{say}$$

where

$$S_{i_s j_s}^s = 2A_{i_s}^s A_{j_s}^s - A_{i_s}^s A_{i_s}^s - A_{j_s}^s A_{j_s}^s$$

$$K_k = \frac{1}{2}\left(1 - \frac{1}{2^k}\right)$$

The array is therefore

$$\prod_{s=1}^n A_{i_s}^s A_{j_s}^s - K_k \sum_{s=1}^n S_{i_s j_s}^s \prod_{\substack{s'=1 \\ s' \neq s}}^n A_{i_{s'}}^{s'} A_{j_{s'}}^{s'}$$

$$+ K_k^2 \sum_{\substack{s,s'=1 \\ s \neq s'}}^n S_{i_s j_s}^s S_{i_{s'} j_{s'}}^{s'} \prod_{s''} A_{i_{s''}}^{s''} A_{j_{s''}}^{s''}$$

$$+ \text{ etc.}$$

in which the s subscripts can never be the same.

Now let each of the terms be written out in terms of genotypes, and genotypic values inserted in place of genotypic symbols, and suppose terms are identified as follows:

$$y = \prod_{s=1}^n A_{i_s}^s A_{j_s}^s$$

$$d_1 = \sum_{s=1}^n S_{i_s j_s}^s \prod_{\substack{s'=1 \\ s' \neq s}}^n A_{i_{s'}}^{s'} A_{j_{s'}}^{s'}$$

$$d_2 = \sum_{\substack{s,s'=1 \\ s' \neq s}}^n S_{i_s j_s}^s S_{i_{s'} j_{s'}}^{s'} \prod_{s''} A_{i_{s''}}^{s''} A_{j_{s''}}^{s''}$$

and so on. Corresponding to each individual in the population there is a y, a d_1, a d_2, and so on up to a d_n. Let the expectations over the population be as follows:

$$E(y) = \mu$$

$$E(d_1) = \delta_1, \qquad E(d_2) = \delta_2, \quad \cdots, \quad E(d_n) = \delta_n$$

$$V(y) = \sigma_{yy}, \qquad V(d_1) = \sigma_{11}, \quad V(d_2) = \sigma_{22}, \quad \cdots, \quad V(d_n) = \sigma_{nn}$$

$$\text{Cov}(y, d_j) = \sigma_{yj}, \qquad \text{Cov}(d_j, d_{j'}) = \sigma_{jj'}$$

Then we can immediately write down:

Variance of kth generation means of 0th generation individuals

$$= \sigma_{yy} + K_k^2\sigma_{11} + K_k^4\sigma_{22} + K_k^6\sigma_{33} + \cdots$$
$$- 2K_k\sigma_{y1} + 2K_k^2\sigma_{y2} - 2K_k^3\sigma_{y3} + \cdots$$
$$- 2K_k^3\sigma_{12} + 2K_k^4\sigma_{13} - 2K_k^5\sigma_{14} + \cdots$$
$$- 2K_k^5\sigma_{23} + 2K_k^6\sigma_{24} - 2K_k^7\sigma_{25} + \cdots$$
$$+ \text{etc.}$$

or

$$\sigma_{yy} + \sum_m K_k^{2m}\sigma_{mm} + 2\sum_{m=1}^{n}(-1)^m K_k^m\sigma_{ym} + \sum_{\substack{m\neq m'\\=1}}^{n}(-1)^{m+m'}K_k^{m+m'}\sigma_{mm'}$$

Covariance of individual in 0th generation and its kth degree offspring

$$= \sigma_{yy} - K_k\sigma_{y1} + K_k^2\sigma_{y2} - K_k^3\sigma_{y3} + \text{etc.}$$
$$= \sigma_{yy} + \sum_{m=1}^{n}(-1)^m K_k^m\sigma_{ym}$$

Covariance of independent kth and lth degree progeny means of individuals in oth generation

$$= \sigma_{yy} + K_k K_l\sigma_{11} + K_k^2 K_l^2\sigma_{22} + \text{etc.}$$
$$- (K_k + K_l)\sigma_{y1} + (K_k^2 + K_l^2)\sigma_{y2} - \text{etc.}$$
$$- (K_k K_l^2 + K_k^2 K_l)\sigma_{12} + (K_k K_l^3 + K_k^3 K_l)\sigma_{13} - \text{etc.}$$
$$+ \text{etc.}$$
$$= \sigma_{yy} + \sum_{m=1}^{n}(-1)^m(K_k^m + K_l^m)\sigma_{ym} + \sum_{m,m'=1}^{n}(-1)^{m+m'}K_k^m K_l^{m'}\sigma_{mm'}$$

It would also be of interest to obtain the covariance of kth and lth progeny of rth generation individuals within $(r-1)$th generation families. It will be recalled that we gave a very simple general formula for this covariance in the case of one locus. It is left to the reader to show that a somewhat analogous formula holds. An examination and discussion of the relation between experimental and theoretical covariances is given by Horner and Weber (1956).

20.4 MEAN AND VARIANCE OF AN INBRED POPULATION

Consider the population

$$\prod_{=1}^{n}\left(\sum_m p_m^i A_m^i\right)^2$$

which has the random mating structure, the gene frequency of A_m^i, which is the mth allele at the ith locus, being p_m^i. The summation on m for particular i ranges over the number of alleles at the ith locus.   When this population is inbred to a degree measured by F and there is no selection and no linkage, the genotypic array of the resultant population is

$$\prod_{i=1}^{n} \left\{ \sum_{m,m'} [(1 - F)p_m^i p_{m'}^i + F\delta_{mm'} p_m^i] A_m^i A_{m'}^i \right\}$$

where $\delta_{mm'}$ is the Kronecker delta and is unity if m equals m' and 0 otherwise.

We wish to obtain the mean and variance of this population.   To do so we note that the genotypic value of

$$\prod_{i=1}^{n} A_{m_i}^i A_{m_i'}^i = \mu + \sum_i \alpha_{m_i}^i + \sum_i \alpha_{m_i'}^i + \sum_i d_{m_i m_i'}^i$$
$$+ \sum_{i,i'} (\alpha\alpha)_{m_i m_{i'}} + \text{etc.}$$

and the right-hand side can be written formally as

$$\prod_{i=1}^{n} (1 + \alpha_{m_i}^i)(1 + \alpha_{m_i'}^i)$$

provided that in the resultant expression unity is replaced by μ, $\alpha_{m_i}^i \alpha_{m_i'}^{i}$ is replaced by $d_{m_i m_i'}^i$, and, for example, $\alpha_{m_i}^i \alpha_{m_i'}^i \alpha_{m_i'}^{i'}$ is replaced by $(d^i \alpha^{i'})_{m_i m_i' m_{i'}}$ (cf. Kempthorne, 1955).

The mean of the inbred population is therefore

$$\prod_{i=1}^{n} \sum_{m,m'} [(1 - F)p_{m_i}^i p_{m_i'}^i + F\delta_{m_i m_i'} p_{m_i}^i](1 + \alpha_{m_i}^i)(1 + \alpha_{m_i'}^i)$$

provided we expand the product of factors involving the α's first.   Consider this product and the terms therein.   The first term will be unity and will occur with all genotypes; hence this term gives μ.   Now consider terms like $\alpha_{m_i}^i$.   These will have the coefficient

$$\sum_{m_i'} [(1 - F)p_{m_i}^i p_{m_i'}^i + F\delta_{m_i m_i'} p_{m_i}^i]$$

which is clearly $p_{m_i}^i$, and, since

$$\sum_{m_i} p_{m_i}^i \alpha_{m_i}^i = 0$$

such terms give zero. By the same argument, any term involving a product of α's, one from each locus, will lead to zero. Now consider a term such as $\alpha^i_{m_i}\alpha^i_{m'_i}$, which is of course $d^i_{m_i m'_i}$. This term yields

$$\sum_{m_i m'_i}[(1 - F)p^i_{m_i}p^i_{m'_i} + F\delta_{m_i m'_i}p^i_{m_i}]d^i_{m_i m'_i}$$

The first term of the product gives

$$(1 - F)\sum_{m_i m'_i}p^i_{m_i}p^i_{m'_i}d^i_{m_i m'_i}$$

which is zero since dominance deviations sum to zero over either chromosome involved. The second term gives

$$\sum_{m_i, m'_i}(F\delta_{m_i m'_i}p^i_{m'_i})d^i_{m_i m'_i}$$

which is clearly equal to

$$F\sum_{m_i}p^i_{m_i}d^i_{m_i m_i}$$

Hence, if

$$D_1 = \sum_i\sum_{m_i}p^i_{m_i}d^i_{m_i m_i}$$

we have the over-all contribution from terms of this type equal to

$$FD_1$$

By an entirely similar argument we see that only dominance deviations enter into the mean of the population and that the dominance $\times$ dominance $\times \cdots \times$ dominance deviation from k loci involves F^k. If then

$$D_k = \sum_{(k)}\Big(\sum_{m_i}\sum_{m_{i'}}\cdots\Big)p^i_{m_i}p^{i'}_{m_{i'}}\cdots(d\,d\cdots d)_{m_i m_i m_{i'} m_{i'}\cdots}$$

where $\sum_{(k)}$ denotes summation over all sets of k loci, μ_I the mean of the inbred population is given by

$$\mu_I = \mu_R + FD_1 + F^2D_2 + F^3D_3 + \ldots \tag{1}$$

where for explicitness we have labeled μ as μ_R, the mean of the original random mating population. Note in passing that the D_j's are defined in terms of the dominance deviations of the original random mating population. The equation (1) has considerable interest on its own merits. It shows that, if there are no dominance deviations, no dominance $\times$ dominance deviations, and so on, then the mean of the population does not change under inbreeding. If there were no dominance $\times$ dominance, dominance $\times$ dominance $\times$ dominance, etc. deviations, the mean of the inbred population would be linearly related to F in spite of the fact that there is epistacy.   This is offhand a remarkable result because one might guess that the linear relation would hold in the absence of epistacy.   We see by the above argument that there may be epistatic deviations involving "additive" in their name without disturbing the linearity.   Of course, if one knows the result and thinks long enough about it, no argumentation is necessary, and the result is obvious.   The result given in equation (1) is of interest in that it shows that a synthesis of Fisher's least-squares approach to the theory of quantitative inheritance and Wright's F leads to a neat understandable conclusion.   The result could of course have been guessed on the basis of the theory of selfing in relation to quantitative inheritance, given elsewhere in the text (see also Kempthorne, 1956a).

Now we turn to the genotypic variance of the inbred population.   We may here expect considerable difficulty and if we do not get a neat result should not be surprised.   It is important to begin the examination because we shall then see the origin of the awkwardness in the final result. Let us get the total sum of squares of genotypic values in the inbred population.   This is equal to

$$\sum_{(m),(m')} \prod_{i=1}^{n} [(1 - F)p_{m_i}^i p_{m_i'}^i + F\,\delta_{m_i m_i'}p_{m_i}^i] \times$$

$$\prod_{i=1}^{n} (1 + \alpha_{m_i}^i)(1 + \alpha_{m_i'}^i) \prod_{i=1}^{n} (1 + \beta_{m_i}^i)(1 + \beta_{m_i'}^i)$$

where we have used α's to represent one genotypic value and β's to represent the other (equal) genotypic value, because each product must be expanded before the multiplication by genotypic frequency and subsequent addition over all possible genotypes, which is indicated merely by $\sum\limits_{(m)(m')}$.   We now pick off terms in the product and while working with the α's and β's shall at the end of the argument replace β by α.   Clearly we get μ^2 with a coefficient of unity.   Now consider $\alpha_{m_i}^i \beta_{m_i}^i$.   This has a coefficient

$$\sum_{m_i} [(1 - F)p_{m_i}^i p_{m_i'}^i + F\,\delta_{m_i m_i'}p_{m_i}^i]$$

which is clearly equal to $p_{m_i}^i$.   A term like $\alpha_{m_i}^i \beta_{m_i'}^i$ leads to

$$F \sum_{m_i} p_{m_i}^i \alpha_{m_i}^i \beta_{m_i}^i$$

Hence as regards additive effects we get

$$2 \sum_{(l)} \sum_{m_i} p_{m_i}^i (\alpha_{m_i}^i)^2 + 2F \sum_{(l)} \sum_{m_i} p_{m_i}^i (\alpha_{m_i}^i)^2$$

where $\sum\limits_{(l)}$ denotes summation over all loci, or clearly

$$(1 + F)\sigma_A^2$$

This is of course the classical result of Wright (1921) for the case of purely additive genes. Finally for single-locus effects we have

$$\sum_{m_i,m_i'} [(1 - F)p_{m_i}^i p_{m_i'}^i + F \delta_{m_i m_i'} p_m^i](d_{m_i m_i'}^i)^2$$

which is equal to

$$(1 - F)\sigma_{D_i}^2 + F \sum_{m_i} p_{m_i}^i (d_{m_i m_i}^i)^2$$

where $\sigma_{D_i}^2$ is the dominance variance arising from the ith locus. If we let

$$\sum_{(l)} \sum_{m_i} p_{m_i}^i (d_{m_i m_i}^i)^2 = S_{D_I}$$

the total contribution of the dominance deviations to the sum of squares equals

$$(1 - F)\sigma_D^2 + FS_{D_I}$$

As regards products of additive effects and dominance deviations, we get

$$\sum_{m,m'} [(1 - F)p_{m_i}^i p_{m_i'}^i + F \delta_{m_i m_i'} p_{m_i}^i] \alpha_{m_i}^i \beta_{m_i}^i \beta_{m_i'}^i$$

and this gives

$$F \sum_{(l)} \sum_{m_i} p_{m_i}^i (\alpha_{m_i}^i)(d_{m_i m_i}^i)$$

Herein lies the rub in obtaining the total genotypic variance of the inbred population, in that additive effects and dominance deviations which are uncorrelated in the random mating population become correlated in the inbred population. This is, after all, obviously what happens with inbreeding.

For interest we work out one more term, namely the variance from additive × additive contributions. Here we get, for $\alpha_{m_i}^i \alpha_{m_i'}^{i'} \beta_{m_i}^i \beta_{m_{i'}}^{i'}$,

$$\sum_{m_i',m_{i'}'} [(1 - F)p_{m_i}^i p_{m_i'}^i + F \delta_{m_i m_i'}][(1 - F)p_{m_{i'}}^{i'} p_{m_{i'}'}^{i'} + F \delta_{m_{i'} m_{i'}'} p_{m_{i'}}^{i'}]$$

followed by summation over m_i, $m_{i'}$. This term gives

$$\sum p_{m_i}^i p_{m_{i'}}^{i'} [(\alpha\alpha)_{m_i m_{i'}}]^2$$

and in total amounts is $\frac{1}{4}\sigma_{AA}^2$. There are four such terms giving σ_{AA}^2 in all. For a term involving $\alpha_{m_i}^i \alpha_{m_{i'}'}^{i'} \beta_{m_i}^i \beta_{m_{i'}}^{i'}$, we get $F(\sigma_{AA}^2/4)$, and with eight such terms we have $2F\sigma^2_{AA}$ in all. Finally terms like $\alpha^i_{m_i}\alpha^{i'}_{m_{i'}}\beta^i_{m_i}\beta^{i'}_{m_{i'}}$ give $F^2\sigma^2_{AA}$. The total involving σ^2_{AA} is therefore $(1 + F)^2\sigma^2_{AA}$.

It is clear that we shall not easily get a formula by the above route for the genotypic variance in the inbred population, though it is possible that an ingenious mind may obtain an easily comprehensible result. We should, however, note that, if we have two equally frequent alleles at each locus, the covariance of unlike terms is zero.

General Remarks

Our knowledge of covariances between relatives under an inbreeding system for the case of epistacy appears to be nil. We therefore turn to experiments which utilize inbreeding and random mating. It is interesting to note that a synthesis of Wright's inbreeding coefficient F and the components of variance σ^2_A, σ^2_D, σ^2_{AA}, σ^2_{AD}, σ^2_{DD}, etc. occurs.

20.5 THE DIALLEL CROSS

The term "diallel mating" appears to have been used rather widely with some possible lack of precision. One usage is to specify the case in which each of a set of individuals is mated to another set of individuals. The term "diallel cross" has come into prominence in recent years (Jinks, 1954; Hayman, 1954a, b) for the case where all possible crosses, including selfings, are made among a set of *inbred* lines. An early analysis of this situation based on simplifying assumptions was made by Hull (1945, 1952). Some extensive theory on the resultant observations has been developed by Hayman (1954b). Some discussion of this material is given by Kempthorne (1956b), with a description of the general situation with arbitrary epistacy, and by Griffing (1956). In all cases genetical analysis of maternal effects has not been made. This would presumably proceed on the lines of the work presented elsewhere (Chapter 15) on maternal effects.

We shall here present a general framework based on the work of Kempthorne (1956b) and Matzinger (1956), within which the diallel cross gives useful information. We shall make the following assumptions for the analysis of genotypic values:

1. The parents used in the diallel cross are a random sample from the population which would arise by inbreeding without selection, artificial or natural, from a random mating population with arbitrary number of segregating loci and arbitrary number of alleles per locus.

2. There is normal diploid segregation.

3. There is no linkage.

Our treatment holds for the case of inbreeding to any particular F value and not merely to the case of F equals unity. For the application of the genetical analysis to experimental data we shall use the standard assumptions that

1. The genotype and environment combine additively to give the phenotypic values.
2. The genotypes and environments are not associated.

The former assumption can be relaxed if the environments used are a random sample of the appropriate *realistic* population of environments.

The original random mating population is specified by the genotypic array

$$\prod_{i=1}^{n} \left(\sum_{m} p_m^i A_m^i \right)^2$$

where A_m^i is the mth allele at the ith locus, p_m^i is the frequency of this gene, summation extends over the number of alleles at the ith locus (not necessarily the same for all loci), and the product runs from 1 to n where n is the number of segregating loci in the population.

After inbreeding to a degree measured by F the frequency of the genotypes are:

$$A_m^i A_m^i: \quad (p_m^i)^2 + F p_m^i (1 - p_m^i)$$
$$A_m^i A_{m'}^i: \quad 2 p_m^i p_{m'}^i (1 - F)$$

and the frequency of a genotype is the product of factors one for each locus and depending on the genes at that locus. It will be convenient for the mathematical development to use the following notation:

$$\text{Frequency of } A_m^i A_{m'}^i = (1 - F) p_m^i p_{m'}^i + \delta_{mm'} F p_m^i$$

where $\delta_{mm'}$ is the Kronecker delta which is unity if m equals m' and is zero otherwise. Note here that the genotype $A_m^i A_{m'}^i$ with m unequal to m' can be regarded as arising in the two ordered ways $A_m^i A_{m'}^i$ and $A_{m'}^i A_m^i$.

Now let us consider the diallel table as given in Table 20.1, in which the parents are denoted by P_r, and Π_{rs} is the population which results from the mating of P_r as a male to P_s as a female. Our job is to characterize the populations in Table 20.1, and for simplicity we shall consider only means, variances, and covariances.

First we consider means. We wish to find the expectation of the mean of any population Π_{rr} and the expectation of the mean of any population Π_{rs}. The latter case is particularly easy, because the population Π_{rs} arises by the union of random gametes from P_r and random gametes from P_s. Under our assumptions P_r and P_s are random members of the inbred population; so an individual in Π_{rs} arises by union of two random

TABLE 20.1

REPRESENTATION OF DIALLEL CROSS

	P_1	P_2	P_3		P_k
P_1	Π_{11}	Π_{12}	Π_{13}	. . .	Π_{1k}
P_2	Π_{21}	Π_{22}	Π_{23}	. . .	Π_{2k}
P_3	Π_{31}	Π_{32}	Π_{33}	. . .	Π_{3k}
P_k	Π_{k1}	Π_{k2}	Π_{k3}	. . .	Π_{kk}

gametes of the inbred population, and under our assumptions of pure inbreeding and no linkage a random gamete of the inbred population is a random gamete of the original population. Hence the expectation of the genotypic value of an individual in any Π_{rs} $(r \neq s)$ is the mean of the original population, μ say.

For the case of Π_{rr} we must obtain the sire and dam gametes of a random individual P_r. Now the frequency of $A_m^i A_{m'}^i$ at the ith locus is $(1 - F)p_m^i p_{m'}^i + \delta_{mm'} F p_m^i$, and this gives rise to the gametic array

$$\tfrac{1}{2}(A_m^i + A_{m'}^i)$$

The parental array is

$$\sum \left\{ \prod_{i=1}^{n} [(1 - F)p_m^i p_{m'}^i + \delta_{mm'} F p_m^i] A_m^i A_{m'}^i \right\}$$

where summation is over all possible pairs m, m' for each possible locus. The offspring array of the parents is

$$\sum \prod_{i=1}^{n} [(1 - F)p_m^i p_{m'}^i + \delta_{mm'} F p_m^i] \tfrac{1}{4}(A_m^i A_m^i + A_m^i A_{m'}^i + A_{m'}^i A_m^i + A_{m'}^i A_{m'}^i)$$

We have to insert genotypic values in place of genotype symbols in this expression. We shall use the model developed for genotypic values in the case of random mating populations. It will be recalled that the genotypic value of the genotype

$$\prod_{i=1}^{n} A_m^i A_{m'}^i$$

which in full we would write as

$$\prod_{i=1}^{n} A_{m_i}^i A_{m_i'}^i$$

where the subscripts i on m and m' are inserted to specify explicitly the alleles present at the ith locus, is expressible as

$$\mu + \sum_i (\alpha^i_{m_i} + \alpha^i_{m'_i}) + \sum_i d^i_{m_i m'_i}$$
$$+ \sum_{i,i'} [(\alpha^i \alpha^{i'})_{m_i m_{i'}} + (\alpha^i \alpha^{i'})_{m'_i m_{i'}} + (\alpha^i \alpha^{i'})_{m_i m''_{i'}} + (\alpha^i \alpha^{i'})_{m'_i m'_{i'}}]$$
$$+ \text{ etc.}$$

Now this can be written formally as

$$\prod_{i=1}^{n} (1 + \alpha^i_{m_i})(1 + \alpha^i_{m'_i})$$

if we make an obvious correspondence of the terms in the expansion, such as replacing unity by μ, $\alpha^i_{m_i} \alpha^i_{m_i}$ by $d^i_{m_i m_i}$, $\alpha^i_{m_i} \alpha^i_{m_i} \alpha^{i'}_{m_i}$ by $(d^i \alpha^{i'})_{m_i m_i m_{i'}}$, and so on (cf. Kempthorne, 1955). Hence the expectation of the mean of the offspring array is

$$\sum \prod_{i=1}^{n} [(1 - F) p^i_{m_i} p^i_{m'_i} + \delta_{m_i m'_i} F p^i_{m_i}] \times$$
$$\tfrac{1}{4}[(1 + \alpha^i_m)(1 + \alpha^i_m) + (1 + \alpha^i_m)(1 + \alpha^i_{m'}) + (1 + \alpha^i_{m'})(1 + \alpha^i_m)$$
$$+ (1 + \alpha^i_{m'})(1 + \alpha^i_{m'})]$$

We have to look at this expression and deduce a simple expression for it. We see that it is equal to

$$\mu + \left(\frac{1+F}{2}\right) D_1 + \left(\frac{1+F}{2}\right)^2 D_2 + \left(\frac{1+F}{2}\right)^3 D_3 + \cdots$$

as is indeed obvious from the fact that Π_{rr} is an inbred population with coefficient of inbreeding equal to $(1 + F)/2$.

We shall not attempt to get the variance of the means of the populations Π_{rr}. In the case of F equal to unity this is clearly equal to the variance of the population of possible homozygous lines derived from the original population, a quantity which will have in general no relationship to σ^2_A, σ^2_D, σ^2_{AA}, etc. of the original random mating population.

We now turn to variances and covariances. These are contained in the expressions for the variances of sire means, of family means, and so on. The results obtained by Matzinger (1956) for the case of two loci and extended in the intuitively obvious way are as follows:

Variance of sire means

$$V_s = \left(\frac{1+F}{4}\right) \sigma^2_A + \left(\frac{1+F}{4}\right)^2 \sigma^2_{AA} + \left(\frac{1+F}{4}\right)^3 \sigma^2_{AAA} + \cdots$$

Variance between family means

$$V_F = \left(\frac{1+F}{2}\right)\sigma_A^2 + \left(\frac{1+F}{2}\right)^2\sigma_D^2 + \left(\frac{1+F}{2}\right)^2\sigma_{AA}^2 + \left(\frac{1+F}{2}\right)^3\sigma_{AD}^2$$

$$+ \left(\frac{1+F}{2}\right)^4\sigma_{DD}^2 + \left(\frac{1+F}{2}\right)^3\sigma_{AAA}^2 + \cdots$$

Also it is clear that the variance of entries off the diagonal is σ_G^2. It follows that the covariance of individuals within sires, that is, of half-sibs is V_s. Note that, if F equals zero, V_s reduces to the ordinary half-sib covariance, while, if F equals unity, we get

$$\tfrac{1}{2}\sigma_A^2 + \tfrac{1}{4}\sigma_{AA}^2 + \cdots$$

which is the covariance of parent and offspring in the original random mating population and is clearly the correct answer for this case because two half-sibs will have exactly one gene in common at each locus. The covariance between full-sibs, that is, between two individuals with the same parent, reduces to σ_G^2 if F equals unity, which is clearly correct since two full-sibs will have identical genotypes in the case of F equal to unity. In the case F equal to zero we get the usual full-sib covariance in a random mating population.

We will now sketch the derivation of these results. First consider an arbitrary individual in the inbred generation, say

$$\prod_{i=1}^{n} A_{m_i}^i A_{m_i'}^i$$

with frequency

$$\prod_{i=1}^{n} [(1 - F)p_{m_i}^i p_{m_i'}^i + F\,\delta_{m_i m_i'}p_m^i]$$

The whole array of offspring with this individual as sire arises from the sire gametic array

$$\prod_{i=1}^{n} (\tfrac{1}{2}A_{m_i}^i + \tfrac{1}{2}A_{m_i'}^i)$$

and the dam gametic array

$$\prod_{i=1}^{n} \left(\sum_r p_r^i A_r^i\right)$$

The array of offspring is therefore

$$\prod_{i=1}^{n} \left(\frac{1}{2}\sum_r p_r^i A_r^i A_{m_i}^i + \frac{1}{2}\sum_r p_r^i A_r^i A_{m_i'}^i\right)$$

The mean of this array is obtained by inserting

$$(1 + \alpha_r^i)(1 + \alpha_{m_i}^i)$$

in place of $A_r^i A_{m_i}^i$, and similarly for $A_r^i A_{m_i'}^i$, and evaluating the expression according to the procedures used above. So we have to consider

$$\prod_{i=1}^{n} \left[1 + \sum_r p_r^i \alpha_r^i + \tfrac{1}{2}\alpha_{m_i}^i + \tfrac{1}{2}\alpha_{m_i'}^i + \frac{1}{2}\sum_r p_r^i(\alpha_r^i \alpha_{m_i}^i) + \frac{1}{2}\sum_r p_r^i(\alpha_r^i \alpha_{m_i'}^i) \right]$$

This is equal to

$$\mu + \frac{1}{2}\sum_i \alpha_{m_i}^i + \frac{1}{2}\sum_i \alpha_{m_i'}^i + \frac{1}{4}\sum_{i,i'} (\alpha_{m_i}^i \alpha_{m_{i'}}^{i'} + \alpha_{m_i'}^i \alpha_{m_{i'}}^{i'} + \alpha_{m_i}^i \alpha_{m_{i'}'}^{i'} + \alpha_{m_i'}^i \alpha_{m_{i'}'}^{i'})$$

$$+ \frac{1}{8}\sum_{i,i',i''} \alpha_{m_i}^i \alpha_{m_{i'}}^{i'} \alpha_{m_{i''}}^{i''} + \text{etc.}$$

Note that all dominance deviations disappear because they will involve summation weighted by gene frequency.

We now take the square of the offspring mean and sum weighting by

$$\sum_{m,m'} \prod_{i=1}^{n} [(1 - F)p_{m_i}^i p_{m_i'}^i + F \delta_{m_i m_i'} p_{m_i}^i]$$

where summation is over all the possible genotypes as given by all the possible sequences of m_i and m_i'. Clearly we get μ^2. As regards $\alpha_{m_i}^i$, we get

$$\tfrac{1}{4}\sum p_{m_i}^i (\alpha_{m_i}^i)^2$$

and the same quantity from $\alpha_{m_i'}^i$. The product of $\alpha_{m_i}^i$ and $\alpha_{m_i'}^i$ gives $(F/2)\sum p_{m_i}^i(\alpha_{m_i}^i)^2$, so that the additive effects yield in all

$$\frac{1}{4}\frac{\sigma_A^2}{2} + \frac{1}{4}\frac{\sigma_A^2}{2} + \frac{F}{4}\sigma_A^2 = \left(\frac{1+F}{4}\right)\sigma_A^2$$

From quantities like

$$(\alpha_{m_i}^i \alpha_{m_{i'}}^{i'})^2$$

we get $\frac{1}{16} \frac{1}{4}\sigma_{AA}^2$ and there are four such terms. Cross products like $(\alpha_{m_i}^i \alpha_{m_{i'}}^{i'})(\alpha_{m_i}^i \alpha_{m_{i'}'}^{i'})$ give

$$\frac{1}{16}\sum_{m_i} \sum_{m_{i'} m_{i'}'} p_m^i[(1 - F)p_{m_{i'}}^{i'} p_{m_{i'}'}^{i'} + F \delta_{m_{i'} m_{i'}'} p_{m_{i'}}^{i'}](\alpha_{m_i}^i \alpha_{m_{i'}}^{i'})(\alpha_{m_i}^i \alpha_{m_{i'}'}^{i'})$$

$$= \tfrac{1}{8}F\sum_{m_i, m_{i'}} p_{m_i}^i p_{m_{i'}}^{i'}(\alpha_{m_i}^i \alpha_{m_{i'}}^i)^2$$

which leads to $\frac{1}{64}F\sigma_{AA}^2$ or $\frac{1}{8}F\sigma_{AA}^2$ from eight terms like this one. Terms like

$$(\alpha_{m_i}^i\alpha_{m_{i'}}^{i'})(\alpha_{m_i'}^i\alpha_{m_{i'}'}^{i'})$$

give

$$\frac{1}{16}\sum_{m_i,m_i'}\sum_{m_{i'},m_{i'}'}[(1-F)p_m^ip_{m_i'}^i + F\delta_{m_im_i'}p_{m_i}^i][(1-F)p_{m_{i'}}^{i'}p_{m_{i'}'}^{i'}$$

$$+ F\delta_{m_{i'}m_{i'}'}p_{m_{i'}}^{i'}](\alpha_{m_i}^i\alpha_{m_{i'}}^{i'})(\alpha_{m_i'}^i\alpha_{m_{i'}'}^{i'})$$

This gives $\frac{1}{16}F^2(\sigma_{AA}^2/4)$, leading to $\frac{1}{16}F^2\sigma_{AA}^2$ in all. So far then we have

$$\left(\frac{1+F}{4}\right)\sigma_A^2 + \left(\frac{1+F}{4}\right)^2\sigma_{AA}^2$$

In general we may have a product $(\alpha_{r_i}^i\alpha_{r_{i'}}^{i'}\alpha_{r_{i''}}^{i''}\cdots)(\alpha_{s_i}^i\alpha_{s_{i'}}^{i'}\alpha_{s_{i''}}^{i''}\cdots)$ in which

$$r_i \text{ is either } m_i \text{ or } m_i'$$
$$s_i \text{ is either } m_i \text{ or } m_i'$$

with equal frequency. If the two factors in the product differ in k subscripts, we get a coefficient of F^k. Hence, for the additive × additive × $\cdots$ × additive interactions involving t loci, the contribution is

$$2^t\sum_k\frac{t!}{k!(t-k)!}F^k\frac{\sigma_{AA\cdots A}^2}{2^t}\times\frac{1}{(2^t)^2} = \left(\frac{1+F}{4}\right)^t\sigma_{AA\cdots A}^2$$

It is readily apparent that cross products resulting from the squaring lead to zero.

In the case of family means, let the sire genotype be

$$\prod_{i=1}^n(A_{s_i}^iA_{s_{i'}}^i)$$

and the dam genotype be

$$\prod_{i=1}^n(A_{d_i}^iA_{d_{i'}}^i)$$

The frequencies of these can be written down as, respectively,

$$\prod_{i=1}^n[(1-F)p_{s_i}^ip_{s_i'}^i + F\delta_{s_is_i'}p_{s_i}^i]$$

and

$$\prod_{i=1}^n[(1-F)p_{d_i}^ip_{d_i'}^i + F\delta_{d_id_i'}p_{d_i}^i]$$

The offspring genotypic array is

$$\prod_{i=1}^{n} \frac{1}{4^n} (A^i_{s_i} + A^i_{s'_i})(A^i_{d'_i} + A^i_{d_i})$$

so that the genotypic mean of this array is

$$\frac{1}{4^n} \prod_{i=1}^{n} [(1 + \alpha^i_{s_i})(1 + \alpha^i_{d_i}) + (1 + \alpha^i_{s'_i})(1 + \alpha^i_{d_i}) + (1 + \alpha^i_{s_i})(1 + \alpha^i_{d'_i}) \\ + (1 + \alpha^i_{s'_i})(1 + \alpha^i_{d'_i})]$$

We have to square this expression, multiply by the probability of the mating, which is the product of the frequency of the sire and the frequency of the dam, and then sum. Note that, if there were no epistacy, the problem would be entirely trivial, as indeed are many of the problems considered. For our present purposes the genotypic mean of the offspring is best written as

$$\prod_{i=1}^{n} [1 + \tfrac{1}{2}\alpha^i_{s_i} + \tfrac{1}{2}\alpha^i_{s'_i} + \tfrac{1}{2}\alpha^i_{d_i} + \tfrac{1}{2}\alpha^i_{d'_i} + \tfrac{1}{4}(d^i_{s_id_i} + d^i_{s_id'_i} + d^i_{s'_id_i} + d^i_{s'_id'_i})]$$

We will merely illustrate the evaluation by picking off the beginning terms. Clearly we get μ^2, and, since the parental combination of genes is split up as regards the offspring, any product of a term with unity gives zero. As regards $(\alpha^i_{s_i})^2$ we get $\tfrac{1}{4}\sum p_i(\alpha^i_{s_i})^2$, and as regards $(\alpha^i_{s_i})(\alpha^i_{s'_i})$ we get $\tfrac{1}{4}F\sum p_i(\alpha^i_{s_i})^2$, so that these terms give in all $\left(\dfrac{1 + F}{2}\right)\sigma^2_A$. As regards σ^2_D we have

(1) $\tfrac{1}{16}(d^i_{s_id_i})^2$ giving $\tfrac{1}{16}\sigma^2_D \times 4 = \dfrac{\sigma^2_D}{4}$

(2) $\tfrac{1}{16}(d^i_{s_id_i})(d^i_{s_id'_i})$ giving $\dfrac{F}{16}\sigma^2_D \times 8$

(3) $\tfrac{1}{16}(d^i_{s_id_i})(d^i_{s'_id_i})$ giving $\dfrac{F^2}{16}\sigma^2_D \times 4$

or $\left(\dfrac{1 + F}{2}\right)^2 \sigma^2_D$ in all. The other terms are picked off and evaluated correspondingly, though any general proof the author can think of would be exceedingly tedious.

There would be some interest in obtaining covariances involving the diagonal means and the mean of other entries in the same row. Only in the case of F equal to unity does it appear that nice formulas would result. For this case the reader is referred to Kempthorne (1956b) and to Hayman (1954b). Some additional ideas on the interpretation of the diallel cross in a specific situation are given by Horner and Lana (1957).

20.6 THE CORRELATIONS BETWEEN RELATIVES UNDER RANDOM MATING IN AN INBRED POPULATION

We have spent some space on the correlations between relatives under specified systems of inbreeding, in particular full-sibbing, and found that the results were unpleasantly complex, though it is possible (and indeed probable) that a simple representation of the results will be discovered. When we turn to random mating of individuals of a population which results by inbreeding a random mating population to a definite F value, we find that very simple formulas exist for the genotypic variance of offspring, namely σ_G^2, the genotypic variance in the original random mating population, and for the covariance of full-sibs and of half-sibs. These results suggest very strongly the possibility that we can write down the covariance of any two relatives, neither of whom is inbred, in the population resulting from random mating of the inbred population.   We shall not spend much time on this problem.   Let us consider the case of one locus and let the two random individuals, with the relationship under examination, be $X\ (= ab)$ and $Y\ (= cd)$.   Then the genotypic values as deviations from the mean of the random mating population are

$$G_X = \alpha_a + \alpha_b + d_{ab}$$
$$G_Y = \alpha_c + \alpha_d + d_{cd}$$

Their covariance is under our assumptions equal to

$$E(\alpha_a\alpha_c + \alpha_a\alpha_d + \alpha_b\alpha_c + \alpha_b\alpha_d) + E(d_{ab}d_{cd})$$

This is

$$2r_{XY}\sigma_A^2 + u_{XY}\sigma_D^2$$

where

$$r_{XY} = \tfrac{1}{4}\{P(a{=}c) + P(a{=}d) + P(b{=}c) + P(b{=}d)\}$$
$$u_{XY} = P(a{=}c,\, b{=}d) + P(a{=}d,\, b{=}c)$$

Let us check that this formula works for the two cases.   For full-sibs let the diagram be as in Figure 20.1.

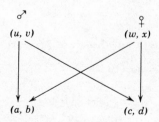

FIGURE 20.1

Let $P(u=v) = F = P(w=x)$. Then, if a and c denote the paternal genes, and b and d the maternal genes, we have as probability arrays

$$a = \tfrac{1}{2}u + \tfrac{1}{2}v$$
$$c = \tfrac{1}{2}u + \tfrac{1}{2}v$$
$$b = \tfrac{1}{2}w + \tfrac{1}{2}x$$
$$d = \tfrac{1}{2}w + \tfrac{1}{2}x$$

so that

$$P(a=c) = \tfrac{1}{2}(1 + F) = P(b=d)$$
$$P(a=d) = P(b=c) = 0$$

and

$$r_{XY} = \tfrac{1}{4}(1 + F) \quad \text{and} \quad 2r_{XY} = \frac{1 + F}{2}$$

Also

$$P(a=c, b=d) = \left(\frac{1 + F}{2}\right)^2$$

and

$$P(a=d, b=c) = 0$$

so

$$u_{XY} = \left(\frac{1 + F}{2}\right)^2$$

Hence the covariance is

$$\left(\frac{1 + F}{2}\right)\sigma_A^2 + \left(\frac{1 + F}{2}\right)^2\sigma_D^2$$

For half-sibs let the diagram be as in Figure 20.2. Then with the same notation as in the full-sib case we have

$$a = \tfrac{1}{2}u + \tfrac{1}{2}v$$
$$b = \tfrac{1}{2}w + \tfrac{1}{2}x$$
$$c = \tfrac{1}{2}w + \tfrac{1}{2}x$$
$$d = \tfrac{1}{2}y + \tfrac{1}{2}z$$

Hence

$$P(a=c) = P(b=d) = P(a=d) = 0$$
$$P(b=c) = \tfrac{1}{2}(1 + F)$$

so

$$r_{XY} = \tfrac{1}{8}(1 + F)$$

and

$$2r_{XY} = \tfrac{1}{4}(1 + F)$$

Also

$$P(a=c, b=d) = P(a=d, b=c) = 0$$

so we get

$$\tfrac{1}{4}(1 + F)\sigma_A^2$$

as the desired covariance.

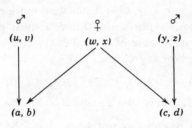

FIGURE 20.2

The parent–offspring covariance encounters difficulties because a correlation in additive values and dominance deviations arises. A slightly different argument shows that for the case of one locus the covariance is

$$(1 + F)\frac{\sigma_A^2}{2} + F\sum_i p_i\alpha_i d_{ii}$$

and it will be noted that the second term is the covariance among homozygotes in the perfectly inbred population of additive effects and dominance deviations of these homozygotes evaluated in the original random mating population.

It is left to the reader to work out other covariances which may be of experimental interest. It is also left as an exercise to the reader to show that the formula extends to the case of an arbitrary number of loci with arbitrary epistacy and no linkage to the form

$$2r_{XY}\sigma_A^2 + u_{XY}\sigma_D^2 + (2r_{XY})^2\sigma_{AA}^2 + (2r_{XY}u_{XY})\sigma_{AD}^2$$
$$+ (u_{XY})^2\sigma_{DD}^2 + \text{etc.}$$

for the case of collateral relatives. The general result given here was indicated for the case of two alleles per locus by Cockerham (1954).

20.7 A PROPOSED EXTENSION OF THE DIALLEL EXPERIMENT

The difficulty in the diallel experiment described above is that the estimates of components of genotypic variance (or linear functions of these) will be rather inaccurate as may be judged by reference to Chapter 13.

The extension originally suggested, in the absence of the genetic theory we now possess, by Dr. G. W. Brown sometime around 1948, is as follows. Take a large random sample of size n of individuals from the inbred population and number them from 1 to n. Then obtain r crosses by the following rules. We require $(n - r - 1)$ to be even and equal to $2k$, say. Then cross line x with lines $x + k + 1$, $x + k + 2$, $\cdots$, $x + k + r$ where, if $x + k + r$ is greater than n, we reduce it by n. This results in $nr/2$ crosses. Thus with 10 lines r must be odd and equal to 3 or 5 or 7 or 9. For the case of r equal 3, k will equal 3, and the crosses that will be made up are as follows:

$(1, 5)$, $(1, 6)$, $(1, 7)$, $(2, 6)$, $(2, 7)$, $(2, 8)$, $(3, 7)$, $(3, 8)$, $(3, 9)$, $(4, 8)$, $(4, 9)$, $(4, 10)$, $(5, 9)$, $(5, 10)$, $(6, 10)$.

The value of this design has not been established from all points of view. Possible points of view are:

1. The estimation of Cov $(F. S)$ and Cov $(H. S)$, for which case we get greater accuracy on Cov $(H. S)$ because the number of degrees of freedom for lines (or sires) is $(n-1)$. This number could be achieved by a balanced experiment with 45 crosses, as opposed to 15 crosses in the proposed experiment.

2. If we were in the position of having a large number of lines and wished to guess the best single and double crosses, we could do so by an analysis which is not unreasonably complicated. It seems obvious that such predictions, which will be based on the absence of certain epistatic effects, will be more accurate than if the same number of crosses were used but with a fixed set of $r/2$ lines used as testers. This point however remains to be established.

The analysis of the proposed experiment for either point of view would be based on a model

$$y_{ij} = \mu + g_i + g_j + \text{error}$$

where y_{ij} is the yield of cross (i, j), though of course point of view (1) above would require in addition the calculation of genetic expectations. It is hoped to publish a full treatment of this design shortly.

20.8 AN EXPERIMENT FOR THE ESTIMATION OF COMPONENTS OF GENOTYPIC VARIANCE

Consider the case of s sires, each mated to a random sample of d dams, and suppose that the progeny of each sire × dam cross are tested in r replicates of a randomized block experiment. This is Experiment I of Comstock and Robinson (1952). Suppose the number of competitive individuals available from the cross of sire i and dam ij in replicate k is equal to n_{ijk}. We suppose that n_{ijk} is greater than zero for all i, j, and k. What is the appropriate analysis of variance? The unequal numbers will result in considerable difficulties in the analysis of variation by an orthogonal analysis of variance, and in such cases, as has been noted elsewhere, a reasonable procedure is to do two analyses of variance which do not "add up": (1) an analysis of variance between and within plots and (2) an analysis of plot means computed, ignoring any differences in their reliabilities. If we denote the yield of the lth individual of the cross sire i × dam ij in replicate k by y_{ijkl}, and the plot means by z_{ijk}, the algebraic expressions for the sums of squares are given in Tables 20.2 and 20.3.

TABLE 20.2

ANALYSIS OF VARIANCE OF PLOT MEANS OF EXPERIMENT

Source	d.f.	S.S.	M.S.
Replicates	$r-1$	$\sum_k \dfrac{Z^2_{..k}}{sd} - \dfrac{Z^2_{...}}{sdr}$	R
Sires	$s-1$	$\sum_i \dfrac{Z^2_{i..}}{dr} - \dfrac{Z^2_{...}}{sdr}$	S
Dams within sires	$s(d-1)$	$\sum_{ij} \dfrac{Z^2_{ij.}}{r} - \sum_i \dfrac{Z^2_{i..}}{dr}$	D
Sire–dams × replicates	$(sd-1)(r-1)$	By difference	I
Total	$rsd-1$	$\sum_{ijk} z^2_{ijk} - \dfrac{Z^2_{...}}{sdr}$	

TABLE 20.3

ANALYSIS OF VARIANCE BETWEEN AND WITHIN PLOTS

Source	d.f.	S.S.	M.S.
Between plots	$sdr-1$	$\sum_{ijk} \dfrac{Y^2_{ijk.}}{n_{ijk}} - \dfrac{Y^2_{...}}{N_{...}}$	
Within plots	$N_{...} - sdr$	By difference	E
Total	$N_{...} - 1$	$\sum_{ijkl} y^2_{ijkl} - \dfrac{Y^2_{...}}{N_{...}}$	

In order to interpret the analysis of variance, we must find the expectations of the mean squares (or sums of squares) in terms of our genetic model. We shall assume that the sires and dams are random members of a population which has resulted from a random mating population by inbreeding to an extent measured by the coefficient of inbreeding F. It will be noted that the case F equal to zero corresponds to the situation when the sires and dams are chosen from a non-inbred random mating population, and that F equal to unity corresponds to the case when the sires and dams are random homozygous individuals resulting from inbreeding to homozygosity of a random mating population. It would appear that the whole continuum of possibilities from F equals zero to F equals unity is of interest.

The genetical structure of the entries in the experiment is as follows:

1. The individuals within a plot are full-sibs.
2. The individuals in different replicates resulting from a particular cross are full-sibs.
3. The individuals in the same or different replicates resulting from a common sire but different dams are half-sibs.

We shall assume that the errors attached to each individual consist of two parts:

(a) A part specific to each individual which is uncorrelated from individual to individual and is denoted by f with appropriate subscripts, with expectation zero and variance σ_f^2.

(b) A part common to all individuals of the same plot which is denoted by e with appropriate subscripts, is uncorrelated between different plots, and has an expectation equal to zero and variance equal to σ_e^2.

We may note in passing that randomization permits us to use this partition of error as an artifice (cf. Kempthorne, 1952, Chapter 8) provided we have homogeneous variabilities over the experiment.

It is immediately evident that the expectation of the mean square within plots is

$$\sigma_f^2 + [\sigma_G^2 - \text{Cov}(F.S)]$$

as can be seen by using the fact that the expectation of the mean square is the expectation of half of the square of the difference between two individuals. In writing this down, we have assumed that the genotypic variance of an offspring is σ_G^2, which is the genotypic variance in the original random mating population, and this is true under our assumptions since throughout the argument we assume absence of linkage and selection.

Now we consider the properties of plot means.   The variance of a plot mean based on n_{ijk} individuals is equal to

$$\sigma_e^2 + \frac{\sigma_f^2}{n_{ijk}} + \frac{1}{n_{ijk}^2} \left[n_{ijk}\sigma_G^2 + n_{ijk}(n_{ijk} - 1) \operatorname{Cov}(F.S) \right]$$

$$= \sigma_e^2 + \operatorname{Cov}(F.S) + \frac{1}{n_{ijk}} \left[\sigma_f^2 + \sigma_G^2 - \operatorname{Cov}(F.S) \right]$$

$$= \sigma_2^2 + \frac{1}{n_{ijk}} \sigma_1^2$$

where

$$\sigma_1^2 = \sigma_f^2 + \sigma_G^2 - \operatorname{Cov}(F.S)$$

$$\sigma_2^2 = \sigma_e^2 + \operatorname{Cov}(F.S)$$

The covariance of two-plot means in different replicates which contain individuals with the full-sib relationship is

$$\frac{1}{n_{ijk}} \cdot \frac{1}{n_{ijk'}} n_{ijk}n_{ijk'} \operatorname{Cov}(F.S) = \operatorname{Cov}(F.S)$$

Similarly the covariance of two-plot means which contain individuals with the half-sib relationship, whether they occur in the same or different replicates is $\operatorname{Cov}(H.S)$.   We can therefore complete Table 20.4, which gives the expectations of mean squares of the analysis of variance in Table 20.2.

TABLE 20.4
EXPECTATIONS OF MEAN SQUARES FOR ANALYSIS OF VARIANCE IN TABLE 20.2

Source	d.f.	Expectation of Mean Square
Replicates	$(r-1)$	$[\sigma_2^2 - \operatorname{Cov}(F.S)] + n_h\sigma_1^2 + \dfrac{sd}{(r-1)} \sum_k r_k^2$
Sires	$(s-1)$	$[\sigma_2^2 - \operatorname{Cov}(F.S)] + n_h\sigma_1^2 + r[\operatorname{Cov}(F.S) - \operatorname{Cov}(H.S)] + rd\operatorname{Cov}(H.S)$
Dams within sires	$s(d-1)$	$[\sigma_2^2 - \operatorname{Cov}(F.S)] + n_h\sigma_1^2 + r[\operatorname{Cov}(F.S) - \operatorname{Cov}(H.S)]$
Sire–dams by replicates	$(sd-1)(r-1)$	$[\sigma_2^2 - \operatorname{Cov}(F.S)] + n_h\sigma_1^2$

$$n_h = \frac{1}{rsd} \sum_{ijk} \frac{1}{n_{ijk}}$$

The basic quantities for the computation of the expectations of mean squares are as follows, where r_k denotes the effect (assumed additive) of the kth replicate $\left(\sum_k r_k = 0\right)$:

$$E(z_{ijk} - \mu)^2 = \sigma_2^2 + \frac{1}{n_{ijk}} \sigma_1^2 + r_k^2$$

$$E(Z_{ij.} - r\mu)^2 = r\sigma_2^2 + \sum_k \frac{1}{n_{ijk}} \sigma_1^2 + r(r-1) \operatorname{Cov}(F.S)$$

$$E(Z_{i..} - r\,d\mu)^2 = r\,d\sigma_2^2 + \sum_{ik} \frac{1}{n_{ijk}} \sigma_1^2$$
$$+ dr(r-1) \operatorname{Cov}(F.S) + dr^2(d-1) \operatorname{Cov}(H.S)$$

$$E(Z_{...} - rsd\mu)^2 = rsd\sigma_2^2 + \sum_{ijk} \frac{1}{n_{ijk}} \sigma_1^2$$
$$+ sdr(r-1) \operatorname{Cov}(F.S) + sdr^2(d-1) \operatorname{Cov}(H.S)$$

$$E(Z_{..k} - s\,d\mu)^2 = s\,d\sigma_2^2 + \sum_{ij} \frac{1}{n_{ijk}} \sigma_1^2 + s\,d(d-1) \operatorname{Cov}(H.S)$$
$$+ s^2\,d^2 r_k^2$$

From the proposed experiment we may therefore obtain estimates as shown in Table 20.5. The genetic interpretation to be placed on the

TABLE 20.5

Parameter	Estimate
σ_1^2	E
$\operatorname{Cov}(H.S)$	$\dfrac{1}{rd}(S-D)$
$\operatorname{Cov}(F.S) - \operatorname{Cov}(H.S)$	$\dfrac{1}{r}(D-I)$
$\operatorname{Cov}(F.S)$	$\dfrac{1}{r}(D-I) + \dfrac{1}{rd}(S-D)$
$\sigma_2^2 - \operatorname{Cov}(F.S) = \sigma_e^2$	$I - n_h E$
$\sigma_f^2 + \sigma_G^2$	$E + \dfrac{1}{r}(D-I) + \dfrac{1}{rd}(S-D)$

estimates enumerated has been worked out for the case when the sires and dams are random individuals from the population resulting by pure inbreeding without selection from a random mating population.   In fact,

$$\sigma_G^2 = \sigma_A^2 + \sigma_D^2 + \sigma_{AA}^2 + \sigma_{AD}^2 + \sigma_{DD}^2 + \cdots$$

$$\text{Cov}\,(F.\,S) = \left(\frac{1+F}{2}\right)\sigma_A^2 + \left(\frac{1+F}{2}\right)^2 \sigma_D^2 + \left(\frac{1+F}{2}\right)^2 \sigma_{AA}^2$$

$$+ \left(\frac{1+F}{2}\right)^3 \sigma_{AD}^2 + \left(\frac{1+F}{2}\right)^4 \sigma_{DD}^2 + \cdots$$

$$\text{Cov}\,(H.\,S) = \left(\frac{1+F}{4}\right)\sigma_A^2 + \left(\frac{1+F}{4}\right)^2 \sigma_{AA}^2 + \left(\frac{1+F}{4}\right)^3 \sigma_{AAA}^2 + \cdots$$

The above results form a basis by which the theory of quantitative inheritance given in this and earlier chapters may be checked.   It will be recalled that no amount of verification can prove a theory to be correct; it can only indicate that a theory gives a reliable representation of pre-scribed situations.   What the author would consider to be a reasonable check on the theory would be the following.   Obtain a number of inbred populations from a specified population by inbreeding to particular values of F, say half a dozen different values, with replication of the inbreeding process by the same and different methods of reaching the same F value. Follow this by an evaluation of the resulting material by several inde-pendently replicated experiments for each replicate of each F population. This would enable estimates of the importance of the various components of genotypic variance with checks on assumptions of the negligibility of higher-order components.   At the same time we should also obtain estimates by obtaining covariances for different relationships under random mating.   It will be recalled that the estimation of components of variance and covariance is difficult in the sense of obtaining accuracy so that very large experiments would be necessary.

In closing it is appropriate to mention the concept of "heritability" in the present connection.*   If we can assume negligibility of some com-ponents of genotypic variance, then we can estimate the non-negligible components.   For instance, a single experiment with a single F (in-breeding) value is sufficient to estimate the additive and dominance variances if we can assume that epistacy is absent.   In any case sufficient assumptions would be made and *should be checked* within the whole

* It is unfortunate in my opinion that the term "heritability" is also used occasionally for the quantity: gain from selection divided by selection differential. This quantity may under special circumstances be equal to heritability defined in other ways, but this may be the exception rather than the rule. It is, for obvious reasons, a good experimental concept.

experiment, to enable the estimation of the total genotypic variance, and the additive and dominance variance, and possibly others. Now heritability in the narrow sense is defined by Lush (1937 and succeeding editions) to be

$$\frac{\sigma_A^2}{\sigma_P^2}$$

and under our assumptions

$$\sigma_P^2 = \sigma_G^2 + \text{environmental variance}$$

In the present case there are two environmental variances, σ_e^2 and σ_f^2, and we could, it may be guessed, make a case for using either one of these, or a composite of the two, or a composite of the two plus another environmental variance (due to variation not measured in the experiment) as a measure of environmental variance. In the present case there seems to be no "airtight" case for any particular one of these, and we are forced to conclude that heritability in the narrow sense without further precise definition of the environmental population is meaningless. This criticism does not apply with the same force to heritability measured in an existent population though the term when evaluated depends on two entirely different sources of variation under our models, namely genotypic and environmental, and is appropriate only in the consideration of certain simple types of selection in an existent population. The same sort of criticism may be leveled at heritability in the broad sense *in the present context* which has σ_G^2 as numerator instead of σ_A^2. There is, however, a very strong case for the consideration of the ratio σ_A^2/σ_G^2 because both parts are genetically determined and are under the assumptions, though not necessarily in fact, properties of the genetic setup. This ratio was first used apparently by Fisher (1918).

We may also note before closing that in the special case of an F_2 population derived from two inbred lines there are two equally frequent alleles per locus. In the absence of epistacy when the genotypic contributions from the ith locus are, respectively, u_i, $a_i u_i$, and $-u_i$, measured about some origin, we have

$$\sigma_A^2 = \tfrac{1}{2}\sum u_i^2$$

$$\sigma_D^2 = \tfrac{1}{4}\sum a_i^2 u_i^2$$

so that

$$\frac{2\sigma_D^2}{\sigma_A^2} = \frac{\sum a_i^2 u_i^2}{\sum u_i^2}$$

which is a measure of mean square dominance, a value greater than unity indicating overdominance (or underdominance or superdominance or what you will), though a value less than unity could result from overdominance at some loci.   The reader is referred in this connection to Comstock and Robinson (1948, 1952).

20.9 EXTENSION OF EXPERIMENT

The obvious extension of the above experiment is to repeat the experiment over a number of years and over a sample of locations in the population of locations of interest.   The details of such an extension are straightforward.   One should, ideally, have orthogonality of everything with everything else: i.e. the same locations in each of the different years and the same parents equally represented over the locations and years. Such experiments are important because the genotypic variance obtained in the experiment described in the previous section is the variance of the genotypic values in a particular location and in a particular year, and these values may vary from year to year.   It would take too much space to give the routine details of the extended experiment.   One would make a partition of genotypic value into a part common to all locations and years, an interaction of genotype and location, of genotype and year, and of genotype and location and year.   There would be corresponding components of genotypic variance and of the covariance of full-sibs and half-sibs.   The analysis of variance would have the usual structure with sources such as sires, sires × years, sires × locations, sires × locations × years, etc., and the coefficients of these components in the expectations of mean squares can be written down at sight of the design by the use of the rules given in Chapter 13, treating locations and years as random factors.   The reader may refer to Rojas and Sprague (1952) for a somewhat similar example of an analysis of variance.   See also Matzinger (1956a), Matzinger and Kempthorne (1956), and Matzinger (1956).

20.10 THE GENERAL MODIFIED DIALLEL CROSS EXPERIMENT

Suppose we have p parents of the same type of origin as in the previous experiment and one analysis *only*, the entries arising from crosses. (Cf. Kempthorne, 1952, Chapter 6.) We suppose that the whole matter is replicated r times and that there are n_{ijk} individuals in the kth replicate of the cross of parents i and j.   Reciprocal crosses may be obtained, and the following analysis would then be performed on the mean.   It may be hoped that some genetical analysis of the difference will be developed in the future.   As in the case of the previous experiment we do an analysis of variance within and between plots and also an analysis of variance of plot means.   The analysis of variance of plot means is derived by the use of the model

$$z_{ijk} = \mu + g_i + g_j + s_{ij} + r_k + l_{ijk}$$

though the resulting mean squares will be interpreted on the basis of their expected values genetically and *not* on the basis of the above model. We suppose in the following that each cross is made only one way. The analysis of variance has the structure given in Table 20.6.

TABLE 20.6

ANALYSIS OF VARIANCE OF CROSSES IN DIALLEL EXPERIMENT

Source	d.f.	S.S.	M.S.
Replicates	$(r-1)$	$\sum_k \dfrac{Z_{..k}^2}{n} - \dfrac{Z_{...}^2}{rn}$	
Sires	$(p-1)$	$\dfrac{1}{r(p-2)}\sum_i Z_{i..}^2 - \dfrac{2(p-1)}{p-2}\dfrac{Z_{...}^2}{rn}$	S
Residual among crosses	$p(p-3)/2$	$\sum_{ij} \dfrac{Z_{ij.}^2}{r} - \dfrac{1}{r(p-2)}\sum_i Z_{i..}^2$ $+ \dfrac{p}{p-2}\dfrac{Z_{...}^2}{rn}$	R
Crosses × replicates	$(r-1)(n-1)$	By difference	I
Total	$rn-1$	$\sum z_{ijk}^2 - \dfrac{Z_{...}^2}{rn}$	

$$n = \frac{p(p-1)}{2}$$

This analysis of variance is obtained as follows:

Replicate sum of squares $= R(\mu, r_k) - R(\mu)$

Sires $\qquad\qquad\qquad\; = R(\mu, g_l) - R(\mu)$

Residual among crosses $= R(\mu, g_l, s_{mn}) - R(\mu, g_l)$

$R(\mu) =$ the reduction in sum of squares due to fitting μ with all other parameters placed equal to zero

$R(\mu, r_k) =$ the reduction in sum of squares due to fitting μ and r_k $(k = 1, 2, \cdots, r)$ with all other parameters placed equal to zero

$R(\mu, g_l) =$ the reduction in sum of squares due to fitting μ and g_l $(l = 1, 2, \cdots, p)$ with all other parameters placed equal to zero

$R(\mu, g_l, s_{mn}) =$ the reduction in sum of squares due to fitting μ, g_l $(l = 1, 2, \cdots, p)$, s_{mn} $(m, n = 1, 2, \cdots, p; \; m \neq n)$ with all other parameters placed equal to zero and is in fact the ordinary sum of squares for crosses

The terms r_k can be ignored in the latter two because crosses are orthogonal to replicates. The exact formulas for the reductions in sums of squares are obtained by writing out the normal equations appropriate to each, fitting and taking the sum of products of estimates and right-hand sides of the normal equations. The normal equations are easy to write down because any parameter occurs in the model with coefficient 1 or 0, so that the normal equation corresponding to any parameter θ, say, has

R.H.S. = sum of observations whose expectations contain θ

and

L.H.S. = the expectation of the right-hand side

noting that the solutions of the equations are estimates and not true values.

We may note in passing that this experiment is the standard one for the estimation of variance due to "general combining ability" and "specific combining ability" (Sprague and Tatum, 1942). The analysis has in the past been done by assuming the g's and s's to be completely independent random variables with variances, respectively, of σ_g^2 and σ_s^2. The above analysis shows that, in the analysis of plot totals,

$$\sigma_g^2 = f^2 \operatorname{Cov} (H.\,S)$$
$$\sigma_s^2 = f^2 [\operatorname{Cov} (F.\,S) - 2 \operatorname{Cov} (H.\,S)]$$

where f is the number of individuals per plot. These equations give presumably the exact meaning to be attached to the two terms. It is appropriate to mention here that there seems to me to be considerable lack of precision in the use of the two concepts, general and specific combining ability, in the literature. The word "general" tends to indicate invariant or all-pervading, but it is apparent that we can talk only about the general combining ability of a line in combination with a set of lines or a population of lines from which we have a random sample. To talk about the specific combining ability of a line seems to be nonsense in that the nicking which may be observed with a particular cross cannot be attributed to either line alone in the cross. It is correct, on the other hand, to talk about the general combining ability *variance* and the specific combining ability *variance* of a set of lines. These are, however, no more or less than what is indicated by the above equations expressing them in terms of the covariances of full- and half-sibs. This should not be taken to mean that it is impossible to give some operational definition of the statement that a certain line has specific combining ability. It merely indicates the need for precision of scientific terminology.

By a procedure exactly analogous to that described for the previous experiment we may obtain the expectations of the mean squares of the analysis of variance in Table 20.6.   They are given in Table 20.7.

TABLE 20.7

EXPECTATIONS OF MEAN SQUARES IN TABLE 20.6

Source	$\sigma_e^2 + n_h \sigma_1^2$	$\operatorname{Cov}(F.S) - 2\operatorname{Cov}(H.S)$	$\operatorname{Cov}(H.S)$	$\dfrac{n}{r-1}\sum r_k^2$
Replicates	1	0	0	1
Sires	1	r	$r(p-2)$	0
Residual among crosses	1	r	0	0
Plot error	1	0	0	0

20.11 ANOTHER EXPERIMENT

Instead of mating s sires, each to a random sample of d dams, we may be in the position that we can use each individual as a sire on any number of dams.*   We would then use a random sample of s sires, each mated to each of d dams.   This is related to Experiment II of Comstock and Robinson (1952).   The structure of the resulting material is indicated in Table 20.8.

TABLE 20.8

GENETIC STRUCTURE OF EXPERIMENT

Dam

Sire	1	2	$\cdots$	d
1	×	×	$\cdots$	×
2	×	×	$\cdots$	×
.	.	.	$\cdots$	.
s	×	×	$\cdots$	×

Now suppose that this is done and that the resulting sd crosses are evaluated in a replicated experiment of r blocks of sd plots, one for each cross.   Suppose that the number of individuals from sire i, dam j in replicate k is n_{ijk}.   We do two analyses of variance as before:

(a) Between and within plots

(b) Between cross-replicate means.

* With many plants we can achieve this by selfing the "sires" and "dams" first. This is possible provided linkage can be ignored.

The expectation of the mean square within plots, E say, is clearly

$$\sigma_f^2 + \sigma_G^2 - \text{Cov}\,(F.\,S)$$

as before. The unweighted analysis of variance of plot means has the structure indicated in Table 20.9, wherein we use z_{ijk} as the plot mean.

TABLE 20.9

ANALYSIS OF VARIANCE OF EXPERIMENT

Source	d.f.	S.S.	M.S.
Replicates	$(r-1)$	$\sum \dfrac{Z_{..k}^2}{sd} - \dfrac{Z_{...}^2}{rsd}$	R
Sires	$(s-1)$	$\sum \dfrac{Z_{i..}^2}{rd} - \dfrac{Z_{...}}{rsd}$	S
Dams	$(d-1)$	$\sum \dfrac{Z_{.j.}^2}{rs} - \dfrac{Z_{...}^2}{rsd}$	D
Sires × dams	$(s-1)(d-1)$	$\sum \dfrac{Z_{ij.}^2}{r} - \sum \dfrac{Z_{i..}^2}{rd}$ $- \sum \dfrac{Z_{.j.}^2}{rs} + \dfrac{Z_{...}^2}{rsd}$	(SD)
Sire–dam combinations × replicates	$(sd-1)(r-1)$	By difference	I
Total	$rsd-1$	$\sum z_{ijk}^2 - \dfrac{Z_{...}^2}{rsd}$	

The expectations of the mean squares in Table 20.9 are obtained as before, noting that individuals from the same sire and dam are full-sibs. and that individuals from the same sire *or* the same dam are half-sibs, The expectations are given in Table 20.10.

TABLE 20.10

EXPECTATIONS OF MEAN SQUARES IN TABLE 20.9

M.S.	Expectation of M.S.
S	$\sigma_e^2 + n_h\sigma_1^2 + r[\text{Cov}\,(F.\,S) - 2\,\text{Cov}\,(H.\,S)] + rd\,\text{Cov}\,(H.\,S)$
D	$\sigma_e^2 + n_h\sigma_1^2 + r[\text{Cov}\,(F.\,S) - 2\,\text{Cov}\,(H.\,S)] + rs\,\text{Cov}\,(H.\,S)$
(SD)	$\sigma_e^2 + n_h\sigma_1^2 + r[\text{Cov}\,(F.\,S) - 2\,\text{Cov}\,(H.\,S)]$
I	$\sigma_e^2 + n_h\sigma_1^2$

To interpret Table 20.10, it will be recalled that

(1) σ_e^2 is the variance of the part of error common to all individuals in a plot

(2) $\sigma_1^2 = \sigma_f^2 + \sigma_G^2 - \text{Cov}\,(F.\,S)$

where σ_f^2 is the variance of the part of error particular to each individual.

Hence we estimate as shown in Table 20.11. The interpretation of Cov $(F.\,S)$ and Cov $(H.\,S)$ will be as in the preceding experiments.

TABLE 20.11

Parameter	Estimate
Cov $(H.\,S)$	$\dfrac{1}{rd}[S - (SD)]$ or $\dfrac{1}{rs}[D - (SD)]$
	or $\dfrac{1}{r(2sd-s-d)}\left[\dfrac{(s-1)S + (d-1)D}{s + d - 2} - (SD)\right]$
Cov $(F.\,S) -$ Cov $(H.\,S)$	$\dfrac{1}{r}[(SD) - I]$
σ_1^2	E
σ_e^2	$I - n_h E$
$\sigma_f^2 + \sigma_G^2$	$E + \text{Cov}\,(F.\,S)$

This experiment may and generally should be repeated over locations and years with the obvious analysis in terms of general genotypic values and interactions of these with locations and years.

It is noteworthy that, in the diallel experiment and the third experiment, the genotypic quantities intrinsic to the interpretation of the experiments are the covariance of half-sibs and the covariance of full-sibs minus twice the covariance of half-sibs. In the absence of epistacy the former is $\frac{1}{4}\sigma_A^2$ and the latter is $\frac{1}{4}\sigma_D^2$. In the first experiment described above, the intrinsic quantities are the covariance of half-sibs as in the other cases and the covariance of full-sibs minus the covariance of half-sibs. The latter would equal $\frac{1}{4}(\sigma_A^2 + \sigma_D^2)$ if there were no epistacy.

Other Notes

Some of the experiments discussed above have been described from an alternative viewpoint by Comstock and Robinson (1952). They have described another experiment, the essential feature of which is back-crossing F_2 populations to parental populations, and have discussed this experiment in the absence of epistacy. Horner (1952) and Horner,

Comstock and Robinson (1955) have examined this experiment for the role of particular types of epistacy. Statistical properties of populations arising from continued backcrossing were also considered.

REFERENCES

Cockerham, C. C. 1954. An extension of the concept of partitioning hereditary variance for analysis of covariance among relatives when epistasis is present. *Genetics*, **39**, 959–882.

Comstock, R. E., and H. F. Robinson. 1948. The components of gentic variance in populations of biparental populations and their use in estimating the average degree of dominance. *Biometrics*, **4**, 254–266.

Comstock, R. E., and H. F. Robinson. 1952. Estimation of average dominance of genes. Chapter 30 of *Heterosis*, edited by J. W. Gowen. Iowa State College Press, Ames.

Fisher, R. A. 1918. The correlation between relatives on the supposition of Mendelian inheritance. *Trans. Roy. Soc. Edinb.*, **52**, 399–433.

Griffing, B. 1956. A generalized treatment of the use of diallel crosses in quantitative inheritance. *Heredity*, **10**, 31–50.

Hayman, B. I. 1954a. The analysis of variance of diallel crosses. *Biometrics*, **10**, 235–244.

Hayman, B. I. 1954b. The theory and analysis of diallel crosses. *Genetics*, **39**, 789–809.

Henderson, C. R. 1955. Personal communication.

Horner, T. W. 1952. Non-allelic gene interaction and the interpretation of quantitative genetic data. Ph.D. Thesis. North Carolina State College.

Horner, T. W., R. E. Comstock, and H. F. Robinson. 1955. Non-allelic gene interaction and the interpretation of quantitative genetic data. *Tech. Bull. N. C. agric. Exp. Sta.*, **118**.

Horner, T. W., and E. P. Lana. 1957. A three-year study of general and specific combining ability in tomatoes. *Proc. Amer. Soc. Hort. Sci.* In press.

Horner, T. W., and C. R. Weber. 1956. Theoretical and experimental study of self-fertilized populations. *Biometrics*, **12**, 404–414.

Hull, F. H. 1945. Regression analyses of yields of hybrid corn and inbred parent lines. *Maize Genet. News Lett.*, **19**, 21–27.

Hull, F. H. 1952. Overdominance and recurrent selection. Chapter 28 of *Heterosis*. Iowa State College Press, Ames.

Jinks, J. L. 1954. The analysis of heritable variation in a diallel cross of *Nicotiana rustica* varieties. *Genetics*, **39**, 767–788.

Jinks, J. L., and B. I. Hayman. 1953. The analysis of diallel crosses. *Maize Genet. News Lett.*, **27**, 48–54.

Kempthorne, Oscar. 1952. *The design and analysis of experiments.* John Wiley & Sons, New York.

Kempthorne, O. 1955. The correlations between relatives in random mating populations. *Proc. XXth Cold Spr. Harb. Symp. quant. Biol.*, 60–75.

Kempthorne, O. 1956a. On the covariances between relatives with general epistasis. *Proc. roy. Soc. Lond.*, B, **145**, 100–108.

Kempthorne, O. 1956b. The theory of the diallel cross. *Genetics*, **41**, 451–459.

Lush, J. L. 1937. *Animal breeding plans* and succeeding editions. Iowa State College Press, Ames.

Matzinger, Dale. 1956. Components of variance of diallel crosses in maize in experiments repeated over locations and years. Ph.D. Thesis. Iowa State College Library.

Matzinger, Dale, and O. Kempthorne. 1956. The modified diallel table with partial inbreeding and interactions with environment. *Genetics*, **41**, 822–833.

Rojas, B. 1951. Analysis of a group of experiments on combining ability in corn. M. S. Thesis. Iowa State College Library.

Rojas, B., and G. F. Sprague. 1952. A comparison of variance components in corn yield trials. III. General and specific combining ability and their interactions with locations and years. *Agron. J.*, **44**, 462–466.

Sprague, G. F., and L. A. Tatum. 1942. General vs. specific combining ability in single crosses of corn. *J. Amer. Soc. Agron.*, **37**, 923–932.

Wright, Sewall. 1921. Systems of mating. II. The effects of inbreeding on the genetic composition of a population. *Genetics*, **6**, 124–143.

Wright, Sewall. 1951. The genetical structure of populations. *Ann. Eugen. Lond.*, **15**, 323–354.

FURTHER READING

Allard, R. W. 1956. The analysis of genetic-environmental interactions by means of diallel crosses. *Genetics*, **41**, 305–318.

Gates, C. E. 1954. The constitution of genetic variances and covariances in self-fertilized crops assuming linkage. Ph.D. Thesis. North Carolina State College Library.

Wright, Sewall. 1952. The theoretical variance within and among subdivisions of a population that is in a steady state. *Genetics*, **37**, 312–321.

PROBLEMS

1. Derive Table 20.4.

2. Derive Table 20.6.

3. Derive Table 20.7.

4. Derive Table 20.10.

5. Describe an experiment to check whether inbreeding has the theoretical effect described in the present chapter. (Hint: Use a few different F values and test, for homogeneity and goodness of fit of deviations from predictions.)

6. Describe an experiment to estimate σ_A^2, σ_D^2, σ_{AA}^2, σ_{AD}^2, and σ_{DD}^2 for a specific population, assuming that all other components of genotypic variance are negligible.

7. Incorporate into the answer of question 6 a test of the adequacy of the assumption that three-factor or higher-order genotypic interactions are negligible.

8. Derive the covariance of first cousins when the mating is at random in an inbred population.

9. Derive the covariance of double first cousins when the mating is at random in an inbred population.

10. Develop a proof of the general result for covariances among relatives arising by random mating in an inbred population.

11. Develop other experiments on the lines of those given in this chapter.

12. Write out the analysis of variance and expectations of mean squares for the case when each of the experiments described in this chapter is repeated over a random sample of locations and years, the basic individuals being the same in all repetitions.

13. Discuss the possibilities for experiments in which we mate at random individuals from two inbred populations with different coefficients of inbreeding.

CHAPTER 21

Populations Derived from Inbred Lines

21.1 INTRODUCTION

We have already considered some aspects of inbred lines as part of the general discussion of partially inbred material. The case in which we have completely homozygous individuals is a sufficiently frequent one, particularly with plants, for a special description to be both necessary and worth while. The great bulk of our knowledge on this case is due to Fisher, Immer, and Tedin (1932), Panse (1940a, b), Powers (1934, 1939, 1941, 1942, 1945, 1950, 1955), Mather (1941, 1942, 1943, 1946, 1949), Comstock and Robinson (1948, 1952), Mather and Vines (1951), Anderson and Kempthorne (1954), Hayman (1954), Hayman and Mather (1955), and Dempster (1955). This knowledge can be classified rather easily according to the order of the statistics involved, first-order statistics being means, second-order statistics being variances and covariances, third-order statistics being third moments about the mean, and so on. Our presentation will follow precisely this breakdown and in the natural order. We shall first give some general background.

Any genetic interpretation of numbers calculated from observations must be based on the properties of those numbers in terms of models which describe the observations in terms of genetic and environmental effects. We shall assume herein that the genetic and environmental forces which combine to produce the phenotypic characteristic that is the observed number, do so in an additive manner. This assumption can be relaxed to some extent, but it would take us too far afield to discuss all the complexities of the general situation. It is also assumed that the genotypes and environments are associated at random. This has the consequence that first-order statistics or means are the sum of a constant environmental contribution and a genetic contribution. Variances will in general contain two parts, one being due to genetic factors and the other a constant environmental variance. In particular situations it may be desirable and even essential to use different environmental variances for different observations, as, for example, observations from different years.

Covariances will not in general contain environmental variance under the models we shall assume, though we could easily envisage a theory in which the environments considered are a correlated sample from a population of environments with a hierarchal or crossed structure, and for which some components of environmental variance would be necessarily included.

Along with the classification of knowledge by the degree of the statistics involved, we also have a classification of knowledge on the basis of the genetic model assumed. We can in fact find in the literature discussions on one or more of the following genetic assumptions:

1. No dominance, no epistacy, no linkage, and no selection of progeny.
2. Dominance, no epistacy, no linkage, and no selection of progeny.
3. Epistacy, no linkage, and no selection of progeny.
4. No dominance, no epistacy, linkage, and no selection of progeny.
5. Dominance, no epistacy, linkage, and no selection of progeny.
6. Dominance, epistacy, linkage, and no selection of progeny.

and so on. To the above methods of classification we may add the assumption about number of alleles, which in the great bulk of work is two, but in isolated cases is more.

Thus we have an extensive multiple classification of possible cases which is partially hierarchal, in that the case of epistacy is always treated to include dominance. One can therefore easily visualize a whole treatise devoted to the subject of this chapter alone.

The case even more primitive than those above in which there are two alleles at each locus, say A_i, a_i, with A_i and a_i having effects independent of i, and with no epistacy, will not be considered here because it is so primitive.

21.2 MEANS OF DERIVED POPULATIONS

Here the most extensive work in the literature is that of Anderson and Kempthorne (1954) who assumed two alleles per locus, an arbitrary number of loci, with arbitrary epistacy and no selection. They used the following model for the genotypic value of an individual with genotype $A_iA_jB_kB_lC_mC_n \cdots$ which allows for any sort of epistacy. This model can be written down by noting that there are, under their assumptions, three possible phases at each locus which can be represented by the numbers 0, 1, 2, where 0 corresponds for example to A_0A_0, 1 to A_0A_1, and 2 to A_1A_1. We let A_0 designate the 0 phase, A_1 the 1 phase, and A_2 the 2 phase, so that a genotype can be written as

$$A_iB_jC_kD_l \cdots$$

Then we may note that formally

$$[\bar{A} + (A_i - \bar{A})] [\bar{B} + (B_j - \bar{B})] [\bar{C} + (C_k - \bar{C})] [\bar{D} + (D_l - \bar{D})] \cdots$$

$$= \bar{A}\bar{B}\bar{C}\bar{D} + (A_i - \bar{A})\bar{B}\bar{C}\bar{D} + \bar{A}(B_j - \bar{B})\bar{C}\bar{D} + \bar{A}\bar{B}(C_k - \bar{C})\bar{D}$$

$$+ \bar{A}\bar{B}\bar{C}(D_l - \bar{D}) + (A_i - \bar{A})(B_j - \bar{B})\bar{C}\bar{D}$$

$$+ (A_i - \bar{A})\bar{B}(C_k - \bar{C})\bar{D} + (A_i - \bar{A})\bar{B}\bar{C}(D_l - \bar{D})$$

$$+ \bar{A}(B_j - \bar{B})(C_k - \bar{C})\bar{D} + \bar{A}(B_j - \bar{B})\bar{C}(D_l - \bar{D})$$

$$+ \bar{A}\bar{B}(C_k - \bar{C})(D_l - \bar{D}) + \text{etc.} \tag{1}$$

This equation (1) holds identically in the letters A, B, C, D, regardless of how $\bar{A}$, $\bar{B}$, $\bar{C}$, $\bar{D}$ are defined.   Now let

$$\bar{A} = \tfrac{1}{4}A_0 + \tfrac{1}{2}A_1 + \tfrac{1}{4}A_2$$
$$\bar{B} = \tfrac{1}{4}B_0 + \tfrac{1}{2}B_1 + \tfrac{1}{4}B_2$$
$$\text{etc.}$$

and let the distinct terms on the right-hand side be each written out as a function of genotypic symbols.   Then the identity still holds.   Finally let the genotypic values be inserted for the genotypic symbols, and we have an equation which can be written as

$$A_i B_j C_k D_l = \mu + \alpha_i + \beta_j + \gamma_k + \delta_l + (\alpha\beta)_{ij} + (\alpha\gamma)_{ik} + (\alpha\delta)_{il}$$

$$+ (\beta\gamma)_{jk} + (\beta\delta)_{jl} + (\gamma\delta)_{kl} + (\alpha\beta\gamma)_{ijk} + (\alpha\beta\delta)_{ijl}$$

$$+ (\alpha\gamma\delta)_{ikl} + (\beta\gamma\delta)_{jkl} + (\alpha\beta\gamma\delta)_{ijkl} \tag{1a}$$

The equation (1a) gives the genotypic value as consisting of

(1) a quantity μ, the same for all genotypes, which is in fact the mean of the random mating equilibrium population with gene frequency equal to one half at all loci,
(2) contributions peculiar to the phase of each locus in the genotype,
(3) contributions peculiar to the phases of each pair of loci in the genotype,
(4) contributions peculiar to the phases of each set of three loci in the genotype,

and so on.

The interpretation of the equation or model (1a) is fairly obvious.   The quantity α_0 is for instance equal to

$$[\nu_0 - (\tfrac{1}{4}\nu_0 + \tfrac{1}{2}\nu_1 + \tfrac{1}{4}\nu_2)]$$

where ν_0 is the mean of the random mating population with $A_0 A_0$ at the A locus and gene frequency of one half at every other locus, ν_1 is the mean of a similar population with A_0A_1 at the A locus, and v_2 is the mean of a similar population with A_1A_1 at the A locus. The quantity α_0 gives then the average effect of phase A_0A_0 at the A locus. The three quantities α_0, α_1, and α_2 satisfy

$$\tfrac{1}{4}\alpha_0 + \tfrac{1}{2}\alpha_1 + \tfrac{1}{4}\alpha_2 = 0$$

and all symbols have this property, for instance,

$$\tfrac{1}{4}(\alpha\beta\gamma)_{0jk} + \tfrac{1}{2}(\alpha\beta\gamma)_{1jk} + \tfrac{1}{4}(\alpha\beta\gamma)_{2jk} = 0$$

We may note also that the effect of phase at any locus is given by three numbers whose weighted average is zero, and that we can if we wish refer to

$$\tfrac{1}{2}(\alpha_2 - \alpha_0) \quad \text{as the direct effect of substituting } A_1 \text{ for } A_0$$

and

$$\alpha_1 - \tfrac{1}{2}(\alpha_0 + \alpha_2) \quad \text{as the dominance effect}$$

The direct effect would be the same as the least-squares effect for a population with gene frequency of one half at every locus.

We shall now prove a general theorem that any population with constant phase frequencies for all loci has a genotypic mean of a specific structure. Consider the population

$$\prod_{i=1}^{n} (pA_0 + 2qA_1 + rA_2)$$

where the product is to be taken over all loci. The mean is equal to

$$\prod_{i=1}^{n} [\bar{A} + p(A_0 - \bar{A}) + 2q(A_1 - \bar{A}) + r(A_2 - \bar{A})]$$

$$= \prod_{i=1}^{n} [\bar{A} + (p - q)(A_0 - \bar{A}) + (r - q)(A_2 - \bar{A})]$$

$$= \mu + (p - q)\sum\alpha_0 + (r - q)\sum\alpha_2$$
$$+ (p - q)^2\sum\alpha_0\alpha_0' + (p - q)(r - q)(\sum\alpha_0\alpha_2' + \sum\alpha_2\alpha_0')$$
$$+ (r - q)^2\sum\alpha_2\alpha_2' + (p - q)^3\sum\alpha_0\alpha_0'\alpha_0''$$
$$+ \text{etc.}$$

where summation is over all pairs, all triplets, etc. of loci. Thus the population mean is of the form

$$\mu + KM_0 + LM_2 + K^2M_{00} + KL(M_{02} + M_{20}) + L^2M_{22}$$
$$+ K^3M_{000} + K^2L(M_{002} + M_{020} + M_{200})$$
$$+ KL^2(M_{022} + M_{202} + M_{220}) + L^3M_{222}$$
$$+ \text{etc.}$$

where

$$K = p - q$$

$$L = r - q$$

$$M_0 = \sum \alpha_0, \qquad M_2 = \sum \alpha_2$$

$$M_{00} = \sum \alpha_0 \alpha_0' \qquad M_{02} = \sum \alpha_0 \alpha_2$$

etc.

The simple populations derived from 2 parents have values of K and L given in Table 21.1.

TABLE 21.1

VALUES OF K AND L FOR POPULATIONS DERIVED FROM
TWO HOMOZYGOUS PARENTS

	K	L
P_1	1	0
P_2	0	1
$P_1 P_2 = F_1$	$-\frac{1}{2}$	$-\frac{1}{2}$
$P_1 F_1 (= B_1)$	$\frac{1}{4}$	$-\frac{1}{4}$
$P_2 F_1 (= B_2)$	$-\frac{1}{4}$	$\frac{1}{4}$
$P_1(P_1 F_1)$	$\frac{5}{8}$	$-\frac{1}{8}$
$P_2(P_1 F_1)$	$-\frac{3}{8}$	$-\frac{1}{8}$
$P_1(P_2 F_1)$	$-\frac{1}{8}$	$-\frac{3}{8}$
$P_2(P_2 F_1)$	$-\frac{1}{8}$	$\frac{5}{8}$
$F_1(P_1 F_1)$	$\frac{1}{8}$	$-\frac{1}{8}$
$F_1(P_2 F_1)$	$-\frac{1}{8}$	$\frac{1}{8}$
$(F_1)S = F_2$	0	0
$(F_2)S = F_3$	$\frac{1}{4}$	$\frac{1}{4}$
$(F_3)S = F_4$	$\frac{3}{8}$	$\frac{3}{8}$
$(P_1 F_1)S$	$\frac{1}{2}$	0
$(P_2 F_1)S$	0	$\frac{1}{2}$

It is now appropriate to say something on how these results could be used. It is clear that, if we can assume that interactions of a particular order are negligible, then we can determine the contribution of each type of interaction to any possible population mean. Scaling tests for the absence of epistacy have been given by Powers (1941) which consist of examining the three comparisons of means:

$$A = 2(P_1 F_1) - P_1 - F_1$$

$$B = 2(P_2 F_1) - P_2 - F_1$$

$$C = 4F_2 - P_1 - P_2 - 2F_1$$

Clearly A, B, and C will be zero if there are no interactions, and if interactions involving three or more loci can be assumed negligible they will be zero if and only if there are no two-loci interactions. An appropriate procedure might be to take, say, a dozen of the populations listed in Table 21.1 to perform a replicated experiment, say, in a completely randomized design so that we can get pure error for each population. We would then have a clean estimate of the error of each mean, and we would be able to test the adequacy of the representation of means by a model including mean and loci effects, or mean, loci effects, and two-loci interactions, and so on. In this way we would determine whether for example it is reasonable to assume interactions involving three or more loci to be negligible, and hence have a test of two-factor interactions which has some reliability.

It is now of interest to consider the case of three or more inbred lines and populations derived from these. Theory for population means in this case can be developed. Under the assumption of two alleles per locus it is worth while to use the concept of a loci group. Let the three parents be denoted by I, II, and III. Then, if we agree to call the phase of each locus in parent I the 0 phase, the loci of parents II and III may be classified as follows.

	Loci Group			
	1	2	3	4
Parent I	0	0	0	0
Parent II	0	2	0	2
Parent III	0	0	2	2

Thus parents I and II are identical with regard to loci groups 1 and 3, parents II and III with regard to loci groups 1 and 2, and finally parents II and III with regard to loci groups 2 and 4. The means of derived populations can be worked out quite easily (Anderson, 1953).

It would be very desirable and indeed essential to develop the theory for the case of multiple alleles. However, such a theory should lead to results which are reasonably comprehensible and useful toward understanding the genetic determination of attributes. Only the case of the diallel cross, based on rather strict assumptions, leads to such results as far as known at present. This matter is discussed elsewhere.

21.3 SECOND-DEGREE STATISTICS OR VARIANCES AND COVARIANCES

We shall here give the results for the case of no epistacy, for the reason that results that are easy to understand and use have been obtained only for this case, with the exception of the diallel cross. (See, however, Hayman and Mather, 1955.) We shall deal only with the case of populations derived from two perfectly inbred lines. The results given below were obtained by Fisher, Immer, and Tedin (1932) or by Mather (1949).

We shall here give the general formula in the absence of epistacy and linkage. Suppose a population has the property that the frequencies of the '0', '1', '2' phases are p, $2q$, and r, respectively, at every locus. Let contributions from these phases be denoted by d_i, $h_.$, and $-d_i$ at the ith locus. Then the mean of the population is

$$(p - r)\sum d_i + 2q\sum h_i$$

and the variance is obtained as the sum of the variance from each locus because of the assumption of no linkage. The variance at any locus is

$$(p + r)d^2 + 2qh^2 - [(p - r)d + 2qh]^2$$
$$= [(p + r) - (p - r)^2]d^2 + 2q(1 - 2q)h^2 - 4q(p - r)\,dh$$

In presenting results Mather (1949) has used D for $\sum d^2$ and H for $\sum h^2$, and to complete the picture we shall use C for $\sum dh$. It may be noted in passing, as has been noted elsewhere in this book, that D and H are multiples of the additive and dominance variance in the F_2 population. In fact, for the general random mating population $p_1^2 AA + 2p_1 q_1 Aa + q_1^2 aa$ with genotypic values d, h, and r for AA, Aa, and aa, respectively,

$$\sigma_A^2 = \sum 2p_1 q_1 [p_1(d - h) + q_1(h + d)]^2$$

which with $p_1 = q_1$ gives

$$\sigma_A^2 = \sum \tfrac{1}{2}d^2 = \tfrac{1}{2}D$$

and

$$\sigma_D^2 = 4\sum p_1^2 q_1^2 h^2$$

which with $p_1 = q_1$ gives

$$\sigma_D^2 = \tfrac{1}{4}H$$

The genotypic variances of the populations which we easily derived from two parents P_1 and P_2 are given in Table 21.2.

In addition to variances, there is need for knowledge of covariances. The covariances in populations which are derived by selfing have already been given in Chapter 17. Other covariances may be worked out easily, and to exemplify the process we shall work out the covariance of backcross $(P_1 F_1)$ individuals with their progeny means obtained by mating at random to the F_2 population. The latter will transmit the gametic array

$$\tfrac{1}{2}A + \tfrac{1}{2}a$$

to offspring for each locus. The computations are given in Table 21.3.

TABLE 21.2

VARIANCES OF DERIVED POPULATIONS

Population	Genotypic Frequencies			Genotypic Variance		
	p	$2q$	r	D	H	C
P_1	1	0	0	0	0	0
P_2	0	0	1	0	0	0
F_1	0	1	0	0	0	0
F_2	$\frac{1}{4}$	$\frac{1}{2}$	$\frac{1}{4}$	$\frac{1}{2}$	$\frac{1}{4}$	0
P_1F_1	$\frac{1}{2}$	$\frac{1}{2}$	0	$\frac{1}{4}$	$\frac{1}{4}$	$-\frac{1}{2}$
P_2F_1	0	$\frac{1}{2}$	$\frac{1}{2}$	$\frac{1}{4}$	$\frac{1}{4}$	$\frac{1}{2}$
$(P_1F_1)P_1$	$\frac{3}{4}$	$\frac{1}{4}$	0	$\frac{3}{16}$	$\frac{3}{16}$	$-\frac{3}{8}$
$(P_1F_1)P_2$	0	$\frac{3}{4}$	$\frac{1}{4}$	$\frac{3}{16}$	$\frac{3}{16}$	$\frac{3}{8}$
$(P_2F_1)P_1$	$\frac{1}{4}$	$\frac{3}{4}$	0	$\frac{3}{16}$	$\frac{3}{16}$	$-\frac{3}{8}$
$(P_2F_1)P_2$	0	$\frac{1}{4}$	$\frac{3}{4}$	$\frac{3}{16}$	$\frac{3}{16}$	$\frac{3}{8}$
F_3	$\frac{3}{8}$	$\frac{1}{4}$	$\frac{3}{8}$	$\frac{3}{4}$	$\frac{3}{4}$	0
F_4	$\frac{7}{16}$	$\frac{1}{8}$	$\frac{7}{16}$	$\frac{7}{8}$	$\frac{7}{64}$	0
F_5	$\frac{15}{32}$	$\frac{1}{16}$	$\frac{15}{32}$	$\frac{15}{16}$	$\frac{15}{256}$	0
F_∞	$\frac{1}{2}$	0	$\frac{1}{2}$	1	0	0

TABLE 21.3

COVARIANCE OF P_1F_1 INDIVIDUALS WITH MEANS OF PROGENY FROM MATING WITH F_2 POPULATION

P_1F_1 Individual	Frequency	Genotypic Value	Gametic Array	Progeny Array	Progeny Mean
AA	$\frac{1}{2}$	d	A	$\frac{1}{2}AA+\frac{1}{2}Aa$	$\frac{1}{2}d+\frac{1}{2}h$
Aa	$\frac{1}{2}$	h	$\frac{1}{2}A+\frac{1}{2}a$	$\frac{1}{4}AA+\frac{1}{2}Aa+\frac{1}{4}aa$	$\frac{1}{2}h$
aa	0	$-d$	a	$\frac{1}{2}Aa+\frac{1}{2}aa$	$\frac{1}{2}h-\frac{1}{2}d$

$$\text{Covariance} = \frac{1}{2}d(\frac{1}{2}d + \frac{1}{2}h) + \frac{1}{2}h(\frac{1}{2}h) - (\frac{1}{2}d + \frac{1}{2}h)(\frac{1}{4}d + \frac{1}{2}h)$$
$$= \frac{1}{4}d^2 - \frac{1}{8}dh \rightarrow \frac{1}{4}D - \frac{1}{8}C$$

21.4 HAYMAN'S DEVICE

Hayman (1954) has given a device which is sometimes useful for problems relating to populations in which there are two alleles per locus, and no epistasy. Using his notation, we let the three phases at the ith locus be denoted by II, Ii, and ii, respectively, and let these be denoted by a variable θ_i which takes the values 1, 0, and -1, respectively, for the three phases. Then, if a genotype is denoted by $\theta = (\theta_1, \theta_2, \cdots, \theta_n)$ and there is no epistacy, the genotypic value is

$$\sum_{i=1}^{n} [d_i\theta_i + h_i(1 - \theta_i^2)]$$

as may be seen merely by substituting $\theta_i = 1$, 0, and -1 in turn. The useful properties of this representation are:

1. The individual with genotype θ_i produces gametes I and i with frequencies $\frac{1}{2}(1 + \theta_i)$ and $\frac{1}{2}(1 - \theta_i)$, respectively.

2. The cross $\theta' \times \theta''$ produces progeny II, Ii, and ii with frequencies $\frac{1}{4}(1 + \theta_i')(1 + \theta_i'')$, $\frac{1}{2}(1 - \theta_i'\theta_i'')$, and $\frac{1}{4}(1 - \theta_i')(1 - \theta_i'')$, respectively, so that the expectations of θ_i and $(1 - \theta_i^2)$ are $\frac{1}{2}(\theta_i' + \theta_i'')$ and $\frac{1}{2}(1 - \theta_i'\theta_i'')$, respectively, and the genotypic mean of the progeny is

$$\frac{1}{2}\sum_i [d_i(\theta_i' + \theta_i'') + h_i(1 - \theta_i'\theta_i'')]$$

As an illustration of the use of this device, consider the crossing of $\theta_1' = 1$ and $\theta_2'' = 0$: i.e. of P_1 and F_1 $(= P_1P_2)$. The frequency of progeny with $\theta = 1$, 0, and -1 are $\frac{1}{2}$, $\frac{1}{2}$, 0, respectively. The progeny mean is $\frac{1}{2}(d + h)$. This particular result is, of course, easy to obtain without any special device.

The reader is referred to Hayman (1954) for an application of the device to the diallel table in which epistacy is assumed to be absent.

The utility of the device appears to be restricted to the case of two alleles at each locus. Hayman (1954) states that the case of q alleles can be represented by p pairs of alleles such that q lies between 2^{p-1} and 2^p. It will be obvious from the treatment of general random mating populations and of the diallel table with multiple alleles given elsewhere in the book that such a representation not only is unnecessary but also may give the impression that the situation is complex rather than inherently simple. It seems to the author a sine qua non that a general genetic theory must deal with an arbitrary number of alleles, and that the biometric relationships must be independent of the number of alleles at each locus, except for the case in which the genetic origin of the material considered ensures that there will be only two alleles per locus. As further clarification of this point the biometric relations should be the same whether we consider three genotypes AA, AB, and BB or the six genotypes A_1A_1, A_1A_2, A_2A_2, A_1B, A_2B, BB, which would result by regarding the A gene as having two indistinguishable variants A_1 and A_2 such that the genotypes A_1A_1, A_1A_2, and A_2A_2 are identical to the AA genotype.

21.5 THE EFFECTS OF LINKAGE ON FIRST- AND SECOND-DEGREE STATISTICS

A great contribution has been made by Mather (1949) to the effects of linkage on some of the statistics considered above. We shall first, however, consider the first-degree statistics.

It is immediately obvious that the effect of linkage on progeny means is zero on the average if there is no epistacy. The effect of linkage on means when we have epistacy can be illustrated by the case of an F_2 population arising by the crossing of AB/ab with AB/ab. The genotypic frequencies are written down quite easily as the square of the gametic array:

$$[\tfrac{1}{2}(1 - r)AB + \tfrac{1}{2}rAb + \tfrac{1}{2}raB + \tfrac{1}{2}(1 - r)ab]^2$$
$$= [\tfrac{1}{4}(AB + Ab + aB + ab) + \tfrac{1}{2}(\tfrac{1}{2} - r)(AB - Ab - aB + ab)]^2$$

The mean of the population is equal to μ, the mean in the absence of linkage, with two corrections. The first is the genotypic expression evaluated by inserting genotypic values in place of genotypic symbols in

$$\tfrac{1}{4}(\tfrac{1}{2} - r)[(AB + ab)^2 - (Ab + aB)^2]$$

or

$$\tfrac{1}{4}(\tfrac{1}{2} - r)(AABB + aabb - AAbb - aaBB)$$

which is related to the additive × additive epistatic deviations. The second is equal to

$$\tfrac{1}{4}(\tfrac{1}{2} - r)^2[(AB + ab)^2 + (Ab + aB)^2 - 2(AB + ab)(Ab + aB)]$$
$$= \tfrac{1}{4}(\tfrac{1}{2} - r)^2[(AABB - 2AABb + AAbb) - 2(AaBB - 2AaBb + Aabb)$$
$$+ (aaBB - 2aaBb + aabb)]$$

It is immediately clear that this is related to the dominance × dominance deviations. We may note in passing that in terms of the Anderson–Kempthorne model this particular term reduces to $-(1 - 2r)^2 A_1 B_1$, which is a rather simple form. These elementary considerations give the clue to the general situation. The general solution will clearly not be simple to get, though we may anticipate that, with selfing, the solution will have a simple form. We shall not explore the matter further here. See in this connection the paper by Cockerham (1956).

As regards the second-degree statistics, we shall give a description of the results of Mather (1949). We consider only the case in which there is no epistacy, and note in passing that the scaling tests based on means will retain their property of detecting epistacy, regardless of whether or not there is linkage, though their sensitivity may be lowered by the presence of linkage. We take the case of populations derived from the crossing of two homozygous parents. Let the parents have genotypes $AABB$ and $aabb$, respectively. Then the F_1 population has genotype AB/ab. Now consider the F_2 population, and suppose that the contributions to the genotypic value are for AA, Aa, and aa equal to d, h, $-d$, respectively, and for BB, Bb, and bb equal to d', h', $-d'$, respectively. The genotypic array for the F_2 population resulting from the selfing of the coupling double heterozygote is

$$[\tfrac{1}{2}(1 - r)AB + \tfrac{1}{2}rAb + \tfrac{1}{2}raB + \tfrac{1}{2}(1 - r)ab]^2$$

or, if we let

$$c = \tfrac{1}{2}(\tfrac{1}{2} - r)$$

it is

$$[(\tfrac{1}{4} + c)AB + (\tfrac{1}{4} - c)Ab + (\tfrac{1}{4} - c)aB + (\tfrac{1}{4} + c)ab]^2$$

It eases the computations to utilize quantities δ_1 and δ_2 which are given by

$$\delta_1 = \tfrac{1}{4} + c$$
$$\delta_2 = \tfrac{1}{4} - c$$

so that $\delta_1 + \delta_2 = \tfrac{1}{2}$, $\delta_1 - \delta_2 = 2c$, $\delta_1^2 - \delta_2^2 = c$, and $\delta_1^2 + \delta_2^2 = \tfrac{1}{8} + 2c^2$. The basis for the computations is given in Table 21.4.

TABLE 21.4

BASIS OF COMPUTATIONS FOR A CASE OF LINKAGE

Genotype	Frequency in F_2	F_2 Value	F_3 Mean	F_2–F_3 Means	F_4 Mean
$AABB$	δ_1^2	$d+d'$	$d+d'$	0	$d+d'$
$AABb$	$2\delta_1\delta_2$	$d+h'$	$d+\tfrac{1}{2}h'$	$\tfrac{1}{2}h'$	$d+\tfrac{1}{4}h'$
$AAbb$	δ_2^2	$d-d'$	$d-d'$	0	$d-d'$
$AaBB$	$2\delta_1\delta_2$	$h+d'$	$\tfrac{1}{2}h+d'$	$\tfrac{1}{2}h$	$\tfrac{1}{4}h+d'$
$AaBb(c)$	$2\delta_1^2$	$h+h'$	$\tfrac{1}{2}h+\tfrac{1}{2}h'$	$\tfrac{1}{2}h+\tfrac{1}{2}h'$	$\tfrac{1}{4}h+\tfrac{1}{4}h'$
$AaBb(r)$	$2\delta_2^2$	$h+h'$	$\tfrac{1}{2}h+\tfrac{1}{2}h'$	$\tfrac{1}{2}h+\tfrac{1}{2}h'$	$\tfrac{1}{4}h+\tfrac{1}{4}h'$
$Aabb$	$2\delta_1\delta_2$	$h-d'$	$\tfrac{1}{2}h-d'$	$\tfrac{1}{2}h$	$\tfrac{1}{4}h-d'$
$aaBB$	δ_2^2	$-d+d'$	$-d+d'$	0	$-d+d'$
$aaBb$	$2\delta_1\delta_2$	$-d+h'$	$-d+\tfrac{1}{2}h'$	$\tfrac{1}{2}h'$	$-d+\tfrac{1}{4}h'$
$aabb$	δ_1^2	$-d-d'$	$-d-d'$	0	$-d-d'$

We therefore find, with S.S. denoting "sum of squares of",

$$F_2 \text{ mean} = \tfrac{1}{2}(h + h')$$

$$F_2\text{-}F_3 \text{ mean} = (\tfrac{1}{2}h + \tfrac{1}{2}h')(4\delta_1\delta_2 + 2\delta_1^2 + 2\delta_2^2)$$

$$= \tfrac{1}{4}(h + h')$$

$$F_3 \text{ mean} = \tfrac{1}{4}(h + h')$$

$$\text{S.S. } F_2 \text{ values} = 2(\delta_1 + \delta_2)^2(d^2 + d'^2 + h^2 + h'^2) + 4(\delta_1^2 - \delta_2^2)dd'$$
$$+ 4(\delta_1^2 + \delta_2^2)hh'$$
$$= \tfrac{1}{2}(d^2 + d'^2) + \tfrac{1}{2}(h^2 + h'^2) + 4cdd' + 4(\tfrac{1}{8} + 2c^2)hh'$$

$$F_2 \text{ variance} = \tfrac{1}{2}(d^2 + d'^2) + \tfrac{1}{4}(h^2 + h'^2) + 4cdd' + 8c^2hh'$$

$$\text{S.S. } F_3 \text{ values} = 2(\delta_1 + \delta_2)^2[d^2 + d'^2 + (\tfrac{1}{2}h)^2 + (\tfrac{1}{2}h')^2] + 4(\delta_1^2 - \delta_2^2)dd'$$
$$+ 4(\delta_1^2 + \delta_2^2)(\tfrac{1}{2}h)(\tfrac{1}{2}h')$$
$$= \tfrac{1}{2}(d^2 + d'^2) + \tfrac{1}{8}(h^2 + h'^2) + 4cdd' + (\tfrac{1}{8} + 2c^2)hh'$$

Variance of F_3 means

$$= \tfrac{1}{2}(d^2 + d'^2) + \tfrac{1}{16}(h^2 + h'^2) + 4cdd' + 2c^2hh'$$

Similarly:

Variance of F_4 means of F_2 individuals

$$= \tfrac{1}{2}(d^2 + d'^2) + \tfrac{1}{16}(h^2 + h'^2) + 4cdd' + \frac{c^2hh'}{2}$$

and, in general, variance of F_k means of F_2 individuals

$$= \tfrac{1}{2}(d^2 + d'^2) + \frac{1}{2^{2k-2}}(h^2 + h'^2) + 4cdd' + \frac{32}{2^{2k-2}}c^2hh'$$

$$= \tfrac{1}{2}(d^2 + d'^2 + 8cdd') + \frac{1}{2^{2k-2}}(h^2 + h'^2 + 32c^2hh')$$

S.S. $(F_2\text{-}F_3)$ values

$$= 2(\delta_1 + \delta_2)^2[(\tfrac{1}{2}h)^2 + (\tfrac{1}{2}h')^2] + 4(\delta_1^2 + \delta_2^2)(\tfrac{1}{2}h)(\tfrac{1}{2}h')$$
$$= \tfrac{1}{2}[(\tfrac{1}{2}h)^2 + (\tfrac{1}{2}h')^2] + (\tfrac{1}{2} + 8c^2)(\tfrac{1}{2}h)(\tfrac{1}{2}h')$$

Variance of $F_2\text{-}F_3$ means

$$= \tfrac{1}{16}(h^2 + h'^2) + 2c^2hh'$$

Variance of $F_2\text{-}F_4$ means

$$= \tfrac{1}{4}(\tfrac{3}{4})^2(h^2 + h'^2) + 8c^2(\tfrac{3}{4})^2hh'$$

or, in general,

Variance of $F_k\text{-}F_l$ means of F_2 individuals

$$= \tfrac{1}{4}\left(\frac{1}{2^{k-2}} - \frac{1}{2^{l-2}}\right)^2 [(h^2 + h'^2) + 32c^2hh']$$

Since

$$\text{Cov}\,(X_1,\,X_2) = \tfrac{1}{2}[V(X_1) + V(X_2) - V(X_1 - X_2)]$$

we have the result:

Covariance of F_k means and F_l means of F_2 individuals

$$= \tfrac{1}{2}(d^2 + d'^2 + 8cdd') + \frac{4}{2^{k+l}}(h^2 + h'^2 + 32c^2hh')$$

We may note therefore that all variances and covariances among F_2 individuals of their progeny means in any generation of subsequent selfing are expressible in terms of

$$D_a = d^2 + d'^2 + 8cdd'$$

and

$$H_a = h^2 + h'^2 + 32c^2hh'$$

For comparison with Mather's results (1949, p. 84) we may note that our

$$c = \tfrac{1}{2}(\tfrac{1}{2} - r)$$

so that

$$8c = 2(1 - 2r)$$

and

$$32c^2 = 2(1 - 2r)^2$$

and that Mather uses p for the recombination percentage. The above results were obtained fairly easily, but succeeding results get gradually more difficult to obtain.

The variance of F_3 individuals within F_2 parents is obtained by noting that

$4\delta_1\delta_2$ of F_2 individuals segregate for the A locus only into

$$\tfrac{1}{4}AA + \tfrac{1}{2}Aa + \tfrac{1}{4}aa$$

$4\delta_1\delta_2$ of F_2 individuals segregate for the B locus only into

$$\tfrac{1}{4}BB + \tfrac{1}{2}Bb + \tfrac{1}{4}bb$$

$2\delta_1^2$ of F_2 individuals are coupling double heterozygotes

$2\delta_2^2$ of F_2 individuals are repulsion heterozygotes

so that the required variance equals

$$4\delta_1\delta_2[\tfrac{1}{2}(d^2 + d'^2) + \tfrac{1}{4}(h^2 + h'^2)]$$
$$+ 2\delta_1^2[\tfrac{1}{2}(d^2 + d'^2) + \tfrac{1}{4}(h^2 + h'^2) + 4cdd' + 8c^2hh']$$
$$+ 2\delta_2^2[\tfrac{1}{2}(d^2 + d'^2) + \tfrac{1}{4}(h^2 + h'^2) - 4cdd' + 8c^2hh']$$

which is

$$\tfrac{1}{4}[(d^2 + d'^2) + 32c^2dd'] + \tfrac{1}{8}[(h^2 + h'^2) + (\tfrac{1}{2} + 8c^2)(32c^2)hh']$$

In the above we utilize the fact that the terms "coupling" and "repulsion" are relevant to the association of d and d', in that, if d and d' arise in the same individual, we use the term "coupling," and, if d and $-d'$ arise in the same individual, we use the term "repulsion." We can translate formulas for the one case into the other by changing d' into $-d'$. If the original individual were a repulsion double heterozygote, all the formulas above should be altered in this way.

In an analogous way we can develop similar formulas for variances of F_3 individuals, of $F_4, F_5, \cdots$ means of F_3 individuals, and the appropriate covariances. The procedure becomes very tedious because the frequencies of F_3 individuals involve δ_1^4 and δ_2^4 as well as lower powers of δ_1 and δ_2. The author knows of no way of getting out formulas neatly, and it does not seem worth while to burden the reader with a large amount of tedious algebra. Undoubtedly someone will find a quick way of deriving all the quantities of interest. Mather and Vines (1951) state some of the results in the form that the intrinsic variances and covariances are of different unspecified natures.

We now turn to some of the other relationships developed by Mather (1949). These are the formulas for the variance of biparental progeny means ($V_{\overline{BIP}}$), the covariance of the F_2 individual value and its progeny mean ($W_{F_2/BIP}$), and the mean variance of biparental progenies ($\bar{V}_{BIP}$), the mating in all cases being at random within the F_2 population. The values for these variances and covariances can be written down immediately in the absence of linkage as

$$V_{\overline{BIP}} = \operatorname{Cov}(F.\,S) = \tfrac{1}{2}\sigma_A^2 + \tfrac{1}{4}\sigma_D^2$$
$$W_{F_2/BIP} = \operatorname{Cov}(P,\,O) = \tfrac{1}{2}\sigma_A^2$$
$$\bar{V}_{BIP} = \tfrac{1}{2}\sigma_A^2 + \tfrac{3}{4}\sigma_D^2$$

with

$$\sigma_A^2 = \tfrac{1}{2}\sum d^2 = \tfrac{1}{2}D \quad \text{and} \quad \sigma_D^2 = \tfrac{1}{4}\sum h^2 = \tfrac{1}{4}H$$

In the case of linkage, we have to revert to the use of Table 21.4 or to use the elementary theory on the progress of a population with linked loci given in Chapter 2. Mather (1949) finds that the above formulas hold if D and H are redefined, as follows:

$$V_{\overline{BIP}} = \tfrac{1}{4}D_a + \tfrac{1}{16}H_a, \Big\}$$
$$W_{F_2/BIP} = \tfrac{1}{4}D_a, \quad\;\Big\}$$
$$\bar{V}_{BIP} = \tfrac{1}{2}D_b + \tfrac{3}{16}H_b,$$

$$D_a = d^2 + d'^2 + 8cdd'$$
$$H_a = h^2 + h'^2 + 32c^2hh'$$
$$D_b = d^2 + d'^2 + 32c^2dd'$$
$$H_b = h^2 + h'^2 + (\tfrac{1}{2} + 8c^2)(32c^2)hh'$$

Mather (1947) also gives results for backcross populations, and Mather and Vines (1951) additional results. We note that, as long as we are concerned with variances, we can merely sum any product terms in d and d', or in h and h' over all pairs of loci.

21.6 DISCUSSION

It would be foolhardy for the author to attempt a discussion of the utilization of the above results in view of the excellent treatment given by Mather (1949, 1951). We shall give only a few remarks on the procedure of utilization:

1. The values given above are genotypic variances and covariances. Phenotypic variances will also involve environmental variance and environment–genotype interaction variance if there be any.

2. No modification of covariance formulas is necessary under most circumstances if designs with randomization are used, or if the results being correlated are from different experiments.

3. The realistic modification of genotypic variance formulas for environmental variance is a difficult problem. If there is no environmental–genotype interaction, we have to add a variance component to theoretical genotypic variance components to obtain expected phenotypic variances. The difficulty then arises of choosing an estimate of environmental variance which may be used to adjust phenotypic variances to genotypic variances. A common procedure is to use observed variances in non-segregating populations such as the true breeding parents or the F_1. We will frequently find that these variances are markedly different. The variance between individuals in either parent population may be very high, expressing the greater susceptibility of inbred material to the vagaries of environment. In fact, there appears to be no general tendency in the magnitudes of the environmental variances that the author has seen (cf. Byrd, 1955). This makes utilization of theoretical variances somewhat hazardous in some situations.

4. The use of transformations to remove epistacy is appropriate, but there may be considerable difficulties in that each set of data may require its own individual transformation, and no general knowledge may accrue. This comes to our attention forcibly when the data on the same populations collected in different years require different transformations (cf. Powers, 1950, 1955).

5. One is faced in all applications with the requirement that two scaling conditions be met: namely, (a) additivity of environmental effects and hence constancy of environmental variance, and (b) additivity of genetic factors; that is, absence of epistacy. There seems to be no reason why these two requirements should be satisfied or even approximately satisfied by a single scale. It appears (to the author) that the problems involved

here merit considerable attention of all workers on the study of quantitative inheritance. The problems are not particular to the type of research which Mather and his coworkers have pursued but occur in all uses of genetic expectations involving variances. If we use covariances only, we need only consider the requirement of no epistacy.

In closing this chapter we apologize to the reader for the absence of a general treatment and a procedure for the development of general formulas in a single attack. It may, however, be remarked that difficulties arise as soon as one becomes involved in inbreeding. A few problems relating to inbred populations are, as we have seen, susceptible to simple general solution, but these are problems in which populations are derived from the inbred populations by random mating, and under these circumstances there is independence of the two genes possessed at any locus by a resulting individual. It is also regrettable that no material on polyploid populations can be included herein.

The reader should refer to the classical paper by Fisher, Immer, and Tedin (1932) for a discussion of third-degree statistics. He should refer to Panse (1940a, b) for a discussion of selection in relation to the results given above. Robson (1956) examines the genetic content of fourth-degree statistics.

All the matters are discussed extensively in *Biometrical Genetics* by Mather (1947), and this work with extensions in Mather and Vines (1951) constitutes a definitive statement of our knowledge on the use of inbred populations. A very detailed study of one set of data is given by Powers (1955), and may be consulted for both general and detailed procedures and for general discussion.

The papers of Comstock and Robinson (1948, 1952) listed below are specifically concerned with average degree of dominance. The papers by Griffing (1950, 1953) give examples of the applications of some techniques. Hull (1952) has worked on this area with particular reference to overdominance and selection procedures for several years. Hayman and Mather (1955) give results on two-locus epistacy. See also Chapter 20.

REFERENCES

Anderson, V. L. 1953. A model for the study of quantitative inheritance. Ph.D. Thesis. Iowa State College Library.

Anderson, V. L., and O. Kempthorne. 1954. A model for the study of quantitative inheritance. *Genetics*, **39**, 883–898.

Byrd, W. F. 1955. Genetic and environmental variances in segregating and non-segregating maize populations. Ph.D. Thesis. Iowa State College Library.

Cockerham, C. C. 1956. Effects of linkage on the covariances between relatives. *Genetics*, **41**, 138–141.

Comstock, R. E., and H. F. Robinson. 1948. The components of genetic variance in populations of biparental progenies and their use in estimating the average degree of dominance. *Biometrics*, **4**, 254–266.

Comstock, R. E., and H. F. Robinson, 1952. Estimation of average dominance of genes. Chapter 30 of *Heterosis*, edited by J. W. Gowen. Iowa State College Press, Ames.

Dempster, Everett, R. 1955. Some genetic problems in controlled populations. *Proc. 3rd Berkeley Symp. math. Statist. Prob.*. In press.

Fisher, R. A., F. R. Immer, and O. Tedin. 1932. The genetical interpretation of statistics of the third degree in the study of quantitative inheritance. *Genetics*, **17**, 107–124.

Griffing, Bruce. 1950. Analysis of quantitative gene action by constant parent regression and related techniques. *Genetics*, **35**, 303–321.

Griffing, Bruce. 1953. The analysis of tomato yield components in terms of genotypic and environmental effects. *Res. Bull.* 397. *Ia. agric. Exp. Sta.*, **397**.

Hayman, B. I. 1954. The theory and analysis of diallel crosses. *Genetics*, **39**, 289–809.

Hayman, B. I., and K. Mather. 1955. The description of genic interactions in continuous variation. *Biometrics*, **11**, 69–82.

Hull, F. H. 1952. Overdominance and recurrent selection. Chapter 28 of *Heterosis*, edited by J. W. Gowen. Iowa State College Press, Ames.

Mather, K. 1941. Variation and selection of polygenic characters. *J. Genet.*, **41**, 159–193.

Mather, K. 1942. The balance of polygenic combinations. *J. Genet.*, **43**, 309–336.

Mather, K. 1943. Polygenic inheritance and natural selection. *Biol. Rev.*, **18**, 32–64.

Mather, K. 1946. Dominance and heterosis. *Amer. Nat.*, **80**, 91–96.

Mather, K. 1949. *Biometrical genetics*. Methuen, London.

Mather, K., and A. Vines. 1951. The inheritance of height and flowering time in a cross of *Nicotiana rustica*. In *Quantitative Inheritance*, Her Majesty's Stationery Office, London.

Panse, V. G. 1940a. The applications of genetics to plant breeding. II. The inheritance of quantitative characters and plant breeding. *J. Genet.*, **40**, 283–302.

Panse, V. G. 1940b. A statistical study of quantitative inheritance. *Ann. Eugen. Lond.*, **10**, 76–105.

Powers, L. 1934. The nature and interaction of genes differentiating habit of growth in a cross between varieties of *Triticum vulgare*. *J. agric. Res.*, **49**, 573–605.

Powers, L. 1939. Studies on the nature of the interactions of the genes differentiating quantitative characters in a cross between *Lycopersicon esculentum* and *L. Pimpinelli folium*. *J. Genet.*, **39**, 139–170.

Powers, L. 1941. Inheritance of quantitative characters in crosses involving two species of *Lycopersicon*. *J. agric. Res.*, **63**, 149–174.

Powers, L. 1942. The nature of the series of environmental variances and the estimation of the genetic variances and the geometric means in crosses involving species of *Lycopersicon*. *Genetics*, **27**, 561–575.

Powers, L. 1945. Relative yields of inbred lines and F_1 hybrids of tomato. *Bot. Gaz.*, **106**, 247–268.

Powers, L. 1950. Determining scales and the use of transformations in studies of weight per locule of tomato fruit. *Biometrics*, **6**, 145–163.

Powers, L. 1955. Components of variance method and partitioning method of genetic analysis applied to weight per fruit of tomato hybrid and parental populations. *Tech. Bull. U.S. Dep. Agric.*, **1131**.

Robinson, H. F., R. E. Comstock, and P. H. Harvey. 1949. Estimates of heritability and the degree of dominance in corn. *Agron. J.*, **41**, 353–359.

Robson, D. S. 1956. Applications of the k_4 statistic to genetic variance component analyses. *Biometrics*, **12**, 433–444.

FURTHER READING

Nelder, J. A. 1952. Some genotypic frequencies and variance components occurring in biometrical genetics. *Heredity*, **6**, 387–394.

Nelder, J. A. 1953. Statistical models in biometrical genetics. *Heredity*, **7**, 111–119.

CHAPTER 22

Infinitesimal Equilibrium Theory of Assortative Mating

22.1 INTRODUCTION

We propose in this chapter to review some rather extensive work by R. A. Fisher which deals with a stationary population in which the attributes are determined by a large number of factors, the genes of which have small or infinitesimal effects. This means for example that, if the population were classified into three groups, AA, Aa, and aa, according to the three possible phases at one locus, the genotypic variability in each group would be essentially the same as in the entire population, but the means would be slightly different, depending on the effects of the genes A and a and on the effects of other genes whose presence is correlated with that of the A, a genes by the effects of assortative mating or homogamy as Fisher termed it. We shall reproduce essentially the mathematical argumentation of Fisher (1918).

The relevance of this theory to real biological populations is a question we shall not attempt to evaluate. It seems quite likely that in a natural population there will be a whole spectrum of genes with regard to their effects, from genes having large negative effects through genes with small effects, to genes having large positive effects. It also seems likely that the great bulk of genetic variability in a natural population will arise from genes having small effects relative to the genotypic standard deviation in the population, but this is pure speculation.

22.2 THE FREQUENCY OF MATINGS

The entire argument will be in terms of genotypic values about the population mean. Let ρ be the marital correlation, and the population variance be V. Then it may be expected that with a large number of genes, each with small effects, the probability that an individual has a value between x and $x + dx$ is

$$M = \frac{1}{(2\pi V)^{1/2}} \exp\left(-\frac{x^2}{2V}\right) dx \tag{1}$$

and likewise the frequency that an individual has a value between y and $y + dy$ is

$$N = \frac{1}{(2\pi V)^{1/2}} \exp\left(-\frac{y^2}{2V}\right) dy \qquad (2)$$

By virtue of the marital correlation ρ, the frequency of matings of individuals in $(x, x + dx)$ and individuals in $(y, y + dy)$ is

$$\frac{1}{[2\pi(1 - \rho^2)]^{1/2}V} \exp\left[-\frac{x^2 - 2\rho xy + y^2}{2(1 - \rho^2)V}\right] dx\, dy \qquad (3)$$

which is equal to

$$\frac{MN}{(1 - \rho^2)^{1/2}} \exp\left[-\frac{\rho^2 x^2 - 2\rho xy + \rho^2 y^2}{2(1 - \rho^2)V}\right] \qquad (4)$$

To obtain the effect of assortative mating we have to determine the frequency of matings of two groups with different genotypes. One group with genotypic values denoted by x may be supposed to have a total frequency of M', a mean equal to a and a variance equal (essentially) to V, and the other group with genotypic values denoted by y, a total frequency of N', a mean equal to b, and a variance equal to V. The probability that an individual will be in the first group and have a genotypic value in $(x, x + dx)$ is

$$\frac{M'}{(2\pi V)^{1/2}} \exp\left[-\frac{(x - a)^2}{2V}\right] dx$$

and the probability that an individual will be in the second group and have a genotypic value in $(y, y + dy)$ is

$$\frac{N'}{(2\pi V)^{1/2}} \exp\left[-\frac{(y - b)^2}{2V}\right] dy$$

and the conditional probability of two such individuals mating is

$$\frac{1}{(1 - \rho^2)^{1/2}} \exp\left[-\frac{(\rho^2 x^2 - 2\rho xy + \rho^2 y^2)}{2(1 - \rho^2)V}\right]$$

Hence the combined probability of the three subevents is

$$\frac{M'N'}{2\pi V} \exp\left\{-\frac{1}{2V}[(x - a)^2 + (y - b)^2]\right\} \frac{1}{(1 - \rho^2)^{1/2}}$$

$$\exp\left[-\frac{(\rho^2 x^2 - 2\rho xy + \rho^2 y^2)}{2(1 - \rho^2)V}\right] dx\, dy \qquad (5)$$

To obtain the probability of an individual of the first group mating with an individual of the second group we merely have to integrate (i.e. sum) this expression over all values of x and y.   This gives

$$M'N' \exp\left(\frac{\rho ab}{V}\right) \tag{6}$$

For those who are interested, the integral is obtained by transforming into a bivariate normal density form.

22.3 THE EQUILIBRIUM FREQUENCIES FOR A SINGLE FACTOR

Let the frequency of A_iA_i individuals be $p_i^2(1 + f_{ii})$ and of A_iA_j individuals be $2p_ip_j(1 + f_{ij})$ where p_i, $i = 1, 2, \cdots, m$ are the frequencies of the m alleles.   Then the f_{ij} are subject to the conditions

$$\sum_{j=1}^{m} p_j f_{ij} = 0, \qquad i = 1, 2, \cdots, m \tag{7}$$

Let the mean deviation of the A_iA_i class of individuals from the population mean be G_{ii}, and of the A_iA_j class be G_{ij}.   Then

$$\sum_{ij} p_i p_j (1 + f_{ii}) G_{ij} = 0 \tag{8}$$

By equation (6) the frequency of matings (A_iA_j) by (A_rA_s), or $(ij) \times (rs)$ for short, is

$$8 p_i p_j p_r p_s (1 + f_{ij})(1 + f_{rs}) \exp\left(\frac{\rho}{V} G_{ij} G_{rs}\right)$$
$$= 8 p_i p_j p_r p_s (1 + f_{ij})(1 + f_{rs}) \left(1 + \frac{\rho}{V} G_{ij} G_{rs}\right) \tag{9}$$

where we have supposed that G_{ij} and G_{rs} are small relative to $\sqrt{V}$, the genotypic standard deviation in the population.   Now consider the A_1A_2 class.   Its frequency we know to be

$$2 p_1 p_2 (1 + f_{12})$$

which must also equal the frequency of A_1A_2 offspring arising from the matings with their appropriate frequencies.   The matings which give rise to A_1A_2 offspring are as follows: $(11) \times (22)$, $(12) \times (12)$, $(11) \times (12)$, $(12) \times (22)$, $(11) \times (2r)$, $(1r) \times (22)$, $(12) \times (1r)$, $(12) \times (2r)$, $(1r) \times (2s)$ where

r, s can take any values from 3 to m. The equilibrium condition is therefore:

$$2p_1p_2(1 + f_{12}) = 2p_1p_2 \left[p_1p_2(1 + f_{11})(1 + f_{22}) \left(1 + \frac{\rho}{V} G_{11}G_{22} \right) \right.$$

$$+ p_1p_2(1 + f_{12})^2 \left(1 + \frac{\rho}{V} G_{12}^2 \right)$$

$$+ p_1^2(1 + f_{11})(1 + f_{12}) \left(1 + \frac{\rho}{V} G_{11}G_{12} \right)$$

$$+ p_2^2(1 + f_{12})(1 + f_{22}) \left(1 + \frac{\rho}{V} G_{12}G_{22} \right)$$

$$+ \sum_r p_1p_r(1 + f_{11})(1 + f_{2r}) \left(1 + \frac{\rho}{V} G_{11}G_{2r} \right)$$

$$+ \sum_r p_2p_r(1 + f_{1r})(1 + f_{22}) \left(1 + \frac{\rho}{V} G_{1r}G_{22} \right)$$

$$+ \sum_r p_1p_r(1 + f_{12})(1 + f_{1r}) \left(1 + \frac{\rho}{V} G_{12}G_{1r} \right)$$

$$+ \sum_r p_2p_r(1 + f_{12})(1 + f_{2r}) \left(1 + \frac{\rho}{V} G_{12}G_{2r} \right)$$

$$\left. + \sum_{r,s} p_rp_s(1 + f_{1r})(1 + f_{2s}) \left(1 + \frac{\rho}{V} G_{1r}G_{2s} \right) \right] \quad (10)$$

where summation over r and s runs from 3 to m.

A shorthand form of equation (10) is

$$2p_1p_2(1 + f_{12}) = 2 \sum_{jk} p_1p_jp_2p_k (1 + f_{1j})(1 + f_{2k}) \left(1 + \frac{\rho}{V} G_{1j}G_{2k} \right) \quad (10a)$$

The factor $2p_1p_2$ may be canceled from both sides of equation (10). We now state that the remaining part on the right-hand side which does not involve ρ is unity because of the conditions (7). This part can in fact be written as

$$\sum p_jp_k(1 + f_{1j})(1 + f_{2k}) = \left[\sum_j p_j(1 + f_{1j}) \right] \left[\sum_k p_k(1 + f_{2k}) \right]$$

$$= \left(\sum_j p_j \right) \left(\sum_k p_k \right)$$

$$= 1$$

With a little consideration the equilibrium condition is seen to reduce to

$$f_{12} = \frac{\rho}{V}\left[\sum_{v=1}^{m} p_v(1 + f_{1v})G_{1v}\right]\left[\sum_{w=1}^{m} p_w(1 + f_{2w})G_{2w}\right]$$

or, if we let

$$H_1 = \sum_{v=1}^{m} p_v(1 + f_{1v})G_{1v}$$

$$H_2 = \sum_{v=1}^{m} p_v(1 + f_{2v})G_{2v}$$

etc.

then

$$f_{12} = \frac{\rho}{V} H_1 H_2 \tag{11}$$

Clearly in general $f_{ij} = (\rho/V)H_i H_j$. Note that we have implicit equations for the f_{ij}'s based *only* on the assumption that the G_{ij}'s are small. This differs from Fisher's result (1918, p. 416, equation XIV*), which in addition utilized an assumption that products of f's and G's are small and may be ignored. This is indeed the case, as can be seen from equation (11), but it is possibly, but not probably, worth while to note the more accurate equation (11). We note that the f's are of the order of G^2 and the H's consist of two parts, one of order G and the other of order G^3, so that to the order of magnitude G^2 it is correct to consider that

$$H_j = \sum_{v=1}^{m} p_v G_{jv} \tag{12}$$

The equation (12) can be surmised from the fact that H_1 and H_2 are, respectively, the means of the subpopulations producing A_1 and A_2 gametes, respectively.

This equilibrium condition merits a little discussion. It is in the author's opinion a rather remarkable equation and just one product of Fisher's genius. First let us consider the case of two alleles, because then the situation is much simpler and easier to visualize. If we let P_{11} be the frequency of A_1A_1 individuals, and $2P_{12}$ the frequency of A_1A_2 individuals, and so on, we have

$$P_{11} = p_1^2 + \frac{\rho}{V} p_1^2 H_1^2$$

$$P_{12} = p_1 p_2 + \frac{\rho}{V} p_1 p_2 H_1 H_2$$

$$P_{22} = p_2^2 + \frac{\rho}{V} p_2^2 H_2^2$$

Now, by the definition of H_1, H_2, we see that to the order of magnitude considered

$$p_1 H_1 + p_2 H_2 = 0$$

so the equations take the form

$$P_{11} = p_1^2 + \delta$$
$$P_{12} = p_1 p_2 - \delta$$
$$P_{22} = p_2^2 + \delta$$

It is noteworthy that this is exactly the structure which arises under inbreeding where it will be recalled δ is equal to Fp_1p_2, F being the coefficient of inbreeding attained. In the present case

$$H_1 = p_1 G_{11} + p_2 G_{12}$$

and, since

$$p_1^2 G_{11} + 2p_1 p_2 G_{12} + p_2^2 G_{22} = 0$$
$$p_1 H_1 = p_1^2 G_{11} - \tfrac{1}{2}(p_1^2 G_{11} + p_2^2 G_{22})$$
$$= \tfrac{1}{2}(p_1^2 G_{11} - p_2^2 G_{22})$$

Hence

$$\delta = \frac{\rho}{4V}(p_1^2 G_{11} - p_2^2 G_{22})^2$$

which is the form given by Fisher (1918, p. 411) for the two-allele case.

There appears to be a tendency in the literature to take the point of view that a natural population will have the same structure as that resulting by inbreeding of a random mating population. If this were so, then δ would have to be of the form Fp_1p_2 where F is independent of gene frequency. We note that this is not at all the case if the Fisher's model presented above is reasonable for natural populations, as indeed it appears to be on a priori grounds. In fact, even though the two-allele case can be represented as one with inbreeding coefficient F, we would have

$$F = -\frac{\rho}{V}H_1 H_2$$

$$= \frac{\rho(p_1^2 G_{11} - p_2^2 G_{22})^2}{4V p_1 p_2}$$

which is clearly dependent on gene frequency. Of course, when we turn to the case of an arbitrary number of loci, m say, we see that such a representation would fail because there is only one F parameter possible, while there are in fact m different quantities $H_1, H_2, \cdots, H_m$ which define the situation. It is also to be noted that the coefficient of inbreeding can take values between 0 and 1 only, so that the frequency of homozygotes is greater than the square of the corresponding gene frequency, whereas such is obviously not the case under assortative mating.

22.4 THE FREQUENCIES OF COMBINATIONS OF PHASES OF TWO FACTORS

The procedure here will be formally identical with that in the preceding section. A second locus will be indicated by the use of a prime, so that the frequency of the phase (ij) (ordered) at the first locus is $p_i p_j (1 + f_{ij})$, and the frequency of the phase (kl) (ordered) at the second locus is $p'_k p'_l (1 + f'_{kl})$. The joint frequency of the two phases will be denoted by

$$p_i p_j (1 + f_{ij}) p'_k p'_l (1 + f'_{kl})(1 + f_{ij \cdot kl})$$

We now set up the equilibrium condition for the frequency of $A_1 A_2 A'_1 A'_2$ or $(12 \cdot 12)$ individuals. The $f_{ij \cdot kl}$ are subject to certain conditions in order that the frequency of $A_i A_j$ individuals be $p_i p_j (1 + f_{ij})$ and of $A'_k A'_l$ individuals be $p'_k p'_l (1 + f'_{kl})$. We suppose that products of f_{ij} or f'_{kl} and $f_{ij \cdot kl}$ can be ignored. The accuracy of this to the appropriate order of magnitude will be verified later. It follows that conditions on the $f_{ij \cdot kl}$ are

$$\sum_{ij} p_i p_j f_{ij \cdot kl} = 0 \tag{13}$$

$$\sum_{kl} p'_k p'_l f_{ij \cdot kl} = 0$$

Also we may ignore the product of two f's, one from each locus, because such a product will be of order G^4. Hence we may write the frequency of $A_i A_j A'_k A'_l$ individuals as

$$p_i p_j p'_k p'_l (1 + f'_{ij \cdot kl})$$

where

$$f'_{ij \cdot kl} = f_{ij \cdot kl} + f_{ij} + f'_{kl} \tag{14}$$

Gametes of the structure $(1 \cdot 1)$, i.e. the first allele at the first locus and the first allele at the second locus, arise from individuals of the following structure:

$$(11 \cdot 11), (11 \cdot 12), \cdot \cdot \cdot, (11 \cdot 1n)$$
$$(12 \cdot 11), (12 \cdot 12), \cdot \cdot \cdot, (12 \cdot 1n)$$
$$\cdot \quad \cdot \quad \cdot \quad \cdot \quad \cdot \quad \cdot \quad \cdot \quad \cdot$$
$$(1m \cdot 11), (1m \cdot 12), \cdot \cdot \cdot, (1m \cdot 1n)$$

where $(12 \cdot 13)$ denotes the genotype with alleles 1 and 2 at the first locus and alleles 1 and 3 at the second locus, and there are m and n alleles at the first and second locus, respectively. The total frequency of such gametes is therefore

$$p_1 p_1'[p_1 p_1'(1 + f_{11 \cdot 11}') + p_1 p_2'(1 + f_{11 \cdot 12}') + \cdots + p_1 p_n'(1 + f_{11 \cdot 1n}')$$
$$+ p_2 p_1'(1 + f_{12 \cdot 11}') + p_2 p_2'(1 + f_{12 \cdot 12}') + \cdots + p_2 p_n'(1 + f_{12 \cdot 1n}')$$
$$+ \cdot \ \cdot \ \cdot \ \cdot \ \cdot \ \cdot \ \cdot \ \cdot \ \cdot \ \cdot \ \cdot \ \cdot \ \cdot \ \cdot$$
$$+ p_m p_1'(1 + f_{1m \cdot 11}') + p_m p_2'(1 + f_{1m \cdot 12}') + \cdots + p_m p_n'(1 + f_{1m \cdot 1n}')]$$
$$= p_1 p_1' + p_1 p_1'[p_1 p_1' f_{11 \cdot 11}' + p_1 p_2' f_{11 \cdot 12}' + \cdots + p_1 p_n' f_{11 \cdot 1n}'$$
$$+ p_2 p_1' f_{12 \cdot 11}' + p_2 p_2' f_{12 \cdot 12}' + \cdots + p_2 p_n' f_{12 \cdot 1n}'$$
$$+ \cdot \ \cdot \ \cdot \ \cdot \ \cdot \ \cdot \ \cdot \ \cdot \ \cdot \ \cdot \ \cdot \ \cdot \ \cdot$$
$$+ p_m p_1' f_{1m \cdot 11}' + p_m p_2' f_{1m \cdot 12}' + \cdots + p_m p_n' f_{1m \cdot 1n}']$$
$$= p_1 p_1' + p_1 p_1' F_{11} \quad \text{say} \tag{15}$$

Similar expressions exist for the frequency of every possible gamete. It can be seen by direct substitution of $f_{ij \cdot kl}$ in terms of f_{ij}, f_{kl}', and $f_{ij \cdot kl}$ that F_{11} has the same value whether written in primed or unprimed quantities.

Individuals having the genotype (12·12) arise either by the union of (1·1) and (2·2) gametes or by union of (1·2) and (2·1) gametes. We now use the relationship for the frequency of mating of two groups, and note that to the appropriate order of magnitude, and with no epistacy, the mean of the group giving (1·1) gametes is $H_1 + H_1'$, and of the group giving (1·2) gametes is $H_1 + H_2'$, and so on. The equilibrium condition that the frequency of (12·12) individuals be constant is

$$2 p_1 p_2 p_1' p_2'(1 + f_{12 \cdot 12}') = p_1 p_1'(1 + f_{11}) p_2 p_2'(1 + F_{22})$$
$$\exp\left[\frac{\rho}{V}(H_1 + H_1')(H_2 + H_2')\right]$$
$$+ p_1 p_2'(1 + F_{12}) p_2 p_1'(1 + F_{21}) \exp\left[\frac{\rho}{V}(H_1 + H_2')(H_2 + H_1')\right] \tag{16}$$

or, expanding and neglecting product terms,

$$2 f_{12 \cdot 12}' = F_{11} + F_{22} + \frac{\rho}{V}(H_1 + H_1')(H_2 + H_2')$$
$$+ F_{12} + F_{21} + \frac{\rho}{V}(H_1 + H_2')(H_2 + H_1') \tag{17}$$

Also

$$2f_{12\cdot12} = 2f'_{12\cdot12} - 2f_{12} - 2f'_{12}$$

$$= 2f'_{12\cdot12} - 2\frac{\rho}{V}H_1H_2 - 2\frac{\rho}{V}H'_1H'_2$$

so

$$2f_{12\cdot12} = F_{11} + F_{22} + F_{12} + F_{21} + \frac{\rho}{V}(H_1 + H_2)(H'_1 + H'_2) \tag{18}$$

Fisher then notes that the equation

$$f_{12\cdot12} = \frac{\rho}{V}(H_1 + H_2)(H'_1 + H'_2) \tag{19}$$

which is analogous to the formula for the single-locus case, leads, with the equations defining the F_{ij}, to

$$F_{ij} = \frac{\rho}{V}H_iH'_j \tag{20}$$

and that (19) and (20) lead to equality in (18). The equation (18) is therefore the equilibrium condition on $f_{12\cdot12}$, with corresponding equations for the other f's.   Note that the $f_{ij\cdot kl}$ are of order of magnitude G^2.

Finally $H_1, H_2, \cdots, H'_1, H'_2, \cdots$ may be evaluated since for instance

$$H_1 = p_1G_{11} + p_2G_{12} + \cdots + p_mG_{1m}$$

where by definition G_{11} is the mean deviation of the A_1A_1 class of individuals.   If we suppose that the contribution about the mean of the genes A_rA_s at the first locus is g_{rs} and of genes $A'_rA'_s$ at the second locus (the primed locus) about the mean is g'_{rs}, the quantity G_{11} is given by

$$G_{11} = \frac{1}{p_1^2(1 + f_{11})}\sum_{ij}p_1^2(1 + f_{11})p'_ip'_j(1 + f'_{ij})(1 + f_{11\cdot ij})(g_{11} + g'_{ij})$$

$$= \sum_{ij}p'_ip'_j(1 + f'_{ij})(1 + f_{11\cdot ij})(g_{11} + g'_{ij})$$

$$= g_{11} + \sum_{ij}p'_ip'_j(1 + f'_{ij})(1 + f_{11\cdot ij})g'_{ij}$$

since

$$\sum_{ij}p'_ip'_j(1 + f'_{ij})(1 + f_{11\cdot ij}) = 1$$

Also

$$G_{12} = g_{12} + \sum_{ij}p'_ip'_j(1 + f'_{ij})(1 + f_{12\cdot ij})g'_{ij}$$

and so on.

Hence

$$H_1 = p_1g_{11} + p_2g_{12} + \cdots + p_mg_{1m}$$
$$+ \sum_k \sum_{ij} p_kp'_ip'_j(1 + f'_{ij})(1 + f_{1k \cdot ij})g'_{ij}$$
$$= h_1 + \sum_{ij} p'_ip'_j(1 + f'_{ij})\left(1 + \sum_k p_kf_{1k \cdot ij}\right)g'_{ij}$$

where

$$h_1 = \sum_j p_jg_{1j}$$

But

$$\sum_k p_kf_{1k \cdot ij} = \frac{\rho}{V}H_1(H'_i + H'_j)$$

so

$$H_1 = h_1 + \frac{\rho}{V}H_1\left[\sum_{ij} p'_ip'_j(1 + f'_{ij})g'_{ij}(H'_i + H'_j)\right]$$

or

$$H_1 = h_1 + \frac{\rho}{V}H_1\sum_i (2p'_ih'_iH'_i)$$

where

$$h'_i = \sum_{j'} p'_jg'_{ij}$$

The argument above may be extended so that the primed locus ranges over all loci except the unprimed one, and we then have the equation

$$H_1 = h_1 + \frac{\rho}{V}H_1S\sum_i (2p'_ih'_iH'_i)$$

where S may be taken to include summation over *all* loci since the contribution of any one locus is small.

Fisher then introduces a constant A such that

$$H_1 = h_1 + AH_1$$

and

$$H_1 = \frac{h_1}{1 - A}$$

where

$$A = \frac{\rho}{V}S\sum(2p_ih_iH_i)$$

or

$$A(1 - A) = \frac{\rho}{V}S\sum 2p_ih_i^2$$

We now note that $S\sum 2p_i h_i^2$ is the additive genetic variance of the random mating population with the same gene frequencies as the given equilibrium population and may be denoted by σ_{AR}^2. Hence

$$A(1 - A) = \frac{\rho}{V} \sigma_{AR}^2$$

The total genotypic variance in the population is equal to the expression

$$S_1 \text{ [frequency of genotype (genotypic value)}^2\text{]}$$

where summation (S_1) is over every possible genotype. Now the genotypic value is equal to the sum of g's, one for each phase at each locus, and so the genotypic value squared is equal to the sum of squares of appropriate g's plus twice the sum of products. It therefore follows that the total genotypic variance is equal to

$$S \sum_{ij} P_{ij} g_{ij}^2 + 2S_2 \sum_{ij} \sum_{kl} P_{ij} P_{kl}' (1 + f_{ij \cdot kl}) g_{ij} g_{kl}'$$

where $P_{ij}\, P_{kl}'$ denote genotypic frequencies, S denotes summation over all the loci and S_2 summation over all pairs of loci. This expression is equal to

$$S_1 \sum_{ij} P_{ij} g_{ij} (g_{ij} + S' \sum_{kl} P_{kl}' f_{ij \cdot kl} g_{kl}')$$

where S' denotes summation over all loci except the one whose contribution is outside the parentheses. The quantity in parentheses is the mean of the class of individuals which have genes (ij) at the locus fixed in the argument and is therefore equal to G_{ij}. Hence we have

$$V = S \sum_{ij} P_{ij} g_{ij} G_{ij}$$

Also, substituting for $f_{ij \cdot kl}$,

$$G_{ij} = g_{ij} + \frac{\rho}{V} (H_i + H_j) S' \sum_{kl} p_{kl}' (H_k' + H_l') g_{kl}'$$

$$= g_{ij} + \frac{\rho}{V(1 - A)^2} (h_i + h_j) S' \sum_{kl} P_{kl}' (h_k' + h_l') g_{kl}'$$

$$= g_{ij} + \frac{\rho}{V(1 - A)^2} (h_i + h_j) \sigma_{AR}^2$$

$$= g_{ij} + \left(\frac{A}{1 - A} \right) (h_i + h_j)$$

Hence

$$V = S \sum_{ij} P_{ij} g_{ij} \left[g_{ij} + \frac{A}{(1-A)} (h_i + h_j) \right]$$

$$= \sigma_{GR}^2 + \frac{A}{(1-A)} \sigma_{AR}^2$$

It therefore follows that

$$\rho \sigma_{AR}^2 = A(1-A)\sigma_{GR}^2 + A^2 \sigma_{AR}^2$$

or

$$A^2 \sigma_{DR}^2 - A \sigma_{GR}^2 + \rho \sigma_{AR}^2 = 0 \qquad (21)$$

where $\sigma_{DR}^2 = \sigma_{GR}^2 - \sigma_{AR}^2$ is the dominance variance in the random mating population. Hence, given a random mating population with, of course, determinate σ_{AR}^2 and σ_{DR}^2, and given ρ, there will be a unique value of A which is the solution for A in the quadratic (21) which is between 0 and 1.

22.5 DESCRIPTION OF FISHER'S FURTHER WORK

Fisher shows that, in a population *at equilibrium* of the type considered above, linkage could be considered as a special case by permitting the phases from two linked loci with say two alleles at each locus to be represented as the phases from a single locus with four alleles.

Fisher then extends his results by letting environment be additive in its effects. If for example we consider height, there are three possible measures:

(1) x, the actual height in a particular environment,
(2) y, the height under a standard environment (or equivalently, averaged over a population of environments),
(3) z, what the height would have been if the effects of the genes were purely additive and given by the least squares procedure.

In present times we would refer to x as the phenotypic value, y as the genotypic value, and z as the additive value, or as the breeding value (Lush, 1937, and succeeding editions).

The regression of x on y is taken to be unity, as would be the practice at the present time. The regression of y on x would be c_1 in Fisher's terminology where

$$c_1 = \frac{\sigma_G^2}{\sigma_G^2 + \sigma_E^2} = \frac{\sigma_G^2}{\sigma_P^2}$$

σ_G^2 being the genotypic variance and σ_E^2 the environment variance. This ratio has achieved considerable prominence since 1918 and is now generally referred to as the heritability or heritability in the broad sense (Lush, 1937 and succeeding editions). The regression of y on z would be unity and the regression of z on y would be c_2 where

$$c_2 = \frac{\sigma_A^2}{\sigma_G^2 - A\sigma_D^2}$$

We note that, if A is zero, then the quantity $c_1 c_2$ which appears frequently in Fisher's calculations would be

$$c_1 c_2 = \frac{\sigma_A^2}{\sigma_P^2}$$

which is nowadays referred to as heritability in the narrow sense (Lush, 1937 and succeeding editions).

Fisher considers the possibilities that the marital correlation is a result of association between mates with regard to

(1) the phenotype x
(2) the genotypic value y, and
(3) the breeding value z.

Table 22.1 is a summary of Fisher's deductions.

In addition, Fisher deduces that the correlation between full-sibs or fraternal correlation is $(c_1/4)[1 + c_2(1 + 2A)]$ and between double first cousins is $(c_1/16)[1 + 3c_2(1 + 4A)]$.

TABLE 22.1

SUMMARY OF CONCLUSIONS

Origin of Correlation

	x	y	z
A Correlations	$c_1 c_2 \rho$	$\rho \dfrac{c_2}{c_1}$	$\dfrac{\rho}{c_1 c_2}$
P–0	$c_1 c_2 \left(\dfrac{1+\rho}{2}\right)$	$\dfrac{c_1 c_2 + A c_1}{2}$	$c_1 c_2 \left(\dfrac{1+A}{2}\right)$
P–kth degree 0	$c_1 c_2 \left(\dfrac{1+\rho}{2}\right)\left(\dfrac{1+A}{2}\right)^{k-1}$	$\left(\dfrac{c_1 c_2 + A c_1}{2}\right)\left(\dfrac{1+A}{2}\right)^{k-1}$	$c_1 c_2 \left(\dfrac{1+A}{2}\right)^{k+1}$

Fisher used correlations quoted by Pearson and Lee (1903) to infer values for ρ, c_1, c_2, and A. We shall not discuss these results because the correlations are unreliable, particularly as regards environmental deviations. It is rather surprising that the human geneticists have not pursued this type of approach with regard to quantitative attributes to at least a fractional extent, compared to the work on genes with large effects. From a number of points of view, scientific, medical, and social, there appears to the author to be need for some analysis of the role of genetic determination in what we might call standard human attributes as opposed to defects.

Finally in the 1918 paper Fisher discussed the interpretation of the statistical effects of dominance, and started the consideration of the dominance ratio which is taken up again in his 1922 paper on the dominance ratio and led to the stochastic treatment of population reproduction.

As a final note on this chapter it is to be realized that the assumptions of a large number of factors with small summary of effects, of no epistacy, and of additive environmental effects may be questionable, and it is clear that Fisher was aware of the deficiencies of the theory. It is remarkable that there has been essentially no further work on the general topic with the exception of Fisher's book (1930) for the nearly forty years up to the present time. It is quite apparent that the elucidation of the situation rests with further deductive work together with clean observational results.

The ideas of this chapter have been applied by Reeve (1956) to the use of assortative mating for the estimation of heritability. See also Reeve (1952, 1955).

REFERENCES

Fisher, R. A. 1918. The correlation between relatives on the supposition of Mendelian inheritance. *Trans. roy. Soc. Edinb.*, **52**, 399–433.

Fisher, R. A. 1922. On the dominance ratio. *Proc. roy. Soc. Edinb*, **42**, 321–341.

Fisher, R. A. 1930. *The genetical theory of natural selection*. Clarendon Press, Oxford.

Lush, J. L. 1937. *Animal breeding plans*. Iowa State College Press, Ames.

Pearson, K., and A. Lee. 1903. On the laws of inheritance in man. *Biometrika*, **2**, 357–462.

Reeve, E. C. R. 1952. Studies in quantitative inheritance. III. Heritabilities and genetic correlation in progeny tests using different mating systems. *J. Genet.*, **51**, 520–542.

Reeve, E. C. R. 1955. The variance of the genetic correlation coefficient. *Biometrics*, **11**, 357–374.

Reeve, E. C. R. 1956. Discussion paper, *Proc. Cold Spr. Harb. Symp. quant. Biol.*, **20**, 76–78.

CHAPTER 23

Selection for Quantitative Characters

23.1 INTRODUCTION

The theory of Mendelian inheritance with regard to unidentifiable genotypes has been developed in the preceding chapters. The main aim of such theory and the application to experimental data from a pure scientific viewpoint is to broaden our understanding of the genetic situation. However, the main application will be to the problems of applied genetics. Our understanding will be the basis for the continual search for "better" genetic material, whether it be corn which yields higher, oats which resists rusts, hogs which have fast growth gains, and so on. The measure of our understanding of the intrinsic genetic situation will be the extent to which we can obtain individuals of desired types. We are thus led to the consideration of selection theory for quantitative attributes. We have seen some of the elementary work on selection theory for the case of identifiable genotypes, though we should mention that this theory is essentially single-locus theory. The theory of quantitative inheritance has one aspect which constitutes its value perhaps more than anything else, namely, that it leads us to a more general view of genetic determination, and a more general view of epistacy. The classical epistatic models of complementary gene action, and duplicate factors for example, are of great interest, but they must surely comprise a very small subset of the totality of possible epistatic effects.

In this chapter we shall be concerned with some elementary aspects of selection theory. It will come as no surprise to the reader who has been through the preceding chapters that selection theory is very limited. We have seen that general representations of populations are possible only under special circumstances, and specifically under random mating, preceded possibly by inbreeding. We shall attempt to give the hard core of present knowledge, and shall deal mainly with entirely additive gene effects. We shall give references only to the pure genetic theory of selection, it being entirely beyond the scope of the book or the author to review the vast experimental work on selection.

It is easy to construct situations in which selection will make not the slightest advance. If, for instance, the heterozygote is superior to both homozygotes, these having equal genotypic values, selection of the superior individuals will merely reproduce the unselected population. The superiority of an individual may arise entirely from epistatic effects, and the progeny resulting from this individual will contain none of these epistatic effects under many circumstances.

23.2 MASS SELECTION IN THE CASE OF ADDITIVE GENE AND ENVIRONMENTAL EFFECTS

In the particular case when we can write

$$P = G + E$$

$$G = \sum_{ij} p_i^j \alpha_i^j$$

where P is the genotype of the individual, G is the genetic contribution, E is the environmental contribution, assumed uncorrelated with G, the α_i^j's are additive effects of genes, the p_i^j's are the gene frequencies in the individual, and the summation over j is over alleles within loci and over i is over loci. It will happen that the total variance of the population of phenotypic values is

$$\sigma_P^2 = \sigma_G^2 + \sigma_E^2$$

Now suppose individuals are selected on the basis of their phenotype. Then the regression of genotype on phenotype will be

$$\frac{\text{Cov}\,(P, G)}{V(P)} = \frac{\sigma_G^2}{\sigma_P^2} = \frac{\sigma_G^2}{\sigma_G^2 + \sigma_E^2}$$

If the mean of the selected individuals differs from the population mean by D, which is the selection differential, the expected genotypic value of the mean of the selected individuals will be

$$D \times \frac{\sigma_G^2}{\sigma_P^2}$$

We may note in passing that the ratio σ_G^2/σ_P^2 is in the case of purely additive gene effects the "heritability" as used by Lush (1937 and succeeding editions). The value of D can be estimated in a specific instance as the difference between the phenotypic values of the selected and original population. Its theoretical value for the common type of mass selection, namely truncation selection, in which the upper p per cent of the population are chosen can be calculated if the distribution of the phenotypic values in the population be known. If for instance $f(x)\,dx$ is the probability that the phenotype of a random individual lies within the range x, $x + dx$, then, if X is defined to be the solution of the equation in X,

$$\frac{p}{100} = \int_X^\infty f(x)\,dx$$

then

$$D = \frac{100}{p} \int_X^\infty (x - \mu)\,f(x)\,dx$$

where μ is the original population mean. If the distribution is in fact normal, it turns out that

$$D = k\sigma_P$$

where k is an easily calculated number. Values for it are given for example by Lush (1945, Table 12, p. 148).

The next question which arises is the nature of the population which will result from the selected individuals, and it is here that the difficulties in the theory arise. Actually what is given above is true, regardless of the nature of the effects of the genes. It can be regarded as giving the effect on genetic structure of the population by considering genotypic values as arising by assigning a score of unity for one allele and zero for all other alleles.

In the case when the genes are additive in their effects, the mean of the population obtained by random mating of the selected individuals will be

$$D \frac{\sigma_G^2}{\sigma_P^2}$$

above the original mean, any offspring having a genotypic value which is the mean of the parental values.

The effect on population variance is easily predicted in this simple case, providing there is random mating and no linkage, from the fact that it will be related to

$$\sum p_i p_{i'}(\alpha_i + \alpha_{i'})^2 - \left(\sum_i p_i \alpha_i\right)^2$$

added over all loci. In the case of two alleles, the variance due to any one locus is proportional to $p(1 - p)$. We can guess that in general, unless the trait is very highly heritable and environmental variance is negligible, the variance of the resulting population is little different from that of the unselected population.

In the case when the gene effects are not additive, we will not know how much gene frequency has changed, so that we will have no means of predicting the population which will result by random mating, or any other system of mating, of the selected individuals.* We can state that, if the gene effects are solely additive, the process of truncation selection with mating of superior animals to superior animals will result in animals which are no less superior on the average, and will give some individuals superior to the parents, providing there is still genetic variability. The fact that selection experiments do not have this result in general is indication that either dominance or epistacy or both are operative, or that the genotypes which would give the superior animals are inviable. The last explanation is no less likely than the others and from many points of view more likely in that the combination of genes producing positive effects may result in some sort of physiological imbalance which renders the genotype inviable.

There is a vast literature on the examination of selection experiments, on how to select the individuals with the preferred phenotypic and genotypic values, for example, by the use of progeny averages, on the relative effectiveness of procedures with regard to the speed of advance possible with various procedures, but the literature on the consequences of selecting according to a particular scheme with regard to the resulting *offspring* generations is very sparse, because the theory becomes very complex. The reader may refer to the texts of Lush (1937 and succeeding editions) and Lerner (1950) for extensive discussions dealing with animal populations. Papers by Nordskog (1948), Hazel (1943), Dickerson and Hazel (1942), Henderson (1952), Robertson (1953) deal with various aspects of selection procedures for animals. As regards plant populations, there is an extensive literature on corn (see Sprague, 1952, for a review). The papers of Panse (1940a, b) should be consulted for consideration of selection in relation to specific gene models. The references given here are without doubt a biased selection, but it would be beyond the scope of this book or the author to attempt any listing, let alone a review of selection experiments.

What is written above refers to selection *for and on the basis of* a single attribute. What makes most actual selection situations more complex is the fact that a combination of attributes and not a single one is desired. The term "single attribute" is here used in the sense that a measurement or combination of measurements is observed, the variances and covariances of this attribute are used in the formulas, and selection is made on the basis of this attribute only. That this is not the best procedure will be seen from the following section.

* See Chapter 16.

23.3 SELECTION WITH KNOWLEDGE OF SEVERAL ATTRIBUTES

We now consider the case in which there are m phenotypic characteristics or attributes say $P_1, P_2, \cdot \cdot \cdot, P_m$ for each individual.† For each we shall assume that the observed value P_{ij} of the ith attribute for the jth individual is composed of two parts, G_{ij} the genotypic value of the ith attribute for the jth individual, and E_{ij} the corresponding environmental effect. Thus we have

$$P_{ij} = G_{ij} + E_{ij}$$

We shall assume that the genotypic values of the various attributes are correlated between individuals as are the environmental effects, but that there is no correlation between the G terms and E terms between individuals. The individuals available from the unselected population are assumed to be a random sample of the population. The environment experienced by each individual is assumed to be a random one.

Suppose it is desired to pick out those individuals, denoted by j, for which

$$M_j = a_1 G_{1j} + a_2 G_{2j} + \cdot \cdot \cdot + a_m G_{mj}$$

is as high as possible. The requirement of linearity is made to enable a mathematical solution. It may be biologically unrealistic. The quantities $a_1, a_2, \cdot \cdot \cdot, a_m$ are taken to be known. They may be relative economic values of the different attributes. If we were interested only in one attribute, say the lth, all the a's except a_l would be zero. In general the index M_j may be termed the value of the jth individual. There are of course many possible values of an individual. We cannot know the G_{ij} in general, and we assume that we have an estimate of G_{ij} which is P_{ij}, equal to $G_{ij} + E_{ij}$. The problem is to construct an index based on the P_{ij} which will be used as a basis for picking out individuals with preferred M values. We note that we have made no restrictions on the nature of the P_{ij}'s or G_{ij}'s, except that certain statistical assumptions must be satisfied.

Our mathematical and statistical knowledge being what it is, we further restrict the problem by requiring that a linear function of the P_{ij} be used for the index. Having gone thus far, we can now consider the purely mathematical problem which is to find numbers $b_1, b_2, \cdot \cdot \cdot, b_m$ such that

$$I_j = b_1 P_{1j} + b_2 P_{2j} + \cdot \cdot \cdot + b_m P_{mj}$$

† An attribute for an individual may be the girth of its sire or the milk production of its dam. It is to be noted that a grandparent can affect an offspring only through a parent of the offspring, but that a prediction formula may be improved in accuracy by including the grandparent in addition to the parent. This serves as another example of the difference between correlation and causation.

and

$$M_j = a_1 G_{1j} + a_2 G_{2j} + \cdots + a_m G_{mj}$$

have as high a correlation as possible.   We shall suppose that

$$\text{Cov}\,(G_{rj},\,G_{sj}) = \sigma_{rs}$$

and

$$\text{Cov}\,(E_{rj},\,E_{sj}) = \tau_{rs}$$

so that σ_{rs} is the genotypic covariance (variance, if $r = s$) of the rth and sth attributes, and τ_{rs} is the environmental covariance of the rth and sth attributes.   It follows immediately that

$$\rho_{IM} = \frac{\displaystyle\sum_{ij} a_i b_j \sigma_{ij}}{\sqrt{\left(\displaystyle\sum_{ik} a_i a_k \sigma_{ik}\right)\left[\displaystyle\sum_{ln} b_l b_n (\sigma_{ln} + \tau_{ln})\right]}}$$

and this is the quantity to be maximized with regard to the b's.   The a's are of course known, so that we may ignore the first term in the denominator.   We have then to maximize K, where

$$\frac{\displaystyle\sum_{ij} a_i b_j \sigma_{ij}}{\left[\displaystyle\sum_{l,n} b_l b_n (\sigma_{ln} + \tau_{ln})\right]^{1/2}} = K$$

This equation may be written

$$\left(\sum_{ij} a_i b_j \sigma_{ij}\right)^2 - K^2 \left[\sum_{ln} b_l b_n (\sigma_{ln} + \tau_{ln})\right]$$

and we have to find the solution to the equations

$$\frac{\partial K}{\partial b_t} = 0, \qquad t = 1, 2, \cdots, m$$

Now

$$2\left(\sum_{ij} a_i b_j \sigma_{ij}\right)\left(\sum_i a_i \sigma_{it}\right) - 2K \frac{\partial K}{\partial b_t}\left[\sum_{ln} b_l b_n (\sigma_{ln} + \tau_{ln})\right]$$
$$- 2K^2 \sum_l b_l (\sigma_{lt} + \tau_{lt}) = 0$$

so the equations to be solved are

$$K^2 \sum_l b_l (\sigma_{lt} + \tau_{lt}) = \left(\sum_{ij} a_i b_j \sigma_{ij}\right)\left(\sum_i a_i \sigma_{it}\right)$$

or, if

$$c_l = \frac{K^2 b_l}{\sum_{ij} a_i b_j \sigma_{ij}}$$

the equations are

$$\sum_l c_l(\sigma_{lt} + \tau_{lt}) = \sum_i a_i \sigma_{it}, \qquad t = 1, 2, \cdots, m$$

This is a set of m equations in m unknowns, the solution to which can be obtained in the ordinary way. We note that the substitution of c's in place of b's merely results in multiplication of the index I by a constant and that this will not affect the correlation of I with M or the relative ratings of the individuals. We may therefore take as the index

$$I_j = c_1 P_{1j} + c_2 P_{2j} + \cdots + c_m P_{mj}$$

where the c's are given by the preceding equation.

It is interesting to note that, even if all a's except one, say a_l, are zero, the index I will depend on the observed values of the other attributes in general. As an example suppose we have two attributes with variances and covariances as follows:

$$\sigma_{11} = 1, \qquad \tau_{11} = 1$$

$$\sigma_{22} = 1, \qquad \tau_{22} = 1$$

$$\sigma_{12} = 0.5, \qquad \tau_{12} = -0.5$$

and we are interested solely in the first attribute, so that $a_1 = 1$, $a_2 = 0$, and the c's are given by the equations

$$2c_1 + 0c_2 = 1$$

$$0c_1 + 2c_2 = 0.5$$

and the best index is

$$I_j = \tfrac{1}{2} P_{1j} + \tfrac{1}{4} P_{2j}$$

rather than

$$P_{1j}$$

as we might suspect without critical thought.

It is also worth noting the converse case in which we select only on the basis of an observed attribute. For this case we will obtain responses to this selection in all attributes which are either genotypically or environmentally correlated with the attribute selected for. If the correlations are linear, the response to a change from the mean δ_1 in attribute 1 will result in a change in δ_2 equal to

$$\frac{\sigma_{12} + \tau_{12}}{\sigma_{11} + \tau_{11}} \delta_1$$

in attribute 2, and it appears that the resultant genotypic change in attribute 2 will be

$$\frac{\sigma_{12}}{\sigma_{11} + \tau_{11}} \delta_1$$

In the absence of errors of estimation of the variance and covariance components, the c's will be obtained exactly, and the rate of progress with regard to M, with p per cent truncation selection and normality of distribution of M, will be equal to

$$k\beta_{MI}\sigma_I = k\rho_{IM}\sigma_M$$

where σ_I, σ_M are the standard deviations of I and M, respectively, in the population of unselected individuals. Note, however, that the progress may be lost immediately by the crossing necessary to produce the next generation. Note also that the rate of progress is proportional to ρ_{IM} and not to ρ_{IM}^2.

There are many statistical problems which arise in the utilization of the above selection index. It will in general be the case that the population variances and covariances will be unknown, and we shall have only estimates of them. The effect of inaccuracies of these estimates on the accuracy of the computed index appears to be unknown. The index will lose some of its accuracy because of the errors of estimation of variance-covariance components and will not be optimum.

Quite apart from the distributional questions about the use of the index, there are more fundamental questions. It is not in the author's opinion possible to make a "blanket" statement that the use of an index constructed as above will lead to faster progress than a selection procedure based on selection for attributes separately; that is, select for G_1 for two generations, then select for G_2 for two generations, and so on. There are no doubt circumstances under which the index will give faster progress than attribute-wise selection, and we may guess that these include linearity of all regressions *throughout* the possible ranges. We can conceivably run into the situation where no progress is made on a compound measure of value because positive selection for one attribute in the measure results in negative selection for another attribute. It does not seem appropriate to speculate on all the possibilities in the present book, but it seems desirable to express the personal opinion that the uncritical use of a selection index without considering the correlational situation we are working in may be very ineffective.

Final Note

The treatment given above is without doubt very skimpy. The reader is referred to Lush (1937), Lerner (1950) and to the genetic journals, practically every issue of which contains some selection experiments. The selection index given above is closely related to discriminant functions (Fisher, 1936, 1938) and was worked out by Smith (1936). A presentation in terms of correlations rather than variances and covariances was given by Hazel (1943).

REFERENCES

Berry, J. C. 1945. Reliability of averages of different numbers of lactation records for comparing dairy cows. *J. Dairy Sci.*, **28**, 355–366.

Bonnier, G. 1936. Progeny tests of dairy sires. *Hereditas Lund*, **22**, 145–166.

Comstock, R. E., and L. M. Winters. 1944. A comparison of the effects of inbreeding and selection on performance in swine. *J. Anim. Sci.*, **3**, 380–389.

Dempster, E. R., and I. M. Lerner. 1947. The optimum structure of breeding flocks I and II. *Genetics*, **32**, 555–579.

Dempster, E. R., and I. M. Lerner. 1950. Heritability of threshold characters. *Genetics*, **35**, 212–236.

Dempster, E. R., I. M. Lerner and D. Lowry. 1952. Continuous selection for egg production in poultry. *Genetics*, **37**, 693–708.

Dickerson, G. E., and J. C. Grimes. 1947. Effectiveness of selection for efficiency of gain in Duroc swine. *J. Anim. Sci.*, **6**, 265–287.

Dickerson, G. E., and L. N. Hazel. 1942. Selection for growth rate and productivity in closed herds of swine. *Abstr. J. Anim. Sci.*, **1**, 342.

Dickerson, G. E., and L. N. Hazel. 1944a. Effectiveness of selection on progeny performance as a supplement to earlier culling in livestock. *J. agric. Res.*, **69**, 459–476.

Dickerson, G. E., and L. N. Hazel. 1944b. Selection for growth rate of pigs and productivity of sows. *J. Anim. Sci.*, **3**, 201–212.

Edwards, J. 1932. The progeny test as a method evaluating the dairy sire. *J. agric. Res.*, **22**, 811–837.

Falconer, D. S. 1952. The problem of environment and selection. *Amer. Nat.*, **86**, 293–298.

Falconer, D. S. 1953. Selection for large and small size in mice. *J. Genet.*, **51**, 470–497.

Falconer, D. S., and J. W. B. King. 1953. A study of selection limits in the mouse. *J. Genet.*, **51**, 561–581.

Fine, N. C., and L. M. Winters. Selection for an increase in growth rate and market score in two inbred lines of swine. *J. Anim. Sci.*, **12**, 251–262.

Fisher, R. A. 1936. The use of multiple measurements in taxonomic problems. *Ann. Eugen. Lond.*, **7**, 179–188.

Fisher, R. A. 1938. The statistical utilization of multiple measurements. *Ann. Eugen. Lond.*, **8**, 376–386.

Fisher, R. A. 1951. Limits of intensive production in animals. *Brit. agric. Bull.*, **4**, 217–218.

Gowen, J. W., editor. 1952. *Heterosis.* Iowa State College Press, Ames.

Hazel, L. N. 1943. The genetic basis for constructing selection indexes. *Genetics,* **28,** 476–490.

Hazel, L. N., and J. L. Lush. 1942. Constructing selection indexes to make maximum progress. *Abstr. J. Anim. Sci.,* **1,** 69–70.

Hazel, L. N., and J. L. Lush. 1942. The efficiency of three methods of selection. *J. Hered.,* **33,** 393–399.

Henderson, C. R. 1952. Specific and general combining ability. Chapter 22 of *Heterosis.* Iowa State College Press, Ames.

Hutchinson, J. B. 1936. An analysis of the efficiency of selection methods used in the improvement of Malvi Cotton. *Indian J. agric. Sci.,* **6,** 672–683.

Hutchinson, J. B. 1940. The application of genetics to plant breeding. I. The genetic interpretation of plant breeding problems. *J. Genet.,* **40,** 271–282.

Johansson, I., and A. Robertson. 1954. Progeny testing in the breeding of farm animals. *Proc. Brit. Soc. Anim. Prod.,* **1952,** 79–105.

Karam, H. A., A. B. Chapman, and A. L. Pope. 1953. Selection lambs under farm flock conditions. *J. Anim. Sci.,* **12,** 148–164.

Krider, J. L., B. W. Fairbanks, W. E. Carrol, and E. Roberts. 1946. Effectiveness of selecting for rapid and for slow growth rate in Hampshire swine. *J. Anim. Sci.,* **5,** 3–15.

Lerner, I. M. 1950. *Population genetics and animal improvement.* University Press, Cambridge.

Lerner, I. M. 1954. *Genetic homeostasis.* Oliver and Boyd, London, 1954.

Lerner, I. M., D. Cruden, and L. W. Taylor. 1949. The relative breeding worth of full sisters. *Poult. Sci.,* **28,** 903–913.

Lerner, I. M., and E. R. Dempster. 1951. Attenuation of genetic progress under continued selection in poultry. *Heredity,* **5,** 75–94.

Lerner, I. M., and L. N. Hazel. 1947. Population genetics of a poultry flock under artificial selection. *Genetics,* **32,** 325–339.

Lush, J. L. 1931. The number of daughters necessary to prove a sire. *J. Dairy Sci.,* **14,** 209–220.

Lush, J. L. 1933. The bull index problem in the light of modern genetics. *J. Dairy Sci.,* **16,** 501–522.

Lush, J. L. 1935. Progeny test and individual performance as indicators of an animal's breeding value. *J. Dairy Sci.,* **18,** 1–19.

Lush, J. L. 1945. *Animal breeding plans.* Iowa State College Press, Ames. 3rd edition.

Lush, J. L. 1944. The optimum emphasis on dam's records when providing dairy sires. *J. Dairy Sci.,* **27,** 937–951.

Lush, J. L. 1947. Family merit and individual merit as bases for selection. *Amer. Nat.,* **81,** 241–261, 362–379.

MacArthur, J. W. 1948. Selection for small and large body size in the house mouse. *Genetics,* **34,** 194–209.

Mather, K., and B. J. Harrison. 1949. The manifold effect of selection. *Hereditas Lund,* **3,** 1–52, 131–162.

Nordskog, A. W. 1948. Periodical trapnesting and family selection for egg production. *Poult. Sci.,* **27,** 713–718.

Nordskog, A. W., and O. Cotterill. 1953. Breeding for egg quality. *Poult. Sci.,* **32,** 1051–1054.

Nordskog, A. W., and A. J. Wyatt. 1952. Genetic improvement as related to size of breeding operations. *Poult. Sci.,* **31,** 1062–1066.

Panse, V. G. 1940a. Application of genetics to plant breeding. II. Inheritance of quantitative characters and plant breeding. *J. Genet.*, **40**, 283–302.

Panse, V. G. 1940b. A statistical study of quantitative inheritance. *Ann. Eugen. Lond.*, **10**, 76–105.

Panse, V. G. 1946. An application of the discriminant function for selection in poultry. *J. Genet.*, **47**, 242–248.

Rendel, J. M., and A. Robertson. 1950. Estimation of genetic gain in milk yield by selecting in a closed herd of dairy cattle. *J. Genet.*, **50**, 1–8.

Rendel, J. M., A. Robertson, and K. A. Alim. 1951. The extent of selection for milk yield in dairy cattle. *Empire J. exp. Agric.*, **19**, 295–301.

Robertson, A. 1953. The use and interpretation of progeny tests in livestock improvement. *Proc. Brit. Soc. Anim. Prod.*, 18th meeting, **1953**, 3–12.

Robertson, A., and J. M. Rendel. 1950. The use of progeny testing with artificial insemination in dairy cattle. *J. Genet.*, **50**, 21–31.

Sismanidis, A. 1942. Selection for an almost invariable character in *Drosphila. J. Genet.*, **44**, 204–215.

Smith, H. F. 1936. A discriminant function for plant selection. *Ann. Eugen. Lond.*, **7**, 240–250.

Sprague, G. F. 1952. Early testing and recurrent selection. Chapter 26 of *Heterosis.* Iowa State College Press, Ames.

Tyler, W. J., and G. Hyatt. 1948. The relative merits of a cow's own record and her progeny test for predicting the butterfat production of her furture daughters. *J. Dairy Sci.*, **31**, 657.

Warren, W. M., and G. E. Dickerson, 1952. Components of performance in selecting for heterosis in swine. *Res. Bull. Univ. Miss.*, **511**.

Wigan, L. G. 1944. Balance and potence in natural populations. *J. Genet.*, **46**, 150–160.

Wigan, L. G., and K. Mather. 1942. Correlated response to selection of polygenic characters. *Ann. Eugen. Lond.*, **11**, 354–364.

Wright, Sewall. 1931. Evolution in Mendelian populations, *Genetics*, **16**, 97–159.

Wright, Sewall. 1932. On the evaluation of dairy sires. *Proc. Amer. Soc. Anim. Prod.*, **1932**, 71–78.

Index

Page numbers in parentheses indicate entry is contained in references, further reading, or, occasionally, problem sections.